						Metals

Metals

Metalloids

Nonmetals

			13 +3 3A	14 +4 4A	-3 15 5A	-2 16 6A	-1 17 7A	Halogens	Nobel gases 18 8A

								2 He 4.00 helium
			5 B 10.81 boron	6 C 12.01 carbon	7 N 14.01 nitrogen	8 O 16.00 oxygen	9 F 19.00 fluorine	10 Ne 20.18 neon

10 8B	11 1B	12 2B	13 Al 26.98 aluminum	14 Si 28.09 silicon	15 P 30.97 phosphorus	16 S 32.07 sulfur	17 Cl 35.45 chlorine	18 Ar 39.95 argon
28 Ni 58.69 nickel	29 Cu 63.55 copper	30 Zn 65.39 zinc	31 Ga 69.72 gallium	32 Ge 72.61 germanium	33 As 74.92 arsenic	34 Se 78.96 selenium	35 Br 79.90 bromine	36 Kr 83.80 krypton
46 Pd 106.42 palladium	47 Ag 107.87 silver	48 Cd 112.41 cadmium	49 In 114.82 indium	50 Sn 118.71 tin	51 Sb 121.75 antimony	52 Te 127.60 tellurium	53 I 126.90 iodine	54 Xe 131.29 xenon
78 Pt 195.08 platinum	79 Au 196.97 gold	80 Hg 200.59 mercury	81 Tl 204.38 thallium	82 Pb 207.2 lead	83 Bi 208.98 bismuth	84 Po (209) polonium	85 At (210) astatine	86 Rn (222) radon
110 — (269)	111 — (272)	112 — (277)		114 — (285)		116 — (289)		

64 Gd 157.25 gadolinium	65 Tb 158.93 terbium	66 Dy 162.50 dysprosium	67 Ho 164.93 holmium	68 Er 167.26 erbium	69 Tm 168.93 thulium	70 Yb 173.04 ytterbium	71 Lu 174.97 lutetium
96 Cm (247) curium	97 Bk (247) berkelium	98 Cf (251) californium	99 Es (252) einsteinium	100 Fm (257) fermium	101 Md (258) mendelevium	102 No (259) nobelium	103 Lr (260) lawrencium

INTRODUCTORY CHEMISTRY

Nivaldo J. Tro

Custom Edition for California State University, Northridge

Taken from:
Introductory Chemistry, Second Edition
by Nivaldo J. Tro

Taken from:

Introductory Chemistry, Second Edition
by Nivaldo J. Tro
Copyright © 2006, 2003 by Pearson Education, Inc.
Published by Prentice Hall
Upper Saddle River, NJ 07458

This special edition published in cooperation with Pearson Custom Publishing.

Printed in the United States of America

10 9 8 7 6 5 4 3 2 1

ISBN 0-536-94384-2

2005180093

MT

Please visit our web site at *www.pearsoncustom.com*

PEARSON CUSTOM PUBLISHING
75 Arlington Street, Suite 300, Boston, MA 02116
A Pearson Education Company

CONTENTS

1
The Chemical World   1

2
Measurement and Problem Solving   11

8

Quantities in Chemical Reactions 233

9

Electrons in Atoms and the Periodic Table 263

10

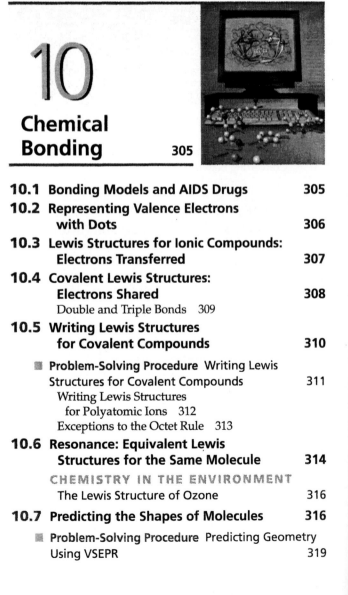

Chemical Bonding 305

13

Solutions   429

TO THE STUDENT

This book is for *you*, and every text feature has you in mind. I have two main goals for you in this course: to see chemistry as you never have before, and to develop the problem-solving skills you need to succeed in chemistry.

I want you to experience chemistry in a new way. Each chapter of this book is written to show you that chemistry is not just something that happens in a laboratory; chemistry surrounds you at every moment. I have worked with several outstanding artists to develop photographs and art that will help you visualize the molecular world. From the opening example to the closing chapter, you will *see* chemistry. I hope that when you finish this course, you think differently about your world because you understand the molecular interactions that underlie everything around you.

I also want you to develop problem-solving skills. No one succeeds in chemistry—or in life, really—without the ability to solve problems. I can't give you a formula for problem solving, but I can give you strategies that will help you develop the *chemical intuition* you need to understand chemical reasoning. Look for several recurring structures throughout this book designed to help you master problem solving. The most important ones are (1) the solution map, a visual aid that helps you navigate your way through a problem; (2) the two-column Examples, in which the left column explains in clear and simple language the purpose of each step of the solution shown in the right column; and (3) the three-column Examples, which describe a problem-solving procedure while demonstrating how it is applied to two different Examples.

Lastly, know that chemistry is not reserved only for those with some special talent or special capability. With the right amount of effort and some clear guidance, anyone can master chemistry, including you.

Sincerely,

Nivaldo J. Tro
tro@westmont.edu

TO THE INSTRUCTOR

I thank all of you who used the first edition of *Introductory Chemistry*—you made this book a success from its first year of publication. The preparation of the second edition has enabled me to further refine and strengthen the text to even better fulfill its foundational mission: teaching chemical skills in the context of relevance.

Introductory Chemistry is designed for a one-semester, college-level, introductory or preparatory chemistry course. Students taking this course need to develop problem-solving skills—but they also must see *why* these skills are important to them and to their world. *Introductory Chemistry* extends chemistry from the laboratory to the student's world. It motivates students to learn chemistry by demonstrating how it plays out in their daily lives.

This is a visual book. Today's students often learn by seeing, so wherever possible, I have used images to help communicate the subject. In developing chemical principles, for example, I worked with several artists to develop multipart images that show the connection between everyday processes visible to the eye and the molecular interactions responsible for those processes. This art has been further refined and improved in the second edition, making the visual impact sharper and more targeted to student learning.

For the same reason, in teaching problem-solving skills, I use a *solution map* to help students see the general logic of working through a multistep problem. Extensive flow charts are also incorporated throughout the book, allowing students to visualize the organization of chemical ideas and concepts. In this edition, I have reworked the color scheme of both the solution maps and the flow charts to increase their pedagogical value, making them more intuitive and more consistent throughout the text. Thus, the solution maps now utilize the colors of the visible spectrum—always in the same order, from violet to red.

At key points throughout this book, I use a *three-column* layout, in which students learn a general procedure for solving problems of a particular type as they see it applied to two worked Examples simultaneously. In this format, the *explanation* of how to solve a problem is placed directly beside the actual steps in the *solution* of the problem. Your positive comments about the pedagogical benefits of this approach in the first edition prompted me to carry the strategy one step further and convert many of the *single-column* worked Examples to a *two-column* format for the second edition. In these Examples, one column describes how the problem is solved and explains the rationale for each step, while the other column shows the actual steps. Many of you said that you use a similar technique in lecture and office hours.

I have also added a new feature entitled *Conceptual Checkpoints* to this edition. These checkpoints are short questions that students can use to test their mastery of key concepts as they read through a chapter. Emphasizing understanding rather than calculation, they are designed to be easy to answer if the student has grasped the essential concept but difficult if he or she has not. The answers to these checkpoints, like the answers to the *Skillbuilder* exercises that follow each worked Example, are given at the end of each chapter.

Some significant improvements have been made to key content areas as well. These include:

- an enhanced discussion of the scientific method in Chapter 1
- a new section on physical separation methods in Chapter 3
- a more intuitive explanation of the mole, focusing on the underlying logic of the concept, in Chapter 6
- a clearer organization of the solubility rules for compounds in Chapter 7

Finally, the real-world relevance of the text has been further strengthened by the addition of half a dozen new interest boxes, dealing with such topics as ion size and nerve impulse transmission, artificial sweeteners, and Kevlar.

The media package that accompanies this book has been greatly enhanced for the second edition. To help both you and your students achieve your goals, we have provided innovative, book-specific, interactive media elements for all of your major instructional needs:

- classroom presentation
- student tutorial
- online assessment and course management

Marginal icons in the text now identify the Student Tutorials, interactive Live Examples, and manipulable 3-dimensional molecular images available to students in OneKey, the Accelerator CD, and the Companion Website that accompany the book. These components (as well as other available supplements) are fully described in the Print and Media Resources section of the Preface that follows.

To help you prepare your lectures more efficiently and teach most effectively, this text is now available in an *Annotated Instructor's Edition*. In addition to the entire student text, the *AIE* includes marginal annotations containing teaching tips, suggestions for dealing with common student misconceptions, ideas for classroom demonstrations, icons that identify the art and tables reproduced as color acetates in the Transparency Pack, and references to relevant instructional articles on a wide range of chemical topics.

I hope this book and the changes in the second edition support you in your mission of teaching students chemistry. Ours is a worthwhile cause, even though it requires constant effort. Please feel free to email me with any questions or comments you might have. I look forward to hearing from you as you use this book in your course.

Sincerely,

Nivaldo J. Tro
tro@westmont.edu

PREFACE

The design and features of this text have been conceived to work together as an integrated whole with a single purpose: to help students understand chemical principles and master problem-solving skills in a context of relevance. Students must not only be able to grasp chemical concepts and solve chemical problems, but also understand how those concepts and problem-solving skills are relevant to their other courses, their eventual career paths, and their daily lives.

Teaching Principles

The development of basic chemical principles—such as those of atomic structure, chemical bonding, chemical reactions, and the gas laws—is one of the main goals of this text. Students must acquire a firm grasp of these principles in order to succeed in the general chemistry sequence or the chemistry courses that support the allied health curriculum. To that end, the book integrates qualitative and quantitative material, and proceeds from concrete concepts to more abstract ones.

Organization of the Text

The main divergence in topic ordering among instructors teaching introductory and preparatory chemistry courses is the placement of electronic structure and chemical bonding. Should these topics come early, at the point where models for the atom are being discussed? Or should they come later, after the student has been exposed to chemical compounds and chemical reactions? Early placement gives students a theoretical framework within which they can understand compounds and reactions. However, it also presents students with abstract models before they understand why they are necessary. I have chosen a later placement for the following reasons:

1. *A later placement seems more flexible.* An instructor who wants to cover atomic theory and bonding earlier can simply cover Chapters 9 and 10 after Chapter 4. However, if atomic theory and bonding were placed earlier, it would be more difficult for the instructor to skip these chapters and come back to them later.
2. *A later placement allows earlier coverage of topics that students can more easily visualize.* Coverage of abstract topics too early in a course can lose some students. Chemical compounds and chemical reactions are more tangible than atomic orbitals, and the relevance of these is easier to demonstrate to the beginning student.
3. *A later placement gives students a reason to learn an abstract theory.* Once students learn about compounds and reactions, they are more easily motivated to learn a theory that explains them in terms of underlying causes.
4. *A later placement follows the scientific method.* In science, we normally make observations, form laws, *and then* build models or theories that explain our observations and laws. A later placement follows this ordering.

Nonetheless, I know that every course is unique and that each instructor chooses to cover topics in his or her own way. Consequently, I have written each chapter for maximum flexibility in topic ordering. In addition, the book is offered in two formats. The full version, *Introductory Chemistry*, contains 19 chapters, including organic chemistry and biochemistry. The shorter version, *Introductory Chemistry Essentials*, contains 17 chapters and omits these topics.

Improving Conceptual Understanding

Students often have difficulty in developing a true understanding of the concepts that underlie chemical behavior. These concepts are important not only as the foundation for problem solving but also as the basis for insight into how the chemical world works. To address this need, we have incorporated a new set of questions at the end of appropriate sections that encourage students to test their grasp of the key principles in the section.

NEW Conceptual Checkpoints

These strategically located conceptual questions

- enhance understanding of chemical principles,
- encourage students to stop and think about the ideas just presented before going on to new material, and
- provide a tool for self-assessment.

Presented in multiple-choice format, the questions are designed so that an attentive student can answer them quickly, with little or no calculation.

Answers to Conceptual Checkpoints are given at the end of each chapter, along with explanations of the reasoning involved.

CONCEPTUAL CHECKPOINT 6.1

Which of these statements is *always* true for samples of atomic elements, regardless of the type of element present in the samples?

(a) If two samples of different elements contain the same number of atoms, they must contain the same number of moles.

(b) If two samples of different elements have the same mass, they must contain the same number of moles.

(c) If two samples of different elements have the same mass, they must contain the same number of atoms.

Answers to Conceptual Checkpoints are given at the end of each chapter, along with explanations of the reasoning involved.

Answers to Conceptual Checkpoints

6.1 (a) The mole is a counting unit; it represents a definite number (Avogadro's number, 6.02×10^{23}). Therefore, a given number of atoms always represents a precise number of moles, regardless of what atom is involved. Atoms of different elements have different masses, so if samples of different elements have the same mass, they *cannot* contain the same number of atoms or moles.

6.2 (a) Avogadro's number was defined so as to make the molar mass of a compound (the mass of one mole, or Avogadro's number of molecules or formula units), *in grams*, numerically equal to the formula mass of the compound in amu. In order for the molar mass *in kilograms* to be numerically equal to the formula mass in amu, we would need 1000 times as many molecules or formula units in a mole. In other words, Avogadro's number would have to be 1000 times larger, or 6.02×10^{26}.

6.3 (b) This compound has the highest ratio of oxygen atoms to chromium atoms, and so must have the greatest mass percent of oxygen.

Developing Problem-Solving Skills

The development of problem-solving skills is the main goal of the text. To this end, *Introductory Chemistry* develops a systematic approach in which problem-solving skills are

- emphasized throughout each chapter,
- developed through many in-chapter Examples,
- reinforced with *Skillbuilder* exercises immediately following each Example,
- reviewed in unique chapter summaries, and
- practiced and synthesized in end-of-chapter exercises.

Starting with the simplest problems involving unit conversions, the text presents students with a basic procedure for solving most chemical problems. This procedure and the Examples that demonstrate its use have a number of special pedagogical features, designed to help students master problem-solving skills through understanding rather than mechanical repetition.

UNIQUE Solution Maps

Many of the Examples employ a unique visual approach in which students are shown how to draw a *solution map* for the problem. They are taught to outline the steps—using conversion factors and equations—needed to get from the information they are given to the information they are trying to find. This technique encourages students to think through the problem and formulate a solution strategy, and helps them see the relationship between the big picture and the individual steps. In response to requests from users of the text, there is a more consistent use of color for the buttons in the solution maps in this edition.

Converting between Grams of a Compound and Grams of a Constituent Element

Now, we have everything we need to solve our sodium problem. Suppose we want to know how many grams of sodium there are in 15 g of NaCl. The chemical formula gives us the relationship between moles of Na and moles of NaCl:

1 mol Na ≡ 1 mol NaCl

To use this relationship, we need *mol* NaCl. But, we have *g* NaCl. We can, however, use the *molar mass* of NaCl to convert from g NaCl to mol NaCl. Then we use the conversion factor from the chemical formula to convert to mol Na. Finally, we use the molar mass of Na to convert to g Na. The solution map is:

Notice that we must convert from g NaCl to mol NaCl *before* we can use the chemical formula as a conversion factor.

NEW Two-Column Examples

In this edition, all but the simplest Examples are presented in a unique two-column format. The left column explains each step, while the right column shows how the step is executed. This format encourages students to think about the reason for each step in the solution and to fit the steps together in the context of an overall plan.

UNIQUE *Skillbuilder* Exercises

Every worked Example in *Introductory Chemistry* is followed by at least one similar but unworked *Skillbuilder* problem, allowing students to make an immediate test of the problem-solving techniques they have just learned. Many important Examples also have an additional *Skillbuilder Plus* problem, affording students further opportunity for practice. For immediate reinforcement, answers to all *Skillbuilder* and *Skillbuilder Plus* problems are given at the end of each chapter.

UNIQUE Three-Column Problem-Solving Procedures

Among the distinctive features of this book are the numerous specific procedures for solving particular types of problems, presented in a unique three-column format. The first column outlines the problem-solving procedure and explains the reasoning that underlies each step. The second and third columns show how the steps are implemented for two typical Examples. Seeing the method applied to solve two related but slightly different problems helps students understand the general procedure in a way that no single Example could convey.

Visualization: Connecting the Macroscopic and Microscopic Worlds

Today's students often absorb information best when it is presented in graphic form or accompanied by some visual reinforcement. While pictures cannot replace clear explanations, they can supplement them in crucial ways. The art program of this book was expressly conceived to help students visualize connections between molecular processes and the behavior of macroscopic objects.

◀ Many concepts are illustrated using a two-part visual image: a photograph of a real-world object or process, and a depiction of what is taking place on the molecular level, either superimposed or shown as a magnified breakout.

▼ Many molecular formulas in the text are depicted not only with structural formulas, but also with space-filling drawings of the molecules for greater clarity and vividness.

▲ Figure 3.11 Vaporization: a physical change If you push the button on a lighter without turning the flint, some of the liquid butane vaporizes to gaseous butane. Since the liquid butane and the gaseous butane are both composed of butane molecules, this is a physical change.

▲ Figure 3.12 Burning: a chemical change If you push the button *and* turn the flint to create a spark, you produce a flame. The butane molecules react with oxygen molecules in air to form new molecules, carbon dioxide and water. This is a chemical change.

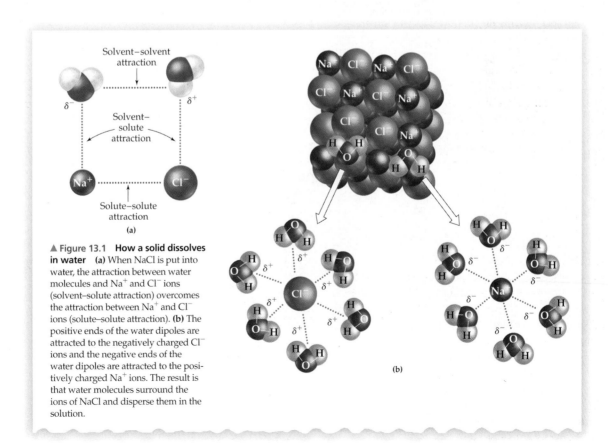

▲ Figure 13.1 How a solid dissolves in water (a) When NaCl is put into water, the attraction between water molecules and Na$^+$ and Cl$^-$ ions (solvent–solute attraction) overcomes the attraction between Na$^+$ and Cl$^-$ ions (solute–solute attraction). (b) The positive ends of the water dipoles are attracted to the negatively charged Cl$^-$ ions and the negative ends of the water dipoles are attracted to the positively charged Na$^+$ ions. The result is that water molecules surround the ions of NaCl and disperse them in the solution.

Creating Interest in Chemistry

Students learn best when they feel that the material is interesting and relevant to their lives. Interest in the field of chemistry and in the topic under study is enhanced by means of two recurring features.

UNIQUE Chapter Openers

Every chapter opens with a description of an everyday situation or practical application that clearly demonstrates the importance of the material covered in that chapter. These openers often involve topics that are particularly relevant to the lives of students, such as health, consumer, environmental, or societal issues. Each chapter introductory narrative is accompanied by a piece of art portraying the content in a striking visual image that combines macroscopic and molecular views. Each chapter introductory narrative is accompanied by a unique and striking visual image, combining macroscopic and molecular views, that brings the content to life for the student.

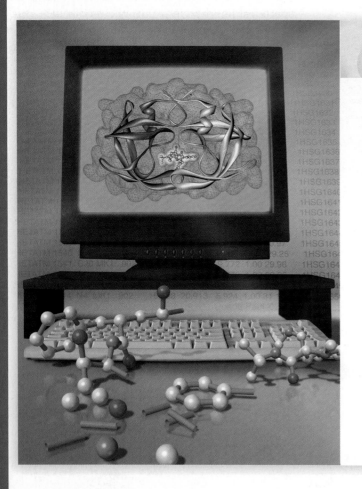

◄ The gold-colored structure on the computer screen is a representation of HIV-protease. The molecule shown in the center is Indinavir, a protease inhibitor.

CHAPTER 10

Chemical Bonding

"The fascination of a growing science lies in the work of the pioneers at the very borderland of the unknown, but to reach this frontier one must pass over well traveled roads ..."

Gilbert N. Lewis (1875–1946)

10.1 Bonding Models and AIDS Drugs
10.2 Representing Valence Electrons with Dots
10.3 Lewis Structures for Ionic Compounds: Electrons Transferred
10.4 Covalent Lewis Structures: Electrons Shared
10.5 Writing Lewis Structures for Covalent Compounds
10.6 Resonance: Equivalent Lewis Structures for the Same Molecule
10.7 Predicting the Shapes of Molecules
10.8 Electronegativity and Polarity: Why Oil and Water Don't Mix

10.1 Bonding Models and AIDS Drugs

Proteins are discussed in more detail in Chapter 19.

In 1989, researchers discovered the structure of a molecule called HIV-protease. HIV-protease is a protein (a class of biological molecules) synthesized by the human immunodeficiency virus (HIV), which causes AIDS. HIV-protease is crucial to the virus's ability to replicate itself. Without HIV-protease, HIV could not spread in the human body because the virus could not copy itself, and AIDS would not develop.

With knowledge of the HIV-protease structure, drug companies set out to design a molecule that would disable protease by sticking to the working part of the molecule (called the *active site*). To design such a molecule, researchers used **bonding theories**—models that predict how atoms bond together to form molecules—to simulate how potential drug molecules would interact with the protease molecule. By the early 1990s, these companies had developed several drug molecules that seemed to work. Since these molecules inhibit the action of HIV-protease, they are called *protease inhibitors*. In human trials, protease inhibitors in combination with other drugs have decreased the viral count in HIV-infected individuals to undetectable levels. Many AIDS patients are still alive today because of the development of these drugs.

Bonding theories are central to chemistry because they predict how atoms bond together to form compounds. They predict what combinations of atoms form compounds and what combinations do not. For example, bonding theories predict why salt is NaCl and not NaCl₂ and why water is H₂O and not H₃O. Bonding theories also explain the shapes of molecules, which in turn determine many of their physical and chemical properties. The bonding theory you will learn in this chapter is called *Lewis theory*, named after the American chemist who developed it, G. N. Lewis (1875–1946). It involves representing electrons as dots and drawing what are called *dot structures* or *Lewis structures* to represent molecules. These structures, which are fairly simple to draw, have tremendous predictive power. It takes just a few minutes to

305

Interest Boxes

Introductory Chemistry has four types of interest boxes: Everyday Chemistry, Chemistry in the Media, Chemistry in the Environment, and Chemistry and Health.

Antifreeze in Frogs

On the outside, wood frogs (*Rana sylvatica*) look like most other frogs. They are only a few inches long and have characteristic greenish-brown skin. However, wood frogs survive cold winters in a remarkable way—they partially freeze. In the frozen state, the frog has no heartbeat, no blood circulation, no breathing, and no brain activity. Within 1 to 2 hours of thawing, however, these vital functions return, and the frog hops off to find food. How is this possible?

Most cold-blooded animals cannot survive freezing temperatures because the water within their cells freezes. As we learned in Section 12.8, when water freezes, it expands, irreversibly damaging cells. When the wood frog hibernates for the winter, however, it secretes large amounts of glucose into its blood and into the interior of its cells. When the temperature drops below freezing, extracellular bodily fluids, such as those in the abdominal cavity, freeze solid. Fluids within cells, however, remain liquid because the high glucose concentration lowers their freezing point. In other words, the concentrated glucose solution within the frog's cells acts as antifreeze, preventing the water within the cells from freezing and allowing the frog to survive.

CAN YOU ANSWER THIS? *The wood frog can survive at body temperatures as low as −8.0 °C. Calculate the molality of a glucose solution ($C_6H_{12}O_6$) required to lower the freezing point of water to −8.0 °C.*

REFERENCE: Another interesting example is discussed in "Freeze-Proof Bugs," Donald DeLorenzo, *J. Chem. Educ.* 1981 58 788

◀ The wood frog survives cold winters by partially freezing. The fluids within the frog's cells, however, remain liquid to temperatures as low as −8 °C. These fluids are protected by a high concentration of glucose that acts as antifreeze, lowering their freezing point.

- *Everyday Chemistry* boxes describe in chemical terms what is happening on the atomic or molecular level in common, everyday processes, such as the bleaching of hair, and explain the properties of familiar materials, such as Kevlar.
- *Chemistry in the Media* boxes discuss chemical topics that have been in the news, such as the controversy over oxygenated fuels.
- *Chemistry in the Environment* boxes deal with environmental issues that are closely tied to chemistry, such as acid rain and the ozone hole.
- *Chemistry and Health* boxes focus on biomedical topics as well as those related to personal health and fitness, such as drug dosage, ulcers and antacids, and isoosmotic solutions for transfusions.

The interest boxes in *Introductory Chemistry* all contain questions that relate directly to the chapter material, helping students apply what they have just learned.

Review and Assessment

UNIQUE Chapter in Review

Each chapter ends with a review consisting of two sections, the first focusing on chemical principles and the second on chemical skills. Each section is itself divided into two columns.

CHAPTER IN REVIEW

Chemical Principles	Relevance
The Mole Concept: The mole is a specific number (6.022×10^{23}) that is defined so as to allow us to easily count atoms or molecules by weighing them. One mole of any element has a mass equivalent to its atomic mass in grams, and a mole of any compound has a mass equivalent to its formula mass in grams. The mass of 1 mol of an element or compound is called the molar mass.	**The Mole Concept:** The mole concept allows us to determine the number of atoms or molecules in a sample from its mass. Just as a hardware store customer wants to know the number of nails in a certain weight of nails, so we want to know the number of atoms in a certain mass of atoms. Since atoms are too small to count, we use their mass.

Converting between Grams of a Compound and Grams of a Constituent Element (Section 6.5)

To convert from grams of a compound to grams of a constituent element, first use the molar mass of the compound to convert from grams of the compound to moles of the compound. Then use the chemical formula to obtain a conversion factor to convert from moles of the compound to moles of the constituent element. Finally, use the molar mass of the constituent element to convert from moles of the element to grams of the element.

To convert from grams of a constituent element to grams of a compound, first use the molar mass of the constituent element to convert from grams of the element to moles of the element. Then use the chemical formula to obtain a conversion factor to convert from moles of the constituent element to moles of the compound. Finally, use the molar mass of the compound to convert from moles of the compound to grams of the compound.

EXAMPLE 6.17   Converting between Grams of a Compound and Grams of a Constituent Element

Find the grams of iron in 79.2 g of Fe_2O_3.

Given: 79.2 g Fe_2O_3

Find: g Fe

Conversion Factors:

Molar mass Fe_2O_3
$$= 2(55.85) + 3(16.00)$$
$$= 159.70 \text{ g/mol}$$
$$2 \text{ mol Fe} = 1 \text{ mol } Fe_2O_3$$

Solution Map:

g Fe_2O_3 → mol Fe_2O_3 → mol Fe → g Fe

$$\frac{1 \text{ mol } Fe_2O_3}{159.70 \text{ g } Fe_2O_3} \qquad \frac{2 \text{ mol Fe}}{1 \text{ mol } Fe_2O_3} \qquad \frac{55.85 \text{ g Fe}}{1 \text{ mol Fe}}$$

Solution:

$$79.2 \text{ g } Fe_2O_3 \times \frac{1 \text{ mol } Fe_2O_3}{159.70 \text{ g } Fe_2O_3} \times \frac{2 \text{ mol Fe}}{1 \text{ mol } Fe_2O_3}$$
$$\times \frac{55.85 \text{ g Fe}}{1 \text{ mol Fe}} = 55.4 \text{ g Fe}$$

- In the Chemical Principles section, the left column summarizes the key principles while the right column tells why each is important.

- In the Chemical Skills section, the left column describes the key skills while the right column contains a worked Example illustrating each skill.

Student Exercises

All chapters contain exercises divided into four types: questions, problems, cumulative problems, and highlight problems. Many new exercises have been added in this edition to provide a full range of assessment opportunities.

◀ The *Questions* are qualitative, requiring the student to summarize important chapter concepts.

Questions

1. Why is reaction stoichiometry important? Can you give some examples?
2. What does it mean to say that two quantities in a chemical reaction are equivalent?
3. Write conversion factors showing the relationships between moles of each of the reactants and products in the following reaction.

   $$N_2(g) + 3\,H_2(g) \longrightarrow 2\,NH_3(g)$$

4. For the reaction in Problem 3, how many molecules of H_2 are required to completely react with two molecules of N_2? How many moles of H_2 are required to completely react with 2 mol of N_2?
5. Write the conversion factor that you would use to convert from moles of Cl_2 to moles of NaCl in the following reaction.

If you have 7 cups of noodles, 27 tomatoes, and 9 cloves of garlic, how many servings of pasta can you make? Which ingredient limits the amount of pasta that is possible?
9. In a chemical reaction, what is the limiting reactant?
10. In a chemical reaction, what is the theoretical yield?
11. In a chemical reaction, what are the actual yield and percent yield?
12. If you are given a chemical equation and specific amounts of each reactant in grams, how would you determine how much product can possibly be made?
13. Consider the following generic chemical reaction.

   $$A + 2\,B \longrightarrow C + D$$

Suppose you have 12 g of A and 24 g of B. Which of the following statements are true?

◀ The *Problems* are quantitative in nature. This section, the longest, is divided by headings into subsections dealing with the major topical areas of the chapter.

Mass Percent Composition

67. A 2.45-g sample of strontium completely reacts with oxygen to form 2.89 g of strontium oxide. Use this data to calculate the mass percent composition of strontium in strontium oxide.

68. A 4.78-g sample of aluminum completely reacts with oxygen to form 6.67 g of aluminum oxide. Use this data to calculate the mass percent composition of aluminum in aluminum oxide.

69. A 1.912-g sample of calcium chloride is decomposed into its constituent elements and found to contain 0.690 g Ca and 1.222 g Cl. Calculate the mass percent composition of Ca and Cl in calcium chloride.

70. A 0.45-g sample of aspirin is decomposed into its constituent elements and found to contain 0.27 g C, 0.020 g H, and 0.16 g O. Calculate the mass percent composition of C, H, and O in aspirin.

71. Copper(II) fluoride contains 37.42% F by mass. Use this percentage to calculate the mass of fluorine in grams contained in 28.5 g of copper(II) fluoride.

72. Silver chloride, often used in silver plating, contains 75.27% Ag. Calculate the mass of silver chloride in grams required to make 4.8 g of silver plating.

▶ *Cumulative Problems* require students to synthesize several of the skills they have learned in the chapter and in previous chapters.

Cumulative Problems

97. A pure copper cube has an edge length of 1.42 cm. How many copper atoms does it contain? (volume of a cube = (edge length)^3; density of copper = 8.96 g/cm^3)

98. A pure silver sphere has a radius of 0.886 cm. How many silver atoms does it contain? (Volume of a sphere = $\frac{4}{3}\pi r^3$; density of silver = 10.5 g/cm^3)

99. A drop of water has a volume of approximately 0.05 mL. How many water molecules does it contain? (density of water = 1.0 g/cm^3).

100. Fingernail-polish remover is primarily acetone (C_3H_6O). How many acetone molecules are in a bottle of acetone with a volume of 325 mL? (density of acetone = 0.788 g/cm^3).

101. Complete the following table:

Substance	Mass	Moles	Number of Particles (atoms or molecules)
Ar	___	4.5×10^{-4}	___
NO$_2$	___	___	1.09×10^{20}
K	.22.4 mg	___	___
C$_8$H$_{18}$	3.76 kg	___	___

102. Complete the following table:

Substance	Mass	Moles	Number of Particles (atoms or molecules)
C$_6$H$_{12}$O$_6$	15.8 g	___	___
Pb	___	___	9.04×10^{21}
CF$_4$	22.5 kg	___	___
C	___	0.0388	___

▶ *Highlight Problems* are set within a context that will be of particular interest to the student because of its timeliness, familiarity, or relevance to some important issue. Such problems often include photographs or art.

All Problems and Cumulative Problems are paired: A problem that is answered in the back of the book (identified by a blue number) is followed by a similar problem without an answer. All answers are available in the instructor's full *Solutions Manual*.

101. A major event affecting global climate is the El Niño/La Niña cycle. In this cycle, equatorial Pacific Ocean waters warm by several degrees Celsius above normal (El Niño) and then cool by several degrees Celsius below normal (La Niña). This cycle affects weather not only in North and South America, but as far away as Africa. Why does a seemingly small change in ocean temperature have such a large impact on weather?

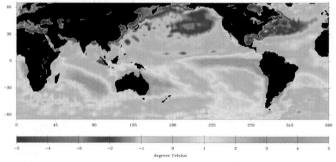

▲ Temperature anomaly plot of the world's oceans for December 23, 1997. The red section off the western coast of South America is the El Niño effect, a warming of the Pacific Ocean along the equator.

Print and Media Resources

 For the Instructor

Annotated Instructor's Edition (0–13–149513–5) with annotations by Carl Hoeger, University of California, San Diego. This special edition contains the entire student text plus marginal annotations to aid instructors in preparing their lectures. Included are suggestions for classroom demonstrations, teaching tips, Transparency Pack icons, and references to articles on the effective presentation of many chemical topics.

Instructor's Resource and Full Solutions Manual (0–13–147062–0) by Mark Ott, Jackson Community College, and Matthew Johll, Illinois Valley Community College. This manual features lecture outlines with presentation suggestions, teaching tips, suggested in-class demonstrations, and topics for classroom discussion. It also contains full solutions to all the end-of-chapter problems from the text.

Test Item File (0–13–147064–7) by Kuruvilla Zachariah, Ohio University. This printed test bank includes more than 1300 questions. A computerized version of the test item file is available in the Instructor's Resource Center.

Transparency Pack (0–13–147069–8) This set contains 175 full-color transparencies from the text. Chosen specifically to put principles into visual perspective, it can save you time while you are preparing your lectures.

Instructor's Resource Center on CD/DVD (0–13–147063–9) This fully searchable and integrated collection of resources is designed to help you make efficient and effective use of your lecture preparation time as well as to enhance your classroom presentations and assessment efforts. This package features the following:

- Nearly all the art from the text, including tables, in JPG and PDF formats; movies; animations; interactive activities; and the *Instructor's Resource Manual* Word™ files.

- Four PowerPoint™ presentations: (1) a lecture outline presentation for each chapter, (2) all the art from the text, (3) the worked Examples from the text, and (4) CRS (Classroom Response System) questions.

- A search engine tool that lets you find relevant resources via a number of different parameters, such as key terms, learning objectives, figure numbers, and resource type.

- The TestGen, a computerized version of the Test Item File that allows you to create and tailor exams to your needs.

ONEKEY   (Access at http://chem.prenhall.com/tro)

OneKey offers the best teaching and learning resources all in one place.

- OneKey for *Introductory Chemistry, Second Edition*, is all your *students* need for access to your course materials anytime, anywhere.

- OneKey is all *you* need to plan and administer your course.

Conveniently organized by text chapter, these compiled resources help you save time and help your students reinforce and apply what they have learned in class.

Student Resources

- The new **WebBook**, a full electronic version of the text with embedded Live Examples, animations, movies, and molecules

- **Live Examples**, an interactive version of selected Examples from the text

- A **3-D Molecule Gallery** to help students visualize many important molecules introduced in the course

- **Quizzes** of multiple-choice and true/false questions featuring hints and answer-specific feedback

- More online resources such as **Research Navigator, Link Library,** and the **Math Tutorial**

Instructor Resources

- Resources from the **Instructor's Resource Center on CD/DVD** (described on the previous page) are also included in OneKey.

Assessment Content

- Multiple choice **Quiz Questions** with hints and feedback

- **Student Tutorials** featuring animations, movies, and molecules with multiple-choice follow-up questions

- **Test Item File** questions

PHGradeAssist 2

- **PH GradeAssist** Available only through OneKey, PH GradeAssist is a timesaving homework and assessment system that allows students unlimited practice with algorithmically generated problems in an online environment. Instructors can administer quizzes and assignments, control the content and assignment parameters, and receive assignments and view performance statistics with the built-in gradebook. This customizable system has a volume built specifically for this text. Content includes selected end-of-chapter questions with detailed feedback as well as links to appropriate **WebBook** sections. The PH GradeAssist platform is going through continual, seamless upgrades, to offer instructors more options and to make the program easier for students to use.

With contributions by Roy Kennedy, Massachusetts Bay Community College; Mark E. Ott, Jackson Community College; Michael Hauser, St. Louis Community College–Meramec; Jeffrey Lehman, Grossmont College; Cary Willard, Grossmont College; and Bette Kreuz, University of Michigan–Dearborn.

COURSE MANAGEMENT

All of the content in **OneKey** is also available in **WebCT** and **Blackboard**. Prentice Hall offers content cartridges for these text-specific Classroom Management Systems. Visit **http://cms.prenhall.com** or contact your Prentice Hall sales representative for details. More basic courses, loaded with just the Test Item file, are also available.

 # For the Student

Study Guide (0–13–147071-X) by Donna Friedman, St. Louis Community College–Florissant Valley. This book assists students through the text material with chapter overviews and practice problems for each major concept in the text, followed by two or three self-tests with answers at the end of each chapter.

Selected Solutions Manual (0–13–147085–2) by Matthew Johll, Illinois Valley Community College. This book provides solutions only to those problems that have a short answer in the text's Answers section (problems numbered in blue in the text).

Math Review Toolkit (0–13–147066–3) by Gary L. Long, Virginia Tech. This print resource, free when packaged with the text, reinforces the skills necessary to succeed in chemistry. Keyed specifically to chapters in *Introductory Chemistry, Second Edition*, it includes additional mathematics review, problem-solving tools, and examples.

◀ *Companion Website*
(Access at **http://chem.prenhall.com/tro**) For students who wish to utilize a Website for additional practice, the Companion Website contains the **Chemical Principles**, **Live Examples**, **Molecule Gallery**, **Practice Quiz**, **True/False**, and **Math Tutorial** modules included in the Course Management Systems described previously.

Student Accelerator CD-ROM
This student CD—which contains animations, movies, and molecules from the Companion Website—accelerates the performance of the Website when students download high-bandwidth media, so that students are not restricted by slow connections. It can also be used apart from the Companion Website if a student doesn't have a live Internet connection. Many of the media elements available on the CD are referenced in the text by means of marginal icons and titles. The *Introductory Chemistry, Second Edition* Accelerator CD comes packaged with every new student textbook for no additional charge.

Acknowledgments

This book has been a group effort, and there are many people whose help has meant a great deal to me. First and foremost, I would like to thank my editor, Kent Porter Hamann, who took a chance on a little-known author from a small liberal-arts college when she signed me to write the first edition of this book. She has believed in me and encouraged me from day one—I am forever indebted to her. I also owe much to Ray Mullaney, whose wisdom and gentle guidance have steered this project throughout, as well as to John Challice and Paul Corey for their unwavering commitment and support.

New to this edition is Dan Schiller, a development editor with an author's instinct and an incredibly sharp eye for detail. I am grateful to Dan for his ideas, his persistence, his deep and broad knowledge, and especially for the many hours he has poured into this project. This book would be much different without him. I deeply appreciate the expertise and professionalism of my copy editor, Amy Schneider, as well as the skill and diligence of Fran Daniele, Simone Lukashov, and their colleagues at Prepare. Thanks are also due to my media editor, Michael Richards, ably assisted by Ed Dodd III and Bridget K. Page; my project manager, Kristen Kaiser; executive marketing manager Steve Sartori; art director Jon Boylan; Patti Burns, Connie Long, and the staff of Artworks; editorial assistant extraordinaire Jackie Howard; and the rest of the Prentice Hall team—they are part of a first-class operation. This text has benefited immeasurably from their talents and hard work. I owe a special debt of gratitude to Quade Paul, who made my ideas come alive in his art.

I am happy to acknowledge the help of my colleagues Allan Nishimura and David Marten, who have supported me in my department while I worked on this book. I am also deeply obligated to my provost, Shirley Mullen, who gives me the freedom to be who I am and encourages me to develop in ways unique to myself. She is an outstanding faculty leader and an inspiration to me.

I am grateful to those who have given so much to me personally while writing this book. First on that list is my wife, Ann. Her patience and love for me are beyond description. I must also thank my children, Michael, Ali, Kyle, and Kaden, whose smiling faces and love of life always inspire me. I come from a large Cuban family, whose closeness and support most people would envy. Thanks to my parents, Nivaldo and Sara; my siblings, Sarita, Mary, and Jorge; my siblings-in-law, Jeff, Nachy, Karen, and John; my nephews and nieces, Germain, Danny, Lisette, Sara, and Kenny. These are the people with whom I celebrate life.

Lastly, I am indebted to the many reviewers, listed next, whose ideas are scattered throughout this book. They have corrected me, inspired me, and sharpened my thinking on how best to teach this subject we call chemistry. I deeply appreciate their commitment to this project.

Reviewers of the 2nd Edition

David S. Ballantine, Jr.,
Northern Illinois University

Colin Bateman,
Brevard Community College

Michele Berkey,
San Juan College

Steven R. Boone,
Central Missouri State University

Bryan E. Breyfogle,
Southwest Missouri State University

Morris Bramlett,
University of Arkansas–Monticello

Frank Carey,
Wharton County Junior College

Robbey C. Culp,
Fresno City College

Michelle Driessen,
University of Minnesota–

Minneapolis

Donna G. Friedman,
St. Louis Community College–Florissant Valley

Crystal Gambino,
Manatee Community College

Steve Gunther,
Albuquerque Technical Vocational Institute

Michael Hauser,
St. Louis Community College–Meramec

Newton P. Hillard, Jr.,
Eastern New Mexico University

Carl A. Hoeger,
University of California–San Diego

Donna K. Howell,
Angelo State University

Nichole Jackson,
Odessa College

T. G. Jackson,
University of South Alabama

Donald R. Jones,
Lincoln Land Community College

Roy Kennedy,
Massachusetts Bay Community College

Blake Key,
Northwestern Michigan College

Kirk Kawagoe,
Fresno City College

Rebecca A. Krystyniak,
St. Cloud State University

Laurie LeBlanc,
Cuyamaca College

Ronald C. Marks,
Warner Southern College

Carol A. Martinez,
Albuquerque Technical Vocational Institute

Charles Michael McCallum,
University of the Pacific

Robin McCann,
Shippensburg University

Victor Ryzhov,
Northern Illinois University

Theodore Sakano,
Rockland Community College

Deborah G. Simon,

Santa Fe Community College

Mary Sohn,
Florida Institute of Technology

Peter-John Stanskas,
San Bernardino Valley College

James G. Tarter,
College of Southern Idaho

Ruth M. Topich,
Virginia Commonwealth University

Eric Trump,
Emporia State University

Mary Urban,
College of Lake County

Richard Watt,
University of New Mexico

Lynne Zeman,
Kirkwood Community College

Reviewers of the 1st Edition

Lori Allen
University of Wisconsin—Parkside

Laura Andersson
Big Bend Community College

Danny R. Bedgood
Arizona State University

Christine V. Bilicki
Pasadena City College

Warren Bosch
Elgin Community College

Bryan E. Breyfogle
Southwest Missouri State University

Carl J. Carrano
Southwest Texas State University

Donald C. Davis
College of Lake County

Donna G. Friedman
St. Louis Community College at Florissant Valley

Leslie Wo-Mei Fung

Loyola University of Chicago

Dwayne Gergens
San Diego Mesa College

George Goth
Skyline College

Jan Gryko
Jacksonville State University

Roy Kennedy
Massachusetts Bay Community College

C. Michael McCallum
University of the Pacific

Kathy Mitchell
St. Petersburg Junior College

Bill Nickels
Schoolcraft College

Bob Perkins
Kwantlen University College

Mark Porter
Texas Tech University

Caryn Prudenté
University of Southern Maine

Connie M. Roberts
Henderson State University

Rill Ann Reuter
Winona State University

Jeffery A. Schneider
SUNY–Oswego

Kim D. Summerhays
University of San Francisco

Ronald H. Takata
Honolulu Community College

Calvin D. Tormanen
Central Michigan University

Eric L. Trump
Emporia State University

CHAPTER 1

The Chemical World

"Imagination is more important than knowledge."

Albert Einstein (1879–1955)

1.1 Soda Pop Fizz

Open a can of soda pop and you hear the familiar "chchchch" of pressure release. Take a sip and you feel the carbon dioxide bubbles on your tongue. Shake the can before you open it and you will be sprayed with the liquid. A can of soda pop, like most things, is a chemical mixture. Soda pop consists primarily of sugar, water, and carbon dioxide. It is the unique combination of these chemicals that gives soda pop its properties. Do you want to know why soda pop tastes sweet? You need to know about sugar and solutions of sugar with water. We learn about solutions in Chapter 13. Do you want to know why soda fizzes when you open it? You need to understand gases and their ability to dissolve in liquids and how that ability changes with changing pressure. We learn about gases in Chapter 11. Do you want to know why drinking too much soda pop makes you gain weight? You need to understand energy and the production of energy by chemical reactions. We discuss energy in Chapter 3 and chemical reactions in Chapter 7. You need not go any farther than your own home and your own everyday experiences to discover chemical questions. Chemicals compose virtually everything: the soda; this book; your pencil; indeed, even your own body.

► Virtually everything around you is composed of chemicals.

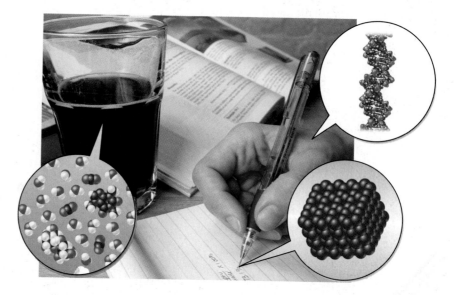

◄ Soda pop is a mixture of carbon dioxide and water and a few other substances that give flavor and color. When soda pop is poured into a glass, some of the carbon dioxide molecules come out of the mixture, producing the familiar fizz.

1

Chemists are particularly interested in the connections between the properties of substances and the particles that compose them. For example, why does soda pop fizz? Like all substances, soda pop is composed of tiny particles called atoms. Atoms are so small that a single drop of soda pop contains about one billion trillion of them. In soda pop, as in most substances, these atoms are bound together to form several different types of molecules. The molecules important to fizzing are carbon dioxide and water. Carbon dioxide molecules consist of three atoms—one carbon and two oxygen—held together in a straight line by chemical bonds.

Water molecules also consist of three atoms—one oxygen and two hydrogen—bonded together, but rather than being straight like carbon dioxide, the water molecule is bent.

The details of how atoms bond together to form a molecule—straight, bent, or some other shape—as well as the type of atoms in the molecule, determine *everything* about the substance that the molecule composes. The characteristics of water molecules make water a liquid at room temperature. The characteristics of carbon dioxide molecules make carbon dioxide a gas at room temperature. The characteristics of sugar molecules allow them to interact with our taste buds to produce the sensation of sweetness.

The makers of soda pop use pressure to force gaseous carbon dioxide molecules to mix with liquid water molecules. As long as the can of soda is sealed, the carbon dioxide molecules remain mixed with the water molecules, held there by pressure. When the can is opened, the pressure is released and carbon dioxide molecules escape out of the soda mixture (▼ Figure 1.1). As they do, they create bubbles—the familiar fizz of soda pop.

We will explore the nature of atoms, molecules, and chemical bonds more fully in later chapters. For now, think of atoms and molecules as tiny particles that compose all matter, and chemical bonds as the attachments that hold atoms together.

▶ **Figure 1.1   Where the fizz comes from**   Bubbles in soda pop are pockets of carbon dioxide gas molecules escaping out of the liquid water.

1.2   Chemicals Compose Ordinary Things

▲ The public often has a very narrow view of chemicals, thinking of them only as dangerous poisons or pollutants.

TUTORIAL
Chemistry Examples

Is soda pop composed of chemicals? In the broad definition of chemicals, yes. In fact, there is nothing you can hold or touch that is *not* made of chemicals. Unfortunately, when most people think of chemicals, they envision a can of paint thinner in their garage marked with a skull and crossbones, or they recall headlines about rivers polluted by industrial compounds. But chemicals compose more than just these things—they compose ordinary things, too. Chemicals compose the air we breathe and the water we drink. They compose toothpaste, Tylenol, and toilet paper. Chemicals make up virtually everything we come into contact with. This broader notion of chemicals is what chemists use. Chemistry explains the properties and behavior of chemicals, in the broadest sense, by helping us understand the molecules that compose them.

As you experience the world around you, molecules are interacting to create your experience. Imagine watching a sunset. Molecules are involved in every step. Molecules in air interact with light from the sun, scattering away the blue and green light and leaving the red and orange light to create the color. Molecules in your eyes absorb that light, and as a result are altered in a way that sends a signal to your brain. Molecules in your brain then interpret the signal to produce images and emotions. All of this—mediated by molecules—creates the experience of seeing a sunset.

Chemists are interested in why ordinary things are the way they are. Why is water a liquid? Why is salt a solid? Why does soda fizz? Why is a sunset red? Throughout this book you will learn the answers to these questions and many others. You will learn the connections between the behavior of matter and the behavior of the particles that compose it.

◀ Chemists are interested in knowing why ordinary things, such as water, are the way they are. When a chemist sees a pitcher of water, she thinks of the molecules that compose the liquid and how they determine its properties.

1.3   All Things Are Made of Atoms and Molecules

Professor Richard Feynman, in a lecture to first-year physics students at the California Institute of Technology, said that the most important idea in all human knowledge is that *all things are made of atoms*. Since atoms are usually bound together to form molecules, however, a chemist might add the concept of *molecules* to Feynman's bold assertion. This simple idea—that all

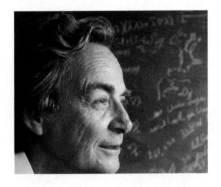

▲ Richard Feynman (1918–1988), Nobel Prize–winning physicist and popular professor at California Institute of Technology.

things are made of atoms and molecules—explains much about our world and our experience of it. Atoms and molecules determine how matter behaves—if they were different, matter would be different. Water molecules, for example, determine how water behaves. Sugar molecules determine how sugar behaves, and the molecules that compose humans determine much about how we behave.

There is a direct connection between the world of atoms and molecules and the world you and I experience every day. Chemists explore this connection. They seek to understand it. A good, simple definition of **chemistry** is the science that tries to understand what matter does by studying what atoms and molecules do.

Chemistry—The science that seeks to understand what matter does by studying what atoms and molecules do.

1.4   The Scientific Method: How Chemists Think

Chemists are scientists and use the **scientific method**—a way of learning that emphasizes observation and experimentation—to understand the world. The scientific method stands in contrast to ancient Greek philosophies that emphasized *reason* as the way to understand the world. Although the scientific method is not a rigid procedure that automatically leads to a definitive answer, it does have key characteristics that distinguish it from other ways of acquiring knowledge. These key characteristics include the observation of nature, the formulation of hypotheses, the testing of hypotheses by experiment, and the formulation of laws and theories.

The first step in acquiring scientific knowledge (▼ Figure 1.2) is often the **observation** or measurement of some aspect of nature. Some observations are simple, requiring nothing more than the naked eye. Other observations emerge from experiments that rely on the use of increasingly sensitive instrumentation. Occasionally, an important observation happens entirely by chance. Alexander Fleming, for example, discovered penicillin when he observed a bacteria-free circle around mold that had accidentally grown on his culture plate. Regardless of how the observation occurs, it usually involves the measurement or description of some aspect of the physical world. For example, Antoine Lavoisier (1743–1794), a French chemist who studied combustion, made careful measurements on the mass of objects before and after burning them in closed containers. He noticed that there was no change in the mass during combustion. Lavoisier made an *observation* about the physical world.

The mass of an object is a measure of the quantity of matter within it.

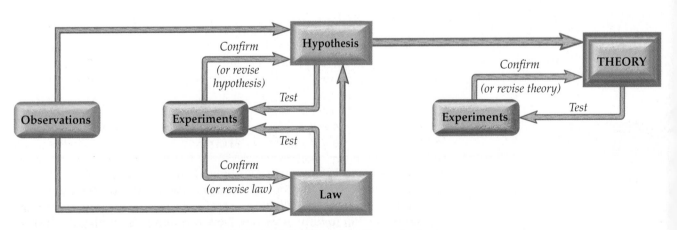

▲ Figure 1.2   **The scientific method**

▶ (Right) Painting of the French chemist Antoine Lavoisier and his wife, Marie, who helped him in his work by illustrating his experiments, recording results, and translating scientific articles from English. (The Metropolitan Museum of Art)
(Far right) John Dalton, the English chemist who formulated the atomic theory.

Observations often lead scientists to formulate a **hypothesis**, a tentative interpretation or explanation of the observations. For example, Lavoisier explained his observations on combustion by hypothesizing that combustion involved the combination of a substance with a component of air. A good hypothesis is *falsifiable*, which means that further testing has the potential to prove it wrong. Hypotheses are tested by **experiments**, highly controlled observations designed to validate or invalidate hypotheses. The results of an experiment may confirm a hypothesis or show it to be mistaken in some way. In the latter case, the hypothesis may have to be modified, or even discarded and replaced by an alternative. Either way, the new or revised hypothesis must then be tested through further experimentation.

Sometimes a number of similar observations can lead to the development of a **scientific law**, a brief statement that synthesizes past observations and predicts future ones. For example, based on his observations of combustion, Lavoisier developed the **law of conservation of mass** that states, "In a chemical reaction matter is neither created nor destroyed." This statement grew out of Lavoisier's observations, but more importantly, it predicted the outcome of similar experiments on any chemical reaction. Laws are also subject to experiments, which can prove them wrong or validate them.

One or more well-established hypotheses may form the basis for a scientific **theory**. Theories try to provide a broader and deeper explanation for what we observe in terms of underlying causes. They are models of the way nature is, and often predict behavior that extends well beyond the observations and laws on which they are founded. A good example of a theory is the **atomic theory** of John Dalton (1766–1844). Dalton explained the law of conservation of mass, as well as other laws and observations, by proposing that all matter was composed of small, indestructible particles called atoms. Dalton's theory was a model of the physical world—it went beyond the laws and observations of the time to explain these laws and observations.

Theories are also tested and validated by experiments. Notice that the scientific method begins with observation, forms laws, hypotheses, and theories based on those observations, and then returns to observation to determine their validity. If a law, hypothesis, or theory is inconsistent with the findings of an experiment, it must be revised and new experiments must be conducted to test the revisions. Over time, poor theories are eliminated, and good theories—those consistent with experiments—remain. Established theories with strong experimental support are the most powerful pieces of scientific knowledge. People unfamiliar with science sometimes say, "That is just a theory," as if theories were mere speculations. However, well-tested theories are as close to truth as we get in science. For example, the idea that all matter is made of atoms is "just a theory," but it is a theory with two hundred years of experimental evidence to support it, including the recent imaging of atoms themselves (◀ Figure 1.3). Established theories should not be taken lightly—they are the pinnacle of scientific understanding.

Scientific theories are also called *models*.

▲ **Figure 1.3   Are atoms real?**   The atomic theory has two hundred years of experimental evidence to support it, including recent images, such as this one, of atoms themselves. This image shows the Japanese characters for "atom" written with individual iron atoms on top of a copper surface.

EVERYDAY Chemistry

Combustion and the Scientific Method

Early chemical theories attempted to explain common phenomena such as combustion. Why did things burn? What was happening to a substance when it burned? Could something that was burned be unburned? Early chemists burned different substances and made observations to try to answer these questions. They observed that things would stop burning if placed in a closed container. They found that many metals would burn to form a white powder that they called a *calx* (now we know that these white powders are oxides of the metal), and that the metal could be recovered from the calx, or unburned, by combining it with charcoal and heating it.

Chemists in the first part of the eighteenth century formed a theory about combustion to explain these observations. In this theory, combustion involved a fundamental substance that they called *phlogiston*. Phlogiston was present in anything that burned and was released during combustion. Flammable objects were flammable because they contained phlogiston. When things were burned in a closed container, they didn't burn for very long because the space within the container became saturated with phlogiston. When things burned in the open, they continued to burn until all of the phlogiston within them was gone. This theory also explained how metals that had burned could be unburned. Charcoal was a phlogiston-rich material—they knew this because it burned so well—and when it was combined with a calx, which was a metal that had been emptied of its phlogiston, it transferred some of its phlogiston into the calx, converting it back into the unburned form of the metal. The phlogiston theory was consistent with all of the observations and was widely accepted as valid.

Like any theory, the phlogiston theory had to be tested continually by experiment. One set of experiments, conducted in the mid-eighteenth century by Louis-Bernard Guyton de Morveau (1737–1816), consisted of weighing metals before and after burning them. In every case the metals *gained* weight when they were burned. However, the phlogiston theory predicted that they should *lose* weight because phlogiston was supposed to be lost during combustion. The phlogiston theory needed modification.

The first modification was to suppose that phlogiston was a very light substance so that it actually "buoyed up" the materials that contained it. When phlogiston was released, the material actually became heavier. Such a modification seemed to fit the observations but also seemed far-fetched. Antoine Lavoisier developed a more likely explanation by devising a completely new theory of combustion. According to Lavoisier, when a substance burned, it actually took something *out* of the air, and when it unburned, it released something back into the air. Lavoisier said that burning objects *fixed* (attached or bonded) the air and that the *fixed* air was released when unburning. In a confirming experiment (▼ Figure 1.4), Lavoisier roasted a mixture of calx and charcoal with the aid of sunlight focused by a giant burning lens, and found that a huge volume of "fixed air" was released in the process. The scientific method had worked. The phlogiston theory was proven wrong, and a new theory of combustion took its place—a theory that, with a few refinements, is still valid today.

CAN YOU ANSWER THIS? *What is the difference between a law and a theory? How does the preceding story demonstrate this difference?*

◄ Figure 1.4 **Focusing on combustion** The great burning lens belonging to the Academy of Sciences. Lavoisier used a similar lens to show that a mixture of *calx* (metal oxide) and charcoal released a large volume of *fixed air* (oxygen) when heated.

1.5   A Beginning Chemist: How to Succeed

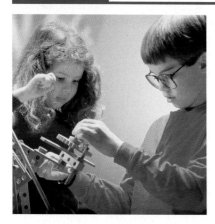

▲ To succeed as a scientist, you must have the curiosity of a child.

You are a beginning chemist. This may be your first chemistry course, but it is probably not your last. To succeed as a beginning chemist, keep these things in mind. First, chemistry requires curiosity and imagination. If you are content knowing that the sky is blue, but don't care *why* it is blue, then you may have to rediscover your curiosity. I say "rediscover" because even children—or better said, *especially* children—have this kind of curiosity. To succeed as a chemist, you must have the curiosity and imagination of a child—you must want to know the *why* of things.

Second, chemistry requires calculation. Throughout this book, I will ask you to calculate things and to quantify information. *Quantification* involves measurement as part of observation—it is one of the most important tools in science. Quantification allows us to go beyond merely saying that this object is hot and that one is cold or that this one is large and that one is small. It allows us to specify the difference precisely. For example, two samples of water may feel equally hot to our hands, but when we measure their temperatures, we find that one is 40 °C and the other is 44 °C. Even small differences can be important in a calculation or experiment, so assigning numbers to observations and manipulating those numbers becomes very important in chemistry.

Lastly, chemistry requires commitment. To succeed in this course, you must commit yourself to learning chemistry. Roald Hoffman, winner of the 1981 Nobel Prize for chemistry, said,

I like the idea that human beings can do anything they want to. They need to be trained sometimes. They need a teacher to awaken the intelligence within them. But to be a chemist requires no special talent, I'm glad to say. Anyone can do it, with hard work.

Professor Hoffman is right. The key to success in this course is hard work, and that requires commitment. You must do your work regularly and carefully. If you do, you will succeed, and you will be rewarded by seeing a whole new world—the world of molecules and atoms. This world exists beneath the surface of nearly everything you encounter. I welcome you to this world and consider it a privilege, together with your professor, to be your guide.

CHAPTER IN REVIEW

Chemical Principles

Matter and Molecules: Chemists are interested in all matter, even ordinary matter such as water or air. You need not go to a chemical storeroom to find chemical questions because chemicals are all around you. Chemistry is the science that tries to understand what matter does by understanding what molecules do.

Relevance

Matter and Molecules: Chemists want to understand matter for several reasons. First, chemists are simply curious—they want to know why. Why are some substances reactive and others not? Why are some substances gases, some liquids, and others solids? Chemists are also practical; they want to understand matter so that they can control it and produce substances that are useful to society and to humankind.

The Scientific Method: Chemists use the scientific method, which makes use of observations, hypotheses, laws, theories, and experiments. Observations involve measuring or observing some aspect of nature. Hypotheses are tentative interpretations of the observations. Laws summarize the results of a large number of observations, and theories are models that explain and give the underlying causes for observations and laws. Hypotheses, laws, and theories are tested and validated by experiment. If they are not confirmed, they must be revised and tested through further experimentation.

The Scientific Method: The scientific method is important because it works as a way to understand the world. Since its inception, knowledge about the natural world and corresponding technologies using that knowledge have grown rapidly. The application of the scientific method has produced knowledge and technology that has raised living standards throughout the world with advances such as increased food production, rapid transportation, unparalleled access to information, and longer life spans.

Success as a Beginning Chemist: To succeed as a beginning chemist, you must be curious and imaginative, be willing to do calculations, and be committed to learning the material.

Success as a Beginning Chemist: Understanding chemistry will give you a deeper appreciation for the world in which you live, and if you choose science as a career, it will be a foundation upon which you will continue to build.

Key Terms

atomic theory [1.4]
chemistry [1.3]
experiment [1.4]

hypothesis [1.4]
law of conservation
   of mass [1.4]

observation [1.4]
scientific law [1.4]

scientific method [1.4]
theory [1.4]

Exercises

Questions   Answers to all questions numbered in blue appear in the Answers section at the back of the book.

1. Why does soda fizz?
2. What are chemicals? Give some examples.
3. What do chemists try to do? How do they understand the natural world?
4. What is meant by the statement, "Matter does what molecules do"? Give an example.
5. Define chemistry.
6. How is chemistry connected to everyday life? Is chemistry relevant only in the chemistry laboratory?
7. Explain the scientific method.
8. Give an example from this chapter of the scientific method at work.

9. What is the difference between a law and a theory?
10. What is the difference between a hypothesis and a theory?
11. What is wrong with the statement, "It is just a theory"?
12. What is the law of conservation of mass and who discovered it?
13. What is the atomic theory and who formulated it?
14. What are three things you need to do to succeed in this course?

Problems

Note: The exercises in the Problems section are paired, and the answers to the odd-numbered exercises (numbered in blue) appear in the Answers section at the back of the book.

15. Examine the opening figure of this chapter. Use the information in Section 1.1 to identify the two molecules sitting next to the cola glass and identify each of the atoms within each molecule.

16. Examine Figure 1.1 and, from a molecular point of view, explain why soda pop fizzes. What molecules are inside a bubble within soda pop?

17. Classify each of the following as an observation, a law, or a theory.
 (a) When a metal is burned in a closed container, the mass of the container and its contents does not change.
 (b) Matter is made of atoms.
 (c) Matter is conserved in chemical reactions.
 (d) When wood is burned in a closed container, its mass does not change.

18. Classify each of the following as an observation, a law, or a theory.
 (a) The star closest to Earth is moving away from Earth at high speed.
 (b) A body in motion stays in motion unless acted upon by a force.
 (c) The universe began as a cosmic explosion called the big bang.
 (d) A stone dropped from an altitude of 450 meters falls to the ground in 9.6 seconds.

19. A chemist in an imaginary universe does an experiment that attempts to correlate the size of an atom with its chemical reactivity. The results are as follows.

Size of Atom	Chemical Reactivity
small	low
medium	intermediate
large	high

 (a) Can you formulate a law from this data?
 (b) Can you formulate a theory to explain the law?

20. A chemist decomposes several samples of water into hydrogen and oxygen and weighs (or more correctly "measures the mass of") the hydrogen and the oxygen obtained. The results are as follows:

Sample Number	Grams of Hydrogen	Grams of Oxygen
1	1.5	12
2	2	16
3	2.5	20

 (a) Can you summarize these observations in a short statement?

Next, the chemist decomposes several samples of carbon dioxide into carbon and oxygen. The results are as follows:

Sample Number	Grams of Carbon	Grams of Oxygen
1	0.5	1.3
2	1.0	2.7
3	1.5	4.0

 (b) Can you summarize these observations in a short statement?
 (c) Can you formulate a law from the observations in **(a)** and **(b)**?
 (d) Can you formulate a theory that might explain your law in **(c)**?

CHAPTER 2

Measurement and Problem Solving

"The important thing in science is not so much to obtain new facts as to discover new ways of thinking about them."

Sir William Lawrence Bragg (1890–1971)

2.1   Measuring Global Temperatures

A unit is a standard, agreed-on quantity by which other quantities are measured.

As scientists grow increasingly concerned about changes in Earth's climate, global warming has become a household term. Average global temperatures affect everything from agriculture to weather and ocean levels. The media have reported that global temperatures are increasing. These reports are based on the work of scientists who—after analyzing records from thousands of temperature-measuring stations around the world—concluded that average global temperatures have risen by 0.6 °C in the last century.

Notice how the scientists reported their results. What if they had reported a temperature increase of simply 0.6 without any *units*? The result would be unclear. Units are extremely important in reporting and working with scientific measurements, and they must always be included. Suppose that the scientists had reported additional zeros with their results—for example, 0.60 °C? or 0.600 °C—or that they had reported the number their computer displayed after averaging many measurements, something like 0.58759824 °C? Would all of these convey the same information? Not really. Scientists agree to a standard way of reporting measured quantities in which the number of reported digits reflects the precision in the measurement—more digits, more precision; fewer digits, less precision. Numbers are usually written so that the uncertainty is in the last reported digit. For example, by reporting a temperature increase of 0.6 °C, the scientists mean 0.6 ± 0.1 °C (± means plus or minus). The temperature rise could be as much as 0.7 °C or as little as 0.5 °C, but it is not 1.0 °C. The degree of certainty in this particular measurement is critical, influencing political decisions that directly affect people's lives.

◀ Measurement is part of our daily lives. In this illustration, a pumpkin is weighed for pricing. **Question:** Can you read the weight on the scale?

11

2.2   Scientific Notation: Writing Large and Small Numbers

▲ Lasers such as this one can measure time periods as short as 1×10^{-15} s.

Science has constantly pushed the boundaries of the very large and the very small. We can, for example, now measure time periods as short as 0.000000000000001 seconds and distances as great as 14,000,000,000 light-years. The many zeros in these numbers are cumbersome to write, so scientists often use **scientific notation** to write them more compactly. In scientific notation, 0.000000000000001 becomes 1×10^{-15}, and 14,000,000,000 becomes 1.4×10^{10}. A number written in scientific notation consists of a **decimal part**, a number that is usually between 1 and 10, and an **exponential part**, 10 raised to an **exponent**, n.

A positive exponent means 1 multiplied by 10 n times.

$$10^0 = 1$$
$$10^1 = 1 \times 10$$
$$10^2 = 1 \times 10 \times 10 = 100$$
$$10^3 = 1 \times 10 \times 10 \times 10 = 1,000$$

A negative exponent $(-n)$ means 1 divided by 10 n times.

$$10^{-1} = \frac{1}{10} = 0.1$$

$$10^{-2} = \frac{1}{10 \times 10} = 0.01$$

$$10^{-3} = \frac{1}{10 \times 10 \times 10} = 0.001$$

To convert a number to scientific notation, we move the decimal point to obtain a number between 1 and 10 and then multiply by 10 raised to the appropriate power. For example, to write 5983 in scientific notation, we move the decimal point to the left three places to get 5.983 (a number between 1 and 10) and then multiply by 1000 to make up for moving the decimal point.

$$5983 = 5.983 \times 1000$$

Since 1000 is 10^3, we write:

$$= 5.983 \times 10^3$$

We can do this in one step by counting how many places we move the decimal point to obtain a number between 1 and 10 and then writing the decimal part multiplied by 10 raised to the number of places we moved the decimal point.

$$5983 = 5.983 \times 10^3$$
$$\overset{}{\underset{3\,2\,1}{\curvearrowleft\curvearrowleft\curvearrowleft}}$$

If the decimal point is moved to the left, as in the previous example, the exponent is positive. If the decimal is moved to the right, the exponent is negative.

$$0.00034 = 3.4 \times 10^{-4}$$
$$\underset{1\,2\,3\,4}{}$$

To express a number in scientific notation:
1. Move the decimal point to obtain a number between 1 and 10.
2. Write the result from Step 1 multiplied by 10 raised to the number of places you moved the decimal point.

   • The exponent is positive if you moved the decimal point to the left.
   • The exponent is negative if you moved the decimal point to the right.

EXAMPLE 2.1   **Scientific Notation**

The U.S. population in 2004 was estimated to be 293,168,000 people. Express this number in scientific notation.

To obtain a number between 1 and 10, move the decimal point to the left 8 decimal places; therefore the exponent is 8. Since the decimal point was moved to the left, the sign of the exponent is positive.

Solution:

$$293{,}168{,}000 \text{ people} = 2.93168 \times 10^{8} \text{ people}$$

SKILLBUILDER 2.1   **Scientific Notation**

The total federal debt in 2004 was approximately $7,132,000,000,000. Express this number in scientific notation.

Note: The answers to all Skillbuilders appear at the end of the chapter.

7.132×10^{12}

EXAMPLE 2.2   **Scientific Notation**

The radius of a carbon atom is approximately 0.000000000070 m. Express this number in scientific notation.

To obtain a number between 1 and 10, move the decimal point to the right 11 decimal places; therefore the exponent is 11. Since the decimal point was moved to the right, the sign of the exponent is negative.

Solution:

$$0.000000000070 \text{ m} = 7.0 \times 10^{-11} \text{ m}$$

SKILLBUILDER 2.2   **Scientific Notation**

Express the number 0.000038 in scientific notation.

3.8×10^{-5}

CONCEPTUAL CHECKPOINT 2.1

The radius of a dust speck is 4.5×10^{-3} mm. In decimal notation, this would be expressed as:

(a) 4500 mm
(b) 0.045 mm
(c) 0.0045 mm
(d) 0.00045 mm

Note: The answers to all Conceptual Checkpoints appear at the end of the chapter.

2.3   Significant Figures: Writing Numbers to Reflect Precision

▲ Since pennies come in whole numbers, 7 pennies means 7.00000 pennies. It is an exact number and therefore never limits significant figures in calculations.

▲ The amount of gold in a 10-g gold bar depends on how precisely it was measured.

If you tell someone you have seven pennies, the meaning is clear. Pennies generally come in whole numbers, and seven pennies means seven whole pennies—it is unlikely that you would have 7.4 pennies. On the other hand, if you tell someone that you have a 10-g gold bar, the meaning is unclear. The actual amount of gold in the bar depends on how precisely it was measured, which in turn depends on the scale or balance that was used to make the measurement. As we just learned, measured quantities are written in a way that reflects the uncertainty in the measurement. If the gold measurement was rough, the bar could be described as containing "10 g of gold." If however, a more precise balance was used, the gold content of the bar could be written as "10.0g." An even more precise measurement would be reported as "10.00 g."

Scientific numbers are reported so that every digit is certain except the last, which is estimated.

For example, suppose a reported number is:

$$\mathbf{45.87}2$$

certain   *estimated*

The first four digits are certain; the last digit is estimated.

Suppose that we weigh an object on a balance with marks at every 1 g, and suppose that the pointer is between the 1-g mark and the 2-g mark (▼ Figure 2.1) but much closer to the 1-g mark. We mentally divide the space between the 1- and 2-g marks into ten equal spaces and estimate that the pointer is at about 1.2 g. We then write the measurement as 1.2 g, indicating that we are sure of the "1" but have estimated the ".2."

A balance with marks every tenth of a gram requires us to write the result with more digits. For example, suppose that on this more precise balance the pointer is between the 1.2-g mark and the 1.3-g mark (▼ Figure 2.2). We again divide the space between the two marks into ten equal spaces and estimate the third digit. For the figure shown, we report 1.26 g.

▶ Figure 2.1   **Estimating tenths of a gram**   This balance has markings every 1 g, so we estimate to the tenths place. To estimate between markings, mentally divide the space into ten equal spaces and estimate the last digit. This reading is 1.2 g.

▲ Figure 2.2   **Estimating hundredths of a gram**   Since this scale has markings every 0.1 g, we estimate to the hundredths place. The correct reading is 1.26 g.

▲ Figure 2.3   **Reading a bathroom scale**

▲ Figure 2.4   **Reading a thermometer**

When a number is expressed in scientific notation, all trailing zeros are counted as significant.

EXAMPLE 2.3   **Reporting the Right Number of Digits**

The bathroom scale in ◀ Figure 2.3 has markings at every 1 lb. Report the reading to the correct number of digits.

Solution:
Since the pointer is between the 147- and 148-lb markings, we mentally divide the space between the markings into ten equal spaces and estimate the next digit. In this case, the result should be reported as:

147.7 lb

What if you estimated a little differently and wrote 147.6 lb? In general, one unit of difference in the last digit is acceptable because the last digit is estimated and different people might estimate it slightly differently. However, if you wrote 147.2 lb, you would clearly be wrong.

SKILLBUILDER 2.3   **Reporting the Right Number of Digits**

A thermometer is used to measure the temperature of a backyard hot tub, and the reading is shown in ◀ Figure 2.4. Write the temperature reading to the right number of digits.   104.5

Counting Significant Figures

The non-place-holding digits in a reported measurement are called **significant figures** (or **significant digits**) and, as we have seen, represent the precision of a measured quantity. The greater the number of significant figures, the greater the precision of the measurement. We can determine the number of significant figures in a written number fairly easily; however, if the number contains zeros, we must distinguish between the zeros that are significant and those that simply mark the decimal place. In the number 0.002, for example, the leading zeros simply mark the decimal place; they *do not* add to the precision of the measurement. In the number 0.00200, the trailing zeros *do* add to the precision of the measurement.

To determine the number of significant figures in a number, follow these rules:

1. All nonzero digits are significant.

1.05   0.0110

2. Interior zeros (zeros between two numbers) are significant.

4.0208   50.1

3. Trailing zeros (zeros after a decimal point) are significant.

5.10   3.00

4. Leading zeros (zeros to the left of the first nonzero number) are not significant. They only serve to locate the decimal point.

Thus, the number 0.0005 has only one significant digit.

5. Zeros at the end of a number but before a decimal point are ambiguous and should be avoided by using scientific notation.

For example, does 350 have two or three significant figures? Write the number as 3.5×10^2 to indicate two significant figures or as 3.50×10^2 to indicate three.

Exact Numbers

Exact numbers have an unlimited number of significant figures. Exact numbers originate from three sources:

- from the accurate counting of discrete objects. For example, 3 atoms means 3.00000 . . . atoms.
- from *defined quantities*, such as the number of centimeters in 1 m. Because 100 cm is defined as 1 m,

  100 cm = 1 m   means   100.00000 . . . cm = 1.0000000 . . . m

  Note that some conversion factors are defined quantities while others are not.

- from integral numbers that are part of an equation. For example, in the equation, $radius = \dfrac{diameter}{2}$, the number 2 is exact and therefore has an unlimited number of significant figures.

EXAMPLE 2.4   Determining the Number of Significant Figures in a Number

How many significant figures are in each of the following numbers?

(a) 0.0035 – 2
(b) 1.080 – 4
(c) 2371 – 4
(d) 2.97 × 10^5 = 3
(e) 1 dozen = 12 = 2
(f) 100,000 = Ambigous

	Solution:
The 3 and the 5 are significant. The leading zeros only mark the decimal place and are not significant.	(a) 0.0035 two significant figures
The interior zero and the trailing zero are significant, as are the 1 and the 8.	(b) 1.080 four significant figures
All digits are significant.	(c) 2371 four significant figures
All digits in the decimal part are significant.	(d) 2.97 × 10^5 three significant figures
Defined numbers have an unlimited number of significant figures.	(e) 1 dozen = 12 unlimited significant figures
This number is ambiguous. Write as 1 × 10^5 to indicate one significant figure or as 1.00000 × 10^5 to indicate six significant figures.	(f) 100,000 ambiguous

SKILLBUILDER 2.4   Determining the Number of Significant Figures in a Number

How many significant figures are in each of the following numbers?

(a) 58.31 – 4
(b) 0.00250 – 3
(c) 2.7 × 10^3 – 2
(d) 1 cm = 0.01 m – 1
(e) 0.500 – 3
(f) 2100 – Ambigous

CONCEPTUAL CHECKPOINT 2.2

A researcher reports that the Spirit rover on the surface of Mars recently measured the temperature to be −25.49 °F. This means that the actual temperature can be assumed to be:

(a) between −25.490 °F and −25.499 °F
(b) between −25.48 °F and −25.50 °F
(c) between −25.4 °F and −25.5 °F
(d) exactly −25.49 °F

Chemistry IN THE MEDIA

The COBE Satellite and Very Precise Measurements That Illuminate Our Cosmic Past

Since the earliest times, humans have wondered about the origins of our planet. Science has slowly probed this question and has developed theories for how the universe and the Earth began. The most accepted theory today for the origin of the universe is the big bang theory. According to the big bang theory, the universe began in a tremendous expansion about 13.7 billion years ago and has been expanding ever since. A measurable prediction of this theory is the presence of a remnant "background radiation" from the expansion of the universe itself. That remnant is characteristic of the current temperature of the universe. When the big bang occurred, the temperature of the universe was very hot and the associated radiation very bright. Today, 16 billion years later, the temperature of the universe is very cold and the background radiation very faint.

In the early 1960s, Robert H. Dicke, P. J. E. Peebles, and their coworkers at Princeton University began to build a device that might measure this background radiation and thus take a direct look into the cosmological past and provide evidence for the big bang theory. At about the same time, quite by accident, Arno Penzias and Robert Wilson of Bell Telephone Laboratories measured excess radio noise on one of their communications satellites. As it turned out, this noise was the background radiation that the Princeton scientists were looking for. The two groups published papers together in 1965 reporting their findings along with the corresponding temperature of the universe, about 3 degrees above absolute zero, or 3 K. (We will define temperature measurement scales in Chapter 3. For now, know that 3 K is an extremely low temperature, several hundred degrees below zero on the Fahrenheit scale.)

In 1989, the Cosmic Background Explorer (COBE) satellite was developed by NASA's Goddard Space Flight Center to measure the background radiation more precisely. It was launched in late 1989 and determined that the background radiation corresponded to a universe with a temperature of 2.735 K. (Notice the difference in significant figures from the previous measurement.) The satel-lite went on to measure tiny fluctuations in the background radiation that amount to temperature differences of 1 part in 100,000. These fluctuations, though small, are an important prediction of the big bang theory. Scientists announced that the COBE satellite had produced the strongest evidence yet for the big bang theory of the creation of the universe. This is the way that science works. Measurement, and precision in measurement, are important to understanding the world—so important that we dedicate most of this chapter just to the concept of measurement.

CAN YOU ANSWER THIS? *How many significant figures are there in each of the preceding temperature measurements (3 K, 2.735 K)?*

▲ The COBE Satellite, launched in 1989 to measure background radiation. Background radiation is a remnant of the big bang that is believed to have formed the universe.

2.4   Significant Figures in Calculations

When we use measured quantities in calculations, the results of the calculation must reflect the precision of the measured quantities. We should not lose or gain precision during mathematical operations.

Multiplication and Division

In multiplication or division, the result carries the *same number of significant figures* as the factor with the fewest significant figures.

For example:

$$\underset{\text{(3 sig. figures)}}{5.02} \times \underset{\text{(5 sig. figures)}}{89.665} \times \underset{\text{(2 sig. figures)}}{0.10} = 45.0118 = \underset{\text{(2 sig. figures)}}{45}$$

The intermediate result (in blue) is rounded to two significant figures to reflect the least precisely known number (0.10), which has two significant figures.
For division, we follow the same rule.

$$\underset{\text{(4 sig. figures)}}{5.892} \div \underset{\text{(3 sig. figures)}}{6.10} = 0.96590 = \underset{\text{(3 sig. figures)}}{0.966}$$

The intermediate result (in blue) is rounded to three significant figures to reflect the least precisely known number (6.10), which has three significant figures.

Rounding

When rounding to the correct number of significant figures:

Round down if the last (or leftmost) digit dropped is 4 or less;
round up if the last (or leftmost) digit dropped is 5 or more.

For example, consider rounding each of the following to two significant figures.

2.33 rounds to 2.3
2.37 rounds to 2.4
2.34 rounds to 2.3
2.35 rounds to 2.4

Be certain to use only the *last (or leftmost) digit being dropped* to decide in which direction to round—ignore all digits to the right of it. For example, to round 2.349 to two significant figures, only the 4 in the hundredths place (2.349) determines which direction to round—the 9 is irrelevant.

2.349 rounds to 2.3

For calculations involving multiple steps, round only the final answer—do not round off between steps. This prevents small rounding errors from affecting your final answer.

| EXAMPLE 2.5 | **Significant Figures in Multiplication and Division** |

Perform the following calculations to the correct number of significant figures.

(a) $1.01 \times 0.12 \times 53.51 \div 96$
(b) $56.55 \times 0.920 \div 34.2585$

Round the intermediate result (in blue) to two significant figures to reflect the two significant figures in the least precisely known quantities (0.12 and 96).

Solution:

(a) $1.01 \times 0.12 \times 53.51 \div 96 = 0.067556 = 0.068$

Round the intermediate result (in blue) to three significant figures to reflect the three significant figures in the least precisely known quantity (0.920).

(b) $56.55 \times 0.920 \div 34.2585 = 1.51863 = 1.52$

| SKILLBUILDER 2.5 | **Significant Figures in Multiplication and Division** |

Perform the following calculations to the correct number of significant figures.

(a) $1.10 \times 0.512 \times 1.301 \times 0.005 \div 3.4$
(b) $4.562 \times 3.99870 \div 89.5$

Addition and Subtraction

In addition or subtraction, the result carries the *same number of decimal places* as the quantity carrying the fewest decimal places.

For example:

It is sometimes helpful to draw a vertical line directly to the right of the number with the fewest decimal places. The line shows the number of decimal places that should be in the answer.

We round the intermediate answer (in blue) to two decimal places because the quantity with the fewest decimal places (5.74) has two decimal places.
For subtraction, we follow the same rule. For example:

$$\begin{array}{r} 4.8 \\ -\ 3.965 \\ \hline 0.835 = 0.8 \end{array}$$

We round the intermediate answer (in blue) to one decimal place because the quantity with the fewest decimal places (4.8) has one decimal place. Remember: *For multiplication and division, the quantity with the fewest* significant figures *determines the number of significant figures in the answer. For addition and subtraction, the quantity with the fewest* decimal places *determines the number of decimal places in the answer.* In multiplication and division we focus on significant figures, but in addition and subtraction we focus on decimal places.

TUTORIAL
Significant Digits

EXAMPLE 2.6   Significant Figures in Addition and Subtraction

Perform the following calculations to the correct number of significant figures.

(a)
```
      0.987
   +125.1
    −1.22
```

(b)
```
      0.765
    −3.449
    −5.98
```

Round the intermediate answer (in blue) to one decimal place to reflect the quantity with the fewest decimal places (125.1). Notice that 125.1 is not the quantity with the fewest significant figures—it has four while the other quantities only have three—but because it has the fewest decimal places, it determines the number of decimal places in the answer.

Solution:

(a)
```
      0.987
   +125.1
    −1.22
    124.867 = 124.9
```

Round the intermediate answer (in blue) to two decimal places to reflect that the quantity with the fewest decimal places (5.98).

(b)
```
      0.765
    −3.449
    −5.98
    −8.664 = −8.66
```

SKILLBUILDER 2.6   Significant Figures in Addition and Subtraction

Perform the following calculations to the correct number of significant figures.

(a)
```
    2.18
   +5.621
   +1.5870
   −1.8
```

(b)
```
    7.876
   −0.56
  +123.792
```

Calculations Involving Both Multiplication/Division and Addition/Subtraction

In calculations involving both multiplication/division and addition/subtraction, do the steps in parentheses first; determine the number of significant figures in the intermediate answer; then do the remaining steps.

For example:

$$3.489 \times (5.67 - 2.3)$$

We do the subtraction step first.

$$5.67 - 2.3 = 3.37$$

We use the subtraction rule to determine that the intermediate answer (3.37) has only one significant decimal place. To avoid small errors, it is best not to round at this point; instead, underline the least significant figure as a reminder.

$$= 3.489 \times 3.\underline{3}7$$

We then do the multiplication step.

$$3.489 \times 3.\underline{3}7 = 11.758$$
$$= 12$$

We use the multiplication rule to determine that the intermediate answer (11.758) rounds to two significant figures (12) because it is limited by the two significant figures in 3.$\underline{3}$7.

EXAMPLE 2.7 **Significant Figures in Calculations Involving Both Multiplication/Division and Addition/Subtraction**

(a) $6.78 \times 5.903 \times (5.489 - 5.01)$
(b) $19.667 - (5.4 \times 0.916)$

Do the step in parentheses first. Use the subtraction rule to mark 0.4790 to two decimal places since 5.01, the number in the parentheses with the least number of decimal places, has two.

Solution:

(a) $6.78 \times 5.903 \times (5.489 - 5.01)$
$= 6.78 \times 5.903 \times (0.4790)$
$= 6.78 \times 5.903 \times 0.4\underline{7}90$

Then perform the multiplication and round the answer to two significant figures since the number with the least number of significant figures has two.

$6.78 \times 5.903 \times 0.4\underline{7}90 = 19.1707$
$= 19$

Do the step in parentheses first. The number with the least number of significant figures within the parentheses (5.4) has two, so mark the answer to two significant figures.

(b) $19.667 - (5.4 \times 0.916)$
$= 19.667 - (4.9464)$
$= 19.667 - 4.\underline{9}464$

Then perform the subtraction and round the answer to one decimal place since the number with the least number of decimal places has one.

$19.667 - 4.\underline{9}464 = 14.7206$
$= 14.7$

SKILLBUILDER 2.7 **Significant Figures in Calculations Involving Both Multiplication/Division and Addition/Subtraction**

(a) $3.897 \times (782.3 - 451.88)$
(b) $(4.58 \div 1.239) - 0.578$

CONCEPTUAL CHECKPOINT 2.3

Which of the following calculations would have its result reported to the *greater* number of significant figures?

(a) 3 + (15/12)
(b) (3 + 15)/12

2.5   The Basic Units of Measurement

By themselves, numbers have little meaning. Read this sentence: When my son was 7 he walked 3, and when he was 4 he threw his baseball 8 and said his school was 5 away. The sentence is confusing because we don't know what the numbers mean—the **units** are missing. The meaning becomes clear, however, when we add the missing units to the numbers: When my son was 7 *months old* he walked 3 *steps*, and when he was 4 *years old* he threw his baseball 8 *feet* and said his school was 5 *minutes* away. Units make all the difference. In chemistry, units are critical. Never write a number by itself; always use its associated units—otherwise your work will be as confusing as the preceding sentence.

The two most common unit systems are the **English system**, used in the United States, and the **metric system**, used in most of the rest of the world. The English system uses units such as inches, yards, and pounds, while the metric system uses centimeters, meters, and kilograms. The most convenient system for science measurements is based on the metric system and is called the **International System** of units or **SI units**. SI units are a set of standard units agreed on by scientists throughout the world.

The abbreviation SI comes from the French le Système International.

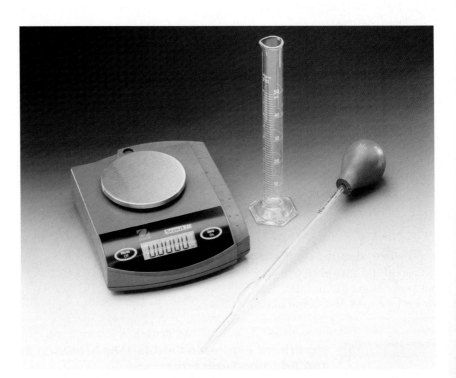

▲ Science uses instruments to make measurements. Every instrument is calibrated in a particular unit without which the measurements would be meaningless.

TABLE 2.1 Important SI Standard Units

Quantity	Unit	Symbol
length	meter	m
mass	kilogram	kg
time	second	s
temperature*	kelvin	K

*Temperature units are discussed in Chapter 3.

The Standard Units

The standard units in the SI system are shown in Table 2.1. They include the **meter (m)** as the standard unit of length; the **kilogram (kg)** as the standard unit of mass; and the **second (s)** as the standard unit of time. Each of these standard units is precisely defined. The meter is defined as the distance light travels in a certain period of time: 1/299,792,458 s. (▼ Figure 2.5). (The speed of light is 3.0×10^8 m/s) The kilogram is defined as the mass of a block of metal kept at the International Bureau of Weights and Measures at Sèvres, France (▼ Figure 2.6). The second is defined using an atomic standard (▼ Figure 2.7).

Most people are familiar with the SI standard unit of time, the second. However, if you live in the United States, you may be less familiar with the meter and the kilogram. The meter is slightly longer than a yard (a yard is 36 inches while a meter is 39.37 inches). Thus, a 100-yd football field measures only 91.4 m.

The kilogram is a measure of mass, which is different from weight. The **mass** of an object is a measure of the quantity of matter within it, while the weight of an object is a measure of the gravitational pull on that matter. Consequently, weight depends on gravity while mass does not. If you were to weigh yourself on Mars, for example, the lower gravity would pull you toward the scale less than Earth's gravity would, resulting in a lower weight. A 150-lb person on Earth would weigh 57 lb on Mars. However, the person's mass, the quantity of matter in his or her body, would remain the same. A kilogram of mass is the equivalent of 2.205 lb of weight on Earth, so if we express mass in kilograms, a 150-lb person on Earth has a mass of approximately 68 kg. A second common unit of mass is the gram (g), defined as follows:

$$1000 \text{ g} = 10^3 \text{ g} = 1 \text{ kg}$$

A nickel (5¢) has a mass of about 5 g.

▲ A nickel has a mass of about 5 g.

▲ **Figure 2.5   The standard of length**   The definition of a meter, established by international agreement in 1983, is the distance that light travels in vacuum in 1/299,792,458 s.
Question: What reasons can you think of why such a precise standard is necessary?

▲ **Figure 2.6   The standard of mass**   A duplicate of the international standard kilogram, called kilogram 20, is kept at the National Institute of Standards and Technology near Washington, D.C.

▲ **Figure 2.7   The standard of time** The second is defined, using an atomic clock, as the duration of 9,192,631,770 periods of the radiation emitted from a certain transition in a cesium-133 atom.

TABLE 2.2 SI Prefix Multipliers

Prefix	Symbol	Multiplier	
tera-	T	1,000,000,000,000	(10^{12})
giga-	G	1,000,000,000	(10^{9})
mega-	M	1,000,000	(10^{6})
kilo-	k	1,000	(10^{3})
deci-	d	0.1	(10^{-1})
centi-	c	0.01	(10^{-2})
milli-	m	0.001	(10^{-3})
micro-	μ	0.000001	(10^{-6})
nano-	n	0.000000001	(10^{-9})
pico-	p	0.000000000001	(10^{-12})
femto-	f	0.000000000000001	(10^{-15})

▲ The diameter of a jelly donut is about 8 cm.   **Question:** Why would you *not* use meters to make this measurement?

TABLE 2.3 Some Common Units and Their Equivalents

Length
1 kilometer (km) = 0.6214 mile (mi)
1 meter (m) = 39.37 inches (in.)
           = 1.094 yards (yd)
1 foot (ft) = 30.48 centimeters (cm)
1 inch (in.) = 2.54 centimeters (cm)
             (exact)

Mass
1 kilogram (kg) = 2.205 pounds (lb)
1 pound (lb) = 453.59 grams (g)
1 ounce (oz) = 28.35 grams (g)

Volume
1 liter (L) = 1000 milliliters (mL)
            = 1000 cubic centimeters
              (cm^3)
1 liter (L) = 1.057 quarts (qt)
1 U.S. gallon (gal) = 3.785 liters (L)

Prefix Multipliers

The SI system uses **prefix multipliers** (Table 2.2) with the standard units. These multipliers change the value of the unit by powers of 10. For example, the kilometer (km) has the prefix *kilo-*, meaning 1000 or 10^3. Therefore:

$$1 \text{ km} = 1000 \text{ m} = 10^3 \text{ m}$$

Similarly, the millisecond (ms) has the prefix *milli-*, meaning 0.001 or 10^{-3}.

$$1 \text{ ms} = 0.001 \text{ s} = 10^{-3} \text{ s}$$

The prefix multipliers allow us to express a wide range of measurements in units that are similar in size to the quantity we are measuring. Choose the prefix multiplier that is most convenient for a particular measurement. For example, to measure the size of a jelly doughnut, use centimeters because jelly doughnuts have a diameter of about 8 cm. A centimeter is a common metric unit and is about equivalent to the width of your pinky finger (2.54 cm = 1 in.). You could have also chosen the decimeter to express the diameter of a jelly doughnut; then the doughnut would measure 0.8 dm. But you should not choose the kilometer since, in that unit, the diameter is 0.00008 km. Pick a unit similar in size to (or smaller than) the quantity you are measuring. Consider expressing the length of a chemical bond, about 1.2×10^{-10} m. Which prefix multiplier should you use? The most convenient one is probably the picometer (pico = 10^{-12}). Chemical bonds measure about 120 pm.

Derived Units

A derived unit is formed from other units. Common derived units include those for **volume**, which is a measure of space. Any unit of length, when cubed (raised to the third power), becomes a unit of volume. Thus, cubic meters (m^3), cubic centimeters (cm^3), and cubic millimeters (mm^3) are all units of volume. In these units, a three-bedroom house has a volume of about 630 m^3, a can of soda pop has a volume of about 350 cm^3, and a rice grain has a volume of about 3 mm^3. We also use the **liter (L)** and milliliter (mL) to express volume. A gallon is equal to 3.785 L. A milliliter is equivalent to 1 cm^3. Table 2.3 lists some common units and their equivalents.

CONCEPTUAL CHECKPOINT 2.4

To express the dimensions of a polio virus, which is about 2.8×10^{-8} m in diameter, the most convenient unit would probably be:

(a) Mm
(b) mm
(c) μm
(d) nm

| 2.6 | **Converting from One Unit to Another** |

Using units as a guide to solving problems is often called *dimensional analysis*.

Units are critical in calculations. Knowing how to work with and manipulate units in calculations is one of the most important skills you will learn in this course. In calculations, units help determine correctness. Units should always be included in calculations, and we will think of many calculations as converting from one unit to another. Units are multiplied, divided, and canceled like any other algebraic quantity.

Remember:

1. Always write every number with its associated unit. Never ignore units; they are critical.
2. Always include units in your calculations, dividing them and multiplying them as if they were algebraic quantities. Do not let units magically appear or disappear in calculations. Units must flow logically from beginning to end.

Consider converting 17.6 in. to centimeters. We know from Table 2.3 that 1 in. = 2.54 cm. How many centimeters are in 17.6 in.? We perform the conversion as follows:

$$17.6 \ \text{in.} \times \frac{2.54 \ \text{cm}}{1 \ \text{in.}} = 44.7 \ \text{cm}$$

The unit *in.* cancels and we are left with *cm* as our final unit. The quantity $\frac{2.54 \ \text{cm}}{1 \ \text{in.}}$ is a **conversion factor** between *in.* and *cm*—it is a fraction with *cm* on top and *in.* on bottom.

For most conversion problems, we are given a quantity in some units and asked to convert the quantity to another unit. These calculations take the following form:

information given × **conversion factor(s)** = **information sought**

Conversion factors are constructed from any two quantities known to be equivalent. In our example, 2.54 cm = 1 in., so we construct the conversion factor by dividing both sides of the equality by 1 in. and cancelling the units.

$$2.54 \ \text{cm} = 1 \ \text{in.}$$
$$\frac{2.54 \ \text{cm}}{1 \ \text{in.}} = \frac{1 \ \text{in.}}{1 \ \text{in.}}$$
$$\frac{2.54 \ \text{cm}}{1 \ \text{in.}} = 1$$

The quantity $\dfrac{2.54\ \text{cm}}{1\ \text{in.}}$ is equal to 1 and can be used to convert between inches and centimeters.

Suppose we want to perform the conversion the other way, from centimeters to inches. If we try to use the same conversion factor, the units do not cancel correctly.

$$44.7\ \text{cm} \times \frac{2.54\ \text{cm}}{1\ \text{in.}} = \frac{114\ \text{cm}^2}{\text{in.}}$$

The units in the answer, as well as the value of the answer, are incorrect. The unit $\text{cm}^2/\text{in.}$ is not correct, and, based on our knowledge of centimeters and inches, we know that 44.7 cm cannot be equivalent to 114 in. In solving problems, always look at the final units to see if they are correct and also look at the magnitude of the answer to see if it makes sense. In this case, our mistake was in how we used the conversion factor. It must be inverted.

$$44.7\ \cancel{\text{cm}} \times \frac{1\ \text{in.}}{2.54\ \cancel{\text{cm}}} = 17.6\ \text{in.}$$

Conversion factors can be inverted because they are equal to 1 and the inverse of 1 is 1.

$$\frac{1}{1} = 1$$

Therefore,

$$\frac{2.54\ \text{cm}}{1\ \text{in.}} = 1 = \frac{1\ \text{in.}}{2.54\ \text{cm}}.$$

In this book, we diagram conversions such as the preceding ones using a **solution map**. A solution map is a visual outline that shows the strategic route required to solve a problem. For unit conversion, the solution map focuses on units and how to convert from one unit to another. The solution map for converting from inches to centimeters is:

The solution map for converting from centimeters to inches is:

Each arrow in a solution map for a unit conversion has an associated conversion factor with the units of the previous step in the denominator and the units of the following step in the numerator. For one-step problems such as these, the solution map is only moderately helpful, but for multistep problems, it becomes a powerful way to develop a problem-solving strategy. The procedure for solving unit conversion problems using the solution map is given in the left column of the following box. The middle and right columns demonstrate examples of how to use the procedure.

Solving Unit Conversion Problems

	EXAMPLE 2.8	EXAMPLE 2.9
	Unit Conversion	**Unit Conversion**
	Convert 7.8 km to miles.	Convert 0.825 m to millimeters.
1. Write down the *given* quantity and its unit(s).	**Given:** 7.8 km	**Given:** 0.825 m
2. Write down the quantity that you are asked to *find* and its unit(s).	**Find:** mi	**Find:** mm
3. Write down the appropriate *conversion factor(s)*. Some of these will be given in the problem. Others you find in tables within the text.	**Conversion Factors:** 1 km = 0.6214 mi (This conversion factor is from Table 2.3.)	**Conversion Factors:** 1 mm = 10^{-3} m (This conversion factor is from Table 2.2.)
4. Write a *solution map* for the problem. Begin with the *given* quantity and draw an arrow symbolizing each conversion step. Below each arrow, write the appropriate conversion factor for that step. Focus on the units. The solution map should end at the *find* quantity.	**Solution Map:** $$\frac{0.6214 \text{ mi}}{1 \text{ km}}$$ The conversion factor is written so that km, the unit we are converting *from*, is on the bottom and mi, the unit we are converting *to*, is on the top.	**Solution Map:** $$\frac{1 \text{ mm}}{10^{-3} \text{ m}}$$ The conversion factor is written so that m, the unit we are converting *from*, is on the bottom and mm, the unit we are converting *to*, is on the top.
5. Follow the solution map to solve the problem. Begin with the *given* quantity and its units. Multiply by the appropriate conversion factor(s), canceling units, to arrive at the *find* quantity.	**Solution:** $$7.8 \text{ km} \times \frac{0.6214 \text{ mi}}{1 \text{ km}} = 4.84692 \text{ mi}$$	**Solution:** $$0.825 \text{ m} \times \frac{1 \text{ mm}}{10^{-3} \text{ m}} = 825 \text{ mm}$$
6. Round the answer to the correct number of significant figures. Follow the significant-figure rules in Sections 2.3 and 2.4. Remember that exact conversion factors do not limit the number of significant figures in your answer.	4.84692 mi = 4.8 mi We round to two significant figures, since the quantity given has two significant figures. (If possible, obtain conversion factors to enough significant figures so that they do not limit the number of significant figures in the answer.)	825 mm = 825 mm We leave the answer with three significant figures, since the quantity given has three significant figures and the conversion factor is a definition, which therefore does not limit the number of significant figures in the answer.
7. Check your answer. Make certain that the units are correct and that the magnitude of the answer makes physical sense.	The units, mi, are correct. The magnitude of the answer is reasonable. A mile is longer than a kilometer, so the value in miles should be smaller than the value in kilometers.	The units, mm, are correct and the magnitude is reasonable. A millimeter is shorter than a meter, so the value in millimeters should be larger than the value in meters.

SKILLBUILDER 2.8	SKILLBUILDER 2.9
Unit Conversion	**Unit Conversion**
• Convert 56.0 cm to inches.	• Convert 5,678 m to kilometers.

If you needed to convert distance in meters to distance in kilometers, which of these conversion factors would you use?

(a) $1 \text{ m}/10^3 \text{ km}$

(b) $10^3 \text{ m}/1 \text{ km}$

(c) $1 \text{ km}/10^3 \text{ m}$

(d) $10^3 \text{ km}/1 \text{ m}$

2.7 Solving Multistep Conversion Problems

When solving multistep conversion problems, we follow the preceding procedure but simply add more steps to the solution map. Every step in the solution map must have a conversion factor with the units of the previous step in the denominator and the units of the following step in the numerator. For example, suppose we want to convert 194 cm to feet. We set up the problem as we outlined earlier.

Given: 194 cm

Find: ft

Conversion Factors:

$$2.54 \text{ cm} = 1 \text{ in.}$$

$$12 \text{ in.} = 1 \text{ ft}$$

Now we can build our solution map. We start with the quantity given and focus on the units. We use the first conversion factor to convert centimeters to inches and the second to convert inches to feet.

Solution Map:

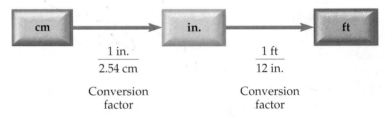

Once the solution map is complete, we follow it to solve the problem.

Solution:

$$194 \text{ cm} \times \frac{1 \text{ in.}}{2.54 \text{ cm}} \times \frac{1 \text{ ft}}{12 \text{ in.}} = 6.3648 \text{ ft}$$

We then round to the correct number of significant figures—in this case, three (from 194 cm, which has three significant figures).

Since one foot is *defined* as 12 in., it does not limit significant figures.

$$6.3648 \text{ ft} = 6.36 \text{ ft}$$

Finally, we check the answer. The units of the answer, ft, are the correct ones and the magnitude seems about right. Since a foot is larger than a centimeter, it is reasonable that the value in feet is smaller than the value in centimeters.

EXAMPLE 2.10 **Solving Multistep Unit Conversion Problems**

An Italian recipe for making creamy pasta sauce calls for 0.75 L of cream. Your measuring cup measures only in cups. How many cups of cream should you use?

4 cups = 1 quart

1. Write down the quantity that is *given* and its unit(s).	**Given:** 0.75 L
2. Write down the quantity that you are asked to *find* and its unit(s).	**Find:** cups
3. Write down the appropriate *conversion factor(s)*. The second conversion factor is from Table 2.3. Note: It is okay if you don't have all the necessary conversion factors at this point. You will discover what you need as you work through the problem.	**Conversion Factors:** 4 cups = 1 qt 1.057 qt = 1 L

4. Write a *solution map*. Focus on the units, finding the appropriate conversion factors with the units of the previous step in the denominator and the units of the next step in the numerator.

Solution Map:

$$\frac{1.057\ qt}{1\ L} \qquad \frac{4\ cups}{1\ qt}$$

5. Follow the solution map. Starting with the quantity that is given and its units, multiply by the appropriate conversion factors, canceling units, to arrive at the quantity that you are trying to find in the desired units.

Solution:

$$0.75\ \cancel{L} \times \frac{1.057\ \cancel{qt}}{1\ \cancel{L}} \times \frac{4\ cups}{1\ \cancel{qt}} = 3.171\ cups$$

6. Round the final answer. Round to two significant figures, since the quantity given has two significant figures.

$$3.171\ cups = 3.2\ cups$$

7. Check your answer. The answer has the right units (cups) and seems reasonable. We know that a cup is smaller than a liter, so the value in cups should be larger than the value in liters.

SKILLBUILDER 2.10   **Solving Multistep Unit Conversion Problems**

Suppose a recipe calls for 1.2 cups of oil. How many liters is this?

LIVE EXAMPLE

EXAMPLE 2.11   **Solving Multistep Unit Conversion Problems**

A running track measures 255 m per lap. To run 10.0 km, how many laps should you run?

Set up the problem in the standard way. Notice that the quantity 255 m per lap is a conversion factor between m and laps.	**Given:** 10.0 km **Find:** number of laps **Conversion Factors:** 1 lap = 255 m 1 km = 10^3 m

Build the solution map beginning with km and ending at laps. Focus on the units.

Solution Map:

$$\frac{10^3\ m}{1\ km} \qquad \frac{1\ lap}{255\ m}$$

Follow the solution map to solve the problem. The intermediate answer (in blue) is rounded to three significant figures, because it is limited by the three signficant figures in the given quantity, 10.0 km.

Solution:

$$10.0 \ \text{km} \times \frac{10^3 \ \text{m}}{1 \ \text{km}} \times \frac{1 \ \text{lap}}{255 \ \text{m}} = 39.216 \ \text{laps} = 39.2 \ \text{laps}$$

The units of the answer are correct and the value of the answer makes sense—if a lap is 255 m, there are about 4 laps to each km (1000 m), so you would have to run about 40 laps to cover 10 km.

SKILLBUILDER 2.11 **Solving Multistep Unit Conversion Problems**

A running track measures 1056 ft per lap. To run 15.0 km, how many laps should you run? (1 mi = 5280 ft)

SKILLBUILDER PLUS

An island is 5.72 nautical mi from the coast. How far is the island in meters? (1 nautical mile = 1.151 mi)

Chemistry AND HEALTH

Drug Dosage

The unit of choice in specifying drug dosage is the milligram (mg). Pick up a bottle of aspirin, Tylenol, or any other common drug and the label tells you how many milligrams of the active ingredient are contained in each tablet, as well as the number of tablets to take per dose. The following table shows the mass of the active ingredient in several common pain relievers, all reported in milligrams. The rest of the tablet is composed of inactive ingredients such as cellulose (or fiber) and starch.

The recommended adult dose for many of these pain relievers is one or two tablets every four to eight hours (depending on the specific pain reliever). Notice that the extra-strength version of each pain reliever just contains a higher dose of the same compound found in the regular-strength version. For the pain relievers listed, three regular-strength tablets are the equivalent of two extra-strength tablets (and probably cost less).

The dosages given in the table are fairly standard for each drug, regardless of the brand. For example, when you look on your drugstore shelf, you will find many different brands of regular-strength ibuprofen, some sold under the generic name and others sold under their brand names (such as Advil). However, if you look closely at the labels, you will find that they all contain the same thing: 200 mg of the compound ibuprofen. There is no difference in the compound or in the amount of the compound. Yet these pain relievers will most likely all have different prices. Choose the least expensive. Why pay more for the same thing?

CAN YOU ANSWER THIS? *Convert each of the doses in the table to ounces. Why are drug dosages not listed in ounces?*

Drug Mass per Pill for Common Pain Relievers

Pain Reliever	Mass of Active Ingredient per Pill
aspirin	325 mg
aspirin, extra strength	500 mg
ibuprofen (Advil)	200 mg
ibuprofen, extra strength	300 mg
acetaminophen (Tylenol)	325 mg
acetaminophen, extra strength	500 mg

2.8   Units Raised to a Power

The unit cm³ is often abbreviated as cc.

When converting quantities with units raised to a power, such as cubic centimeters (cm^3), the conversion factor must also be raised to that power. For example, suppose we want to convert the size of a motorcycle engine reported as 1255 cm³ to cubic inches. We know that

$$2.54 \text{ cm} = 1 \text{ in.}$$

Most tables of conversion factors do not include conversions between cubic units, but we can derive them from the conversion factors for the basic units. We cube both sides of the preceding equality to obtain the proper conversion factor.

$$(2.54 \text{ cm})^3 = (1 \text{ in.})^3$$
$$(2.54)^3 \text{ cm}^3 = 1^3 \text{ in.}^3$$
$$16.387 \text{ cm}^3 = 1 \text{ in.}^3$$

2.54 cm = 1 in. is an exact conversion factor. After cubing, we retain five significant figures so that the conversion factor does not limit the four significant figures of our original quantity (1255 cm³).

We can do the same thing in fractional form.

$$\frac{1 \text{ in.}}{2.54 \text{ cm}} = \frac{(1 \text{ in.})^3}{(2.54 \text{ cm})^3} = \frac{1 \text{ in.}^3}{16.387 \text{ cm}^3}$$

We then proceed with the conversion in the normal way.

Solution Map:

$$\frac{1 \text{ in.}^3}{16.387 \text{ cm}^3}$$

Solution: $1255 \text{ cm}^3 \times \dfrac{1 \text{ in.}^3}{16.387 \text{ cm}^3} = 76.5851 \text{ in.}^3 = 76.59 \text{ in.}^3$

EXAMPLE 2.12   Converting Quantities Involving Units Raised to a Power

A circle has an area of 2,659 cm². What is its area in square meters?

Set up the problem in the standard way.

Given: $2,659 \text{ cm}^2$

Find: m^2

Conversion Factor: $1 \text{ cm} = 0.01 \text{ m}$

Draw a solution map beginning with cm² and ending with m². Notice that you must square the conversion factor.

Solution Map:

$$\frac{(0.01 \text{ m})^2}{(1 \text{ cm})^2}$$

Follow the solution map to solve the problem. Round the answer to four significant figures to reflect the four significant figures in the given quantity. The conversion factor is exact and therefore does not limit the number of signficant figures.

Solution:

$$2,659 \text{ cm}^2 \times \frac{(0.01 \text{ m})^2}{(1 \text{ cm})^2}$$
$$= 2,659 \text{ cm}^2 \times \frac{10^{-4} \text{ m}^2}{1 \text{ cm}^2}$$
$$= 0.265900 \text{ m}^2$$
$$= 0.2659 \text{ m}^2$$

The units of the answer are correct, and the magnitude makes physical sense. A square meter is much larger than a square centimeter, so the value in square meters should be much smaller than the value in square centimeters.

SKILLBUILDER 2.12   Converting Quantities Involving Units Raised to a Power

An automobile engine has a displacement (a measure of the size of the engine) of 289.7 in.³. What is its displacement in cubic centimeters?

EXAMPLE 2.13   Solving Multistep Problems Involving Units Raised to a Power

The average annual per person oil consumption in the United States is 15,615 dm³. What is this value in cubic inches?

Set up the problem in the standard way. The conversion factors come from Tables 2.2 and 2.3.

Given: 15,615 dm³

Find: volume in in.³

Conversion Factors:

$$1 \text{ dm} = 0.1 \text{ m}$$
$$1 \text{ cm} = 0.01 \text{ m}$$
$$2.54 \text{ cm} = 1 \text{ in.}$$

Write a solution map beginning with dm³ and ending with in.³. Each of the conversion factors must be cubed, since the quantities involve cubic units.

Solution Map:

$$\boxed{\text{dm}^3} \rightarrow \boxed{\text{m}^3} \rightarrow \boxed{\text{cm}^3} \rightarrow \boxed{\text{in.}^3}$$

$$\frac{(0.1 \text{ m})^3}{(1 \text{ dm})^3} \qquad \frac{(1 \text{ cm})^3}{(0.01 \text{ m})^3} \qquad \frac{(1 \text{ in.})^3}{(2.54 \text{ cm})^3}$$

Follow the solution map to solve the problem.

Round the answer to five significant figures to reflect the five significant figures in the least precisely known quantity (15,615 dm³). The conversion factors are all exact and therefore do not limit the number of significant figures.

Solution:

$$15,615 \text{ dm}^3 \times \frac{(0.1 \text{ m})^3}{(1 \text{ dm})^3} \times \frac{(1 \text{ cm})^3}{(0.01 \text{ m})^3} \times \frac{(1 \text{ in.})^3}{(2.54 \text{ cm})^3}$$
$$= 9.5289 \times 10^5 \text{ in.}^3$$

The units of the answer are correct and the magnitude makes sense. A cubic inch is smaller than a cubic decimeter, so the value in cubic inches should be larger than the value in cubic decimeters.

SKILLBUILDER 2.13   Solving Multistep Problems Involving Units Raised to a Power

How many cubic inches are there in 3.25 yd³?

CONCEPTUAL CHECKPOINT 2.6

You know that there are 3 ft in a yard. How many cubic feet are there in a cubic yard?

(a) 3
(b) 6
(c) 9
(d) 27

2.9   Density

Why do some people pay more than $3000 for a bicycle made of titanium? A steel frame would be just as strong for a fraction of the cost. The difference between the two, of course, is mass—for a given volume of metal, titanium has less mass, and is therefore lighter than the steel bike. We describe this

▲ Top-end bicycle frames are made of titanium because of its low density and high relative strength. Titanium has a density of 4.50 g/cm³, while iron, for example, has a density of 7.86 g/cm³.

Remember that cubic centimeters and milliliters are equivalent units.

TABLE 2.4 Densities of Some Common Substances

Substance	Density (g/cm³)
water	1.0
ice	0.92
ethanol	0.789
lead	11.4
copper	8.96
gold	19.3
aluminum	2.7
platinum	21.4
iron	7.86
titanium	4.50
charcoal, oak	0.57
glass	2.6

property by saying that titanium is *less dense* than steel. The **density** of a substance is the ratio of its mass to its volume.

$$\text{Density} = \frac{\text{Mass}}{\text{Volume}} \quad \text{or} \quad d = \frac{m}{V}$$

Density is a fundamental property of materials that differs from one substance to another. The units of density are those of mass divided by those of volume, most conveniently expressed in grams per cubic centimeter or grams per milliliter. See Table 2.4 for a list of the densities of same common substances. Aluminum is among the least dense structural metals with a density of 2.70 g/cm³, while platinum is among the densest with a density of 21.4 g/cm³. Titanium has a density of 4.50 g/cm³.

● Calculating Density

The density of a substance is calculated by dividing the mass of a given amount of the substance by its volume. For example, a sample of liquid has a volume of 22.5 mL and a mass of 27.2 g. To find its density, we use the equation highlighted above.

$$d = \frac{m}{V} = \frac{27.2 \text{ g}}{22.5 \text{ mL}} = 1.21 \text{ g/mL}$$

We can use a solution map for solving problems involving equations, but it takes a slightly different form than for pure conversion problems. In a solution map for a problem involving an equation, the solution map shows how the *equation* takes you from the *given* quantities to the *find* quantity. The solution map for this problem is:

$$d = \frac{m}{V}$$

The solution map shows how the values of m and V, when substituted into the equation $d = \frac{m}{V}$, give the desired result, d.

EXAMPLE 2.14   Calculating Density

A jeweler offers to sell a ring to a woman, telling her that it is made of platinum. Noting that the ring felt a little light, the woman decides to perform a test to determine the ring's density. She places the ring on a balance and finds that it has a mass of 5.84 g. She then finds that the ring *displaces* 0.556 cm³ of water. Is the ring made of platinum? The density of platinum is 21.4 g/cm³. (The displacement of water is a common way to measure the volume of irregularly shaped objects. To say that an object *displaces* 0.556 cm³ of water means that when the object is submerged in a container of water filled to the brim, 0.556 cm³ overflows. Therefore, the volume of the object is 0.556 cm³.)

If the ring is platinum, its density should match that of platinum. You are given the mass and volume of the ring. Find the density using the density equation.

Given:

$$m = 5.84 \text{ g}$$

$$V = 0.556 \text{ cm}^3$$

Find: density in g/cm³

Equation: $d = \dfrac{m}{V}$

Draw a solution map. Begin with mass and volume and end with density.

Solution Map:

$$d = \frac{m}{V}$$

Substitute the given values into the density equation and compute the density. The density of the ring is much too low to be platinum, and therefore the ring is a fake.

Solution:

$$d = \frac{m}{V} = \frac{5.84\text{ g}}{0.556\text{ cm}^3} = 10.5\text{ g/cm}^3$$

SKILLBUILDER 2.14   **Calculating Density**

The woman takes the ring back to the jewelry shop, where she is met with endless apologies. They accidentally had made the ring out of silver rather than platinum. They give her a new ring that they promise is platinum. This time when she checks the density, she finds the mass of the ring to be 9.67 g and its volume to be 0.452 cm³. Is this ring genuine?

Density as a Conversion Factor

Density can also be thought of as a conversion factor between mass and volume. We may know the mass of an object and want to calculate its volume or vice versa. For example, suppose we need 68.4 g of a liquid with a density of 1.32 g/cm³ and only have a graduated cylinder to measure its volume. How much volume should we measure? We can set up this problem like a standard conversion problem.

Given: 68.4 g

Find: volume in mL

Conversion Factors:

$$1.32\text{ g/cm}^3$$
$$1\text{ cm}^3 = 1\text{ mL}$$

Density is a conversion factor between mass and volume. To convert from g to mL we need to invert the density because we want g, the unit we are converting from, to be on the bottom and cm³, the unit we are converting to, on the top. Our solution map is:

Solution Map:

Solution: $68.4\text{ g} \times \dfrac{1\text{ cm}^3}{1.32\text{ g}} \times \dfrac{1\text{ mL}}{1\text{ cm}^3} = 51.8\text{ mL}$

We must measure 51.8 mL to obtain 68.4 g of the liquid.

EXAMPLE 2.15   **Density as a Conversion Factor**

The gasoline in an automobile gas tank has a mass of 60.0 kg and a density of 0.752 g/cm³. What is its volume in cm³?

Set up the problem as usual. You are given the mass in kilograms and asked to find the volume in cubic centimeters. Density is the conversion factor between mass and volume.

Given: 60.0 kg

Find: volume in cm³

Conversion Factors:
   0.752 g/cm³
   1000 g = 1 kg

Build the solution map starting with kg and ending with cm³.

Solution Map:

$$ \boxed{kg} \longrightarrow \boxed{g} \longrightarrow \boxed{cm^3} $$

$$ \frac{1000 \text{ g}}{1 \text{ kg}} \qquad \frac{1 \text{ cm}^3}{0.752 \text{ g}} $$

Follow the solution map to solve the problem.

Solution: $60.0 \text{ kg} \times \dfrac{1000 \text{ g}}{1 \text{ kg}} \times \dfrac{1 \text{ cm}^3}{0.752 \text{ g}} = 7.98 \times 10^4 \text{ cm}^3$

SKILLBUILDER 2.15 **Density as a Conversion Factor**

A drop of acetone (nail polish remover) has a mass of 35 mg and a density of 0.788 g/cm³. What is its volume in cubic centimeters?

SKILLBUILDER PLUS

A steel cylinder has a volume of 246 cm³ and a density of 7.93 g/cm³. What is its mass in kilograms?

Chemistry AND HEALTH

Density, Cholesterol, and Heart Disease

Substances are often separated and classified according to their density. A class of substances classified in this way are lipoproteins, carriers of cholesterol in the blood. Cholesterol is found in animal-derived foods such as beef, eggs, fish, poultry, and milk products and is used by the body for several purposes. However, excessive amounts of cholesterol in the blood—which can be caused by both genetic factors and diet—may result in the deposition of cholesterol in arterial walls, leading to a condition called atherosclerosis, or blocking of the arteries. These blockages are dangerous because they inhibit blood flow to important organs, causing heart attacks and strokes. The risk of stroke and heart attack increases with increasing blood cholesterol levels (Table 2.5).

Cholesterol is carried in the blood by lipoproteins, which are classified by their density. The main carriers of blood cholesterol are low-density lipoproteins (LDLs). LDLs, also called bad cholesterol, have a density of 1.04 g/cm³. They are bad because they tend to deposit cholesterol on arterial walls and therefore increase the risk of stroke and heart attack. Cholesterol is also carried by high-density lipoproteins (HDLs). HDLs, also called good cholesterol, have a density of 1.13 g/cm³. HDLs transport cholesterol to the liver for processing and excretion and therefore have a tendency to reduce cholesterol on arterial walls. Too low a level of HDLs (below 35 mg/100 mL) is considered a risk factor for heart disease. Exercise, along with a diet low in saturated fats, is believed to raise HDL levels in the blood while lowering LDL levels.

CAN YOU ANSWER THIS? *What mass of low-density lipoprotein is contained in a cylinder that is 1.25 cm long and 0.50 cm in diameter? (The volume of a cylinder, V, is given by $V = \pi r^2 \ell$, where r is the radius of the cylinder and ℓ is its length.)*

Clogged artery

▲ Too many low-density lipoproteins in the blood can lead to blocking of arteries.

TABLE 2.5 Risk of Stroke and Heart Attack vs. Blood Cholesterol Level

Risk Level	Total Blood Cholesterol (mg/100 mL)	LDL (mg/100 mL)
low	<200	<130
borderline	200–239	130–159
high	240+	160+

2.10   Numerical Problem-Solving Strategies and the Solution Map

In this chapter, you have seen a few examples of how to solve numerical problems. The ability to solve a numerical problem is one of the most important things you will learn in this course. When you first look at a problem, what should you do? Some students simply get stuck—they have trouble getting started. To avoid this, develop a strategy to attack and solve problems. What should you do first? What next? In Section 2.6, we developed a strategy or a procedure to solve simple unit conversion problems. We then learned how to modify that procedure to work with multistep unit conversion problems and problems involving an equation. We will now summarize these procedures and generalize our strategy to apply to most of the numerical problems we encounter in this book. As we did in Section 2.6, we provide the general procedure for solving numerical problems in the left column of the following box. The center and right columns show two examples where this procedure is applied.

LIVE EXAMPLE

Solving Numerical Problems	**EXAMPLE 2.16** **Unit Conversion** A 23.5-kg sample of ethanol is needed for a large-scale reaction. What volume in liters of ethanol should be used? The density of ethanol is 0.789 g/cm³.	**EXAMPLE 2.17** **Unit Conversion with Equation** A 55.9-kg person displaces 57.2 L of water when submerged in a water tank. What is the density of the person in grams per cubic centimeter?

1. Write down the *given* quantity and its units.
    Scan the problem for one or more numbers and their units. This number (or numbers) is (are) the starting point(s) of the calculation.
	Given: 23.5 kg ethanol	**Given:** $m = 55.9$ kg
		                   $V = 57.2$ L

2. Write down the *find* quantity and its units. Scan the problem to determine what you are asked to find. Sometimes the units of this quantity are implied; other times they are specified.	**Find:** volume in L	**Find:** density in g/cm³

3. Write down the appropriate *conversion factors* and/or *equations*.
    Sometimes these conversion factors are given in the problem. Other times they are in tables. You may not get them all at this point—that's okay. For problems involving equations, familiarity and practice will help you know what equation to use.
	Conversion Factors:
	    0.789 g/cm³
	    1000 g = 1 kg
	    1000 mL = 1 L
	    1 mL = 1 cm³
		Conversion Factors and Equation:
		    1000 g = 1 kg
		    1000 mL = 1 L
		    1 cm³ = 1 mL
		
		    $d = \dfrac{m}{V}$

4. Write a *solution map* for the problem. • For problems involving only *conversions*, focus on units. The solution map shows how to get from the units in the *given* quantity to the units in the *find* quantity. • For problems involving *equations*, focus on the equation. The solution map shows how the equation takes you from the *given* quantity (or quantities) to the *find* quantity.	**Solution Map:** $$\frac{1000\ g}{1\ kg} \quad \frac{1\ cm^3}{0.789\ g} \quad \frac{1\ mL}{1\ cm^3} \quad \frac{1L}{1000\ mL}$$	**Solution Map:** $$\boxed{m, V} \rightarrow \boxed{d}$$ $$d = \frac{m}{V}$$
5. Follow the solution map to solve the problem. • For problems involving only *conversions*, begin with the *given* quantity and its units. Multiply by the appropriate conversion factor(s), canceling units, to arrive at the *find* quantity. • For problems involving *equations*, solve the equation for the *find* quantity. (Use algebra to rearrange the equation so that the *find* quantity is isolated on one side.) Gather each of the quantities that must go into the equation in the correct units. (Convert to the correct units using additional solution maps if necessary.) Finally, substitute the numerical values and their units into the equation and compute the answer.	**Solution:** $$23.5\ \cancel{kg} \times \frac{1000\ \cancel{g}}{1\ \cancel{kg}} \times \frac{1\ \cancel{cm^3}}{0.789\ \cancel{g}} \times$$ $$\frac{1\ \cancel{mL}}{1\ \cancel{cm^3}} \times \frac{1\ L}{1000\ \cancel{mL}} = 29.7845\ L$$	**Solution:** $$d = \frac{m}{V}$$ The equation is already solved for the *find* quantity. Convert mass from kilograms to grams. $$m = 55.9\ \cancel{kg} \times \frac{1000\ g}{1\ \cancel{kg}}$$ $$= 5.59 \times 10^4\ g$$ Convert volume from liters to cubic centimeters. $$57.2\ \cancel{L} \times \frac{1000\ \cancel{mL}}{1\ \cancel{L}} \times \frac{1\ cm^3}{1\ \cancel{mL}} =$$ $$57.2 \times 10^3\ cm^3$$ Compute density. $$d = \frac{m}{V} \times \frac{55.9 \times 10^3}{57.2 \times 10^3\ cm^3}$$ $$= 0.9772727\ \frac{g}{cm^3}$$
6. Round the answer to the correct number of significant figures. Use the significant-figure rules from Sections 2.3 and 2.4.	$$29.7845\ L = 29.8\ L$$	$$0.9772727\ \frac{g}{cm^3} = 0.977\ \frac{g}{cm^3}$$
7. Check both the magnitude and units of the answer for correctness. Does the magnitude of the answer make sense? Are the units correct?	The units are correct (L) and the magnitude is reasonable. Since the density is less than 1 g/cm³, the computed volume (29.8 L) should be greater than the mass (23.5 kg). **SKILLBUILDER 2.16** **Unit Conversion** A pure gold metal bar displaces 0.82 L of water. What is its mass in kilograms? (The density of gold is 19.3 g/cm³.)	The units are correct. Since the mass in kilograms and the volume in liters were very close to each other in magnitude, it makes sense that the density is close to 1 g/cm³. **SKILLBUILDER 2.17** **Unit Conversion with Equation** A gold-colored pebble is found in a stream. Its mass is 23.2 mg and its volume is 1.20 mm³. What is its density in grams per cubic centimeter? Is it gold? (density of gold = 19.3 g/cm³)

CHAPTER IN REVIEW

Chemical Principles

Uncertainty: Measured quantities are reported so that the number of digits reflects the certainty in the measurement. Write measured quantities so that every digit is certain except the last, which is estimated.

Units: Measured quantities usually have units associated with them. The most convenient unit system for scientific use is the International System. The SI unit for length is the meter; for mass, the kilogram; and for time, the second. Prefix multipliers such as *kilo-* or *milli-* are often used in combination with these basic units. The SI units of volume are units of length raised to the third power, but liters or milliliters are often used as well.

Density: The density of a substance is its mass divided by its volume, $d = m/V$, and is usually reported in units of grams per cubic centimeter or grams per milliliter. Density is a fundamental property of all substances and generally differs from one substance to another.

Relevance

Uncertainty: Measurement is a hallmark of science, and the precision of a measurement must be communicated with the measurement so that others know how reliable the measurement is. When you write or manipulate measured quantities you must show and retain the precision with which the measurement was made.

Units: The units in a measured quantity communicate what the quantity actually is. Without an agreed-on system of units, scientists could not communicate their measurements. Units are also important in calculations, and the tracking of units throughout a calculation is essential.

Density: The density of substances is an important consideration in choosing materials from which to make things. Airplanes, for example, are made of low-density materials while bridges are made of higher-density materials. Density is also important as a conversion factor between mass and volume and vice versa.

Chemical Skills

Scientific Notation (Section 2.2)

To express a number in scientific notation:

- Move the decimal point to obtain a number between 1 and 10.

- Write the decimal part multiplied by 10 raised to the number of places you moved the decimal point.

- The exponent is positive if you moved the decimal point to the left and negative if you moved the decimal point to the right.

Reporting Measured Quantities to the Right Number of Digits (Section 2.3)

Report measured quantities so that every digit is certain except the last, which is estimated.

Examples

EXAMPLE 2.18   **Scientific Notation**

Express the number 45,000,000 in scientific notation.

$$45,000,000$$
$$7\ 6\ 5\ 4\ 3\ 2\ 1$$

$$4.5 \times 10^7$$

EXAMPLE 2.19   **Reporting Measured Quantities to the Right Number of Digits**

Record the volume of liquid in the graduated cylinder to the correct number of digits. Laboratory glassware is calibrated—and should therefore be read—from the bottom of the meniscus (see figure).

Since the graduated cylinder has markings every 0.1 mL, the measurement should be recorded to the nearest 0.01 mL. In this case, that is 4.57 mL.

Counting Significant Digits (Section 2.3)

The following digits should always be counted as significant:

- nonzero digits

- interior zeros

- trailing zeros after a decimal point

The following digits should never be counted as significant:

- zeros to the left of the first nonzero number

The following digits are ambiguous and should be avoided by using scientific notation:

- zeros at the end of a number, but before a decimal point

EXAMPLE 2.20   Counting Significant Digits

How many significant figures are in the following numbers?

1.0050	five significant figures
0.00870	three significant figures
5,400	Write as 5.4×10^3, 5.40×10^3, or 5.400×10^3, depending on the number of significant figures intended.

Rounding (Section 2.4)

When rounding numbers to the correct number of significant figures, round down if the last digit dropped is 4 or less; round up if the last digit dropped is 5 or more.

EXAMPLE 2.21   Rounding

Round 6.442 and 6.456 to two significant figures.

6.442 rounds to 6.4
6.456 rounds to 6.5

Significant Figures in Multiplication and Division (Section 2.4)

The result of a multiplication or division should carry the same number of significant figures as the factor with the least number of significant figures.

EXAMPLE 2.22   Significant Figures in Multiplication and Division

Perform the following calculation and report the answer to the correct number of significant figures.

$$8.54 \times 3.589 \div 4.2$$
$$= 7.297$$
$$= 7.3$$

Round the final result to two significant figures to reflect the two significant figures in the factor with the least number of significant figures (4.2).

Significant Figures in Addition and Subtraction (Section 2.4)

The result of an addition or subtraction should carry the same number of decimal places as the quantity carrying the least number of decimal places.

EXAMPLE 2.23   Significant Figures in Addition and Subtraction

Perform the following operation and report the answer to the correct number of significant figures.

$$\begin{array}{r} 3.098 \\ 0.67 \\ -0.9452 \\ \hline 2.8228 = 2.82 \end{array}$$

Round the final result to two decimal places to reflect the two decimal places in the quantity with the least number of decimal places (0.67).

Significant Figures in Calculations Involving Both Addition/Subtraction and Multiplication/Division (Section 2.4)

In calculations involving both addition/subtraction and multiplication/division, do the steps in parentheses first, keeping track of how many significant digits are in the answer by underlining the least significant digit, then do the remaining steps. It is best to not round off until the very end.

EXAMPLE 2.24   Significant Figures in Calculations Involving Both Addition/Subtraction and Multiplication/Division

Perform the following operation and report the answer to the correct number of significant figures.

$8.16 \times (5.4323 - 5.411)$
$= 8.16 \times 0.0213$
$= 0.1738$
$= 0.17$

Unit Conversion (Sections 2.6, 2.7)

Solve unit conversion problems by following these steps.

1. Write down the given quantity and its units.

2. Write down the quantity to find and/or its units.

3. Write down the appropriate conversion factor(s).

4. Draw a solution map.

EXAMPLE 2.25   Unit Conversion

Convert 108 ft to meters.

Given: 108 ft

Find: m

Conversion Factors:

$1 \text{ m} = 39.37 \text{ in.}$
$1 \text{ ft} = 12 \text{ in.}$

Solution Map:

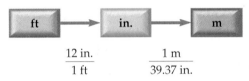

$$\frac{12 \text{ in.}}{1 \text{ ft}} \qquad \frac{1 \text{ m}}{39.37 \text{ in.}}$$

5. Follow the solution map. Starting with the given quantity and its units, multiply by the appropriate conversion factor(s), canceling units, to arrive at the quantity to find in the desired units.

6. Round the final answer to the correct number of significant figures.

7. Check the answer.

Solution:

$$108 \text{ ft} \times \frac{12 \text{ in.}}{1 \text{ ft}} \times \frac{1 \text{ m}}{39.37 \text{ in.}}$$
$= 32.918 \text{ m}$
$= 32.9 \text{ m}$

Unit Conversion Involving Units Raised to a Power (Section 2.8)

When working problems involving units raised to a power, raise the conversion factors to the same power.

EXAMPLE 2.26   Unit Conversion Involving Units Raised to a Power

How many square meters are in 1.0 km^2?

Given: 1.0 km^2

Find: m^2

Conversion Factors: $1 \text{ km} = 1000 \text{ m}$

Solution Map:

$$\frac{(1000 \text{ m})^2}{(1 \text{ km})^2}$$

Solution:

$$1.0 \text{ km}^2 \times \frac{(1000 \text{ m})^2}{(1 \text{ km})^2}$$
$$= 1.0 \text{ km}^2 \times \frac{1 \times 10^6 \text{ m}^2}{1 \text{ km}^2}$$
$= 1.0 \times 10^6 \text{ m}^2$

Calculating Density (Section 2.10)

The density of an object or substance is its mass divided by its volume.

$$d = \frac{m}{V}$$

| EXAMPLE 2.27 | **Calculating Density** |

An object has a mass of 23.4 g and displaces 5.7 mL of water. What is its density in grams per milliliter?

Given:

$$m = 23.4 \text{ g}$$
$$V = 5.7 \text{ mL}$$

Find: density in g/mL

Solution Map:

$$d = \frac{m}{V}$$

Solution:

$$d = \frac{m}{V}$$

$$= \frac{23.4 \text{ g}}{5.7 \text{ mL}}$$

$$= 4.11 \text{ g/mL}$$

$$= 4.1 \text{ g/mL}$$

Density as a Conversion Factor (Section 2.10)

Density can be used as a conversion factor from mass to volume or from volume to mass. To convert between volume and mass, use density directly. To convert between mass and volume, you must invert the density.

| EXAMPLE 2.28 | **Density as a Conversion Factor** |

What is the volume in liters of 321 g of a liquid with a density of 0.84 g/mL?

Given: 321 g

Find: volume in L

Conversion Factors:

$$0.84 \text{ g/mL}$$
$$1 \text{ L} = 1000 \text{ mL}$$

Solution Map:

$$\frac{1 \text{ mL}}{0.84 \text{ g}} \qquad \frac{1 \text{ L}}{1000 \text{ mL}}$$

Solution:

$$321 \text{ g} \times \frac{1 \text{ mL}}{0.84 \text{ g}} \times \frac{1 \text{ L}}{1000 \text{ mL}}$$

$$= 0.382 \text{ L}$$

$$= 0.38 \text{ L}$$

🌑 Key Terms

conversion factor [2.6]	International System [2.5]	prefix multipliers [2.5]	solution map [2.6]
decimal part [2.2]	kilogram (kg) [2.5]	scientific notation [2.2]	units [2.5]
density [2.9]	liter (L) [2.5]	second (s) [2.5]	volume [2.5]
English system [2.5]	mass [2.5]	SI units [2.5]	
exponent [2.2]	meter (m) [2.5]	significant figures	
exponential part [2.2]	metric system [2.5]	(digits) [2.3]	

● Exercises

1. Why is it important to report units with scientific measurements?
2. Why is it important to report a certain number of digits with scientific measurements?
3. Why is scientific notation necessary?
4. If a measured quantity is written correctly, which digits are certain? Which are uncertain?
5. Explain when zeros count as significant digits and when they do not.
6. How many significant digits are there in exact numbers? What kinds of numbers are exact?
7. What limits the number of significant digits in a calculation involving only multiplication and division?
8. What limits the number of significant digits in a calculation involving only addition and subtraction?
9. What are the rules for rounding numbers? What happens if the last digit being dropped is 5 or more? Less than 5?
10. How do significant figures work in calculations involving both addition/subtraction and multiplication/division?
11. What are the basic SI units of length, mass, and time?
12. What are common units of volume?
13. Suppose you are trying to measure the diameter of a Frisbee. What unit and prefix multiplier would you use?
14. What is the difference between mass and weight?

15. Obtain a metric ruler and measure the following objects to the correct number of significant figures.
    (a) quarter (diameter)
    (b) dime (diameter)
    (c) notebook paper (width)
    (d) this book (width)
16. Obtain a stopwatch and measure each of the following to the correct number of significant figures.
    (a) time between your heartbeats
    (b) time it takes you to do the next problem
    (c) time between your breaths
17. Explain why units are important in calculations.
18. How are units treated in a calculation?
19. What is a conversion factor?
20. Write the conversion factor that converts a measurement in inches to feet.
21. Draw a solution map to convert a measurement in grams to pounds.
22. Draw a solution map to convert a measurement in milliliters to gallons.
23. Draw a solution map to convert a measurement in meters to feet.
24. Draw a solution map to convert a measurement in ounces to grams. (1 lb = 16 oz)
25. What is density? Explain why density can work as a conversion factor. Between what quantities does it convert?
26. Explain how you would calculate the density of a substance. Include a solution map in your explanation.

Problems

Note: The exercises in the Problems section are paired, and the answers to the odd-numbered exercises (numbered in blue) appear in the Answers section at the back of the book.

Scientific Notation

27. Express each of the following numbers in scientific notation.
    (a) 32,667,000 (population of California)
    (b) 1,193,000 (population of Hawaii)
    (c) 18,175,000 (population of New York)
    (d) 481,000 (population of Wyoming)

28. Express each of the following numbers in scientific notation.
    (a) 6,364,262,000 (population of the world)
    (b) 1,236,915,000 (population of China)
    (c) 11,051,000 (population of Cuba)
    (d) 3,619,000 (population of Ireland)

29. Express each of the following numbers in scientific notation.
    (a) 0.00000000007461 m (length of a hydrogen–hydrogen chemical bond)
    (b) 0.0000158 mi (number of miles in an inch)
    (c) 0.000000632 m (wavelength of red light)
    (d) 0.000015 m (diameter of a human hair)

30. Express each of the following numbers in scientific notation.
    (a) 0.000000001 s (time it takes light to travel 1 ft)
    (b) 0.143 s (time it takes light to travel around the world)
    (c) 0.000000000001 s (time it takes a chemical bond to undergo one vibration)
    (d) 0.000001 m (approximate size of a dust particle)

31. Express each of the following in decimal notation.
    (a) 6.022×10^{23} (number of carbon atoms in 12.01 g of carbon)
    (b) 1.6×10^{-19} C (charge of a proton in coulombs)
    (c) 2.99×10^{8} m/s (speed of light)
    (d) 3.44×10^{2} m/s (speed of sound)

32. Express each of the following in decimal notation.
    (a) 450×10^{-9} m (wavelength of blue light)
    (b) 13.7×10^{9} years (approximate age of the universe)
    (c) 5×10^{9} years (approximate age of Earth)
    (d) 4.1×10^{1} years (approximate age of this author)

33. Express each of the following in decimal notation.
    (a) 3.89×10^{9}
    (b) 5.9×10^{-4}
    (c) 8.68×10^{12}
    (d) 7.86×10^{-8}

34. Express each of the following in decimal notation.
    (a) 1.90×10^{8}
    (b) 1.4×10^{-2}
    (c) 3.2×10^{3}
    (d) 4.53×10^{-14}

35. Complete the following table.

Decimal Notation	Scientific Notation
2,000,000,000	____
____	1.211×10^{9}
0.000874	____
____	3.2×10^{11}

36. Complete the following table.

Decimal Notation	Scientific Notation
____	4.2×10^{-3}
315,171,000	____
____	1.8×10^{-11}
1,232,000	____

Significant Figures

37. Read each of the following to the correct number of significant figures. Laboratory glassware should always be read from the bottom of the meniscus.

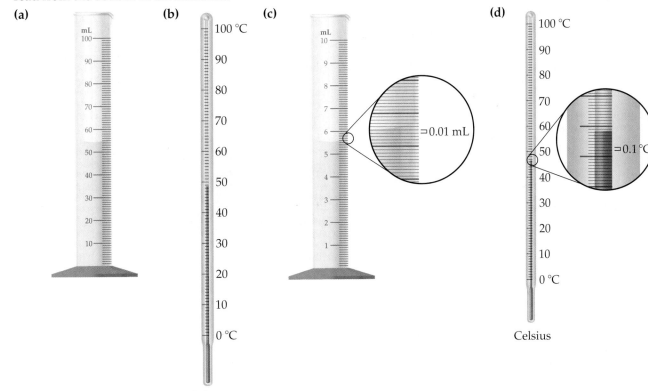

(a)   (b)   (c)   (d)

38. Read each of the following to the correct number of significant figures. Laboratory glassware should always be read from the bottom of the meniscus.

(a)

(b)

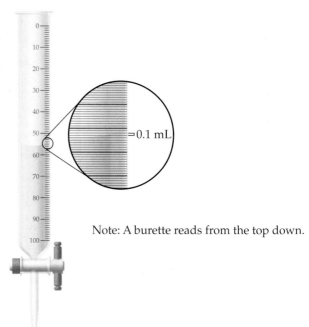

=0.1 mL

Note: A burette reads from the top down.

(c)

Note: A pipette reads from the top down.

(d)

Note: Digital balances normally display mass to the correct number of significant figures for that particular balance.

---

39. For each of the following measured quantities, underline the zeros that are significant and draw an X through the zeros that are not.
   (a) 0.005050 m
   (b) 0.0000000000000060 s
   (c) 220,103 kg
   (d) 0.00108 in.

40. For each of the following measured quantities, underline the zeros that are significant and draw an X through the zeros that are not.
   (a) 0.00010320 s
   (b) 1,322,600,324 kg
   (c) 0.0001240 in.
   (d) 0.02061 m

41. How many significant figures are in each of the following measured quantities?
- **(a)** 0.001125 m
- **(b)** 0.1125 m
- **(c)** 1.12500×10^4 m
- **(d)** 11205 m

42. How many significant figures are in each of the following numbers?
- **(a)** 13001 kg
- **(b)** 13111 kg
- **(c)** 1.30×10^4 kg
- **(d)** 0.00013 kg

43. Determine whether each of the entries in the following table is correct. Correct the ones that are wrong.

Quantity	Significant Figures
(a) 895675 m	6
(b) 0.000869 kg	6
(c) 0.5672100 s	5
(d) 6.022×10^{23} atoms	4

44. Determine whether each of the entries in the following table is correct. Correct the ones that are wrong.

Quantity	Significant Figures
(a) 24 days	2
(b) 5.6×10^{-12} s	3
(c) 3.14 m	3
(d) 0.00383 g	5

Rounding

45. The following numbers are displayed on a calculator. Round each to four significant figures.
- **(a)** 342.985318
- **(b)** 0.009650901
- **(c)** $3.52569241 \times 10^{-8}$
- **(d)** 1,127,436,092

46. The following numbers are displayed on a calculator. Round each to three significant figures.
- **(a)** 9,845.87492
- **(b)** $1.548937483 \times 10^{12}$
- **(c)** 2.3499999995
- **(d)** 0.000045389

47. Round each of the following to two significant figures.
- **(a)** 2.34
- **(b)** 2.35
- **(c)** 2.349
- **(d)** 2.359

48. Round each of the following to three significant figures.
- **(a)** 65.74
- **(b)** 65.749
- **(c)** 65.75
- **(d)** 65.750

49. Each of the following numbers was supposed to be rounded to three significant figures. Find the ones that were incorrectly rounded and correct them.
- **(a)** 42.3492 to 42.4
- **(b)** 56.9971 to 57.0
- **(c)** 231.904 to 232
- **(d)** 0.04555 to 0.046

50. Each of the following numbers was supposed to be rounded to two significant figures. Find the ones that were incorrectly rounded and correct them.
- **(a)** 1.249×10^3 to 1.3×10^3
- **(b)** 3.999×10^2 to 40
- **(c)** 56.21 to 56.2
- **(d)** 0.009964 to 0.010

Significant Figures in Calculations

51. Perform the following calculations to the correct number of significant figures.
- **(a)** $4.5 \times 0.03060 \times 0.391$
- **(b)** $5.55 \div 8.97$
- **(c)** $7.890 \times 10^{12} \div 6.7 \times 10^4$
- **(d)** $67.8 \times 9.8 \div 100.04$

52. Perform the following calculations to the correct number of significant figures.
- **(a)** $89.3 \times 77.0 \times 0.08$
- **(b)** $5.01 \times 10^5 \div 7.8 \times 10^2$
- **(c)** $4.005 \times 74 \times 0.007$
- **(d)** $453 \div 2.031$

53. Determine whether each of the following calculations is performed to the correct number of significant figures. If it is not, correct it.
- **(a)** $34.00 \times 567 \div 4.564 = 4.2239 \times 10^3$
- **(b)** $79.3 \div 0.004 \times 35.4 = 7 \times 10^5$
- **(c)** $89.763 \div 22.4581 = 3.997$
- **(d)** $4.32 \times 10^{12} \div 3.1 \times 10^{-4} = 1.4 \times 10^{16}$

54. Determine whether each of the following calculations is performed to the correct number of significant figures. If it is not, correct it.
- **(a)** $45.3254 \times 89.00205 = 4034.05$
- **(b)** $0.00740 \times 45.0901 = 0.334$
- **(c)** $49857 \div 904875 = 0.05510$
- **(d)** $0.009090 \times 6007.2 = 54.605$

55. Perform the following calculations to the correct number of significant figures.
(a) $87.6 + 9.888 + 2.3 + 100.77$
(b) $43.7 - 2.341$
(c) $89.6 + 98.33 - 4.674$
(d) $6.99 - 5.772$

56. Perform the following calculations to the correct number of significant figures.
(a) $1459.3 + 9.77 + 4.32$
(b) $0.004 + 0.09879$
(c) $432 + 7.3 - 28.523$
(d) $2.4 - 1.777$

57. Determine whether each of the following calculations is performed to the correct number of significant figures. If not, correct it.
(a) $3.8 \times 10^5 - 8.45 \times 10^5 = -4.7 \times 10^5$
(b) $0.00456 + 1.0936 = 1.10$
(c) $8475.45 - 34.899 = 8440.55$
(d) $908.87 - 905.34095 = 3.5291$

58. Determine whether each of the following calculations is performed to the correct number of significant figures. If not, correct it.
(a) $78.9 + 890.43 - 23 = 9.5 \times 10^2$
(b) $9354 - 3489.56 + 34.3 = 5898.74$
(c) $0.00407 + 0.0943 = 0.0984$
(d) $0.00896 - 0.007 = 0.00196$

59. Perform each of the following calculations to the correct number of significant figures.
(a) $(78.4 - 44.889) \div 0.0087$
(b) $(34.6784 \times 5.38) + 445.56$
(c) $(78.7 \times 10^5 \div 88.529) + 356.99$
(d) $(892 \div 986.7) + 5.44$

60. Perform each of the following calculations to the correct number of significant figures.
(a) $(1.7 \times 10^6 \div 2.63 \times 10^5) + 7.33$
(b) $(568.99 - 232.1) \div 5.3$
(c) $(9443 + 45 - 9.9) \times 8.1 \times 10^6$
(d) $(3.14 \times 2.4367) - 2.34$

61. Determine whether each of the following calculations is performed to the correct number of significant figures. If not, correct it.
(a) $(78.56 - 9.44) \times 45.6 = 3152$
(b) $(8.9 \times 10^5 \div 2.348 \times 10^2) + 121 = 3.9 \times 10^3$
(c) $(45.8 \div 3.2) - 12.3 = 2$
(d) $(4.5 \times 10^3 - 1.53 \times 10^3) \div 34.5 = 86$

62. Determine whether each of the following calculations is performed to the correct number of significant figures. If not, correct it.
(a) $(908.4 - 3.4) \div 3.52 \times 10^4 = 0.026$
(b) $(1206.7 - 0.904) \times 89 = 1.07 \times 10^5$
(c) $(876.90 + 98.1) \div 56.998 = 17.11$
(d) $(455 \div 407859) + 1.00098 = 1.00210$

Unit Conversion

63. Perform each of the following conversions within the metric system.
(a) 2.14 kg to grams
(b) 6172 mm to meters
(c) 1316 mg to kilograms
(d) 0.0256 L to milliliters

64. Perform each of the following conversions within the metric system.
(a) 8.95 cm to meters
(b) 1298.4 g to kilograms
(c) 129 cm to millimeters
(d) 2452 mL to liters

65. Perform each of the following conversions within the metric system.
(a) 5.88 dL to liters
(b) 3.41×10^{-5} g to micrograms
(c) 1.01×10^{-8} s to nanoseconds
(d) 2.19 pm to meters

66. Perform each of the following conversions within the metric system.
(a) 1.08 Mm to kilometers
(b) 4.88 fs to picoseconds
(c) 7.39×10^{11} m to gigameters
(d) 1.15×10^{-10} m to picometers

67. Perform the following conversions between the English and metric systems.
(a) 22.5 in. to centimeters
(b) 126 ft to meters
(c) 825 yd to kilometers
(d) 2.4 in. to millimeters

68. Perform the following conversions between the English and metric systems.
(a) 78.3 in. to centimeters
(b) 445 yd to meters
(c) 336 ft to centimeters
(d) 45.3 in. to millimeters

69. Perform the following conversions between the metric and English systems.
(a) 40.0 cm to inches
(b) 27.8 m to feet
(c) 10.0 km to miles
(d) 3845 kg to pounds

70. Perform the following conversions between the metric and English systems.
(a) 254 cm to inches
(b) 89 mm to inches
(c) 7.5 L to quarts
(d) 122 kg to pounds

71. Complete the following table:

m	km	Mm	Gm	Tm
5.08×10^8 m	___	508 Mm	___	___
___	___	27,976 Mm	___	___
___	___	___	___	1.77 Tm
___	1.5×10^5 km	___	___	___
___	___	___	423 Gm	___

72. Complete the following table:

s	ms	μs	ns	ps
1.31×10^{-4} s	___	131 μs	___	___
___	___	___	___	12.6 ps
___	___	___	155 ns	___
___	1.99×10^{-3} ms	___	___	___
___	___	8.66×10^{-5} μs	___	___

73. Convert 2.255×10^{10} g to each of the following units:
(a) kg
(b) Mg
(c) mg
(d) metric tons (1 metric ton = 1000 kg)

74. Convert 1.88×10^{-6} g to each of the following units.
(a) mg
(b) cg
(c) ng
(d) μg

75. A student loses 2.4 lb in one month. How many grams did she lose?

76. A student gains 1.6 lb in two weeks. How many grams did he gain?

77. A runner wants to run 10.0 km. She knows that her running pace is 7.5 mi/h. How many minutes must she run? Hint: Use 7.5 mi/h as a conversion factor between distance and time.

78. A cyclist rides at an average speed of 24 mi/h. If she wants to bike 195 km, how long (in hours) must she ride?

79. A recipe calls for 5.0 qt of milk. What is this quantity in cubic centimeters?

80. A gas can holds 2.0 gal of gasoline. What is this quantity in cubic centimeters?

Units Raised to a Power

81. Fill in the blanks.
(a) $1.0 \text{ km}^2 = $ ___ m^2
(b) $1.0 \text{ cm}^3 = $ ___ m^3
(c) $1.0 \text{ mm}^3 = $ ___ m^3

82. Fill in the blanks.
(a) $1.0 \text{ ft}^2 = $ ___ in.^2
(b) $1.0 \text{ yd}^2 = $ ___ ft^2
(c) $1.0 \text{ m}^2 = $ ___ yd^2

83. The hydrogen atom has a volume of approximately $6.2 \times 10^{-31} \text{ m}^3$. Convert this volume into each of the following units:
(a) cubic picometers
(b) cubic nanometers
(c) cubic angstroms (1 angstrom = 10^{-10} m)

84. Earth has a surface area of 197 million square miles. Convert this area into each of the following units:
(a) square kilometers
(b) square megameters
(c) square decimeters

85. A modest-sized house has an area of 215 m². What is its area in the following units?
(a) km^2 (b) dm^2 (c) cm^2

86. A classroom has a volume of 285 m³. What is its volume in the following units?
(a) km^3 (b) dm^3 (c) cm^3

87. Total U.S. farmland occupies 954 million acres. How many square miles is this? (1 acre = 43,560 ft²; 1 mi = 5280 ft)

88. The average U.S. farm occupies 435 acres. How many square miles is this? (1 acre = 43,560 ft²; 1 mi = 5280 ft)

Density

89. A sample of an unknown metal has a mass of 35.4 g and a volume of 3.11 cm³. Calculate its density and identify the metal by comparison to Table 2.4.

90. A new penny has a mass of 2.49 g and a volume of 0.349 cm³. Is the penny made of pure copper?

91. Glycerol is a syrupy liquid often used in cosmetics and soaps. A 2.50-L sample of pure glycerol has a mass of 3.15×10^3 g. What is the density of glycerol in grams per cubic centimeter?

92. An aluminum engine block has a volume of 4.77 L and a mass of 12.88 kg. What is the density of the aluminum in grams per cubic centimeter?

93. A supposedly gold crown is tested to determine its density. It is found to displace 10.7 mL of water and has a mass of 206 g. Could the crown be made of gold?

94. A vase is said to be solid platinum. It is found to displace 18.65 mL of water and has a mass of 157 g. Could the vase be solid platinum?

95. Ethylene glycol (antifreeze) has a density of 1.11 g/cm³.
    (a) What is the mass in grams of 417 mL of this liquid?
    (b) What is the volume in liters of 4.1 kg of this liquid?

96. Acetone (fingernail-polish remover) has a density of 0.7857 g/cm³.
    (a) What is the mass in grams of 28.56 mL of acetone?
    (b) What is the volume in milliliters of 6.54 g of acetone?

Cumulative Problems

97. A thief uses a bag of sand to replace a gold statue that sits on a weight-sensitive, alarmed pedestal. The bag of sand and the statue have exactly the same volume, 1.75 L.
    (a) Calculate the mass of each object. (density of gold =19.3 g/cm³; density of sand = 3.00 g/cm³)
    (b) Did the thief set off the alarm? Explain.

98. One of the particles that compose atoms is called the proton. The proton has a radius of approximately 1.0×10^{-13} cm and a mass of 1.7×10^{-24} g. Determine the density of a proton. (volume of a sphere $= \frac{4}{3}\pi r^3$; $\pi = 3.14$)

99. A block of metal has a volume of 13.4 in.³ and weighs 5.14 lb. What is its density in grams per cubic centimeter?

100. A log is known to be either oak or pine. It displaces 2.7 gal of water and weighs 19.8 lb. Is the log oak or pine? (density of oak = 0.9 g/cm³; density of pine = 0.4 g/cm³)

101. The density of aluminum is 2.7 g/cm³. What is its density in kilograms per cubic meter?

102. The density of platinum is 21.4 g/cm³. What is its density in pounds per cubic inch?

103. A typical backyard swimming pool holds 150 yd³ of water. What is the mass in pounds of the water?

104. An iceberg has a volume of 8975 ft³. What is the mass in kilograms of the iceberg?

105. The mass of fuel in an airplane must be carefully accounted for before takeoff. If a 747 contains 155,211 L of fuel, what is the mass of the fuel in kilograms? Assume the density of the fuel to be 0.768 g/cm³.

106. A backpacker carries 2.5 L of white gas as fuel for her stove. How many pounds does the fuel add to her load? Assume the density of white gas to be 0.79 g/cm³.

107. Honda produces a hybrid electric car called the Honda Insight. The Insight has both a gasoline-powered engine and an electric motor and has an EPA gas mileage rating of 70 mi/gal on the highway. What is the Insight's rating in kilometers per liter?

108. You rent a car in Germany with a gas mileage rating of 10.3 km/L. What is its rating in miles per gallon?

Highlight Problems

109. In 1999, NASA lost a $94 million orbiter because one group of engineers used metric units in their calculations while another group used English units. Consequently, the orbiter descended too far into the Martian atmosphere and burned up. Suppose that the orbiter was to have established orbit at 155 km and that one group of engineers specified this distance as 1.55×10^5 m. Suppose further that a second group of engineers programmed the orbiter to go to 1.55×10^5 ft. What was the difference in kilometers between the two altitudes? How low did the probe go?

▲ The $94 million Mars Climate Orbiter was lost in the Martian atmosphere in 1999 because two groups of engineers failed to communicate to each other the units that they used in their calculations.

110. A NASA satellite showed that in 2003 the ozone hole was much larger than it was in 2002. The 2003 hole measured 1.04×10^7 mi^2 in diameter, while the diameter of the 2002 hole was 6.9×10^6 mi^2. Calculate the difference in size between the two holes in square meters.

▶ A layer of ozone gas (a form of oxygen) in the upper atmosphere protects Earth from harmful ultraviolet radiation in sunlight. Human-made chemicals react with the ozone and deplete it, especially over the Antarctic at certain times of the year (the so-called ozone hole). The region of low ozone concentration in 2003 (represented here by the dark blue color) was larger than in 2002.

111. In 1999, scientists discovered a new class of black holes with masses 100 to 10,000 times the mass of our sun, but occupying less space than our moon. Suppose that one of these black holes has a mass of 1×10^3 suns and a radius equal to one-half the radius of our moon. What is its density in grams per cubic centimeter? The mass of the sun is 2.0×10^{30} kg, and the radius of the moon is 2.16×10^3 mi. (Volume of a sphere $= \dfrac{4}{3}\pi r^3$).

112. A titanium bicycle frame contains the same amount of titanium as a titanium cube measuring 6.8 cm on a side. Use the density of titanium to calculate the mass in kilograms of titanium in the frame. What would be the mass of a similar frame composed of iron?

Titanium

6.8 cm

▶ A titanium bicycle frame contains the same amount of titanium as a titanium cube measuring 6.8 cm on a side.

Answers to Skillbuilder Exercises

Skillbuilder 2.1 $\$7.132 \times 10^{12}$

Skillbuilder 2.2 3.8×10^{-5}

Skillbuilder 2.3   103.4 °F

Skillbuilder 2.4   **(a)** four significant figures **(b)** three significant figures **(c)** two significant figures **(d)** unlimited significant figures **(e)** three significant figures **(f)** ambiguous

Skillbuilder 2.5   **(a)** 0.001 or 1×10^{-3} **(b)** 0.204

Skillbuilder 2.6   **(a)** 7.6 **(b)** 131.11

Skillbuilder 2.7   **(a)** 1288 **(b)** 3.12

Skillbuilder 2.8   22.0 in.

Skillbuilder 2.9   5.678 km

Skillbuilder 2.10   0.29 L

Skillbuilder 2.11   46.6 laps

Skillbuilder Plus, p. 30 1.06×10^4 m

Skillbuilder 2.12   4747 cm^3

Skillbuilder 2.13 1.52×10^5 in.^{3}

Skillbuilder 2.14   Yes, the density is 21.4 g/cm^3 and matches that of platinum.

Skillbuilder 2.15 4.4×10^{-2} cm^3

Skillbuilder Plus, p. 35   1.95 kg

Skillbuilder 2.16   16 kg

Skillbuilder 2.17 $d = 19.3$ g/cm^3; yes, it is gold.

Answers to Conceptual Checkpoints

2.1 (c) Multiplying by 10^{-3} is equivalent to moving the decimal point three places to the left.

2.2 (b) The last digit is considered to be uncertain by ±1.

2.3 (c) The result of the calculation in **(a)** would be reported as 4; the result of the calculation in **(b)** would be reported as 1.5.

2.4 (d) The diameter would be expressed as 28 nm.

2.5 (c) Kilometers must appear in the numerator and meters in the denominator, and the conversion factor in **(d)** is incorrect (10^3 km ≠ 1 m).

2.6 (d) (3 ft) × (3 ft) × (3 ft) = 27 ft^3

Matter and Energy

"Thus, the task is, not so much to see what no one has yet seen; but to think what nobody has yet thought, about that which everybody sees."

Erwin Schrödinger (1887–1961)

3.1   In Your Room

Look around your room—what do you see? You might see your desk, your bed, or a glass of water. Maybe you have a window and can see trees, grass, or mountains. You can certainly see this book and possibly the table it sits on. What are these things made of? They are made of matter, which we will define more carefully shortly. For now, know that all you see is matter—your desk, your bed, the glass of water, the trees, the mountains, and this book. Some of what you don't see is matter as well. For example, you are constantly breathing air, which is also matter, into and out of your lungs. You feel the matter in air when you feel wind on your skin. Virtually everything is made of matter.

Think about the differences between different kinds of matter. Air is different from water, and water is different from wood. One of our first tasks as we learn about matter is to identify the similarities and differences among different kinds of matter. How are sugar and salt similar? How are air and water different? Why are they different? Why is a mixture of sugar and water similar to a mixture of salt and water but different from a mixture of sand and water? As students of chemistry, we are particularly interested in the similarities and differences between various kinds of matter and how these reflect the similarities and differences between their component atoms and molecules. We want to understand the connection between the macroscopic world and the microscopic one.

◄ Everything that you can see in this room is made of matter. As chemists, we are interested in how the differences between different kinds of matter are related to the differences between the molecules and atoms that compose it. The molecular structures shown here are water molecules on the left and carbon atoms in graphite on the right.

51

3.2   What Is Matter?

Matter is defined as anything that occupies space and has mass. Some types of matter—such as steel, water, wood, and plastic—are easily visible to our eyes. Other types of matter—such as air or microscopic dust—are impossible to see without magnification. Matter may sometimes appear smooth and continuous, but actually it is not. Matter is ultimately composed of **atoms**, tiny particles too small to see (▼ Figure 3.1). In many cases, these atoms are bonded together to form **molecules**, two or more atoms joined to one another in specific arrangements. Recent advances in microscopy have allowed us to image the atoms (▼ Figure 3.2) and molecules (▼ Figure 3.3) that compose matter, sometimes with stunning clarity.

(a)

(b)

▲ **Figure 3.1   Atoms and molecules**   All matter is ultimately composed of atoms. **(a)** In some substances, such as aluminum, the atoms exist as independent particles. **(b)** In other substances, such as in alcohol, several atoms bond together in well-defined structures called molecules.

▲ **Figure 3.2   Scanning tunneling microscope image of nickel atoms**   A scanning tunneling microscope (STM) creates an image by scanning a surface with a tip of atomic dimensions. It can distinguish individual atoms, as in this photo.

▲ **Figure 3.3   Scanning tunneling microscope image of a DNA molecule**   DNA is the hereditary material that encodes the operating instructions for most cells in living organisms.

▶ Figure 3.4 **Three states of matter**   Water exists as ice (solid), water (liquid), and steam (gas). In ice, the water molecules are closely spaced and do not move relative to one another. In liquid water, the water molecules are closely spaced but are free to move around and past each other. In steam, water molecules are separated by large distances and do not interact significantly with one another.

Matter		
Solid	Liquid	Gas

3.3 Classifying Matter According to Its State: Solid, Liquid, and Gas

(a) Crystalline solid (ordered)

(b) Amorphous solid (Not ordered)

▲ Figure 3.5 **Types of solid matter** **(a)** In a crystalline solid, atoms or molecules occupy specific positions to create a well-ordered, three-dimensional structure. **(b)** In an amorphous solid, atoms do not have any long-range order.

There are three common **states of matter: solid, liquid**, and **gas** (▲ Figure 3.4). In solid matter, atoms or molecules pack close to each other in fixed locations. Although neighboring atoms or molecules may vibrate or oscillate, they do not move around each other, giving solids their familiar fixed volume and rigid shape. Ice, diamond, quartz, and iron are all good examples of solid matter. Solid matter may be **crystalline**, in which case its atoms or molecules arrange in geometric patterns with long-range, repeating order (◀ Figure 3.5a), or it may be **amorphous**, in which case its atoms or molecules do not have long-range order (Figure 3.5b). Good examples of *crystalline* solids include salt (▼ Figure 3.6) and diamond; the well-ordered, geometric shapes of salt and diamond crystals reflect the well-ordered geometric arrangement of their atoms. Good examples of *amorphous* solids include glass, rubber, and plastic.

In liquid matter, atoms or molecules are close to each other (about as close as in a solid) but are free to move around and by each other. Like solids, liquids have a fixed volume because their atoms or molecules are in close contact. Unlike solids, however, liquids assume the shape of their container because the atoms or molecules are free to move relative to one another. Water, gasoline, alcohol, and mercury are all good examples of liquid matter.

▶ Figure 3.6 **Salt: a crystalline solid**   Sodium chloride is an example of a crystalline solid. The well-ordered, cubic shape of salt crystals is due to the well-ordered, cubic arrangement of its atoms.

MOLECULE
Sodium Chloride

In gaseous matter, atoms or molecules are separated by large distanc and are free to move relative to one another. Since the atoms or molecules th compose gases are not in contact with one another, gases are **compressib** (▼ Figure 3.7). When you inflate a bicycle tire, for example, you push m atoms and molecules into the same space, compressing them and making t tire harder. Gases always assume the shape and volume of their containe Good examples of gases include oxygen, helium, and carbon dioxide. T properties of solids, liquids, and gases are summarized in Table 3.1.

TABLE 3.1 Properties of Liquids, Solids, and Gases

State	Atomic/Molecular Motion	Atomic/Molecular Spacing	Shape	Volume	Compressibilit
solid	oscillation/vibration about fixed point	close together	definite	definite	incompressible
liquid	free to move relative to one another	close together	indefinite	definite	incompressible
gas	free to move relative to one another	far apart	indefinite	indefinite	compressible

▶ **Figure 3.7   Why gases are compressible**   Since the atoms or molecules that compose gases are not in contact with one another, gases are compressible.

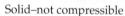
Solid–not compressible   Gas–compressible

3.4   Classifying Matter According to Its Composition: Elements, Compounds, and Mixtures

▲ Helium is a pure substance composed only of helium atoms.

In addition to classifying matter according to its state, we can classify according to its composition (▶ Figure 3.8). Matter may be either a **pu substance**, composed of only one type of atom or molecule, or it may be **mixture**, composed of two or more different types of atoms or molecules co bined in variable proportions.

Pure substances are those composed of only one type of atom or molecu Helium and water are both good examples of pure substances. The atoms th compose helium are all helium atoms, and the molecules that compose wat are all water molecules—no other atoms or molecules are mixed in.

Pure substances can themselves be divided into two types: elements ar compounds. Helium is a good example of an **element**, a substance that ca not be broken down into simpler substances. The graphite in pencils is also element—carbon. No chemical transformation can decompose graphite in simpler substances; it is pure carbon. All known elements are listed in the p riodic table in the inside front cover of this book and in alphabetical order o the inside back cover of this book.

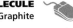

▲ **Figure 3.8   Classification of matter**   Matter may be a pure substance or it may be a mixture. A pure substance may be either an element (such as copper) or a compound (such as sugar), and a mixture may be either homogeneous (such as soda pop) or heterogeneous (such as hydrocarbon and water).

MOLECULE
Graphite

A compound is composed of different atoms that are chemically united (bonded). A mixture is composed of different substances that are not chemically united, but simply mixed together.

A pure substance can also be a **compound**, a substance composed of two or more elements in fixed definite proportions. Compounds are more common than pure elements because most elements are chemically reactive and combine with other elements to form many different compounds. Water, table salt, and sugar are good examples of compounds; they can all be decomposed into simpler substances. For example, if you heat sugar on a pan over a flame, you decompose it into carbon (an element) and gaseous water (a new compound). The black substance left on your pan after burning is the carbon; the water escapes into the air as steam.

The majority of matter that we encounter is in the form of mixtures. A cup of apple juice, a flame, salad dressing, and soil are all examples of mixtures; they contain several substances with proportions that vary from one sample to another. Other common mixtures include air, seawater, and brass. Air is a mixture composed primarily of nitrogen and oxygen gas. Seawater is a mixture composed primarily of salt and water, and brass is a mixture composed of copper and zinc. Each of these mixtures can have different proportions of its constituent

▶ Air and seawater are good examples of mixtures. Air contains primarily nitrogen and oxygen. Seawater contains primarily salt and water.

components. For example, metallurgists vary the relative amounts of co
per and zinc in brass to tailor the metal's properties to its intended use
the higher the zinc content relative to the copper content, the more brit
the brass.

Mixtures themselves can be classified according to how uniformly t
substances within them mix. In a **heterogeneous mixture**, such as oil ai
water, the composition varies from one region to another. In a **homogeneo
mixture**, such as salt water, the composition is the same throughout. Hom
geneous mixtures have uniform compositions because the atoms or molecul
that compose them mix uniformly. Remember that the properties of matt
are determined by the atoms or molecules that compose it.

To summarize, as shown in Figure 3.8:
- Matter may be a pure substance or it may be a mixture.
- A pure substance may be either an element or a compound.
- A mixture may be either homogenous or heterogeneous.
- Mixtures may be composed of two or more elements, two or more compoun
  or a combination of both.

EXAMPLE 3.1   Classifying Matter

Classify each of the following as a pure substance or a mixture. If it is a pu
substance, classify it as an element or a compound; if it is a mixture, classi
it as homogeneous or heterogeneous.

(a) lead fishing weight – *Element*
(b) seawater – *homogeneous*
(c) distilled water – *compound*
(d) Italian salad dressing – *heterogeneous*

Solution:

Begin by examining the alphabetical listing of pure elements inside the ba
cover of this text. If the substance appears in that table, it is a pure substan
and an element. If it is not in the table, but is a pure substance, then it is
compound. If the substance is not a pure substance, then it is a mixture. U
your knowledge about the mixture to determine whether it is homogeneo
or heterogeneous.

(a) Lead is listed in the table of elements. It is a pure substance and an element.

(b) Seawater is composed of several substances including salt and water; it
    a mixture. It has a uniform composition, so it is a homogeneous mixtur

(c) Distilled water is not listed in the table of elements, but it is a pure su
    stance (water); therefore it is a compound.

(d) Italian salad dressing contains a number of substances and is therefore
    mixture. It usually separates into at least two distinct regions with d
    ferent composition and is therefore a heterogeneous mixture.

SKILLBUILDER 3.1   Classifying Matter

Classify each of the following as a pure substance or a mixture. If it is a pu
substance, classify it as an element or a compound. If it is a mixture, classi
it as homogeneous or heterogeneous.

(a) mercury in a thermometer – *element*
(b) exhaled air – *homogeneous*
(c) minestrone soup – *heterogeneous*
(d) sugar – *compound*

Note: The answers to all Skillbuilders appear at the end of the chapter.

▲ Water is a pure substance composed only of water molecules.

3.5 How We Tell Different Kinds of Matter Apart: Physical and Chemical Properties

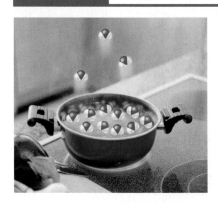

▲ Figure 3.9 **A physical property**
The boiling point of water is a physical property, and boiling is a physical change. When water boils, it turns into a gas, but the water molecules are the same in both the liquid water and the gaseous steam.

In our daily life, we distinguish one substance from another based on the substance's properties. For example, we distinguish water from alcohol based on their different smells, or we distinguish ketchup from mustard based on their different colors and flavors. The characteristics we use to distinguish one substance from another are called **properties**. Different substances have unique properties that characterize them and distinguish them from other substances.

In chemistry, we differentiate between **physical properties**, those that a substance displays without changing its composition, and **chemical properties**, those that a substance displays only through changing its composition. For example, the characteristic odor of gasoline is a physical property—gasoline does not change its composition when it exhibits its odor. On the other hand, the flammability of gasoline is a chemical property—gasoline does change its composition when it burns.

The atoms or molecules that compose a substance do not change when the substance displays its physical properties. For example, the boiling point of water—a physical property—is 100 °C. When water boils, it changes from a liquid to a gas, but the gas is still water (◄ Figure 3.9). On the other hand, the susceptibility of iron to rust is a chemical property—iron must change into iron oxide to display this property (▼ Figure 3.10). Physical properties include odor, taste, color, appearance, melting point, boiling point, and density. Chemical properties include corrosiveness, flammability, acidity, toxicity, and other chemical characteristics.

Iron oxide or rust

Iron atoms

▶ Figure 3.10 **A chemical property**
The susceptibility of iron to rusting is a chemical property, and rusting is a chemical change. When iron rusts, it turns from iron to iron oxide.

EXAMPLE 3.2	**Physical and Chemical Properties**

Determine whether each of the following is a physical or chemical property.

(a) the tendency of copper to turn green when exposed to air - chemical

(b) the tendency of automobile paint to dull over time - chemical

(c) the tendency of gasoline to evaporate quickly when spilled - physical

(d) the low mass (for a given volume) of aluminum relative to other metals - physical

Solution:

(a) Copper turns green because it reacts with gases in air to form com[...]
pounds; this is a chemical property.

(b) Automobile paint dulls over time because it can fade (decompose) du[...]
to sunlight or it can react with oxygen in air. In either case, this is a cher[...]
ical property.

(c) Gasoline evaporates quickly because it has a low boiling point; this is[...]
physical property.

(d) Aluminum's low mass (for a given volume) relative to other metals [...]
due to its low density; this is a physical property.

SKILLBUILDER 3.2   **Physical and Chemical Properties**

Determine whether each of the following is a physical or chemical propert[...]

(a) the explosiveness of hydrogen gas *— chemical*
(b) the bronze color of copper *— physical*
(c) the shiny appearance of silver *— physical*
(d) the ability of dry ice to vaporize *— chemical*

3.6   How Matter Changes: Physical and Chemical Changes

Every day, we witness changes in matter: Ice melts, iron rusts, and fruit ripens, f[...]
example. What happens to the atoms and molecules that compose these substanc[...]
during the change? The answer depends on the kind of change. In a **physic[...]
change**, matter changes its appearance but not its composition. For example, whe[...]
ice melts, it looks different—water looks different from ice—but its composition [...]
the same. Solid ice and liquid water are both composed of water molecules, s[...]
melting is a physical change. Similarly, when glass shatters, it looks different, b[...]
its composition remains the same—it is still glass, so this is again a physical chang[...]
On the other hand, in a **chemical change**, matter *does* change its composition. F[...]
example, copper turns green upon continued exposure to air because it reacts wi[...]
gases in air to form new compounds. This is a chemical change.

The differences between physical and chemical changes are not always a[...]
parent. Only chemical examination of the substances before and after th[...]
change can verify whether the change is physical or chemical. For many case[...]
however, we can identify chemical and physical changes based on what w[...]
know about them. Phase changes, such as melting or boiling, or changes th[...]
involve merely appearance, such as those produced by cutting or crushing, a[...]
always physical changes. Changes involving chemical reactions—often ev[...]
denced by heat exchange or color changes—are chemical changes.

The main difference between chemical and physical changes is related [...]
the changes at the molecular and atomic level. In physical changes, the atom[...]
that compose the matter *do not* change their fundamental associations, eve[...]
though the matter may change its appearance. In chemical changes, atoms [...]
change their fundamental associations, resulting in matter with a new ider[...]
tity. *A physical change results in a different form of the same substance, while a cher[...]
ical change results in a completely new substance.*

Consider physical and chemical changes in liquid butane, the substanc[...]
used to fuel butane lighters. In many lighters, you can see the liquid butar[...]
through the plastic case of the lighter. If you push the fuel button on the light[...]
without turning the flint, some of the liquid butane vaporizes to gaseor[...]
butane—you can usually hear hissing as it leaks out (► Figure 3.11). Since th[...]
liquid butane and the gaseous butane are both composed of butane molecule[...]
this is a physical change. On the other hand, if you push the button *and* turn th[...]
flint to create a spark, a chemical change occurs. The butane molecules react wi[...]
oxygen molecules in air to form new molecules, carbon dioxide and wat[...]
(► Figure 3.12). The change is chemical because the molecules that compose th[...]
butane have changed into different molecules.

Phase changes are transformations from one state of matter (such as solid or liquid) to another.

TUTORIAL
Mixtures and Compounds

MOLECULE
Butane

Gaseous
butane

Liquid
butane

▲ Figure 3.11   **Vaporization:
a physical change**   If you push the
button on a lighter without turning
the flint, some of the liquid butane
vaporizes to gaseous butane. Since
the liquid butane and the gaseous
butane are both composed of butane
molecules, this is a physical change.

Carbon dioxide
and water
molecules

Liquid
butane

▲ Figure 3.12   **Burning: a chemical
change**   If you push the button *and*
turn the flint to create a spark, you produce a flame. The butane molecules
react with oxygen molecules in air to
form new molecules, carbon dioxide
and water. This is a chemical change.

EXAMPLE 3.3   **Physical and Chemical Changes**

Determine whether each of the following is a physical or chemical change.

(a) the rusting of iron *– chemical*   *✓ Physical*
(b) the evaporation of fingernail-polish remover (acetone) from the skin
(c) the burning of coal *– chemical*
(d) the fading of a carpet upon repeated exposure to sunlight
                                    chemical.

Solution:

(a) Iron rusts because it reacts with oxygen in air to form iron oxide; therefore this is a chemical change.

(b) When fingernail-polish remover (acetone) evaporates, it changes from
liquid to gas, but it remains acetone; therefore, this is a physical change.

(c) Coal burns because it reacts with oxygen in air to form carbon dioxide;
this is a chemical change.

(d) A carpet fades on repeated exposure to sunlight because the molecules
that give the carpet its color are decomposed by sunlight; this is a chemical change.

SKILLBUILDER 3.3   **Physical and Chemical Changes**

Determine whether each of the following is a physical or chemical change.

(a) copper metal forming a blue solution when it is dropped into colorless
nitric acid   *(chemical)*
(b) a passing train flattening a penny placed on a railroad track *– physical*
(c) ice melting into liquid water *– physical*
(d) a match igniting a firework
                          chemical

▲ **Figure 3.13   Separating a mixture of two liquids by distillation**   The liquid with the lower boiling point vaporizes first. The vapors are collected and cooled until they condense back into liquid form.

▲ **Figure 3.14   Separating a solid from a liquid by filtration**

⬤ Separating Mixtures through Physical Changes

TUTORIAL
Paper Chromatography of Ink

Chemists often want to separate mixtures into their components. Such separations can be easy or difficult, depending on the components in the mixture. In general, mixtures are separable because the different components have different properties. Various techniques that exploit these differences can be used to achieve separation. For example, oil and water are immiscible (do not mix) and have different densities. For this reason, oil floats on top of water and can be separated from water by **decanting**—carefully pouring off—the oil into another container. Mixtures of miscible liquids can usually be separated by **distillation**, a process in which the mixture is heated to boil off the more **volatile** (easily vaporizable) liquid. The volatile liquid is then recondensed in a condenser and collected in a separate flask (▲ Figure 3.13). If a mixture is composed of a solid and a liquid, the two can be separated by **filtration**, in which the mixture is poured through filter paper usually held in a funnel (▲ Figure 3.14).

⬤ 3.7   Conservation of Mass: There Is No New Matter

As we have seen, our planet, our air, and even our own bodies are composed of matter. Chemical changes do not destroy matter, nor do they create new matter. Recall from Chapter 1 that Antoine Lavoisier, by studying combustion, established the law of conservation of mass, which states:

Matter is neither created nor destroyed in a chemical reaction.

During chemical changes, the total amount of matter remains constant. How does this happen? When we burn butane in a lighter, the butane slowly disappears. Where does it go? It combines with oxygen to form carbon dioxide and water that go into the surrounding air. The mass of the carbon dioxide and water that form, however, must exactly equal the mass of the butane and oxygen that combined.

We examine the quantitative relationships in chemical reactions in Chapter 8.

For example, 58 g of butane will react with 208 g of oxygen to form 176 g of carbon dioxide and 90 g of water.

Butane + Oxygen ⟶ Carbon dioxide + Water
58 g + 208 g ⟶ 176 g + 90 g
266 g = 266 g

The sum of the masses of the butane and oxygen, 266 g, is equal to the sum of the masses of the carbon dioxide and water, which is also 266 g. Matter is conserved.

EXAMPLE 3.4 Conservation of Mass

A chemist forms 16.6 g of potassium iodide by combining 3.9 g of potassium with 12.7 g of iodine. Show that these results are consistent with the law of conservation of mass.

Solution:
The sum of the masses of the potassium and iodine is:

3.9 g + 12.7 g = 16.6 g

The sum of the masses of potassium and iodine equals the mass of the product, potassium iodide. The results are consistent with the law of conservation of mass.

SKILLBUILDER 3.4 Conservation of Mass

Suppose 12 g of natural gas combines with 48 g of oxygen in a flame. The chemical change produces 33 g of carbon dioxide and how many grams of water?

3.8 Energy

▲ Water behind a dam contains potential energy. As the water flows through the dam, the potential energy is converted to kinetic energy (the energy associated with motion) and then to electrical energy.

Matter is one of the two major components of our universe. The other major component is **energy**, defined as *the capacity to do work*. You may at first think that chemistry is concerned only with matter, but the behavior of matter is driven in large part by energy. As we shall see in later chapters, it is the flow of energy that determines what chemical changes will take place and the direction of chemical reactions. So understanding energy is critical to understanding chemistry. Like matter, energy is conserved. The **law of conservation of energy** states:

> Energy can neither be created nor destroyed.

The total amount of energy is constant and cannot change; energy can be changed from one form to another or transferred from one object to another, but not created.

An object possessing energy can do work on another object—it can cause the other object to move. For example, a moving billiard ball contains **kinetic energy**, energy associated with its motion. It can collide with another billiard ball and cause it to move. Water behind a dam contains **potential energy**, energy associated with its position. The water can flow from a higher position to a lower position through the dam, turn a turbine, and produce electrical energy. **Electrical energy** is the energy associated with the flow of electrical charge. Chemical systems contain **chemical energy**, energy associated with potential chemical changes—such as the burning of gasoline—that can move or heat other objects. When we drive a car, we use chemical energy stored in gasoline to move the car forward. When we heat a home, we use chemical energy stored in natural gas to produce heat and warm the air in the house.

Units of Energy

Since energy can be converted from one form to another, all forms of energy can be quantified in the same units. The SI unit of energy is the joule (J), named after the English scientist James Joule (1818–1889), who demonstrated that energy could be converted from one type to another as long as the total energy was conserved. A second unit of energy in common use is the **calorie (cal)**, the amount of energy required to raise the temperature of 1 g of water by 1 °C. A calorie is a larger unit than a joule: 1 cal = 4.184 J. A related energy unit is the nutritional or capital C **Calorie (Cal)**, equivalent to 1000 little c calories. Electricity bills usually come in yet another energy unit, the **kilowatt-hour (kWh)**. Electricity costs about $0.15 per kilowatt-hour. Table 3.2 shows various energy units and their conversion factors. Table 3.3 shows the amount of energy required for various processes in each of these units.

TABLE 3.2 Energy Conversion Factors

1 calorie (cal)	=	4.184 joules (J)
1 Calorie (Cal)	=	1000 calories (cal)
1 kilowatt-hour (kWh)	=	3.60×10^6 joules (J)

TABLE 3.3 Energy Use in Various Units

Unit	Energy Required to Raise Temperature of 1 g of Water by 1 °C	Energy Required to Light 100-W Bulb for 1 Hour	Energy Used by Average U.S. Citizen in 1 Day
joule (J)	4.18	3.6×10^5	9.0×10^8
calorie (cal)	1	8.6×10^4	2.15×10^8
Calorie (Cal)	0.001	86	215,000
kWh	1.1×10^{-6}	0.10	250

Chemistry IN THE MEDIA

Perpetual Motion

The law of conservation of energy has significant implications for energy use. The best we can do with energy is break even; we can't continually draw energy from a device without putting energy into it. A device that supposedly produces energy without the need for energy input is called a *perpetual motion machine* (▶ Figure 3.15) and, according to the law of conservation of energy, cannot exist. Occasionally, the media report or speculate on the discovery of a system that appears to produce more energy than it consumes. For example, I once heard a radio talk show on the subject of energy and gasoline costs. The reporter suggested that we simply design an electric car that recharges itself while you drive. The battery in the electric car would charge during operation in the same way that the battery in a conventional car recharges, except the electric car would run with energy from the battery. People have dreamed of perpetual motion machines such as this for decades. However, such ideas violate the law of conservation of energy because they produce energy without any energy input. In the case of the perpetually moving electric car, the fault lies in the idea that driving the electric car can recharge the battery—it can't.

The reason that the battery in a conventional car recharges is that energy from gasoline combustion is converted into electrical energy that then charges the battery. The electric car needs energy to move forward and the battery would eventually discharge. Some new hybrid cars (electric and gasoline-powered) can capture energy from braking and use that energy to recharge the battery.

▲ Figure 3.15   **A proposed perpetual motion machine**   The rolling balls supposedly keep the wheel perpetually spinning.   **Question:** Can you explain why this would not work?

However, they could never run indefinitely without adding fuel. Our society has a continual need for energy, and as our current energy resources dwindle, new energy sources will be required. Unfortunately, those sources must also follow the law of conservation of energy—energy must be conserved.

CAN YOU ANSWER THIS? *A friend asks you to invest in a new flashlight he invented that never needs batteries. What kind of questions should you ask before writing a check?*

| EXAMPLE 3.5 | **Conversion of Energy Units** |

A candy bar contains 225 Cal of nutritional energy. How many joules does it contain?

Solve this problem using the procedure to solve numerical problems from Chapter 2 (Section 2.10). Here you are given energy in Calories and asked to convert it to energy in joules.

Given: 225 Cal

Find: J

Conversion Factors:
1000 calories = 1 Cal
4.184 J = 1 cal

Draw a solution map. Begin with Cal, convert to cal, and then convert to J.

Solution Map:

$$\frac{1000 \text{ cal}}{1 \text{ Cal}} \qquad \frac{4.184 \text{ J}}{1 \text{ cal}}$$

Follow the solution map to solve the problem and round to the correct number of significant digits.

Solution:

$$225 \text{ Cal} \times \frac{1000 \text{ cal}}{1 \text{ Cal}} \times \frac{4.184 \text{ J}}{1 \text{ cal}} = 9.41 \times 10^5 \text{ J}$$

| SKILLBUILDER 3.5 | **Conversion of Energy Units** |

The complete combustion of a small wooden match produces approximately 512 cal of heat. How many kilojoules are produced?

| SKILLBUILDER PLUS |

Convert 2.75×10^4 kJ to calories.

| CONCEPTUAL CHECKPOINT 3.1 |

Suppose a salesperson wants to make an appliance seem as efficient as possible. In which of the following units would the yearly energy consumption of the appliance have the lowest numerical value and therefore seem most efficient?

(a) J
(b) cal
(c) Cal
(d) kWh

Note: The answers to all Conceptual Checkpoints appear at the end of the chapter.

3.9   Temperature: Random Molecular and Atomic Motion

The temperature of matter is related to the random motion of the atoms and molecules that compose it. The hotter an object is, the greater the motion and the higher the temperature. We should be careful to not confuse temperature and heat. Heat, which has the units of energy, refers to the *exchange* of thermal energy caused by a temperature difference. Temperature is a *measure* of the thermal energy of matter. There are three different temperature scales in common use. The most familiar in the United States is the **Fahrenheit (°F) scale**. On the Fahrenheit scale, water freezes at 32 °F and boils at 212 °F. Room temperature is approximately 75 °F. The Fahrenheit scale was initially set up by assigning 0 °F to the freezing point of a concentrated saltwater solution and 100 °F to body temperature.

The scale often used by scientists is the **Celsius (°C) scale**. On this scale, water freezes at 0 °C and boils at 100 °C. Room temperature is approximately 25 °C.

▶ Figure 3.16   **Comparison of the Fahrenheit, Celsius, and Kelvin temperature scales**   The Fahrenheit degree is five-ninths the size of a Celsius degree. The Celsius degree and the kelvin degree are the same size.

The Fahrenheit and Celsius scales differ in both the size of their respective ⟨de⟩grees and the temperature each calls "zero" (▲ Figure 3.16). Both the Fahren⟨heit⟩ and Celsius scales contain negative temperatures. However, a third temperat⟨ure⟩ scale, called the **Kelvin (K) scale**, avoids negative temperatures by assigning ⟨0⟩ to the coldest temperature possible, absolute zero. Absolute zero (−273 ⟨°C⟩ or −459 °F) is the temperature at which molecular motion virtually stops. The⟨re⟩ is no lower temperature. The kelvin degree, or **kelvin**, is the same size as the C⟨el⟩sius degree—the only difference is the temperature that each scale calls zero.

Conversions between these temperature scales are achieved using the f⟨ol⟩lowing formulas.

$$K = °C + 273$$
$$°C = \frac{(°F - 32)}{1.8}$$

For example, suppose we want to convert 212 K to Celsius. Following the p⟨ro⟩cedure for solving numerical problems (Section 2.10), we write:

Given: 212 K

Find: °C

Equation: The equation that relates the given quantity (K) to the fi⟨nd⟩ quantity (°C) is:

$$K = °C + 273$$

Solution Map: We then build a solution map.

$$K = °C + 273$$

In a solution map involving a formula, the formula establishes the relationship between the variables. However, the formula under the arrow is not necessarily solved for the correct variable until later, as is the case here.

Solution: The equation below the arrow shows the relationship betwee⟨n K⟩ and °C, but it is not in the correct form. We must solve the equation for °C.

$$K = °C + 273$$
$$°C = K - 273$$

Finally, we substitute the given value for K and compute the answer to the correct number of significant figures.

$$°C = 212 - 273$$
$$= -61 \, °C$$

EXAMPLE 3.6 **Converting between Celsius and Kelvin Temperature Scales**

Convert −25 °C to kelvin.

Set up the problem in the normal way. You are given a temperature in °C and asked to find K. Use the equation that shows the relationship between the given quantity (°C) and the find quantity (K).	**Given:** −25 °C **Find:** K **Equation:** $$K = °C + 273$$
Build the solution map.	**Solution Map:**

$$K = °C + 273$$

Follow the solution map to solve the problem by substituting the correct value for °C and computing the answer to the correct number of significant figures.	**Solution:** $$K = °C + 273$$ $$K = -25 \, °C + 273 = 248 \, K$$

SKILLBUILDER 3.6 **Converting between Celsius and Kelvin Temperature Scales**

Convert 358 K to Celsius.

EXAMPLE 3.7 **Converting between Fahrenheit and Celsius Temperature Scales**

Convert 55 °F to Celsius.

Set up the problem in the normal way. You are given a temperature in °F and asked to find °C. Use the equation that shows the relationship between the given quantity (°C) and the find quantity (K).	**Given:** 55 °F **Find:** °C **Equation:** $°C = \dfrac{(°F - 32)}{1.8}$
Build the solution map.	**Solution Map:**

$$°C = \frac{(°F - 32)}{1.8}$$

Substitute the given value into the equation and compute the answer to the correct number of significant figures.	**Solution:** $$°C = \frac{(°F - 32)}{1.8}$$ $$°C = \frac{(55 - 32)}{1.8} = 12.778 \, °C = 13 \, °C$$

SKILLBUILDER 3.7 **Converting between Fahrenheit and Celsius Temperature Scales**

Convert 139 °C to Fahrenheit.

EXAMPLE 3.8   **Converting between Fahrenheit and Kelvin Temperature Scales**

Convert 310 K to Fahrenheit.

Set up the problem in the normal way. You are given a temperature in K and asked to find °F. This problem requires two equations: one relating K and °C and the other relating °C and °F.	**Given:** 310 K **Find:** °F **Equations:** $$K = °C + 273$$ $$°C = \frac{(°F - 32)}{1.8}$$

Build the solution map, which requires two steps: one to convert from K to °C and one to convert from °C to °F.

Solution Map:

$$K = °C + 273 \qquad °C = \frac{(°F - 32)}{1.8}$$

The first equation must be solved for °C. Substitute into this equation to convert from K to °C.	**Solution:** $$K = °C + 273$$ $$°C = K - 273$$ $$°C = 310 - 273 = 37\,°C$$
The second equation must be solved for °F. Substitute into this equation to convert from °C to °F and compute the answer to the correct number of significant digits.	$$°C = \frac{(°F - 32)}{1.8}$$ $$1.8\,°C = (°F - 32)$$ $$°F = 1.8\,°C + 32$$ $$°F = 1.8(37) + 32 = 98.6\,°F = 99\,°F$$

SKILLBUILDER 3.8   **Converting between Fahrenheit and Kelvin Temperature Scales**

Convert −321 °F to kelvin.

CONCEPTUAL CHECKPOINT 3.2

Which of the following temperatures is identical on both the Celsius and the Fahrenheit scale?

(a) 100°
(b) 32°
(c) 0°
(d) −40°

3.10   Temperature Changes: Heat Capacity

All substances change temperature when they are heated, but how much they change for a given amount of heat varies significantly from one substance to another. For example, if you put a steel skillet on a flame, its

TABLE 3.4 Specific Heat Capacities of Some Common Substances

Substance	Specific Heat Capacity (J/g °C)
lead	0.128
gold	0.128
silver	0.235
copper	0.385
iron	0.449
aluminum	0.903
ethanol	2.42
water	4.184

It is simply by coincidence that lead and gold have the same value of specific heat capacity.

temperature rises rapidly. However, if you put some water in the skillet, the temperature increase is much slower. Why? The first reason is that when you add water, the same amount of heat energy must warm more matter, so the temperature rises more slowly. The second and more significant reason is that water is more resistant to temperature change than steel. This is because water has a higher **heat capacity**. The heat capacity of a substance is the quantity of heat energy (usually in joules) required to change the temperature of a given amount of the substance by 1 °C. When the amount of the substance is expressed in grams, the heat capacity is called the **specific heat capacity** (or simply the **specific heat**) and has units of joules per gram degree Celsius (J/g °C). Table 3.4 shows the values of the specific heat capacity for several substances.

Notice that water has the highest heat capacity on the list—changing its temperature requires a lot of heat. If you have traveled from an inland geographical region to a coastal one and have felt the drop in temperature, you have experienced the effects of water's high heat capacity. On a summer day in California, for example, the temperature difference between Sacramento (an inland city) and San Francisco (a coastal city) can be 30 °F; San Francisco enjoys a cool 68 °F, while Sacramento bakes at near 100 °F. Yet the intensity of sunlight falling on these two cities is the same. Why the large temperature difference? The difference between the two locations is the presence of the Pacific Ocean, which practically engulfs San Francisco. Water, with its high heat capacity, absorbs much of the sun's heat without undergoing a large increase in temperature, keeping San Francisco cool. The land surrounding Sacramento, on the other hand, with its low heat capacity, cannot absorb a lot of heat without a large increase in temperature—it has a lower *capacity* to absorb heat without a large temperature increase.

Similarly, only two U.S. states have never recorded a temperature above 100 °F. One of them is obvious: Alaska. It is too far north to get that hot. The other one, however, may come as a surprise. It is Hawaii. The water that surrounds the only island state, having a high heat capacity, moderates the temperature, keeping Hawaii from ever getting too hot.

▲ San Francisco enjoys cool weather even in summer months because of the high heat capacity of the surrounding ocean.

 CONCEPTUAL CHECKPOINT 3.3

If you wanted to heat a metal plate to as high a temperature as possible for a given energy input, you would make the plate out of:

(a) copper
(b) iron
(c) aluminum
(d) it would make no difference

Coolers, Camping, and the Heat Capacity of Water

Have you ever loaded a cooler with ice and then added room-temperature drinks? If you have, you know that the ice quickly melts. In contrast, if you load your cooler with chilled drinks, the ice lasts for hours. Why the difference? The answer is related to the high heat capacity of water within the drinks. As we just learned, water must absorb a lot of heat to raise its temperature, but it must also re-lease a lot of heat to lower its temperature. When the warm drinks are placed into the ice, they release heat, which then melts the ice. The chilled drinks, on the other hand, are already cold, so they do not release much heat. It is always better to load your cooler with chilled drinks—that way, the ice will last the rest of the day.

CAN YOU ANSWER THIS? *Suppose you are cold-weather camping and decide to heat some objects to bring into your sleep-ing bag for added warmth. You place a large water jug and a rock of equal mass close to the fire. Over time, both the rock and the water jug warm to about 38 °C (100 °F). If you could bring only one into your sleeping bag, which one should you bring to keep you the warmest? Why?*

▲ The ice in a cooler loaded with cold drinks lasts much longer than the ice in a cooler loaded with warm drinks.
Question: Can you explain why?

3.11   Energy and Heat Capacity Calculations

The specific heat capacity of a substance can be used to quantify the relationship between the amount of heat added to a given amount of the substance and the cor-responding temperature increase. The equation that relates these quantities is:

$$\text{Heat} = \text{Mass} \times \text{Specific heat capacity} \times \text{Temperature change}$$
$$q = m \times C \times \Delta T$$

where q is the amount of heat in joules, m is the mass of the substance in grams, C is the specific heat capacity in joules per gram per degree Celsius, and ΔT is the temperature change in Celsius. The symbol Δ means *the change in*, so ΔT means *the change in temperature*. For example, suppose you are making a cup of tea and want to know how much heat energy will warm 235 g of water (about 8 oz) from 25 °C to 100.0 °C (boiling). We set up this problem as follows:

ΔT in °C is equal to ΔT in K but is not equal to ΔT in °F.

Given: 235 g water

25 °C initial temperature (T_i)

100.0 °C final temperature (T_f)

Find: amount of heat needed, q

Equation: The equation that relates the given and find quantities is:

$$q = m \cdot C \cdot \Delta T$$

Solution Map:

$$q = m \cdot C \cdot \Delta T$$

In addition to m and ΔT, the equation requires C, the heat specific capacity of water. Our next step is to gather all of the required quantities for the equation (C, m, and ΔT) in the correct units. These are:

$$C = 4.18 \, \text{J/g} \, °\text{C}$$
$$m = 235 \, \text{g}$$

The other required quantity is ΔT. The change in temperature is the difference between the final temperature (T_f) and the initial temperature (T_i).

$$\Delta T = T_f - T_i$$
$$= 100.0 \, °\text{C} - 25 \, °\text{C} = 75 \, °\text{C}$$

Solution: Finally, we substitute the correct values into the equation and compute the answer to the correct number of significant figures.

$$q = m \times C \times \Delta T$$
$$= 235 \, \cancel{g} \times 4.18 \frac{\text{J}}{\cancel{g} \, °\cancel{C}} \times 75 \, °\cancel{C}$$
$$= 7.367 \times 10^4 \, \text{J} = 7.4 \times 10^4 \, \text{J}$$

When discussing energy transfer, we often define the object of our study (such as a flask in which a chemical reaction is occurring) as *the system* and the parts of the universe with which the system exchanges energy as *the surroundings*. Energy is then transferred between the system and its surroundings

It is critical that you substitute each of the correct variables into the equation in the correct units and cancel units as you compute the answer. If, during this process, you learn that one of your variables is not in the correct units, convert it to the correct units using the skills you learned in Chapter 2. Notice that the sign of q is positive ($+$) if the substance is increasing in temperature (heat going into the substance) and negative ($-$) if the substance is decreasing in temperature (heat going out of the substance).

EXAMPLE 3.9   Relating Heat Energy to Temperature Changes

Gallium is a solid metal at room temperature but melts at 29.9 °C. If you hold gallium in your hand, it melts from body heat. How much heat must 2.5 g of gallium absorb from your hand to raise its temperature from 25.0 °C to 29.9 °C? The specific heat capacity of gallium is 0.372 J/g °C.

You are given the mass of gallium and its initial and final temperature and asked to find the amount of heat absorbed.

Given: 2.5 g gallium
$T_i = 25.0 \, °\text{C}$
$T_f = 29.9 \, °\text{C}$
$C = 0.372 \, \text{J/g} \, °\text{C}$

Find: q

The equation that relates the given and find quantities is the specific heat capacity equation.

Equation: $q = m \cdot C \cdot \Delta T$

The solution map shows that the specific heat capacity equation relates the given and find quantities.

Solution Map:

$$q = m \cdot C \cdot \Delta T$$

Before solving the problem, you must gather the necessary quantities —C, m, and ΔT—in the correct units.

Solution:

$$C = 0.372 \text{ J/g °C}$$
$$m = 2.5 \text{ g}$$
$$\Delta T = 29.9 \text{ °C} - 25.0 \text{ °C} = 4.9 \text{ °C}$$

Then substitute the correct variables into the equation, canceling units, and compute the answer to the right number of significant figures.

$$q = m \times C \times \Delta T$$
$$= 2.5 \text{ \cancel{g}} \times 0.372 \frac{\text{J}}{\cancel{\text{g}} \, \cancel{\text{°C}}} \times 4.9 \text{ \cancel{°C}} = 4.557 \text{ J} = 4.6 \text{ J*}$$

*This is the amount of heat required to raise the temperature to the melting point. Actually melting the gallium requires additional heat.

SKILLBUILDER 3.9   Relating Heat Energy to Temperature Changes

You find a copper penny (pre-1982) in the snow and pick it up. How much heat is absorbed by the penny as it warms from the temperature of the snow, -5.0 °C, to the temperature of your body, 37.0 °C? Assume the penny is pure copper and has a mass of 3.10 g. You can find the heat capacity of copper in Table 3.4 (p. 67).

SKILLBUILDER PLUS

The temperature of a lead fishing weight rises from 26 °C to 38 °C as it absorbs 11.3 J of heat. What is the mass of the fishing weight in grams?

EXAMPLE 3.10   Relating Heat Capacity to Temperature Changes

A chemistry student finds a shiny rock that she suspects is gold. She weighs the rock on a balance and obtains the mass, 14.3 g. She then finds that the temperature of the rock rises from 25 °C to 52 °C upon absorption of 174 J of heat. Find the heat capacity of the rock and determine whether the value is consistent with the heat capacity of gold.

You are given the mass of the "gold" rock, the amount of heat absorbed, and the initial and final temperature. You are asked to find the heat capacity.

Given: 14.3 g
174 J of heat absorbed
$T_i = 25$ °C
$T_f = 52$ °C

The equation that relates the given and find quantities is the heat capacity equation.

Find: C

Equation: $q = m \cdot C \cdot \Delta T$

The solution map shows how the heat capacity equation relates the given and find quantities.

Solution Map:

$$q = m \cdot C \cdot \Delta T$$

Before solving the problem, you must gather the necessary quantities —m, q, and ΔT—in the correct units.

Solution:

$$m = 14.3 \text{ g}$$
$$q = 174 \text{ J}$$
$$\Delta T = 52 \text{ °C} - 25 \text{ °C} = 27 \text{ °C}$$

Solve the equation for C and then substitute the correct variables into the equation, canceling units, and compute the answer to the right number of significant figures.

$$q = m \cdot C \cdot \Delta T$$
$$C = \frac{q}{m \, \Delta T}$$

$$C = \frac{174 \text{ J}}{14.3 \text{ g} \times 27 \text{ °C}} = 0.4506 \frac{\text{J}}{\text{g °C}} = 0.45 \frac{\text{J}}{\text{g °C}}$$

By comparing the computed value of the heat capacity (0.45 J/g °C) with the heat capacity of gold from Table 3.4 (0.128 J/g °C), we conclude that the rock could not be pure gold.

SKILLBUILDER 3.10   **Relating Heat Capacity to Temperature Changes**

A 328 g sample of water absorbs 5.78×10^3 J of heat. Find the change in temperature for the water. If the water is
initially at 25.0 °C, what is its final temperature?

CHAPTER IN REVIEW

Chemical Principles

Relevance

Matter: Matter is anything that occupies space and has mass. It is composed of atoms, which are often bonded together as molecules. Matter can exist as a solid, a liquid, or a gas. Solid matter can be either amorphous or crystalline.

Matter: Understanding matter is relevant because everything is made of matter—you, me, the chair you sit on, and the air we breathe. The physical universe basically contains only two things: matter and energy. So we begin our study of chemistry by defining and classifying these two building blocks of the universe.

Classification of Matter: Matter can be classified according to its composition. Pure matter is composed of only one type of substance; that substance may be an element (a substance that cannot be decomposed into simpler substances) or it may be a compound (a substance composed of two or more elements in fixed definite proportions.) Mixtures are composed of two or more different substances whose proportions may vary from one sample to the next. Mixtures can be either homogeneous, having the same composition throughout, or heterogeneous, having a composition that varies from region to region.

Classification of Matter: Since ancient times, humans have tried to understand matter and harness it for their purposes. The earliest humans shaped matter into tools and used the transformation of matter—especially fire—to keep warm and to cook food. To manipulate matter, we must understand it. Fundamental to this understanding is the connection between the properties of matter and the molecules and atoms that compose it. If matter is composed of a single type of atom or molecule, it is a pure substance. If it is composed of two or more types of atoms or molecules, it is a mixture.

Properties and Changes of Matter: The properties of matter can be divided into two types: physical and chemical. The physical properties of matter are those that are displayed without a change in composition. The chemical properties of matter can be displayed only with a change in composition. The changes in matter can themselves be divided into physical and chemical. In a physical change, the appearance of matter may change but its composition does not. In a chemical change, the composition of matter changes.

Properties and Changes of Matter: The physical and chemical properties of matter make the world around us the way it is. For example, a physical property of water is its boiling point at sea level—100 °C. The physical properties of water—and all matter—are determined by the atoms and molecules that compose it. If water molecules were different—even slightly different—water would boil at a different temperature. Imagine a world where water boiled at room temperature.

Conservation of Mass: Whether the changes in matter are chemical or physical, matter is always conserved. In a chemical change the masses of the matter undergoing the chemical change must equal the sum of the masses of matter resulting from the chemical change.

Conservation of Mass: The conservation of matter is relevant to, for example, pollution. We often think that we create pollution, but actually, we are powerless to create anything. Matter cannot be created. So pollution is simply misplaced matter—matter that has been put into places it does not belong.

Energy: Besides matter, energy is the other major component of our universe. Like matter, energy is conserved—it can be neither created nor destroyed. Energy comes in various different types, and these can be converted from one to another. Some common units of energy are the joule (J), the calorie (cal), the nutritional Calorie (Cal), and the kilowatt-hour (kWh).

Energy: Our society's energy sources will not last forever because as we burn fossil fuels—our primary energy source—we convert chemical energy, stored in molecules, to kinetic and thermal energy. The kinetic and thermal energy is not readily available to be used again. Consequently, our energy resources are dwindling, and the conservation of energy implies that we will not be able simply to create new energy—it must come from somewhere.

Temperature: The temperature of matter is related to the random motions of the molecules and atoms that compose it—the greater the motion, the higher the temperature. Temperature is commonly measured on three scales: Fahrenheit (°F), Celsius (°C), and Kelvin (K).

Temperature: The temperature of matter and its measurement is relevant to many everyday phenomena. Humans are constantly interested in the weather, and air temperature is a fundamental part of weather. We use body temperature as one measure of human health and global temperature as one measure of the planet's health.

Heat Capacity: The temperature change that a sample of matter undergoes upon absorption of a given amount of heat is related to the heat capacity of the substance composing the matter. Water has one of the highest heat capacities, meaning that it is most resistant to rapid temperature changes.

Heat Capacity: The heat capacity of water explains why it is cooler in coastal areas, which are near large bodies of high-heat-capacity water, than in inland areas, which are surrounded by low-heat-capacity land. It also explains why it takes longer to cool a refrigerator filled with liquids than an empty one.

Chemical Skills

Examples

Classifying Matter (Sections 3.3, 3.4)

Begin by examining the alphabetical listing of elements in the back of this text. If the substance is listed in that table, it is a pure substance and an element.

If the substance is not listed in that table, use your knowledge about the substance to determine whether it is a pure substance. If it is a pure substance not listed in the table, then it is a compound.

If it is not a pure substance, then it is a mixture. Use your knowledge about the mixture to determine whether it has uniform composition throughout (homogeneous) or nonuniform composition (heterogeneous).

EXAMPLE 3.11   Classifying Matter

Classify each of the following as a pure substance or a mixture. If it is a pure substance, classify it as an element or compound. If it is a mixture, classify it as homogeneous or heterogeneous.

(a) pure silver *element*
(b) swimming-pool water *homogeneous*
(c) dry ice (solid carbon dioxide) *compound*
(d) blueberry muffin *heterogeneous!*

Solution:

(a) Pure element; silver appears in the element table.
(b) Homogeneous mixture; pool water contains at least water and chlorine in variable proportions, and it is uniform throughout.
(c) Compound; dry ice is a pure substance (carbon dioxide), but it is not listed in the table.
(d) Heterogeneous mixture; a blueberry muffin is a mixture of several things and has nonuniform composition.

Physical and Chemical Properties (Section 3.5)

To distinguish between physical and chemical properties, ask whether the substance changes composition while displaying the property. If it *does not* change composition, the property is physical; if it *does*, the property is chemical.

EXAMPLE 3.12   Physical and Chemical Properties

Determine whether each of the following is a physical or chemical property.

(a) the tendency for platinum jewelry to scratch easily *physical*
(b) the ability of sulfuric acid to burn the skin *chemical*
(c) the ability of hydrogen peroxide to bleach hair *chemical*
(d) the density of lead relative to other metals *physical*

Solution:

(a) Physical; scratched platinum is still platinum.
(b) Chemical; the acid chemically reacts with the skin to produce the burn.
(c) Chemical; the hydrogen peroxide chemically reacts with hair to bleach it.
(d) Physical; the heaviness can be felt without changing the lead into anything else.

Physical and Chemical Changes (Section 3.6)

To distinguish between physical and chemical changes, ask whether the substance changes composition during the change. If it *does not* change composition, the change is physical; if it *does*, the change is chemical.

EXAMPLE 3.13   Physical and Chemical Changes

Determine whether each of the following is a physical or chemical change.

(a) the explosion of gunpowder in the barrel of a gun *chemical*
(b) the melting of gold in a furnace *physical*
(c) the bubbling that occurs upon mixing baking soda and vinegar *chemical*
(d) the bubbling that occurs when water boils *physical*

Solution:

(a) Chemical; the gunpowder reacts with oxygen during the explosion.
(b) Physical; the liquid gold is still gold.
(c) Chemical; the bubbling is a result of a chemical reaction between the two substances to form new substances, one of which is carbon dioxide released as bubbles.
(d) Physical; the bubbling is due to liquid water turning into gaseous water, but it is still water.

Conservation of Mass (Section 3.7)

The sum of the masses of the substances involved in a chemical change must be the same before and after the change.

EXAMPLE 3.14   Conservation of Mass

An automobile runs for 10 minutes and burns 47 g of gasoline. The gasoline combined with oxygen from air and formed 132 g of carbon dioxide and 34 g of water. How much oxygen was consumed in the process?

Solution:
The total mass after the chemical change is:

$$132 \text{ g} + 34 \text{ g} = 166 \text{ g}$$

The total mass before the change must also be 166 g.

$$47 \text{ g} + \text{g oxygen} = 166 \text{ g}$$

So, the mass of oxygen consumed is the total mass (166 g) minus the mass of gasoline (47 g).

$$\text{grams of oxygen} = 166 \text{ g} - 47 \text{ g} = 119 \text{ g}$$

Conversion of Energy Units (Section 3.8)

Solve energy unit conversion problems using the problem-solving procedure that we learned in Section 2.10.

- Write down the given quantity and its units.
- Write down the quantity to find and/or its units.
- Write down the appropriate conversion factor(s).

- Write a solution map.

LIVE EXAMPLE
EXAMPLE 3.15   Conversion of Energy Units

Convert 1.7×10^3 kWh (the amount of energy used by the average U.S. citizen in one week) into calories.

Given: 1.7×10^3 kWh

Find: cal

Conversion Factors:

$$1 \text{ kWh} = 3.60 \times 10^6 \text{ J}$$
$$1 \text{ cal} = 4.18 \text{ J}$$

Solution Map:

$$\frac{3.60 \times 10^6 \text{ J}}{1 \text{ kWh}} \qquad \frac{1 \text{ cal}}{4.18 \text{ J}}$$

- Starting with the given quantity and its units, multiply by the appropriate conversion factor(s), canceling units, to arrive at the quantity to find in the desired units.

- Round the final answer to the correct number of significant figures.

- Check the answer.

Solution:

$$1.7 \times 10^3 \ \cancel{kWh} \times \frac{3.60 \times 10^6 \ \cancel{J}}{1 \ \cancel{kWh}} \times \frac{1 \ cal}{4.18 \ \cancel{J}}$$

$$= 1.464 \times 10^9 \ cal$$

$$1.464 \times 10^9 \ cal = 1.5 \times 10^9 \ cal$$

The unit of the answer, cal, is correct. The magnitude of th answer makes sense since cal is a smaller unit than kWh

---

Converting between Celsius and Kelvin Temperature Scales (Section 3.9)

Solve temperature conversion problems using the problem-solving procedure that we learned in Section 2.10. Take the steps appropriate for equations.

- Write down the given and find quantities.

- Write down the appropriate equation that relates K and °C.

- Draw a solution map. Use the appropriate equation that relates the given quantities to the find quantities.

- Solve the equation for the find quantity (°C).

- Substitute the appropriate quantity into the equation and compute the answer to the correct number of significant figures.

- Check the answer.

EXAMPLE 3.16   Converting between Celsius an Kelvin Temperature Scales

Convert 257 K to Celsius.

Given: 257 K

Find: °C

Equation: K = °C + 273

Solution Map:

$$K = °C + 273$$

Solution:

$$K = °C + 273$$
$$°C = K - 273$$
$$°C = 257 - 273 = -16 \ °C$$

The answer has the correct unit, and its magnitud seems correct (see Figure 3.14).

Converting between Fahrenheit and Celsius Temperature Scales (Section 3.9)

- Write down the given and find quantities.

- Write down the appropriate equation that relates °C and °F.

- Draw a solution map.

- Solve the equation for the find quantity (°F).

- Substitute the appropriate quantity into the equation and compute the answer to the correct number of significant figures.

- Check the answer.

EXAMPLE 3.17   Converting between Fahrenhei and Celsius Temperature Scales

Convert 62.0 °C to Fahrenheit.

Given: 62.0 °C

Find: °F

Equation: $°C = \dfrac{(°F - 32)}{1.8}$

Solution Map:

$$°C = \frac{(°F - 32)}{1.8}$$

Solution:

$$°C = \frac{(°F - 32)}{1.8}$$
$$1.8 \ (°C) = °F - 32$$
$$°F = 1.8 \ (°C) + 32$$
$$°F = 1.8 \ (62.0) + 32 = 143.60 \ °F = 144 \ °F$$

The answer has the correct unit, and its magnitud seems correct (see Figure 3.14).

Energy, Temperature Change, and Heat Capacity Calculations (Sections 3.10, 3.11)

| EXAMPLE 3.18 | Energy, Temperature Change, and Heat Capacity Calculations |

What is the temperature change in 355 mL of water upon absorption of 34 kJ of heat?

- Write down the given and find quantities.

Given: 355 mL water; 34 kJ of heat

Find: ΔT

- Write down the equation that relates the given and find quantities.

Equation: $q = m \cdot C \cdot \Delta T$

- Build a solution map, writing the appropriate equation—the one showing the relationship between the given and find quantities—below the arrow.

Solution Map:

$$\boxed{q, m, C} \longrightarrow \boxed{\Delta T}$$

$$q = m \cdot C \cdot \Delta T$$

- Collect each of the quantities required in the equation in the correct units.

The value for q must be converted from kJ to J:

$$q = 34 \ \text{kJ} \times \frac{1000 \ \text{J}}{1 \ \text{kJ}} = 3.4 \times 10^4 \ \text{J}$$

The value for m must be converted from milliliters to grams; use the density of water, 1.0 g/mL, to convert milliliters to grams.

$$m = 355 \ \text{mL} \times \frac{1.0 \ \text{g}}{1 \ \text{mL}} = 355 \ \text{g}$$

$$C = 4.18 \ \text{J/g} \ ^\circ\text{C}$$

- Solve the equation for the find quantity (ΔT).

- Substitute the appropriate quantities into the equation and compute the answer to the correct number of significant figures.

Solution:

$$q = m \times C \times \Delta T$$

$$\Delta T = \frac{q}{mC}$$

$$\Delta T = \frac{3.4 \times 10^4 \ \text{J}}{355 \ \text{g} \times 4.18 \ \text{J/g} \ ^\circ\text{C}}$$

$$= 22.91 \ ^\circ\text{C} = 23 \ ^\circ\text{C}$$

- Check the answer.

The answer has the correct units and the magnitude seems correct. If the magnitude of the answer were a huge number—such as 3×10^6, for example—we would go back and look for a mistake. If water were to go above 100 °C, it would boil, so such a large answer would be unlikely.

Key Terms

amorphous [3.3]	decanting [3.6]	homogeneous	molecules [3.2]
atoms [3.2]	distillation [3.6]	mixture [3.4]	physical changes [3.6]
calorie (c) [3.8]	electrical energy [3.8]	kelvin (K) [3.9]	physical properties [3.5]
Calorie (C) [3.8]	element [3.4]	Kelvin (K) scale [3.9]	potential energy [3.8]
Celsius (°C) scale [3.9]	energy [3.8]	kilowatt-hour (kWh) [3.8]	properties [3.5]
chemical changes [3.6]	Fahrenheit (°F) scale [3.9]	kinetic energy [3.8]	pure substance [3.4]
chemical energy [3.8]	filtration [3.6]	law of conservation of	solid [3.3]
chemical properties [3.5]	gas [3.3]	energy [3.8]	specific heat [3.10]
compound [3.4]	heat capacity [3.10]	liquid [3.3]	state of matter [3.3]
compressible [3.3]	heterogeneous	matter [3.2]	volatile [3.6]
crystalline [3.3]	mixture [3.4]	mixture [3.4]	

Exercises

Questions   Answers to all questions numbered in blue appear in the Answers section at the back of the book.

1. Define matter and give some examples.
2. What is matter composed of?
3. What are the three states of matter?
4. What are the properties of a solid?
5. What is the difference between a crystalline solid and an amorphous solid?
6. What are the properties of a liquid?
7. What are the properties of a gas?
8. Why are gases compressible?
9. What is a mixture?
10. What is the difference between a homogeneous mixture and a heterogeneous mixture?
11. What is a pure substance?
12. What is an element? A compound?
13. What is the difference between a mixture and a compound?
14. What is a physical property? What is a chemical property?
15. What is the difference between a physical change and a chemical change?
16. What is the law of conservation of mass?
17. What is the definition of energy?
18. What is the law of conservation of energy?

19. Name some different kinds of energy.
20. What are three common units for energy?
21. What are three common units for measuring temperature?
22. How do the three temperature scales differ?
23. What is heat capacity?
24. Why are coastal geographic regions normally cooler in the summer than inland geographic regions?
25. The following equation can be used to convert Fahrenheit temperature to Celsius temperature.

$$°C = \frac{(°F - 32)}{1.8}$$

Use algebra to change the equation to convert Celsius temperature to Fahrenheit temperature.
26. The following equation can be used to convert Celsius temperature to kelvin temperature.

$$K = °C + 273$$

Use algebra to change the equation to convert kelvin temperature to Celsius temperature.

Problems

Note: The exercises in the Problems section are paired, and the answers to the odd-numbered exercises (numbered in blue) appear in the Answers section at the back of the book.

Classifying Matter

27. Classify each of the following pure substances as an element or a compound.
    (a) aluminum
    (b) sulfur
    (c) methane
    (d) acetone

28. Classify each of the following pure substances as an element or a compound.
    (a) carbon
    (b) baking soda (sodium bicarbonate)
    (c) nickel
    (d) gold

29. Classify each of the following mixtures as homogeneous or heterogeneous.
    (a) coffee
    (b) chocolate sundae
    (c) apple juice
    (d) gasoline

30. Classify each of the following mixtures as homogeneous or heterogeneous.
    (a) baby oil
    (b) chocolate chip cookie
    (c) water and gasoline
    (d) wine

31. Classify each of the following as a pure substance or a mixture. If it is a pure substance, classify it as an element or a compound. If it is a mixture, classify it as homogeneous or heterogeneous.
    (a) helium gas
    (b) clean air
    (c) rocky road ice cream
    (d) concrete

32. Classify each of the following as a pure substance or a mixture. If it is a pure substance, classify it as an element or a compound. If it is a mixture, classify it as homogeneous or heterogeneous.
    (a) urine
    (b) pure water
    (c) Snickers bar
    (d) soil

Physical and Chemical Properties and Physical and Chemical Changes

33. Classify each of the following properties as physical or chemical.
   (a) the tendency of silver to tarnish
   (b) the shine of chrome
   (c) the color of gold
   (d) the flammability of propane gas

34. Classify each of the following properties as physical or chemical.
   (a) the boiling point of ethyl alcohol
   (b) the temperature at which dry ice evaporates
   (c) the flammability of ethyl alcohol
   (d) the smell of perfume

35. The following list contains several properties of ethylene (a ripening agent for bananas). Which are physical properties and which are chemical?

   • colorless
   • odorless
   • flammable
   • gas at room temperature
   • 1 L has a mass of 1.260 g under standard conditions
   • mixes with acetone
   • polymerizes to form polyethylene

36. The following list contains several properties of ozone (a pollutant in the lower atmosphere but part of a protective shield against UV light in the upper atmosphere). Which are physical and which are chemical?

   • bluish color
   • pungent odor
   • very reactive
   • decomposes on exposure to ultraviolet light
   • gas at room temperature

37. Determine whether each of the following changes is physical or chemical.
   (a) A balloon filled with hydrogen gas explodes upon contact with a spark.
   (b) The liquid propane in a barbecue evaporates away because the user left the valve open.
   (c) The liquid propane in a barbecue ignites upon contact with a spark.
   (d) Copper metal turns green on exposure to air and water.

38. Determine whether each of the following changes is physical or chemical.
   (a) Sugar dissolves in hot water.
   (b) Sugar burns in a pot.
   (c) A metal surface becomes dull because of continued abrasion.
   (d) A metal surface becomes dull on exposure to air.

39. A block of aluminum is **(a)** ground into aluminum powder and then **(b)** ignited. It then emits flames and smoke. Classify **(a)** and **(b)** as chemical or physical changes.

40. Several pieces of graphite from a mechanical pencil are **(a)** broken into tiny pieces. Then the pile of graphite is **(b)** ignited with a hot flame. Classify **(a)** and **(b)** as chemical or physical changes.

The Conservation of Mass

41. An automobile gasoline tank holds 42 kg of gasoline. When the gasoline burns, 168 kg of oxygen are consumed and carbon dioxide and water are produced. What is the total combined mass of carbon dioxide and water that is produced?

42. In the explosion of a hydrogen-filled balloon, 0.50 g of hydrogen reacted with 4.0 g of oxygen to form how many grams of water vapor? (Water vapor is the only product.)

43. Are the following data sets on chemical changes consistent with the law of conservation of mass?
   (a) A 7.5-g sample of hydrogen gas completely reacts with 60.0 g of oxygen gas to form 67.5 g of water.
   (b) A 60.5-g sample of gasoline completely reacts with 243 g of oxygen to form 206 g of carbon dioxide and 88 g of water.

44. Are the following data sets on chemical changes consistent with the law of conservation of mass?
   (a) A 12.8-g sample of sodium completely reacts with 19.6 g of chlorine to form 32.4 g of sodium chloride.
   (b) An 8-g sample of natural gas completely reacts with 32 g of oxygen gas to form 17 g of carbon dioxide and 16 g of water.

45. In a butane lighter, 9.7 g of butane combine with 34.7 g of oxygen to form 29.3 g carbon dioxide and how many grams of water?

46. A 56-g sample of iron reacts with 24 g of oxygen to form how many grams of iron oxide?

Conversion of Energy Units

47. Perform each of the following conversions.
  (a) 32.5 J to calories
  (b) 562 cal to joules
  (c) 35.7 kJ to calories
  (d) 287 cal to kilojoules

48. Perform each of the following conversions.
  (a) 456 cal to joules
  (b) 22.3 J to Calories
  (c) 234 kJ to Calories
  (d) 12.4 Cal to joules

49. Perform each of the following conversions.
  (a) 25 kWh to joules
  (b) 249 cal to Calories
  (c) 113 cal to kilowatt-hours
  (d) 44 kJ to calories

50. Perform each of the following conversions.
  (a) 345 Cal to kilowatt-hours
  (b) 23 J to calories
  (c) 5.7×10^3 J to kilojoules
  (d) 326 kJ to joules

51. Complete the following table:

J	cal	Cal	kWh
225 J	___	5.38×10^{-2} Cal	___
___	8.21×10^5 cal	___	___
___	___	___	295 kWh
___	___	155 Cal	___

52. Complete the following table:

J	cal	Cal	kWh
7.88×10^6 J	1.88×10^6 cal	___	___
___	___	1154 Cal	___
___	88.4 cal	___	___
___	___	___	125 kWh

53. An energy bill indicates that the customer used 955 kWh in July. How many joules did the customer use?

54. A television uses 25 kWh of energy per year. How many joules does it use?

55. An adult eats food whose nutritional energy totals approximately 2.2×10^3 Cal per day. The adult burns 2.0×10^3 Cal per day. How much excess nutritional energy, in kilojoules, does the adult consume per day? If 1 lb of fat is stored by the body for each 14.6×10^3 kJ of excess nutritional energy consumed, how long will it take this person to gain 1 lb?

56. How many joules of nutritional energy are in a bag of chips whose label reads 245 Cal? If 1 lb of fat stored by the body for each 14.6×10^3 kJ of excess nutritional energy consumed, how many bags of chips contain enough nutritional energy to result in 1 lb of body fat?

Converting between Temperature Scales

57. Perform each of the following temperature conversions.
  (a) 212 °F to Celsius (temperature of boiling water)
  (b) 77 K to Fahrenheit (temperature of liquid nitrogen)
  (c) 25 °C to kelvins (room temperature)
  (d) 98.6 °F to kelvins (body temperature)

58. Perform each of the following temperature conversions.
  (a) 102 °F to Celsius
  (b) 0 K to Fahrenheit
  (c) −48 °C to Fahrenheit
  (d) 273 K to Celsius

59. The coldest temperature ever measured in the United States was −80 °F on January 23, 1971, in Prospect Creek, Alaska. Convert that temperature to Celsius and kelvin (assume that −80 °F is accurate to two significant figures).

60. The warmest temperature ever measured in the United States was 134 °F on July 10, 1913, in Death Valley, California. Convert that temperature to Celsius and kelvin.

61. Vodka will not freeze in the freezer because it contains a high percentage of ethanol. The freezing point of pure ethanol is −114 °C. Convert that temperature to Fahrenheit and kelvin.

62. Liquid helium boils at 4.2 K. Convert this temperature to Fahrenheit and Celsius.

63. Complete the following table:

Kelvin	Fahrenheit	Celsius
0.0 K	___	−273.0 °C
___	82.5 °F	___
___	___	8.5 °C

64. Complete the following table:

Kelvin	Fahrenheit	Celsius
273.0 K	___	0.0 °C
___	−40.0 °F	___
385 K	___	___

Energy, Heat Capacity, and Temperature Changes

65. Calculate the amount of heat required to raise the temperature of a 97-g sample of water from 42 °C to 67 °C.

66. Calculate the amount of heat required to raise the temperature of a 27-g sample of water from 5 °C to 22 °C.

67. Calculate the amount of heat required to heat a 45-kg sample of ethanol from 11.0 °C to 19.0 °C.

68. Calculate the amount of heat required to heat a 3.5-kg gold bar from 21 °C to 67 °C.

69. If 89 J of heat are added to a pure gold coin with a mass of 12 g, what is its temperature change?

70. If 57 J of heat are added to an aluminum can with a mass of 17.1 g, what is its temperature change?

71. An iron nail with a mass of 12 g absorbs 15 J of heat. If the nail was initially at 28 °C, what is its final temperature?

72. A 45-kg sample of water absorbs 345 kJ of heat. If the water was initially at 22.1 °C, what is its final temperature?

73. Calculate the temperature change that occurs when 248 cal of heat are added to 24 g of water.

74. A lead fishing weight with a mass of 57 g absorbs 146 cal of heat. If its initial temperature is 47 °C, what is its final temperature?

75. An unknown metal with a mass of 28 g absorbs 58 J of heat. Its temperature rises from 31.1 °C to 39.9 °C. Calculate the heat capacity of the metal and identify it using Table 3.4.

76. An unknown metal is suspected to be gold. When 2.8 J of heat are added to 5.6 g of the metal, its temperature rises by 3.9 °C. Are these data consistent with the metal being gold?

77. When 56 J of heat are added to 11 g of a liquid, its temperature rises from 10.4 °C to 12.7 °C. What is the heat capacity of the liquid?

78. When 47.5 J of heat are added to 13.2 g of a liquid, its temperature rises by 1.72 °C. What is the heat capacity of the liquid?

79. Two identical coolers are packed for a picnic. Each cooler is packed with eighteen 12-oz soft drinks and 3 lb of ice. However, the drinks that went into cooler A were refrigerated for several hours before they were packed in the cooler, while the drinks that went into cooler B were packed at room temperature. When the two coolers are opened three hours later, most of the ice in cooler A is still ice, while nearly all of the ice in cooler B has melted. Explain this difference.

80. A 100-g block of iron metal and 100 g of water are each warmed to 75 °C and placed into two identical insulated containers. Two hours later, the two containers are opened and the temperature of each substance is measured. The iron metal has cooled to 38 °C while the water has cooled only to 69 °C. Explain this difference.

Cumulative Problems

81. Calculate the final temperature of 245 mL of water initially at 32 °C upon absorption of 17 kJ of heat.

82. Calculate the final temperature of 32 mL of ethanol initially at 11 °C upon absorption of 562 J of heat. (density of ethanol = 0.789 g/mL)

83. A pure gold ring with a volume of 1.57 cm^3 is initially at 11.4 °C. When it is put on, it warms to 29.5 °C. How much heat did the ring absorb? (density of gold = 19.3 g/cm^3)

84. A block of aluminum with a volume of 98.5 cm^3 absorbs 67.4 J of heat. If its initial temperature was 32.5 °C, what is its final temperature? (density of aluminum = 2.70 g/cm^3)

85. How much heat in kilojoules is required to heat 56 L of water from 85 °F to 212 °F?

86. How much heat in joules is required to heat a 43-g sample of aluminum from 72 °F to 145 °F?

87. What is the temperature change in Celsius when 29.5 L of water absorbs 2.3 kWh of heat?

88. If 1.45 L of water is initially at 25.0 °C, what will its temperature be after absorption of 9.4×10^{-2} kWh of heat?

89. A water heater contains 55 gal of water. How many kilowatt-hours of energy are necessary to heat the water in the water heater by 25 °C?

90. A room contains 48 kg of air. How many kilowatt-hours of energy are necessary to heat the air in the house from 7 °C to 28 °C? The heat capacity of air is 1.03 J/g °C.

91. A backpacker wants to carry enough fuel to heat 2.5 kg of water from 25 °C to 100.0 °C. If the fuel he carries produces 36 kJ of heat per gram, how much fuel should he carry? (For the sake of simplicity, assume that the transfer of heat is 100% efficient.)

92. A cook wants to heat 1.35 kg of water from 32.0 °C to 100.0 °C. If he uses natural gas to heat the water how much natural gas will he need to burn? Natural gas produces 49.3 kJ of heat per gram. (For the sake of simplicity, assume that the transfer of heat is 100% efficient.)

93. Evaporating sweat cools the body because evaporation absorbs 2.44 kJ per gram of water evaporated. Estimate the mass of water that must evaporate from the skin to cool a body by 0.50 °C, if the mass of the body is 95 kg and its heat capacity is 4.0 J/g °C. (Assume that the heat transfer is 100% efficient.)

94. When ice melts, it absorbs 0.33 kJ per gram. How much ice is required to cool a 12.0-oz drink from 75 °F to 35 °F, if the heat capacity of the drink is 4.18 J/g °C? (Assume that the heat transfer is 100% efficient.)

95. A 15.7-g aluminum block is warmed to 53.2 °C and plunged into an insulated beaker containing 32.5 g of water initially at 24.5 °C. The aluminum and the water are allowed to come to thermal equilibrium. Assuming that no heat is lost, what is the final temperature of the water and aluminum?

96. 25.0 mL of ethanol (density = 0.789 g/mL) initially at 7.0 °C is mixed with 35.0 mL of water (density = 1.0 g/mL) initially at 25.3 °C in an insulated beaker. Assuming that no heat is lost, what is the final temperature of the mixture?

Highlight Problems

97. Classify each of the following molecular pictures as a pure substance or a mixture.

(a)

(b)

(c)

(d)

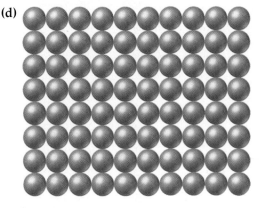

98. Classify each of the following molecular pictures as a pure substance or a mixture. If it is a pure substance, classify it as an element or a compound. If it is a mixture, classify it as homogeneous or heterogeneous.

(a)

(b)

(c)

(d)

99. The following molecular drawing shows images of acetone molecules before and after a change. Was the change chemical or physical?

100. The following molecular drawing shows images of methane molecules and oxygen molecules before and after a change. Was the change chemical or physical?

101. A major event affecting global climate is the El Niño/La Niña cycle. In this cycle, equatorial Pacific Ocean waters warm by several degrees Celsius above normal (El Niño) and then cool by several degrees Celsius below normal (La Niña). This cycle affects weather not only in North and South America, but as far away as Africa. Why does a seemingly small change in ocean temperature have such a large impact on weather?

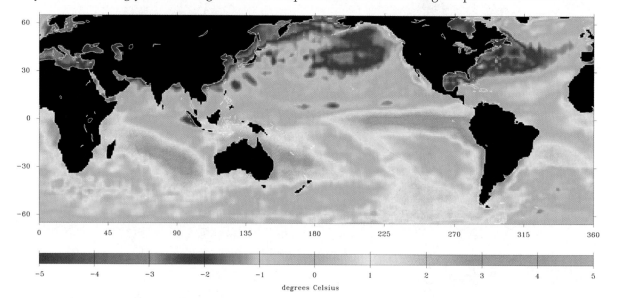

▲ Temperature anomaly plot of the world's oceans for December 23, 1997. The red section off the western coast of South America is the El Niño effect, a warming of the Pacific Ocean along the equator.

102. Global warming refers to the rise in average global temperature due to the increased concentration of certain gases, called greenhouse gases, in our atmosphere. The earth's oceans, because of their high heat capacity, can absorb heat and therefore act to slow down global warming. How much heat would be required to warm the earth's oceans by 1.0 °C? Assume that the volume of earth's oceans is 137×10^7 km^3 and that the density of seawater is 1.03 g/cm^3. Also assume that the heat capacity of seawater is the same as that of water.

▲ The earth's oceans moderate temperatures by absorbing heat during warm periods.

103. Examine the following data for the maximum and minimum average temperatures of San Francisco and Sacramento in the summer and in the winter.

SAN FRANCISCO (COASTAL CITY)

January		August	
High	Low	High	Low
57.4 °F	43.8 °F	64.4 °F	54.5 °F

SACRAMENTO (INLAND CITY)

January		August	
High	Low	High	Low
53.2 °F	37.7 °F	91.5 °F	57.7 °F

(a) Notice the difference between the August high in San Francisco and Sacramento. Why is it much hotter in the summer in Sacramento?
(b) Notice the difference between the January low in San Francisco and Sacramento. How might the heat capacity of the ocean contribute to this difference?

Answers to Skillbuilder Exercises

Skillbuilder 3.1 (a) pure substance, element
(b) mixture, homogeneous
(c) mixture, heterogeneous
(d) pure substance, compound
Skillbuilder 3.2 (a) chemical (b) physical
(c) physical (d) physical
Skillbuilder 3.3 (a) chemical (b) physical
(c) physical (d) chemical
Skillbuilder 3.4 27 g
Skillbuilder 3.5 2.14 kJ

Skillbuilder Plus, p. 63 6.57×10^6 cal
Skillbuilder 3.6 85 °C
Skillbuilder 3.7 282 °F
Skillbuilder 3.8 77 K
Skillbuilder 3.9 50.1 J
Skillbuilder Plus, p. 70 7.4 g
Skillbuilder 3.10 $\Delta T = 4.21$ °C; $T_f = 29.2$ °C

Answers to Conceptual Checkpoints

3.1 (d) kWh is the largest of the four units listed, so the numerical value of the yearly energy consumption would be lowest if expressed in kWh.
3.2 (d) You can confirm this by substituting each of the Fahrenheit temperatures into the equation in Section 3.9 and solving for the Celsius temperature.

3.3 (a) Because copper has the lowest specific heat capacity of the three metals, it will experience the greatest temperature change for a given energy input.

CHAPTER 4

Atoms and Elements

"Nothing exists except atoms and empty space; everything else is opinion."

Democritus (460–370 B.C.)

4.1   Experiencing Atoms at Tiburon

My wife and I recently enjoyed a visit to the northern California seaside town of Tiburon. Tiburon sits next to San Francisco Bay with views of the water, the city of San Francisco, and the surrounding mountains. As we walked along the waterside path, I felt the breeze as it blew over the bay. I could hear the water lapping on the shore, and I could smell the sea air. What was the cause of these sensations? The answer is simple—atoms.

Since all matter is made of atoms, it is atoms that we experience in our sensations. The atom is the fundamental building block of everything we hear, feel, see, and experience. When we feel the wind on our skin, we are feeling atoms. When we hear the lapping water, we are hearing atoms. When we touch a shoreside rock, we are touching atoms, and when we smell the sea air, we are smelling atoms. We eat atoms, we breathe atoms, and we excrete atoms. Atoms are the building blocks of matter; they are the basic units from which nature builds. They are all around us and compose everything, including our own bodies.

Atoms are incredibly small. A single pebble from the shoreline contains more atoms than we could ever count. The number of atoms in a single pebble far exceeds the number of pebbles on the bottom of San Francisco Bay. To get an idea of how small atoms are, imagine that every atom within a small pebble were the size of the pebble itself; then the pebble would be larger than Mt. Everest (▶ Figure 4.1) Atoms are small—yet they compose everything.

The key to connecting the microscopic world with the macroscopic world is the atom. Atoms compose matter; their properties determine matter's properties. An *atom* is the smallest identifiable unit of an element. There are about ninety-one different elements in nature, and consequently about ninety-one different kinds of atoms. In addition, scientists have succeeded in making about twenty synthetic elements (not found in nature). In this chapter, we learn about atoms: what they are made of, how they differ from one another, and how they are structured. We also learn about the elements that atoms compose and some of the properties of those elements.

As we learned in Chapter 3, many atoms exist not as free particles but as groups of atoms bound together to form molecules. Nevertheless, all matter is ultimately made of atoms.

The exact number of naturally occurring elements is controversial because some elements previously considered only synthetic may actually occur in nature in very small quantities.

◀ All matter is composed of atoms. Seaside rocks are often composed of silicates, compounds of silicon and oxygen atoms. Seaside air, like all air, contains nitrogen and oxygen molecules, but it may also contain substances called amines. The amine shown here is triethylamine, which is emitted by decaying fish. Triethylamine is one of the compounds responsible for the fishy smell of the seaside.

▲ **Figure 4.1   The size of the atom**   If every atom within a pebble were the size of the pebble itself, then the pebble would be larger than Mt. Everest.

4.2   Indivisible: The Atomic Theory

▲ Diogenes and Democritus, as imagined by a medieval artist. Democritus is the first person on record to have postulated that matter was composed of atoms.

If we simply examine matter, even under a microscope, it is not obvious that matter is composed of tiny particles. In fact, it appears to be just the opposite. If we divide a sample of matter into smaller and smaller pieces, it seems that we could divide it forever. From our perspective, matter seems continuous. The first person recorded as thinking otherwise was Democritus (460–370 B.C.), a Greek philosopher who theorized that matter was ultimately composed of small, indivisible particles he called *atomos,* or "atoms," meaning "indivisible." Democritus suggested that if you divided matter into smaller and smaller pieces, you would eventually end up with tiny, indestructible particles—atoms.

Democritus' ideas were not widely accepted, and it was not until the early nineteenth century that John Dalton formalized a theory of atoms that gained broad acceptance. Dalton's atomic theory has three parts:

1. Each element is composed of tiny indestructible particles called atoms.
2. All atoms of a given element have the same mass and other properties that distinguish them from the atoms of other elements.
3. Atoms combine in simple, whole-number ratios to form compounds.

Today, the evidence for the atomic theory is overwhelming. Recent advances in microscopy have allowed scientists not only to image individual atoms but also to pick them up and move them (▼ Figure 4.2). Matter is indeed composed of atoms.

▶ **Figure 4.2   Writing with atoms**
Scientists at IBM used a special microscope, called a scanning tunneling microscope (STM), to move xenon atoms to form the letters *IBM.* The cone shape of these atoms is due to the peculiarities of the instrumentation. Atoms are, in general, spherical in shape.

EVERYDAY Chemistry

Atoms and Humans

All matter is composed of atoms. What does that mean? What does it imply? It means that everything before you is composed of tiny particles too small to see. It means that even you and I are composed of these same particles. We acquired those particles from the food we have eaten over the years. The average carbon atom in our own bodies has been used by twenty other living organisms before we got it and will be used by other organisms after we die.

The idea that all matter is composed of atoms has far-reaching implications. It implies that our bodies, our hearts, and even our brains are composed of atoms acting according to the laws of chemistry and physics. Some have viewed this as a devaluation of human life. We have always wanted to distinguish ourselves from everything else, and the idea that we are made of the same basic particles as all other matter takes something away from that distinction . . . or does it?

CAN YOU ANSWER THIS? *Do you find the idea that you are made of atoms disturbing? Why or why not?*

4.3   The Nuclear Atom

Electric charge is more fully defined in Section 4.4. For now, think of it as an inherent property of electrons that causes them to interact with other charged particles.

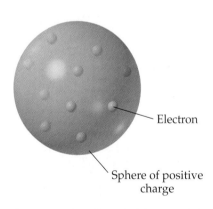

▲ **Figure 4.3   Plum pudding model of the atom**   In the model suggested by J. J. Thomson, negatively charged electrons (yellow) were held in a sphere of positive charge (red).

Electron

Sphere of positive charge

TUTORIAL
Rutherford's Experiment: Blueberry Muffins and Plum Pudding

By the end of the nineteenth century, scientists were convinced that matter was composed of atoms, the permanent, indestructible building blocks from which all substances are constructed. However, an English physicist named J. J. Thomson (1856–1940) complicated the picture by discovering an even smaller and more fundamental particle called the **electron**. Thomson discovered that electrons are negatively charged, that they are much smaller and lighter than atoms, and that they are uniformly present in many different kinds of substances. The indestructible building block called the atom could apparently be "chipped."

The discovery of negatively charged particles within atoms raised the question of a balancing positive charge. Atoms were known to be charge-neutral, so they must contain positive charge that balanced the negative charge of electrons. But how did the positive and negative charges within the atom fit together? Were atoms just a jumble of even more fundamental particles? Were they solid spheres, or did they have some internal structure? Thomson proposed that the negatively charged electrons were small particles held within a positively charged sphere. This model, the most popular of the time, became known as the plum pudding model (plum pudding is an English dessert) (◄ Figure 4.3). The picture suggested by Thomson was—to those of us not familiar with plum pudding—like a blueberry muffin, where the blueberries are the electrons and the muffin is the positively charged sphere.

In 1909, Ernest Rutherford (1871–1937), who had worked under Thomson and adhered to his plum pudding model, performed an experiment in an attempt to confirm it. His experiment proved it wrong instead. In his experiment, Rutherford directed tiny, positively charged particles—called alpha-particles—at an ultrathin sheet of gold foil (► Figure 4.4). These particles were to act as probes of the gold atoms' structure. If the gold atoms were indeed like blueberry muffins or plum pudding—with their mass and charge spread throughout the entire volume of the atom—these speeding probes should pass right through the gold foil with minimum deflection. Rutherford performed the experiment, but the results were not as he expected. A majority of the particles did pass directly through the foil, but some particles were deflected, and some (1 in 20,000) even bounced back. The results puzzled Rutherford, who found them "about as credible as if you had fired a 15-inch shell at a piece of tissue paper and it came back and hit you." What must the structure of the atom be in order to explain this odd behavior?

▶ **Figure 4.4   Rutherford's gold foil experiment**   Tiny particles called alpha-particles were directed at a thin sheet of gold foil. Most of the particles passed directly through the foil. A few, however, were deflected—some of them at sharp angles.

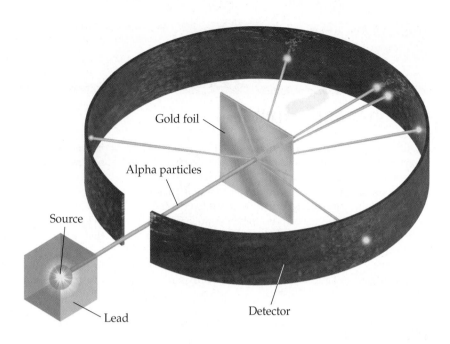

Gold foil

Alpha particles

Source

Lead

Detector

TUTORIAL
Rutherford Experiment:
Nuclear Atom

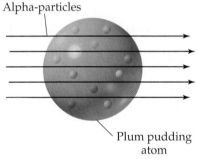

Alpha-particles

Plum pudding
atom

(a) Rutherford's expected result

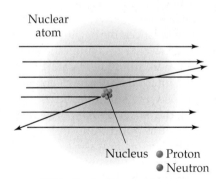

Nuclear
atom

Nucleus   ● Proton
           ● Neutron

(b) Rutherford's actual result

▲ **Figure 4.5   Discovery of the atomic nucleus   (a)** Expected result of Rutherford's gold foil experiment. If the plum pudding model were correct, the alpha-particles would pass right through the gold foil with minimal deflection. **(b)** Actual result of Rutherford's gold foil experiment. A small number of alpha-particles were deflected or bounced back. The only way to explain the deflections was to suggest that most of the mass and all of the positive charge of an atom must be concentrated in a space much smaller than the size of the atom itself.

Rutherford created a new model to explain his results (◀ Figure 4.5). He concluded that matter must not be as uniform as it appears. It must contain large regions of empty space dotted with small regions of very dense matter. In order to explain the deflections he observed, the mass and positive charge of an atom must all be concentrated in a space much smaller than the size of the atom itself. Using this idea, he proposed the **nuclear theory of the atom**, which has three basic parts:

1. Most of the atom's mass and all of its positive charge are contained in a small core called the *nucleus*.
2. Most of the volume of the atom is empty space through which the tiny, negatively charged electrons are dispersed.
3. There are as many negatively charged electrons outside the nucleus as there are positively charged particles (*protons*) inside the nucleus, so that the atom is electrically neutral.

Later work by Rutherford and others demonstrated that the atom's **nucleus** contains both positively charged **protons** and neutral particles called **neutrons**. The dense nucleus makes up more than 99.9% of the mass of the atom, but occupies only a small fraction of its volume. The electrons are distributed through a much larger region, but don't have much mass (▶ Figure 4.6). For now, you can think of these electrons like the water droplets that make up a cloud—they are dispersed throughout a large volume, but weigh almost nothing.

Rutherford's nuclear theory was a success and is still valid today. The revolutionary part of this theory is the idea that matter—at its core—is much less uniform than it appears. If the nucleus of the atom were the size of this dot ·, the average electron would be about 10 m away. Yet the dot would contain almost the entire mass of the atom. Imagine what matter would be like if atomic structure broke down. What if matter were composed of atomic nuclei piled on top of each other like marbles? Such matter would be incredibly dense; a single grain of sand composed of solid atomic nuclei would have a mass of 5 million kg (or a weight of about 10 million lb). Astronomers believe there are some places in the universe where such matter exists: neutron stars and black holes.

▶ Figure 4.6 **The nuclear atom** In this model, 99.9% of the atom's mass is concentrated in a small, dense nucleus that contains protons and neutrons. The rest of the volume of the atom is mostly empty space occupied by negatively charged electrons. The number of electrons outside the nucleus is equal to the number of protons inside the nucleus. In this image, the nucleus is greatly enlarged and the electrons are portrayed as particles.

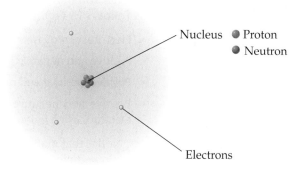

Nucleus ● Proton
● Neutron

Electrons

4.4 The Properties of Protons, Neutrons, and Electrons

▲ If a proton had the mass of a baseball, an electron would have the mass of a rice grain. The proton is nearly 2000 times as massive as an electron.

Protons and neutrons have very similar masses. In SI units, the mass of the proton is 1.67262×10^{-27} kg, and the mass of the neutron is a close 1.67493×10^{-27} kg. A more common unit to express these masses, however, is the **atomic mass unit (amu)**, defined as one-twelfth of the mass of a carbon atom containing six protons and six neutrons. In this unit, a proton has a mass of 1.0073 amu and a neutron has a mass of 1.0087 amu. Electrons, by contrast, have an almost negligible mass of 0.00091×10^{-27} kg, or approximately 0.00055 amu.

The proton and the electron both have electrical **charge**. The proton's charge is +1 and the electron's charge is −1. The charge of the proton and the electron are equal in magnitude but opposite in sign, so that when the two particles are paired the charges exactly cancel. The neutron has no charge.

What is electrical charge? Electrical charge is a fundamental property of protons and electrons, just as mass is a fundamental property of matter. Most matter is charge-neutral because protons and electrons occur together and their charges cancel. However, you have probably experienced excess electrical charge when brushing your hair on a dry day. The brushing action results in the accumulation of electrical charge on the hair strands, which then repel each other, causing your hair to stand on end.

EVERYDAY Chemistry

Solid Matter?

If matter really is mostly empty space as Rutherford suggested, then why does it appear so solid? Why can I tap my knuckles on the table and feel a solid thump? Matter appears solid because the variation in the density is on such a small scale that our eyes can't see it. Imagine a jungle gym one hundred stories high and the size of a football field. It is mostly empty space. Yet if you viewed it from an airplane, it would appear as a solid mass. Matter is similar. When you tap your knuckle on the table, it is much like one giant jungle gym (your finger) crashing into another (the table). Even though they are both primarily empty space, one does not fall into the other.

CAN YOU ANSWER THIS? *Use the jungle gym analogy to explain why most of Rutherford's alpha-particles went right through the gold foil and why a few bounced back. Remember that his gold foil was extremely thin.*

▲ Matter appears solid and uniform because the variation in density is on a scale too small for our eyes to see. Just as this scaffolding appears solid at a distance, so matter appears solid to us.

Positive (red) and negative (yellow) charges attract.

Positive–positive and negative–negative charges repel.

+1 + (−1) = 0

Positive and negative charges cancel.

▲ **Figure 4.7 The properties of electrical charge**

We can summarize the nature of electrical charge as follows (◄ Figure 4.7):

- Electrical charge is a fundamental property of protons and electrons.
- Positive and negative electrical charges attract each other.
- Positive–positive and negative–negative charges repel each other.
- Positive and negative charges cancel each other so that a proton and an electron, when paired, are charge-neutral.

Notice that matter is usually charge-neutral due to the canceling effect of protons and electrons. When matter does acquire charge imbalances, these imbalances usually equalize quickly, often in dramatic ways. For example, the shock you receive when touching a doorknob during dry weather is the equalization of a charge imbalance that developed as you walked across the carpet. Lightning is an equalization of charge imbalances that develop during electrical storms.

If you had a sample of matter—even a tiny sample, such as a sand grain—that was composed of only protons or only electrons, the forces around that matter would be extraordinary, and the matter would be unstable. Luckily, that is not the way matter is—protons and electrons exist together, canceling each other's charge and making matter charge-neutral. The properties of protons, neutrons, and electrons are summarized in Table 4.1.

TABLE 4.1 Subatomic Particles

	Mass (kg)	Mass (amu)	Charge
proton	1.67262×10^{-27}	1.0073	+1
neutron	1.67493×10^{-27}	1.0087	0
electron	0.00091×10^{-27}	0.00055	−1

✔ CONCEPTUAL CHECKPOINT 4.1

An atom with which of these compositions would have a mass of approximately 12 amu and be charge-neutral?

(a) 6 protons and 6 electrons

(b) 3 protons, 3 neutrons, and 6 electrons

(c) 6 protons, 6 neutrons, and 6 electrons

(d) 12 neutrons and 12 electrons

▶ Matter is normally charge-neutral, having equal numbers of positive and negative charges that exactly cancel. When the charge balance of matter is disturbed, as in an electrical storm, it quickly rebalances, often in dramatic ways such as lightning.

Negative charge buildup

Charge equalization

Positive charge buildup

▶ Figure 4.8   **The number of protons in the nucleus defines the element**

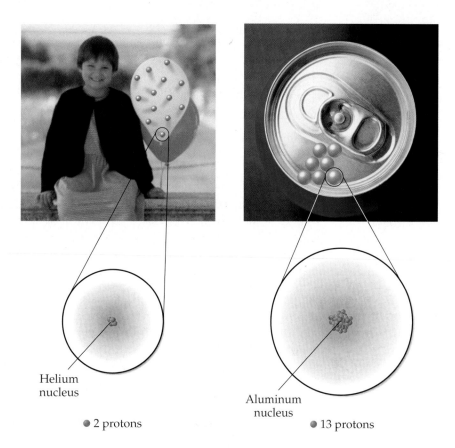

Helium
nucleus
● 2 protons

Aluminum
nucleus
● 13 protons

4.5   Elements: Defined by Their Numbers of Protons

We have seen that atoms are composed of protons, neutrons, and electrons. However, it is the number of protons in the nucleus of an atom that identifies it as a particular element. For example, atoms with 2 protons in their nucleus are helium atoms, atoms with 13 protons in their nucleus are aluminum atoms, and atoms with 92 protons in their nucleus are uranium atoms. The number of protons in an atom's nucleus defines the element (▲ Figure 4.8). Every aluminum atom has 13 protons in its nucleus—if it had a different number of protons, it would be a different element. The number of protons in the nucleus of an atom is called the **atomic number** and is given the symbol **Z**.

The periodic table of the elements (▶ Figure 4.9) lists all known elements according to their atomic numbers. Each element is represented by a unique **chemical symbol**, a one- or two-letter abbreviation for the element that appears directly below its atomic number on the periodic table. The chemical symbol for helium is He; for aluminum, Al; and for uranium, U. The chemical symbol and the atomic number always go together. If the atomic number is 13, the chemical symbol must be Al. If the atomic number is 92, the chemical symbol must be U. This is just another way of saying that the number of protons defines the element.

Most chemical symbols are based on the English name of the element. For example, the symbol for carbon is C; for silicon, Si; and for bromine, Br. Some elements, however, have symbols based on their Latin names. For example, the symbol for potassium is K, from the Latin *kalium*, and the symbol for sodium is Na, from the Latin *natrium*. Other elements with symbols based on their Greek or Latin names include the following:

lead	Pb	*plumbum*
mercury	Hg	*hydrargyrum*
iron	Fe	*ferrum*
silver	Ag	*argentum*
tin	Sn	*stannum*
copper	Cu	*cuprum*

▲ Figure 4.9 **The periodic table of the elements**

The names of elements were often given to describe their properties. For example, *argon* originates from the Greek word *argos*, meaning "inactive," referring to argon's chemical inertness (it does not react with other elements). *Bromine* originates from the Greek word *bromos*, meaning "stench," referring to bromine's strong odor. Other elements were named after countries. For example, polonium was named after Poland, francium was named after France, and americium was named after the United States of America. Still other elements were named after scientists. Curium was named after Marie Curie, and mendelevium was named after Dmitri Mendeleev. Every element's name, symbol, and atomic number are listed in the periodic table (inside front cover) and in an alphabetical listing (inside back cover) in this book.

Curium

96

Cm

(247)

▶ The name *bromine* originates from the Greek word *bromos*, meaning "stench." Bromine vapor, seen as the red-brown gas in this photograph, has a strong odor.

◀ Curium is named after Marie Curie, a chemist who helped discover radioactivity and also discovered two new elements. Curie won two Nobel Prizes for her work.

EXAMPLE 4.1   **Atomic Number, Atomic Symbol, and Element Name**

Find the atomic symbol and atomic number for each of the following elements.

(a) silicon
(b) potassium
(c) gold
(d) antimony

Solution:

As you become familiar with the periodic table, you will be able to quickly locate elements on it. For now, it might be easier to find them in the alphabetical listing on the inside back cover of this book, but you should also find their position in the periodic table.

Element	Symbol	Atomic Number
silicon	Si	14
potassium	K	19
gold	Au	79
antimony	Sb	51

SKILLBUILDER 4.1   **Atomic Number, Atomic Symbol, and Element Name**

Find the name and atomic number for each of the following elements.

(a) Na – Sodium – 12
(b) Ni – Nickel
(c) P – phororpus
(d) Ta – Tantum

4.6   Looking for Patterns: The Periodic Law and the Periodic Table

The organization of the periodic table has its origins in the work of Dmitri Mendeleev (1834–1907), a nineteenth-century Russian chemistry professor. In his time, about sixty-five different elements had been discovered. Through the work of a number of chemists, much was known about each of these elements, including their relative masses, chemical activity, and some of their physical properties. However, there was no systematic way of organizing them.

▲ Dmitri Mendeleev, a Russian chemistry professor who proposed the periodic law and arranged early versions of the periodic table, shown on a Russian postage stamp.

Periodic means "recurring regularly." The properties of the elements, when listed in order of increasing relative mass, formed a *repeating pattern*.

1							2
H							He

3	4	5	6	7	8	9	10
Li	Be	B	C	N	O	F	Ne
11	12	13	14	15	16	17	18
Na	Mg	Al	Si	P	S	Cl	Ar

19	20
K	Ca

▲ **Figure 4.11   Making a periodic table**   If we place the elements from Figure 4.10 in a table, we can arrange them in rows so that similar properties align in the same vertical columns. This is similar to Mendeleev's first periodic table.

▲ Silicon, a metalloid used extensively in the computer and electronics industries. This silicon wafer is being etched to make computer chips.

1	2	3	4	5	6	7	8	9	10	11	12	13	14	15	16	17	18	19	20
H	He	Li	Be	B	C	N	O	F	Ne	Na	Mg	Al	Si	P	S	Cl	Ar	K	Ca

▲ **Figure 4.10   Recurring properties**   The elements shown are listed in order of increasing atomic number (Mendeleev used relative mass, which is similar). The color of each element represents its properties. Notice that the properties (colors) of these elements form a repeating pattern.

In 1869, Mendeleev noticed that certain groups of elements had similar properties. Mendeleev found that if he listed the elements in order of increasing relative mass, those similar properties recurred in a regular pattern (▲ Figure 4.10). Mendeleev summarized these observations in the **periodic law**:

When the elements are arranged in order of increasing relative mass, certain sets of properties recur periodically.

Mendeleev then organized all the known elements in a table in which relative mass increased from left to right and elements with similar properties were aligned in the same vertical columns (◄ Figure 4.11). Since many elements had not yet been discovered, Mendeleev's table contained some gaps, which allowed him to predict the existence of yet-undiscovered elements. For example, Mendeleev predicted the existence of an element he called *eka-silicon*, which fell below silicon on the table and between gallium and arsenic. In 1886, eka-silicon was discovered by German chemist Clemens Winkler (1838–1904), and found to have almost exactly the properties that Mendeleev had anticipated. Winkler named the element germanium, after his home country.

Mendeleev's original listing has evolved into the modern **periodic table**. In the modern table, elements are listed in order of increasing atomic number rather than increasing relative mass. The modern periodic table also contains more elements than Mendeleev's original table because many more have been discovered since his time.

Mendeleev's periodic law was based on observation. Like all scientific laws, the periodic law summarized many observations but did not give the underlying reason for the observation—only theories do that. For now, we accept the periodic law as it is, but in Chapter 9 we examine a powerful theory that explains the law and gives the underlying reasons for it.

The elements in the periodic table can be broadly classified as metals, nonmetals, and metalloids (► Figure 4.12). **Metals** occupy the left side of the periodic table and have similar properties: They are good conductors of heat and electricity; they can be pounded into flat sheets (malleability); they can be drawn into wires (ductility); they are often shiny; and they tend to lose electrons when they undergo chemical changes. Good examples of metals include iron, magnesium, chromium, and sodium.

Nonmetals occupy the upper right side of the periodic table. The dividing line between metals and nonmetals is the zigzag diagonal line running from boron to astatine. Nonmetals have more varied properties—some are solids at room temperature, others are gases—but as a whole they tend to be poor conductors of heat and electricity and they all tend to gain electrons when they undergo chemical changes. Good examples of nonmetals include oxygen, nitrogen, chlorine, and iodine.

Most of the elements that lie along the zigzag diagonal line dividing metals and nonmetals are called **metalloids**, or *semimetals*, and show mixed properties. Metalloids are also called **semiconductors** because of their intermediate electrical conductivity, which can be changed and controlled. This property makes semiconductors useful in the manufacture of the electronic devices central to computers, cell phones, and many other modern gadgets. Good examples of metalloids include silicon, arsenic, and germanium.

1A 1		Metals															8A 18
1 H	2A 2	Nonmetals										3A 13	4A 14	5A 15	6A 16	7A 17	2 He
3 Li	4 Be	Metalloids										5 B	6 C	7 N	8 O	9 F	10 Ne
11 Na	12 Mg	3B 3	4B 4	5B 5	6B 6	7B 7	8B 8	9	10	1B 11	2B 12	13 Al	14 Si	15 P	16 S	17 Cl	18 Ar
19 K	20 Ca	21 Sc	22 Ti	23 V	24 Cr	25 Mn	26 Fe	27 Co	28 Ni	29 Cu	30 Zn	31 Ga	32 Ge	33 As	34 Se	35 Br	36 Kr
37 Rb	38 Sr	39 Y	40 Zr	41 Nb	42 Mo	43 Tc	44 Ru	45 Rh	46 Pd	47 Ag	48 Cd	49 In	50 Sn	51 Sb	52 Te	53 I	54 Xe
55 Cs	56 Ba	57 La	72 Hf	73 Ta	74 W	75 Re	76 Os	77 Ir	78 Pt	79 Au	80 Hg	81 Tl	82 Pb	83 Bi	84 Po	85 At	86 Rn
87 Fr	88 Ra	89 Ac	104 Rf	105 Db	106 Sg	107 Bh	108 Hs	109 Mt	110	111	112		114		116		

Lanthanides	58 Ce	59 Pr	60 Nd	61 Pm	62 Sm	63 Eu	64 Gd	65 Tb	66 Dy	67 Ho	68 Er	69 Tm	70 Yb	71 Lu
Actinides	90 Th	91 Pa	92 U	93 Np	94 Pu	95 Am	96 Cm	97 Bk	98 Cf	99 Es	100 Fm	101 Md	102 No	103 Lr

▲ Figure 4.12   **Metals, nonmetals, and metalloids**   The elements in the periodic table can be broadly classified as metals, nonmetals, and metalloids.

EXAMPLE 4.2   Classifying Elements as Metals, Nonmetals, or Metalloids

Classify each of the following elements as a metal, nonmetal, or metalloid.

(a) Ba — *Metal*
(b) I — *Non Metal*
(c) O — *Non metal*
(d) Te — *metalloid*

Solution:

(a) Barium is on the left side of the periodic table; it is a metal.

(b) Iodine is on the right side of the periodic table; it is a nonmetal.

(c) Oxygen is on the right side of the periodic table; it is a nonmetal.

(d) Tellurium is in the middle-right section of the periodic table, along the line that divides the metals from the nonmetals; it is a metalloid.

SKILLBUILDER 4.2   Classifying Elements as Metals, Nonmetals, or Metalloids

Classify each of the following elements as a metal, nonmetal, or metalloid.

(a) S — *Non Metal*
(b) Cl — *Non Metal*
(c) Ti — *Metal*
(d) Sb — *metalloid*

The periodic table can also be broadly divided into **main-group elements**, whose properties tend to be more predictable based on their position in the periodic table, and **transition elements** or **transition metals**, whose properties

▶ Figure 4.13   **Main-group and transition elements**   The periodic table can be broadly divided into main-group elements, whose properties can generally be predicted based on their position, and transition elements, whose properties tend to be less predictable based on their position.

Main group elements		Transition elements										Main group elements					

Group number

(periodic table as shown in figure, Periods 1–7, groups 1A–8A and 1B–8B/3B–2B with element symbols and atomic numbers)

Main-group elements are in columns labeled with a number and the letter A. Transition elements are in columns labeled with a number and the letter B.

A competing numbering system does not use letters, but only the numbers 1–18. Both numbering systems are shown in Figure 4.12.

The noble gases are inert (or unreactive) compared to other elements. However, some noble gases, especially the heavier ones, will form a limited number of compounds with other elements under special conditions.

are less easily predictable based simply on their position in the periodic tab (▲ Figure 4.13). Each column within the main-group elements in the periodic table is called a **family** or **group** of elements and is designated with a number and a letter printed directly above the column.

The elements within a group usually have similar properties. For example, the Group 8A elements, called the **noble gases**, are chemically iner gases. The most familiar noble gas is probably helium, used to fill buoya balloons. Helium, like the other noble gases, is chemically stable—it wor combine with other elements to form compounds—and is therefore safe put into balloons. Other noble gases include neon, often used in neon sign argon, which makes up a small percentage of our atmosphere; krypton; and xenon. The Group 1A elements, called the **alkali metals**, are all very rea tive metals. A marble-sized piece of sodium explodes violently whe dropped into water. Other alkali metals include lithium, potassium, and rubidium. The Group 2A elements, called the **alkaline earth metals**, a also fairly reactive, although not quite as reactive as the alkali metals. Ca cium, for example, reacts fairly vigorously when dropped into water b will not explode as easily as sodium. Other alkaline earth metals includ

Noble gases

▲ The periodic table with Groups 1A, 2A, and 8A highlighted.

▲ The noble gases include helium (used in balloons), neon (found in neon signs), argon, krypton, and xenon.

Alkaline Earth Metals

Alkali metals

| Li |
| Na |
| K |
| Rb |
| Cs |

| Be |
| Mg |
| Ca |
| Sr |
| Ba |

Halogens

| F |
| Cl |
| Br |
| I |
| At |

▲ The alkali metals include lithium (shown in the first photo), sodium (shown in the second photo reacting with water), potassium, rubidium, and cesium.

▲ The alkaline earth metals include beryllium, magnesium (shown burning in the first photo), calcium (shown reacting with water in the second photo), strontium, and barium.

▲ The halogens include fluorine, chlorine (shown in the first photo), bromine, iodine (shown in the second photo), and astatine.

TUTORIAL
Periodic Properties

TUTORIAL
Interactive Periodic Table

magnesium, a common low-density structural metal; strontium; and barium. The Group 7A elements, called the **halogens**, are very reactive nonmetals. The most familiar halogen is probably chlorine, a greenish-yellow gas with a pungent odor. Because of its reactivity, chlorine is often used as a sterilizing and disinfecting agent. Other halogens include bromine, a redbrown liquid that easily evaporates into a gas; iodine, a purple solid; and fluorine, a pale yellow gas.

EXAMPLE 4.3   **Groups and Families of Elements**

To which group or family of elements does each of the following elements belong?

(a) Mg — Alkali Earth
(b) N — 5A
(c) K   Alkali metal
(d) Br   — Halogens

Solution:

(a) Mg is in Group 2A; it is an alkaline earth metal.

(b) N is in Group 5A.

(c) K is in Group 1A; it is an alkali metal.

(d) Br is in Group 7A; it is a halogen.

SKILLBUILDER 4.3   **Groups and Families of Elements**

To which group or family of elements does each of the following element belong?

(a) Li
(b) B
(c) I
(d) Ar

CONCEPTUAL CHECKPOINT 4.2

Which of these statements can NEVER be true?

(a) An element can be both a transition element and a metal.
(b) An element can be both a transition element and a metalloid.
(c) An element can be both a metalloid and a halogen.
(d) An element can be both a main-group element and a halogen.

4.7   Ions: Losing and Gaining Electrons

In chemical reactions, atoms often lose or gain electrons to form charged particles called **ions**. For example, neutral lithium (Li) atoms contain 3 protons and 3 electrons; however, in reactions, lithium atoms lose one electron (e^-) form Li^+ ions.

$$Li \longrightarrow Li^+ + e^-$$

The Li^+ *ion* contains 3 protons but only 2 electrons, resulting in a net charge of $1+$. Ion charges are usually written with the magnitude of the charge first followed by the sign of the charge. For example, a positive two charge is written $2+$ and a negative two charge is written as $2-$. The charge of an ion depends on how many electrons were gained or lost and is given by the following formula

The charge of an ion is shown in the upper right corner of the symbol.

$$\text{Ion charge} = \text{number of protons} - \text{number of electrons}$$
$$= \#p - \#e^-$$

where "p" stands for *proton* and "e^-" stands for *electron*.
For the Li^+ ion:

$$\text{Ion charge} = 3 - 2 = 1+$$

Neutral fluorine (F) atoms contain 9 protons and 9 electrons; however, chemical reactions fluorine atoms gain one electron to form F^- ions:

$$F + e^- \longrightarrow F^-$$

The F^- *ion* contains 9 protons and 10 electrons, resulting in a -1 charge.

$$\text{Ion charge} = 9 - 10$$
$$= 1-$$

Positively charged ions, such as Li^+, are called **cations**, and negatively charged ions, such as F^-, are called **anions**. Ions behave very differently than the atoms from which they are formed. Neutral sodium atoms, for example are extremely reactive, reacting violently with most things they contact. Sodium cations (Na^+), on the other hand, are relatively inert—we eat them all the time in sodium chloride (table salt). In nature, cations and anions always occur together so that, again, matter is charge-neutral.

EXAMPLE 4.4   **Determining Ion Charge from Numbers of Protons and Electrons**

Determine the charge of each of the following ions.

(a) a magnesium ion with 10 electrons *Mg ~12*
(b) a sulfur ion with 18 electrons *– 16* *0*
(c) an iron ion with 23 electrons *- 26*

Solution:
To determine the charge of each ion, we use the ion charge equation.

$$\text{Ion charge} = \#p - \#e^-$$

The number of electrons is given in the problem. The number of protons is obtained from the element's atomic number in the periodic table.

(a) magnesium with atomic number 12

$$\text{Ion charge} = \overset{P}{12} - \overset{E}{10} = 2+ \ (Mg^{2+})$$

(b) sulfur with atomic number 16

$$\text{Ion charge} = \overset{P}{16} - \overset{E}{18} = 2- \ (S^{2-})$$

(c) iron with atomic number 26

$$\text{Ion charge} = \overset{P}{26} - \overset{E}{23} = 3+ \ (Fe^{3+})$$

SKILLBUILDER 4.4   **Determining Ion Charge from Numbers of Protons and Electrons**

Determine the charge of each of the following ions.

(a) a nickel ion with 26 electrons *– 28-26 = 2+*
(b) a bromine ion with 36 electrons *– 36-35 = 1-*
(c) a phosphorus ion with 18 electrons *= 15-18 = 3-*

LIVE EXAMPLE

EXAMPLE 4.5   **Determining the Number of Protons and Electrons in an Ion**

Find the number of protons and electrons in the Ca^{2+} ion.

2 = 20 - e

From the periodic table, find that the atomic number for calcium is 20, so calcium has 20 protons. The number of electrons can be found using the ion charge equation.	**Solution:** *#e- = 20-2 = 18* $\text{Ion charge} = \#p - \#e^-$ $2+ = 20 - \#e^-$ $\#e^- = 20 - 2 = 18$

Therefore the number of electrons is 18. The Ca^{2+} ion has 20 protons and 18 electrons.

SKILLBUILDER 4.5   **Determining the Number of Protons and Electrons in an Ion**

Find the number of protons and electrons in the S^{2-} ion.   *2- = 16 #e-*   *16+2 = 18 neutron*

#e- = 16+2 = 18   *16 electrons*

⬤ Ions and the Periodic Table

We have learned that in chemical reactions metals have a tendency to lose electrons and nonmetals have a tendency to gain them. For many main-group elements, we can use the periodic table to predict how many electrons tend to be lost or gained. The number above each *main group* column in the periodic table—1 through 8–gives the number of *valence electrons* for the elements

▲ Figure 4.14 **Elements that form predictable ions**

An important exception to this rule is helium—it is in column 8A, but has only 2 valence electrons.

in that column. We discuss the concept of valence electrons more fully Chapter 9, but for now, think of valence electrons as the outermost electrons an atom. For example, since oxygen is in column 6A, we know it has 6 valen electrons; since magnesium is in column 2A, we know it has 2 valence ele trons, and so on. Valence electrons are particularly important because, as shall see in Chapter 10, it is these electrons that take part in chemical bondir

The key to predicting the charge acquired by a particular metal or no metal when it ionizes is as follows:

Main-group elements tend to form ions that have the same number of valence electrons as the nearest noble gas.

For example, the closest noble gas to oxygen is neon. When oxygen ioniz it acquires two additional electrons for a total of 8 valence electrons—the sai number as neon. The closest noble gas to magnesium is also neon. Therefc magnesium loses its 2 valence electrons to attain the same number of valen electrons as neon.

In accordance with this principle, the alkali metals (Group 1A) tend lose 1 electron and therefore form 1+ ions, while the alkaline earth met. (Group 2A) tend to lose 2 electrons and therefore form 2+ ions. The haloge (Group 7A) tend to gain 1 electron and therefore form 1− ions. The groups the periodic table that form predictable ions are shown in ▲ Figure 4.14 . familiar with these groups and the ions they form. In Chapter 9, we exami a theory that more fully explains why these groups form ions as they do.

EXAMPLE 4.6 **Charge of Ions from Position in Periodic Table**

Based on their position in the periodic table, what ions will barium and iodi tend to form?

Solution:
Since barium is in Group 2A, it will tend to form a cation with a 2+ charge (Ba^2
Since iodine is in Group 7A, it will tend to form an anion with a 1− charge (I

SKILLBUILDER 4.6 **Charge of Ions from Position in Periodic Table**

Based on their position in the periodic table, what ions will potassium a sulfur tend to form?

CONCEPTUAL CHECKPOINT 4.3

Which of these pairs of ions would have the same total number of electrons?

(a) Na^+ and Mg^{2+}
(b) F^- and Cl^-
(c) O^- and O^{2-}
(d) Ga^{3+} and Fe^{3+}

4.8 Isotopes: When the Number of Neutrons Varies

All atoms of a given element have the same number of protons; however, they do not necessarily have the same number of neutrons. Since neutrons have nearly the same mass as protons (1 amu), this means that—contrary to what John Dalton originally proposed in his atomic theory—all atoms of a given element *do not* have the same mass. For example, all neon atoms in nature contain 10 protons, but they may have 10, 11, or 12 neutrons (▼ Figure 4.15). All three types of neon atoms exist, and each has a slightly different mass. Atoms with the same number of protons but different numbers of neutrons are called **isotopes**. Some elements, such as beryllium (Be) and aluminum (Al), have only one naturally occurring isotope, while other elements, such as neon (Ne) and chlorine (Cl), have two or more.

Percent means "per hundred." 90.48% means that 90.48 atoms out of 100 are the isotope with 10 neutrons.

Fortunately, the relative amount of each different isotope in a naturally occurring sample of a given element is always the same. For example, in any natural sample of neon atoms, 90.48% of them are the isotope with 10 neutrons, 0.27% are the isotope with 11 neutrons, and 9.25% are the isotope with 12 neutrons. This means that out of 10,000 neon atoms, for example, 9048 have 10 neutrons, 27 have 11 neutrons, and 925 have 12 neutrons. These percentages are called the **percent natural abundance** of the isotopes. The preceding numbers are for neon, but all elements have their own unique percent natural abundance of isotopes.

The sum of the number of neutrons and protons in an atom is called the **mass number** and is given the symbol **A**.

▼ Figure 4.15 **Isotopes of neon** Naturally occurring neon contains three different isotopes, Ne-20 (with 10 neutrons), Ne-21 (with 11 neutrons), and Ne-22 (with 12 neutrons).

A = Number of protons + Number of neutrons

For neon, with 10 protons, the mass numbers of the three different naturally occurring isotopes are 20, 21, and 22, corresponding to 10, 11, and 12 neutrons, respectively.

● Ne-21
● Ne-22
● Ne-20

TABLE 4.2 Neon Isotopes

Symbol	Number of Protons	Number of Neutrons	A (Mass Number)	Percent Natural Abundance
Ne-20 or $^{20}_{10}$Ne	10	10	20	90.48%
Ne-21 or $^{21}_{10}$Ne	10	11	21	0.27%
Ne-22 or $^{22}_{10}$Ne	10	12	22	9.25%

Isotopes are often symbolized in the following way:

Mass number

Atomic number

$^{A}_{Z}$X

Chemical symbol

where X is the chemical symbol, A is the mass number, and Z is the atomic number.

For example, the symbols for the neon isotopes are:

$$^{20}_{10}\text{Ne} \quad ^{21}_{10}\text{Ne} \quad ^{22}_{10}\text{Ne}$$

Notice that the chemical symbol, Ne, and the atomic number, 10, are redundant: If the atomic number is 10, the symbol must be Ne, and vice versa. The mass numbers, however, are different, reflecting the different number of neutrons in each isotope.

A second common notation for isotopes is the chemical symbol (or chemical name) followed by a hyphen and the mass number of the isotope.

X—A

Chemical symbol or name

Mass number

In this notation, the neon isotopes are:

Ne-20   neon-20

Ne-21   neon-21

Ne-22   neon-22

We summarize what we have learned about the neon isotopes in Table 4.2.

Notice that all isotopes of a given element have the same number of protons (otherwise they would be a different element). Notice also that the mass number is the *sum* of the number of protons and the number of neutrons. The number of neutrons in an isotope is the difference between the mass number and the atomic number.

In general, mass number increases with increasing atomic number.

EXAMPLE 4.7 | **Atomic Numbers, Mass Numbers, and Isotope Symbols**

What are the atomic number (Z), mass number (A), and symbols of the carbon isotope with 7 neutrons?

Solution: $6+7=13$

From the periodic table, we find that the atomic number (Z) of carbon is 6, so carbon atoms have 6 protons. The mass number (A) for the isotope with 7 neutrons is the sum of the number of protons and the number of neutrons.

$$A = 6 + 7 = 13$$

So, Z = 6, A = 13, and the symbols for the isotope are C-13 and $^{13}_{6}$C.

SKILLBUILDER 4.7 Atomic Numbers, Mass Numbers, and Isotope Symbols

7 (handwritten) *14.01* (handwritten)

What are the atomic number, mass number, and symbols for the chlorine isotope with 18 neutrons?

17+18 = $^{35}_{17}Cl$ (handwritten)

EXAMPLE 4.8 Numbers of Protons and Neutrons from Isotope Symbols

How many protons and neutrons are in the following chromium isotope?

$^{52}_{24}Cr$ — proton / neutron (N−P) (handwritten)

The number of protons is equal to Z (lower left number).	**Solution:** $\#p = Z = 24$
The number of neutrons is equal to A (upper left number) − Z (lower left number).	$\#n = A - Z$ $= 52 - 24$ $= 28$

SKILLBUILDER 4.8 Numbers of Protons and Neutrons from Isotope Symbols

How many protons and neutrons are in the following potassium isotope?

$^{39}_{19}K$

39−19 = 20, P=19, N=20, p=19, N=20 (handwritten)

CONCEPTUAL CHECKPOINT 4.4

If an atom with a mass number of 27 has 14 neutrons, it must be an isotope of which element?

(a) silicon
(b) aluminum
(c) cobalt
(d) niobium

4.9 Atomic Mass

Some books call this average atomic mass or atomic weight instead of simply atomic mass.

An important part of Dalton's atomic theory was that all atoms of a given element have the same mass. However, we just learned that because of isotopes, the atoms of a given element may have different masses, so Dalton was not completely correct. We can, however, calculate an average mass—called the **atomic mass**—for each element. The atomic mass of each element is listed in the periodic table directly beneath the element's symbol; it represents the average mass of the atoms that compose that element. For example, the periodic table lists the atomic mass of chlorine as 35.45 amu. Naturally occurring chlorine consists of 75.77% chlorine-35 (mass 34.97 amu) and 24.23% chlorine-37 (mass 36.97 amu). Its atomic mass is:

$$\text{Atomic mass} = (0.7577 \times 34.97 \text{ amu}) + (0.2423 \times 36.97 \text{ amu})$$
$$= 35.45 \text{ amu}$$

Notice that the atomic mass of chlorine is closer to 35 than 37, because naturally occurring chlorine contains more chlorine-35 atoms than chlorine-37 atoms. Notice also that when percentages are used in calculations, they must always be converted to their decimal value. To convert a percentage to its decimal value, simply divide by 100. For example:

$$75.77\% = 75.77/100 = 0.7577$$
$$24.23\% = 24.23/100 = 0.2423$$

Chemistry IN THE ENVIRONMENT

Radioactive Isotopes at Hanford, Washington

Nuclei of the isotopes of a given element are not all equally stable. For example, naturally occurring lead is composed primarily of Pb-206, Pb-207, and Pb-208. Other isotopes of lead also exist, but their nuclei are unstable. Scientists can make some of these other isotopes, such as Pb-185, in the laboratory. However, within seconds of their synthesis, Pb-185 atoms emit a few energetic subatomic particles from their nuclei and change into different isotopes of different elements (which are themselves unstable). These emitted subatomic particles are called **nuclear radiation**, and the isotopes that emit them are termed **radioactive**. Nuclear radiation, always associated with unstable nuclei, can be harmful to humans and other living organisms because the energetic particles interact with and damage biological molecules. Some isotopes, such as Pb-185, emit significant amounts of radiation only for a very short time. Others, however, remain radioactive for a long time—in some cases millions or even billions of years.

The nuclear power and nuclear weapons industries both produce by-products containing unstable isotopes of several different elements. Many of these isotopes emit nuclear radiation for a long time, and their disposal is an environmental problem. For example, in Hanford, Washington, which for fifty years produced fuel for nuclear weapons, 177 underground storage tanks contain 55 million gallons of high-level nuclear waste. Certain radioactive isotopes within that waste will produce nuclear radiation for the foreseeable future. Unfortunately, some of the underground storage tanks are aging and leaks have allowed some of the waste to seep into the environment. While the danger from short-term external exposure to this waste is minimal, ingestion of the waste through contamination of drinking water or food supplies would pose significant health risks. Consequently, Hanford is now the site of the largest environmental cleanup project in U.S. history. The U.S. government expects the project to take more than twenty years and cost about $10 billion.

Radioactive isotopes are not always harmful, however, and many have beneficial uses. For example, technetium-99 (Tc-99) is often given to patients to diagnose disease. The radiation emitted by Tc-99 helps doctors image internal organs or detect infection.

CAN YOU ANSWER THIS? *Give the number of neutrons in each of the following isotopes: Pb-206, Pb-207, Pb-208, Pb-185, Tc-99.*

▲ Storage tanks at Hanford, Washington, contain 55 million gallons of high-level nuclear waste. Each tank pictured here holds 1 million gallons.

In general, the atomic mass is calculated according to the following equation:

$$\textbf{Atomic mass} = (\textbf{Fraction of isotope 1} \times \textbf{Mass of isotope 1}) +$$
$$(\textbf{Fraction of isotope 2} \times \textbf{Mass of isotope 2}) +$$
$$(\textbf{Fraction of isotope 3} \times \textbf{Mass of isotope 3}) + \cdots$$

where the fractions of each isotope are the percent natural abundances converted to their decimal values. Atomic mass is useful because it allows us to assign a characteristic mass to each element, and as we will see in Chapter 6, it allows us to quantify the number of atoms in a sample of that element.

EXAMPLE 4.9   Calculating Atomic Mass

Gallium has two naturally occurring isotopes: Ga-69 with mass 68.9256 amu and a natural abundance of 60.11%, and Ga-71 with mass 70.9247 amu and a natural abundance of 39.89%. Calculate the atomic mass of gallium.

Convert the percent natural abundances into decimal form by dividing by 100.	**Solution:** $$\text{Fraction Ga-69} = \frac{60.11}{100} = 0.6011$$ $$\text{Fraction Ga-71} = \frac{39.89}{100} = 0.3989$$
Use the fractional abundances and the atomic masses of the isotopes to compute the atomic mass according to the atomic mass definition given earlier.	$$\begin{aligned}\text{Atomic mass} &= (0.6011 \times 68.9256 \text{ amu}) \\ &\quad + (0.3989 \times 70.9247 \text{ amu}) \\ &= 41.4312 \text{ amu} + 28.2919 \text{ amu} \\ &= 69.7231 = 69.72 \text{ amu}\end{aligned}$$

SKILLBUILDER 4.9   Calculating Atomic Mass

Magnesium has three naturally occurring isotopes with masses of 23.99, 24.99, 25.98 amu and natural abundances of 78.99%, 10.00%, and 11.01%. Calculate the atomic mass of magnesium.

CHAPTER IN REVIEW

Chemical Principles

Relevance

The Atomic Theory: Democritus, an ancient Greek philosopher, is the first person on record to assert that matter is ultimately composed of small, indestructible particles. It was not until 2000 years later, however, that John Dalton introduced a formal atomic theory stating that matter is composed of atoms; atoms of a given element have unique properties that distinguish them from atoms of other elements; and atoms combine in simple, whole-number ratios to form compounds.

The Atomic Theory: The concept of atoms is important because it explains the physical world. You and everything you see are made of atoms. To understand the physical world, we must begin by understanding atoms. Atoms are the key concept—they determine the properties of matter.

Discovery of the Atom's Nucleus: Rutherford's gold foil experiment probed atomic structure and his results led to the nuclear model of the atom, which, with minor modifications to accommodate neutrons, is still valid today. In this model, the atom is composed of protons and neutrons—which compose most of the atom's mass and are grouped together in a dense nucleus—and electrons, which compose most of the atom's volume. Protons and neutrons have similar masses (1 amu) while electrons have a much smaller mass (≈ 0 amu).

Discovery of the Atom's Nucleus: We can see wh this is relevant by asking, what if it were otherwise What if matter were *not* mostly empty space? While w cannot know for certain, it seems probable that suc matter would not form the diversity of substances re quired for life—and then, of course, we would not b around to ask the question.

Charge: Protons and electrons both have electrical charge; the charge of the proton is +1 and the charge of the electron is −1. The neutron has no charge. When protons and electrons combine in atoms, their charges cancel.

Charge: Electrical charge is relevant to much of ou modern world. Many of the machines and computer we depend on are powered by electricity, which is sim ply the movement of electrical charge.

The Periodic Table: The periodic table tabulates all known elements in order of increasing atomic number. The periodic table is arranged so that similar elements are grouped in columns. Elements on the left side of the periodic table are metals and tend to lose electrons in their chemical changes. Elements on the upper right side of the periodic table are nonmetals and tend to gain electrons in their chemical changes. Elements between the two are called metalloids. Columns of elements in the periodic table have similar properties and are called groups or families.

The Periodic Table: The periodic table helps us orga nize the elements in ways that allow us to predict the properties. Helium, for example, is not toxic in sma amounts because it is an inert gas—it does not reac with anything. The gases in the column below it on th periodic table are also inert gases and form a family o group of elements called the noble gases. By tabulatin the elements and grouping similar ones together, w begin to understand their properties.

Atomic Number: The most fundamental characteristic of an atom is the number of protons in its nucleus; this number is called the atomic number (Z) and defines the element.

Ions: When an atom gains or loses electrons it becomes an ion. Positively charged ions are called cations and negatively charged ions are called anions. Cations and anions occur together so that matter is ordinarily charge-neutral.

Isotopes: While all atoms of a given element have the same number of protons, they do not necessarily have the same number of neutrons. Atoms of the same element with different numbers of neutrons are called isotopes. Isotopes are characterized by their mass number (A), the sum of the number of protons and the number of neutrons in their nucleus.

Each naturally occurring sample of an element has the same percent natural abundance of each isotope. These percentages, together with the mass of each isotope, are used to compute the atomic mass of the element, a weighted average of the masses of the individual isotopes.

Isotopes: Isotopes are relevant because they influenc tabulated atomic masses. To understand these masse we must understand the presence and abundance o isotopes. In nuclear processes—processes in which th nuclei of atoms actually change—the presence of diffe ent isotopes becomes even more important. Some iso topes are not stable—they lose subatomic particles an are transformed into other elements. The emission o subatomic particles by unstable nuclei is called r. dioactive decay. In many situations, such as in diagno ing and treating certain diseases, nuclear radiation extremely useful. In other situations, such as in the di posal of radioactive waste, it can pose environment problems.

Chemical Skills

Examples

Determining Ion Charge from Numbers of Protons and Electrons (Section 4.7)

- From the periodic table or from the alphabetical list of elements, find the atomic number of the element; this number is equal to the number of protons.
- Use the ion charge equation to compute charge.

$$\text{Ion charge} = \#p - \#e^-$$

| **EXAMPLE 4.10** | **Determining Ion Charge from Numbers of Protons and Electrons** |

Determine the charge of a selenium ion with 36 electrons.

Solution:
Selenium is atomic number 34; therefore it has 34 protons.

$$\text{Ion charge} = 34 - 36 = -2$$

Determining the Number of Protons and Electrons in an Ion (Section 4.7)

- From the periodic table or from the alphabetical list of elements, find the atomic number of the element; this number is equal to the number of protons.
- Use the ion charge equation and substitute in the known values.

$$\text{Ion charge} = \#p - \#e^-$$

- Solve the equation for the number of electrons.

| **EXAMPLE 4.11** | **Determining the Number of Protons and Electrons in an Ion** |

Find the number of protons and electrons in the O^{2-} ion.

Solution:
The atomic number of O is 8; therefore it has 8 protons.

$$\text{Ion charge} = \#p - \#e^-$$
$$-2 = 8 - \#e^-$$
$$\#e^- = 8 + 2 = 10$$

The ion has 8 protons and 10 electrons.

Determining Atomic Numbers, Mass Numbers, and Isotope Symbols for an Isotope (Section 4.8)

- From the periodic table or from the alphabetical list of elements, find the atomic number of the element.
- The mass number (A) is equal to the atomic number plus the number of neutrons.
- Write the symbol for the isotope by writing the symbol for the element with the mass number in the upper left corner and the atomic number in the lower left corner.
- The other symbol for the isotope is simply the chemical symbol followed by a hyphen and the mass number.

| **EXAMPLE 4.12** | **Determining Atomic Numbers, Mass Numbers, and Isotope Symbols for an Isotope** |

What are the atomic number (Z), mass number (A), and symbols for the iron isotope with 30 neutrons?

Solution:
The atomic number of iron is 26.

$$A = 26 + 30 = 56$$

The mass number is 56.

$$^{56}_{26}\text{Fe}$$

Fe-56

Number of Protons and Neutrons from Isotope Symbols (Section 4.8)

- The number of protons is equal to Z (lower left number).
- The number of neutrons is equal to A (upper left number) − Z (lower left number).

| **EXAMPLE 4.13** | **Number of Protons and Neutrons from Isotope Symbols** |

How many protons and neutrons are in $^{62}_{28}\text{Ni}$?

Solution:
28 protons

$$\#n = 62 - 28 = 34 \text{ neutrons}$$

Calculating Atomic Mass from Percent Natural Abundances and Isotopic Masses (Section 4.9)

- Convert the natural abundances from percent to decimal values by dividing by 100.

- Find the atomic mass by multiplying the fractions of each isotope by their respective masses and adding.

- Round to the correct number of significant figures.
- Check your work.

LIVE EXAMPLE

EXAMPLE 4.14   Calculating Atomic Mass from Percent Natural Abundances and Isotopic Masses

Copper has two naturally occurring isotopes: Cu-63 with mass 62.9395 amu and a natural abundance of 69.17%, and Cu-65 with mass 64.9278 amu and a natural abundance of 30.83%. Calculate the atomic mass of copper.

Solution:

$$\text{Fraction Cu-63} = \frac{69.17}{100} = 0.6917$$

$$\text{Fraction Cu-65} = \frac{30.83}{100} = 0.3083$$

$$\text{Atomic mass} = (0.6917 \times 62.9395 \text{ amu})$$
$$+ (0.3083 \times 64.9278 \text{ amu})$$
$$= 43.5353 \text{ amu} + 20.0107 \text{ amu}$$
$$= 63.5460 \text{ amu}$$
$$= 63.55 \text{ amu}$$

Key Terms

alkali metals [4.6]
alkaline earth metals [4.6]
anions [4.7]
atomic mass [4.9]
atomic mass unit (amu) [4.4]
atomic number (Z) [4.5]
cations [4.7]
charge [4.4]
chemical symbol [4.5]

electron [4.3]
family (of elements) [4.6]
group (of elements) [4.6]
halogens [4.6]
ions [4.7]
isotopes [4.8]
main-group elements [4.6]
mass number (A) [4.8]
metalloids [4.6]

metals [4.6]
neutrons [4.3]
noble gases [4.6]
nonmetals [4.6]
nuclear radiation [4.9]
nuclear theory of the atom [4.3]
nucleus [4.3]
percent natural abundance [4.8]

periodic law [4.6]
periodic table [4.6]
protons [4.3]
radioactive [4.8]
semiconductor [4.6]
transition elements [4.6]
transition metals [4.6]

Exercises

Questions

1. Why is it important to understand atoms?
2. What is an atom?
3. What did Democritus contribute to our modern understanding of matter?
4. What are three main ideas in Dalton's atomic theory?
5. Describe Rutherford's gold foil experiment and the results of that experiment. How did these results contradict the plum pudding model of the atom?
6. What are the main ideas in the nuclear theory of the atom?
7. List the three subatomic particles and their properties.
8. What is electrical charge?
9. Is matter usually charge-neutral? How would matter be different if it were not charge-neutral?

10. What does the atomic number of an element specify?
11. What is a chemical symbol?
12. Give some examples of how elements got their names.
13. What was Dmitri Mendeleev's main contribution to our modern understanding of chemistry?
14. What is the main idea in the periodic law?
15. How is the periodic table organized?
16. What are the properties of metals? Where are metals found on the periodic table?
17. What are the properties of nonmetals? Where are nonmetals found on the periodic table?
18. Where on the periodic table do you find metalloids?
19. What is a family or group of elements?

20. Locate each of the following on the periodic table and give their group number.
   (a) alkali metals
   (b) alkaline earth metals
   (c) halogens
   (d) noble gases
21. What is an ion?
22. What is an anion? What is a cation?
23. Locate each of the following groups on the periodic table and list the charge of the ions they tend to form.
   (a) Group 1A
   (b) Group 2A
   (c) Group 3A
   (d) Group 6A
   (e) Group 7A
24. What are isotopes?
25. What is the percent natural abundance of isotopes?
26. What is the mass number of an isotope?
27. What notations are commonly used to specify isotopes? What do each of the numbers in these symbols mean?
28. What is the atomic mass of an element?

Problems

Atomic and Nuclear Theory

29. Which of the following statements are *inconsistent* with Dalton's atomic theory as it was originally stated? Why?
   (a) All carbon atoms are identical.
   (b) Helium atoms can be split into two hydrogen atoms.
   (c) An oxygen atom combines with 1.5 hydrogen atoms to form water molecules.
   (d) Two oxygen atoms combine with a carbon atom to form carbon dioxide molecules.

30. Which of the following statements are *consistent* with Dalton's atomic theory as it was originally stated? Why?
   (a) Calcium and titanium atoms have the same mass.
   (b) Neon and argon atoms are the same.
   (c) All cobalt atoms are identical.
   (d) Sodium and chlorine atoms combine in a 1:1 ratio to form sodium chloride.

31. Which of the following statements are *inconsistent* with Rutherford's nuclear theory as it was originally stated? Why?
   (a) Helium atoms have two protons in the nucleus and two electrons outside the nucleus.
   (b) Most of the volume of hydrogen atoms is due to the nucleus.
   (c) Aluminum atoms have 13 protons in the nucleus and 22 electrons outside the nucleus.
   (d) The majority of the mass of nitrogen atoms is due to their 7 electrons.

32. Which of the following statements are *consistent* with Rutherford's nuclear theory as it was originally stated? Why?
   (a) Atomic nuclei are small compared to the size of atoms.
   (b) The volume of an atom is mostly empty space.
   (c) Neutral potassium atoms contain more protons than electrons.
   (d) Neutral potassium atoms contain more neutrons than protons.

Protons, Neutrons, and Electrons

33. Which of the following statements about electrons are true?
   (a) Electrons repel each other.
   (b) Electrons are attracted to protons.
   (c) Some electrons have a charge of −1 and some have no charge.
   (d) Electrons are much lighter than neutrons.

34. Which of the following statements about electrons are false?
   (a) Most atoms have more electrons than protons.
   (b) Electrons have a charge of −1.
   (c) If an atom has an equal number of protons and electrons, it will be charge-neutral.
   (d) Electrons experience an attraction to protons.

35. Which of the following statements about protons are true?
   (a) Protons have twice the mass of neutrons.
   (b) Protons have the same magnitude of charge as electrons, but are opposite in sign.
   (c) Most atoms have more protons than electrons.
   (d) Protons have a charge of +1.

36. Which of the following statements about protons are false?
   (a) Protons have about the same mass as neutrons.
   (b) Protons have about the same mass as electrons.
   (c) Some atoms don't have any protons.
   (d) Protons have the magnitude of charge as neutrons, but opposite in sign.

37. How many electrons would it take to equal the mass of a proton?

38. A helium nucleus has two protons and two neutrons. How many electrons would it take to equal the mass of a helium nucleus?

39. What mass of electrons would be required to just neutralize the charge of 1.0 g of protons?

40. What mass of protons would be required to just neutralize the charge of 1.0 g of electrons?

Elements, Symbols, and Names

41. Find the atomic number (Z) for each of the following elements.
    (a) Co
    (b) Ir
    (c) U
    (d) Si
    (e) Be

42. Find the atomic number (Z) for each of the following elements.
    (a) Al
    (b) Sn
    (c) Ca
    (d) Fr
    (e) Xe

43. How many protons are in the nucleus of each of the following atoms?
    (a) Mn
    (b) Ag
    (c) Au
    (d) Pb
    (e) S

44. How many protons are in the nucleus of each of the following atoms?
    (a) Y
    (b) N
    (c) Ne
    (d) K
    (e) Mo

45. Give the symbol and atomic number corresponding to each of the following elements.
    (a) carbon
    (b) nitrogen
    (c) sodium
    (d) potassium
    (e) copper

46. Give the symbol and atomic number corresponding to each of the following elements.
    (a) boron
    (b) neon
    (c) silver
    (d) mercury
    (e) curium

47. Give the name and the atomic number corresponding to the symbol for each of the following elements.
    (a) Au
    (b) Si
    (c) Ni
    (d) Zn
    (e) W

48. Give the name and the atomic number corresponding to the symbol for each of the following elements.
    (a) Ta
    (b) H
    (c) S
    (d) As
    (e) Br

49. Fill in the blanks to complete the following table.

Element Name	Element Symbol	Atomic Number
_____	Au	79
Tin	_____	_____
_____	As	_____
Copper	_____	29
_____	Fe	_____
_____	_____	80

50. Fill in the blanks to complete the following table.

Element Name	Element Symbol	Atomic Number
_____	Al	13
Iodine	_____	_____
_____	Sb	_____
Sodium	_____	_____
_____	Rn	86
_____	_____	82

The Periodic Table

51. Classify each of the following elements as a metal, nonmetal, or metalloid.
    (a) Sr
    (b) Mg
    (c) F
    (d) N
    (e) As

52. Classify each of the following elements as a metal, nonmetal, or metalloid.
    (a) Na
    (b) Ge
    (c) Si
    (d) Br
    (e) Ag

53. Which of the following elements would you expect to lose electrons in chemical changes?
    (a) potassium
    (b) sulfur
    (c) fluorine
    (d) barium
    (e) copper

54. Which of the following elements would you expect to gain electrons in chemical changes?
    (a) nitrogen
    (b) iodine
    (c) tungsten
    (d) strontium
    (e) gold

55. Which of the following elements are main-group elements?
    (a) Te
    (b) K
    (c) V
    (d) Re
    (e) Ag

56. Which of the following elements are *not* main-group elements?
    (a) Al
    (b) Br
    (c) Mo
    (d) Cs
    (e) Pb

57. Which of the following elements are alkaline earth metals?
    (a) sodium
    (b) aluminum
    (c) calcium
    (d) barium
    (e) lithium

58. Which of the following elements are alkaline earth metals?
    (a) rubidium
    (b) tungsten
    (c) magnesium
    (d) cesium
    (e) beryllium

59. Which of the following elements are alkali metals?
    (a) sodium
    (b) potassium
    (c) silver
    (d) magnesium
    (e) cesium

60. Which of the following elements are alkali metals?
    (a) barium
    (b) niobium
    (c) lithium
    (d) rubidium
    (e) calcium

61. Classify each of the following as a halogen, a noble gas, or neither.
    (a) Cl
    (b) Kr
    (c) F
    (d) Ga
    (e) He

62. Classify each of the following as a halogen, a noble gas, or neither.
    (a) Ne
    (b) Br
    (c) S
    (d) Xe
    (e) I

63. To what group number does each of the following elements belong?
    (a) oxygen
    (b) aluminum
    (c) silicon
    (d) tin
    (e) phosphorus

64. To what group number does each of the following elements belong?
    (a) germanium
    (b) nitrogen
    (c) sulfur
    (d) carbon
    (e) boron

65. Which of the following elements do you expect to be most like sulfur? Why?
    (a) nitrogen
    (b) oxygen
    (c) fluorine
    (d) lithium
    (e) potassium

66. Which of the following elements do you expect to be most like magnesium? Why?
    (a) potassium
    (b) silver
    (c) bromine
    (d) calcium
    (e) lead

67. Which of the following pairs of elements do you expect to be most similar? Why?
    (a) Si and P
    (b) Cl and F
    (c) Na and Mg
    (d) Mo and Sn
    (e) N and Ni

68. Which of the following pairs of elements do you expect to be most similar? Why?
    (a) Ti and Ga
    (b) N and O
    (c) Li and Na
    (d) Ar and Br
    (e) Ge and Ga

69. Fill in the blanks to complete the following table.

Chemical Symbol	Group Number	Group Name	Metal or Nonmetal
K	____	____	metal
Br	____	halogens	____
Sr	____	____	____
He	8A	____	____
Ar	____	____	____

70. Fill in the blanks to complete the following table.

Chemical Symbol	Group Number	Group Name	Metal or Nonmetal
Cl	7A	____	____
Ca	____	____	metal
Xe	____	____	nonmetal
Na	____	alkali metal	____
F	____	____	____

Ions

71. Complete each of the following.
    (a) $Na \longrightarrow Na^+ +$ _____
    (b) $O + 2e^- \longrightarrow$ _____
    (c) $Ca \longrightarrow Ca^{2+} +$ _____
    (d) $Cl + e^- \longrightarrow$ _____

72. Complete each of the following.
    (a) $Mg \longrightarrow$ _____ $+ 2e^-$
    (b) $Ba \longrightarrow Ba^{2+} +$ _____
    (c) $I + e^- \longrightarrow$ _____
    (d) $Al \longrightarrow$ _____ $+ 3e^-$

73. Determine the charge of each of the following ions.
    (a) oxygen ion with 10 electrons
    (b) aluminum ion with 10 electrons
    (c) titanium ion with 18 electrons
    (d) iodine ion with 54 electrons

74. Determine the charge of each of the following ions.
    (a) tungsten ion with 68 electrons
    (b) tellurium ion with 54 electrons
    (c) nitrogen ion with 10 electrons
    (d) barium ion with 54 electrons

75. Determine the number of protons and electrons in each of the following ions.
    (a) K^+
    (b) S^{2-}
    (c) Sr^{2+}
    (d) Cr^{3+}

76. Determine the number of protons and electrons in each of the following.
    (a) Ga^{3+}
    (b) Se^{2-}
    (c) Al^{3+}
    (d) Br^-

77. Determine whether each of the following is true or false. If false, correct it.
    (a) The Ti^{2+} ion contains 22 protons and 24 electrons.
    (b) The I^- ion contains 53 protons and 54 electrons.
    (c) The Mg^{2+} ion contains 14 protons and 12 electrons.
    (d) The O^{2-} ion contains 8 protons and 10 electrons.

78. Determine whether each of the following is true or false. If false, correct it.
    (a) The Fe^+ ion contains 29 protons and 26 electrons.
    (b) The Cs^+ ion contains 55 protons and 56 electrons.
    (c) The Se^{2-} ion contains 32 protons and 34 electrons.
    (d) The Li^+ ion contains 3 protons and 2 electrons.

79. Predict the ion formed by each of the following:
    (a) Rb
    (b) K
    (c) Al
    (d) O

80. Predict the ion formed by each of the following:
    (a) F
    (b) N
    (c) Mg
    (d) Na

81. Predict how many electrons will most likely be gained or lost by each of the following:
    (a) Ga
    (b) Li
    (c) Br
    (d) S

82. Predict how many electrons will most likely be gained or lost by each of the following:
    (a) I
    (b) Ba
    (c) Cs
    (d) Se

83. Fill in the blanks to complete the following table.

Symbol	Ion Commonly Formed	Number of Electrons in Ion	Number of Protons in Ion
Te	___	54	___
In	___	___	49
Sr	Sr^{2+}	___	___
___	Mg^{2+}	___	12
Cl	___	___	___

84. Fill in the blanks to complete the following table.

Symbol	Ion Commonly Formed	Number of Electrons in Ion	Number of Protons in Ion
F	___	___	9
___	Be^{2+}	2	___
Br	___	36	___
Al	___	___	13
O	___	___	___

Isotopes

85. What are the atomic number and mass number for each of the following isotopes?
(a) the hydrogen isotope with 1 neutron
(b) the chromium isotope with 27 neutrons
(c) the calcium isotope with 20 neutrons
(d) the tantalum isotope with 108 neutrons

86. How many neutrons are in an atom with the following atomic numbers and mass numbers?
(a) $Z = 28$, $A = 58$
(b) $Z = 92$, $A = 238$
(c) $Z = 21$, $A = 45$
(d) $Z = 18$, $A = 40$

87. Write isotopic symbols of the form $^A_Z X$ for each of the following isotopes.
(a) the oxygen isotope with 8 neutrons
(b) the fluorine isotope with 10 neutrons
(c) the sodium isotope with 12 neutrons
(d) the aluminum isotope with 14 neutrons

88. Write isotopic symbols of the form X-A (for example, C-13) for each of the following isotopes.
(a) the iodine isotope with 74 neutrons
(b) the phosphorus isotope with 16 neutrons
(c) the uranium isotope with 234 neutrons
(d) the argon isotope with 22 neutrons

89. Write the symbol of each of the following in the form $^A_Z X$.
(a) cobalt-60
(b) neon-22
(c) iodine-131
(d) plutonium-244

90. Write the symbol of each of the following in the form $^A_Z X$.
(a) U-235
(b) V-52
(c) P-32
(d) Xe-144

91. Determine the number of protons and neutrons in each of the following:
(a) $^{23}_{11}Na$ (b) $^{266}_{88}Ra$
(c) $^{208}_{82}Pb$ (d) $^{14}_{7}N$

92. Determine the number of protons and neutrons in each of the following:
(a) $^{33}_{15}P$ (b) $^{40}_{19}K$
(c) $^{222}_{86}Rn$ (d) $^{99}_{43}Tc$

93. Carbon-14, present within living organisms and substances derived from living organisms, is often used to establish the age of fossils and artifacts. Determine the number of protons and neutrons in a carbon-14 isotope and write its symbol in the form $^A_Z X$.

94. Plutonium-239 is used in nuclear bombs. Determine the number of protons and neutrons in plutonium-239 and write its symbol in the form $^A_Z X$.

Atomic Mass

95. Rubidium has two naturally occurring isotopes: Rb-85 with mass 84.9118 amu and a natural abundance of 72.17%, and Rb-87 with mass 86.9092 amu and a natural abundance of 27.83%. Calculate the atomic mass of rubidium.

96. Silicon has three naturally occurring isotopes: Si-28 with mass 27.9769 amu and a natural abundance of 92.21%, Si-29 with mass 28.9765 amu and a natural abundance of 4.69%, and Si-30 with mass 29.9737 amu and a natural abundance of 3.10%. Calculate the atomic mass of silicon.

97. Bromine has two naturally occurring isotopes (Br-79 and Br-81) and an atomic mass of 79.904 amu.
(a) If the natural abundance of Br-79 is 50.69%, what is the natural abundance of Br-81?
(b) If the mass of Br-81 is 80.9163 amu, what is the mass of Br-79?

98. Silver has two naturally occurring isotopes (Ag-107 and Ag-109).
(a) Use the periodic table to find the atomic mass of silver.
(b) If the natural abundance of Ag-107 is 51.84%, what is the natural abundance of Ag-109?
(c) If the mass of Ag-107 is 106.905, what is the mass of Ag-109?

99. An element has two naturally occurring isotopes. Isotope 1 has a mass of 120.9038 amu and a relative abundance of 57.4%, and isotope 2 has a mass of 122.9042 amu and a relative abundance of 42.6%. Find the atomic mass of this element and, by comparison to the periodic table, identify it.

100. Copper has two naturally occurring isotopes. Cu-63 has a mass of 62.939 amu and relative abundance of 69.17%. Use the atomic weight of copper to determine the mass of the other copper isotope.

Cumulative Problems

101. Electrical charge is sometimes reported in coulombs (C). On this scale, 1 electron has a charge of -1.6×10^{-19} C. Suppose your body acquires -125 mC (millicoulombs) of charge on a dry day. How many excess electrons has it acquired? (Hint: Use the charge of an electron in coulombs as a conversion factor between charge and electrons.)

102. How many excess protons are in a positively charged object with a charge of $+398$ mC (millicoulombs)? The charge of 1 proton is $+1.6 \times 10^{-19}$ C.

103. The hydrogen atom contains 1 proton and 1 electron. The radius of the proton is approximately 1.0 fm (femtometers) and the radius of the hydrogen atom is approximately 53 pm (picometers). Calculate the volume of the nucleus and the volume of the atom for hydrogen. What percentage of the hydrogen atom's volume is occupied by the nucleus?

104. Carbon-12 contains 6 protons and 6 neutrons. The radius of the nucleus is approximately 2.7 fm and the radius of the atom is approximately 70 pm. Calculate the volume of the nucleus and the volume of the atom. What percentage of the carbon atom's volume is occupied by the nucleus?

105. Prepare a table such as Table 4.2 for the four different isotopes of Sr that have the following natural abundances and masses.

Sr-84	0.56%	83.9134 amu
Sr-86	9.86%	85.9093 amu
Sr-87	7.00%	86.9089 amu
Sr-88	82.58%	87.9056 amu

Use your table and the preceding atomic masses to calculate the atomic mass of strontium.

106. Determine the number of protons and neutrons in each of the following isotopes of chromium and use the following natural abundances and masses to calculate its atomic mass.

Cr-50	4.345%	49.9460 amu
Cr-52	83.89%	51.9405 amu
Cr-53	9.50%	52.9407 amu
Cr-54	2.365%	53.9389 amu

107. Fill in the blanks to complete the following table.

Symbol	Z	A	Number of Protons	Number of Electrons	Number of Neutrons	Charge
Zn^+	_	_	_	_	34	1+
_	25	55	_	22	_	_
_	_	_	15	15	16	_
O^{2-}	_	16	_	_	_	2-
_	_	_	16	18	18	_

108. Fill in the blanks to complete the following table.

Symbol	Z	A	Number of Protons	Number of Electrons	Number of Neutrons	Charge
Mg^{2+}	_	25	_	_	13	2+
_	22	48	_	18	_	_
_	16	_	_	_	16	2-
Ga^{3+}	_	71	_	_	_	_
_	_	_	82	80	125	_

109. Europium has two naturally occurring isotopes: Eu-151 with a mass of 150.9198 and a natural abundance of 47.8%, and Eu-153. Use the atomic mass of europium to find the mass and natural abundance of Eu-153.

110. Rhenium has two naturally occurring isotopes: Re-185 with a natural abundance of 37.40%, and Re-187 with a natural abundance of 62.60%. The sum of the masses of the two isotopes is 371.9087 amu. Find the masses of the individual isotopes.

111. In Chapter 1, we learned the difference between observations, laws, and theories. Give two examples of theories from this chapter and explain why they are theories.

112. In Chapter 1, we learned the difference between observations, laws, and theories. Give one example of a law from this chapter and explain why it is a law.

Highlight Problems

113. The figure is a representation of fifty atoms of a fictitious element with the symbol Nt and atomic number 120. Nt has three isotopes represented by the following colors: Nt-304 (red), Nt-305 (blue), and Nt-306 (green).

(a) Assuming that the figure is statistically representative of naturally occurring Nt, what is the percent natural abundance of each Nt isotope?

(b) Use the following masses of each isotope to calculate the atomic mass of Nt. Then draw a box for the element similar to the boxes for each element shown in the periodic table in the inside front cover of this book. Make sure your box includes the atomic number, symbol, and atomic mass. (Assume that the percentages from part (a) are good to four significant figures)

Nt-304   303.956 amu

Nt-305   304.962 amu

Nt-306   305.978 amu

114. Neutron stars are believed to be composed of solid nuclear matter, primarily neutrons.

(a) If the radius of a neutron is 1.0×10^{-13} cm, calculate the density of a neutron in g/cm^3. (volume of a sphere $= \frac{4}{3}\pi r^3$)

(b) Assuming that a neutron star has the same density as a neutron, calculate the mass in kilograms of a small piece of a neutron star the size of a spherical pebble with a radius of 0.10 mm.

Answers to Skillbuilder Exercises

Skillbuilder 4.1 (a) sodium, 11 (b) nickel, 28
(c) phosphorus, 15 (d) tantalum, 73

Skillbuilder 4.2 (a) nonmetal (b) nonmetal
(c) metal (d) metalloid

Skillbuilder 4.3 (a) alkali metal (b) Group 3A
(c) halogen (d) noble gas

Skillbuilder 4.4 (a) +2 (b) −1 (c) −3

Skillbuilder 4.5 16 protons, 18 electrons

Skillbuilder 4.6 K^+ and S^{2-}

Skillbuilder 4.7 $Z = 17$, $A = 35$, Cl-35 and $^{35}_{17}Cl$

Skillbuilder 4.8 19 protons, 20 neutrons

Skillbuilder 4.9 24.31 amu

Answers to Conceptual Checkpoints

4.1 (c) The mass in amu is approximately equal to the number of protons plus the number of neutrons. In order to be charge-neutral, the number of protons must equal the number of electrons.

4.2 (b) All of the metalloids are main-group elements (see Figures 4.12 and 4.13).

4.3 (a) Both these ions have 10 electrons.

4.4 (b) This atom must have $(27 - 14) = 13$ protons; the element with an atomic number of 13 is Al.

PART
2
Nat'l
people
flex-sc
dental/
$150-$2
train.
Please e

CLAIM
No exp n
Data Entry
Full trainin
vided.   Co
800-819-93

Own a c
Put it f
$3500-$7
www.wile
1-800-343-8

Wanted: 5 teac
starters to w
home. Step-by
train.

Across

1. A type of sugar
16. Element N
26. Thirsty?
42. Part of water
51. Not real sugar
66. _____ composition

bby

may
mer
r

ANSWE

CHAPTER 5

Molecules and Compounds

"Almost all aspects of life are engineered at the molecular level, and without understanding molecules, we can only have a very sketchy understanding of life itself."

Francis Harry Compton Crick (1916–2004)

5.1   Sugar and Salt

Sodium, a shiny metal (▼ Figure 5.1) that dulls almost instantly upon exposure to air, is extremely reactive and poisonous. If you were to consume any appreciable amount of elemental sodium, you would need immediate medical help. Chlorine, a pale yellow gas (▼ Figure 5.2), is equally reactive and poisonous. Yet the compound formed from these two elements, sodium chloride, is the

◀ Ordinary table sugar is a compound called sucrose. A sucrose molecule, such as the one shown here, contains carbon, hydrogen, and oxygen atoms. However, the properties of sucrose are very different from those of carbon, hydrogen, and oxygen. The properties of a compound are, in general, different from the properties of the elements that compose it.

▲ Figure 5.1   Elemental sodium
Sodium is an exremely reactive metal that dulls almost instantly upon exposure to air.

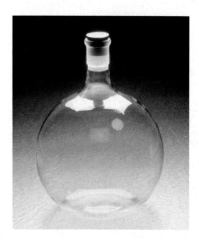

▲ Figure 5.2   Elemental chlorine
Chlorine is a yellow gas with a pungent odor. It is highly reactive and poisonous.

117

▶ Figure 5.3 **Sodium chloride** The compound formed by sodium and chlorine is table salt.

relatively harmless flavor enhancer that we call table salt (▲ Figure 5.3). When elements combine to form compounds, their properties change completely.

Consider ordinary sugar. Sugar is a compound composed of carbon, hydrogen, and oxygen. Each of these elements has its own unique properties. Carbon is most familiar to us as the graphite found in pencils or as the diamonds in jewelry. Hydrogen is an extremely flammable gas used as a fuel for the space shuttle, and oxygen is one of the gases that compose air. When these three elements combine to form sugar, however, a sweet, white, crystalline solid results.

In Chapter 4, we learned how protons, neutrons, and electrons compose different elements, each with its own properties and its own chemistry, each different from the other. In this chapter, we learn how these elements combine with each other to form different compounds, each with its own properties and its own chemistry, each different from all the others and different from the elements that compose it. Here is the great wonder of nature, how from such simplicity—protons, neutrons, and electrons—we get such great complexity. It is exactly this complexity, however, that makes life possible. Life could not exist with just ninety-one different elements if they did not combine to form compounds. It takes compounds in all of their diversity to make living organisms.

5.2   Compounds Display Constant Composition

Although some of the substances we encounter in everyday life are elements, most are not—they are compounds. Free atoms are rare in nature. As we learned in Chapter 3, a compound is different from a mixture of elements. In a compound, the elements combine in fixed, definite proportions, while in a mixture, they can have any proportions whatsoever. For example, consider the difference between a mixture of hydrogen and oxygen gas (▶ Figure 5.4), and the compound water (▶ Figure 5.5). A mixture of hydrogen and oxygen gas can have any proportions of hydrogen and oxygen. Water, on the other hand, is composed of water molecules that consist of two hydrogen atoms bonded to one oxygen atom. Consequently, water has a definite proportion of hydrogen to oxygen.

The first chemist to formally state the idea that elements combine in fixed proportions to form compounds was Joseph Proust (1754–1826) in the **law of constant composition**, which states:

All samples of a given compound have the same proportions of their constituent elements.

▶ Figure 5.4   **A mixture**   This balloon is filled with a mixture of hydrogen and oxygen gas. The relative amounts of hydrogen and oxygen are variable. We could easily add either more hydrogen or more oxygen to the balloon.

▶ Figure 5.5   **A chemical compound** This balloon is filled with water, composed of molecules that have a fixed ratio of hydrogen to oxygen. (*Source:* JoLynn E. Funk.)

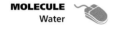

MOLECULE
Water

For example, if we decompose water, we find 16.0 g of oxygen to every 2.0 g of hydrogen, or an oxygen-to-hydrogen mass ratio of:

$$\text{Mass ratio} = \frac{16.0 \text{ g O}}{2.0 \text{ g H}} = 8.0$$

MOLECULE
Ammonia

This is true of any sample of pure water, no matter what its origin (▼ Figure 5.6). The law of constant composition applies not only to water, but to every compound. Consider ammonia, a compound composed of nitrogen and hydrogen. Ammonia contains 14.0 g of nitrogen to every 3.0 g of hydrogen, or a nitrogen-to-hydrogen mass ratio of:

$$\text{Mass ratio} = \frac{14.0 \text{ g N}}{3.0 \text{ g H}} = 4.7$$

Even though atoms combine in whole-number ratios, their *mass* ratios are not necessarily whole numbers.

Again, this ratio is the same for every sample of ammonia—the composition of each compound is constant.

▶ Figure 5.6   **Compounds have fixed composition**   Water will always have a constant ratio of hydrogen to oxygen, no matter what its source.

2 H atoms (○) to every
1 O atom (●)

2 H atoms (○) to every
1 O atom (●)

| EXAMPLE 5.1 | **Constant Composition of Compounds** |

Two samples of carbon dioxide, obtained from different sources, were decomposed into their constituent elements. One sample produced 4.8 g of oxygen and 1.8 g of carbon, and the other sample produced 17.1 g of oxygen and 6.4 g of carbon. Show that these results are consistent with the law of constant composition.

To show this, compute the mass ratio of one element to the other by dividing the larger mass by the smaller one. For the first sample:

Solution:

$$\frac{\text{Mass oxygen}}{\text{Mass carbon}} = \frac{4.8 \text{ g}}{1.8 \text{ g}} = 2.7$$

For the second sample:

$$\frac{\text{Mass oxygen}}{\text{Mass carbon}} = \frac{17.1 \text{ g}}{6.4 \text{ g}} = 2.7$$

Since the ratios are the same for the two samples, these results are consistent with the law of constant composition.

| SKILLBUILDER 5.1 | **Constant Composition of Compounds** |

Two samples of carbon monoxide, obtained from different sources, were decomposed into their constituent elements. One sample produced 4.3 g of oxygen and 3.2 g of carbon, and the other sample produced 7.5 g of oxygen and 5.6 g of carbon. Are these results consistent with the law of constant composition?

5.3   Chemical Formulas: How to Represent Compounds

The reason that compounds have constant composition with respect to mass (as we learned in the previous section) is because they are composed of atoms in fixed ratios.

We represent a compound with a **chemical formula**, which indicates the elements present in the compound and the relative number of atoms of each. For example, H_2O is the chemical formula for water; it indicates that water consists of hydrogen and oxygen atoms in a 2:1 ratio. The formula contains the symbol for each element, accompanied by a subscript indicating the number of atoms of that element. When the subscript is 1, it is omitted.

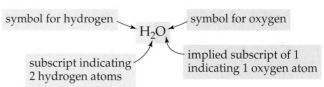

symbol for hydrogen — symbol for oxygen

H_2O

subscript indicating 2 hydrogen atoms

implied subscript of 1 indicating 1 oxygen atom

MOLECULE
Carbon Monoxide

CO   CO₂

▲ The subscripts in a chemical formula are part of what define the compound—if you change a subscript, you change the compound.

Some other common chemical formulas include NaCl for table salt, indicating sodium and chlorine atoms in a 1:1 ratio; CO_2 for carbon dioxide, indicating carbon and oxygen atoms in a 1:2 ratio; and $C_2H_{22}O_{11}$ for table sugar (sucrose), indicating carbon, hydrogen, and oxygen atoms in a 12:22:11 ratio. The subscripts in a chemical formula are part of the compound's definition—if they change, the formula no longer specifies the same compound. For example, CO is the chemical formula for carbon monoxide, an air pollutant with adverse health effects on humans. When inhaled, carbon monoxide interferes with the blood's ability to carry oxygen and can be fatal. CO is the primary substance responsible for deaths of people who inhale too much automobile exhaust. If you change the subscript of the O in CO from 1 to 2, however, you get the formula for a totally different compound. CO_2 is the chemical formula for carbon dioxide, the relatively harmless product of combustion and human respiration. We breathe small amounts of CO_2 all the time with no harmful effects. So, remember:

The subscripts in a chemical formula represent the relative numbers of each type of atom in a chemical compound; they never change for a given compound.

Chemical formulas normally list the most metallic elements first. Therefore, the formula for table salt is NaCl, not ClNa. For compounds that do not include a metal, the more metal-like element is listed first. Recall from Chapter 4 that metals are found on the left side of the periodic table and nonmetals on the upper right side. Therefore, among nonmetals, those to the left in the periodic table are more metal-like than those to the right and are normally listed first. Therefore we write CO_2 and NO, not O_2C and ON. Within a single column in the periodic table, elements toward the bottom are more metal-like than elements toward the top. Therefore we write SO_2, not O_2S. The specific order for listing nonmetal elements in a chemical formula is shown in Table 5.1.

There are a few historical exceptions to this rule, such as the hydroxide ion, which is written as OH^-.

TABLE 5.1 Order of Listing Nonmetal Elements in a Chemical Formula

C	P	N	H	S	I	Br	Cl	O	F

Elements on the left are generally listed before elements on the right.

EXAMPLE 5.2   Writing Chemical Formulas

Write a chemical formula for each of the following:

(a) the compound containing two aluminum atoms to every three oxygen atoms Al_2O_3
(b) the compound containing three oxygen atoms to every sulfur atom SO_3
(c) the compound containing four chlorine atoms to every carbon atom CCl_4

Since aluminum is the metal, it is listed first.

Solution:

(a) Al_2O_3

Since sulfur is below oxygen on the periodic table and since it occurs before oxygen in Table 5.1, it is listed first.

(b) SO_3

Since carbon is to the left of chlorine on the periodic table and since it occurs before chlorine in Table 5.1, it is listed first.

(c) CCl_4

SKILLBUILDER 5.2   Writing Chemical Formulas

Write a chemical formula for each of the following:

(a) the compound containing two silver atoms to every sulfur atom Ag_2S
(b) the compound containing two nitrogen atoms to every oxygen atom N_2O
(c) the compound containing two oxygen atoms to every titanium atom TiO_2

Many times these groups have a charge associated with them and are called *polyatomic ions*. For example, the NO_3 group has a negative charge, NO_3^-. Polyatomic ions are described in more detail in Section 5.7.

Some chemical formulas contain groups of atoms that act as a unit. When several groups of the same kind are present, their formula is set off in parentheses, with a subscript to indicate how many there are. For example, $Mg(NO_3)_2$ indicates a compound containing one magnesium atom and two NO_3 groups.

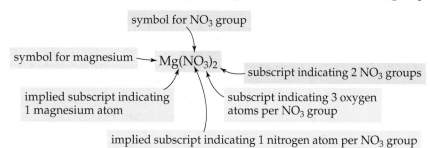

To determine the total number of each type of atom within the parentheses, multiply the subscript outside the parentheses by the subscript for each atom inside the parentheses. Therefore, the preceding formula has the following numbers of each type of atom.

Mg: 1 Mg

N: $1 \times 2 = 2\,N$ (implied 1 inside parentheses times 2 outside parentheses)

O: $3 \times 2 = 6\,O$ (3 inside parentheses times 2 outside parentheses)

EXAMPLE 5.3 | **Total Number of Each Type of Atom in a Chemical Formula**

Determine the number of each type of atom in $Mg_3(PO_4)_2$.

Solution:

Mg: There are three Mg atoms, as indicated by the subscript 3.

P: There are two P atoms, as we see by multiplying the subscript outside the parentheses (2) by the subscript for P inside the parentheses, which is 1 (implied).

O: There are eight O atoms, as we see by multiplying the subscript outside the parentheses (2) by the subscript for O inside the parentheses (4).

SKILLBUILDER 5.3 | **Total Number of Each Type of Atom in a Chemical Formula**

Determine the number of each type of atom in K_2SO_4.

SKILLBUILDER PLUS

Determine the number of each type of atom in $Al_2(SO_4)_3$.

 $Al_2\ S_3O_{12}$

✔ **CONCEPTUAL CHECKPOINT 5.1**

Which of the following formulas represents the greatest number of atoms?

(a) $Al(C_2H_3O_2)_3$
(b) $Al_2(Cr_2O_7)_3$
(c) $Pb(HSO_4)_4$
(d) $Pb_3(PO_4)_4$
(e) $(NH_4)_3PO_4$

5.4   A Molecular View of Elements and Compounds

In Chapter 3, we learned that pure substances could be divided into elements or compounds. We can further subdivide elements and compounds according to the basic units that compose them (▶ Figure 5.7). Pure substances may be elements, or they may be compounds. Elements may be either atomic or molecular. Compounds may be either molecular or ionic.

► Figure 5.7 **A molecular view of elements and compounds**

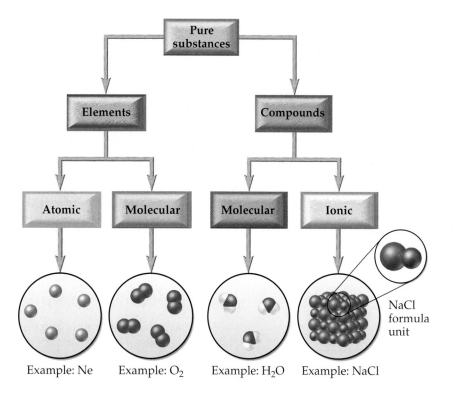

Example: Ne   Example: O₂   Example: H₂O   Example: NaCl

⬤ Atomic Elements

Atomic elements are those that exist in nature with single atoms as their basic units. Most elements fall into this category. For example, helium is composed of helium atoms, copper is composed of copper atoms, and mercury is composed of mercury atoms (▼ Figure 5.8).

⬤ Molecular Elements

Molecular elements do not normally exist in nature with single atoms as their basic units. Instead, these elements exist as *diatomic molecules*—two atoms of that element bonded together—as their basic units. For example, hydrogen is composed of H_2 molecules, oxygen is composed of O_2 molecules, and chlorine is composed of Cl_2 molecules (▼ Figure 5.9). Elements that exist as diatomic molecules are shown in Table 5.2 and in ► Figure 5.10.

A few molecular elements, such as S_8 and P_4, are composed of molecules containing several atoms.

◄ Figure 5.8 **An atomic element**
The basic units that compose mercury, an atomic element and a metal, are single mercury atoms.

► Figure 5.9 **A molecular element**
The basic units that compose chlorine, a molecular element, are diatomic chlorine molecules, each composed of two chlorine atoms.

Diatomic chlorine molecules

▶ **Figure 5.10 Elements that form diatomic molecules** Elements that normally exist as diatomic molecules are highlighted in yellow on this periodic table. Note that six of the seven are nonmetals, including four of the halogens.

TABLE 5.2 Elements That Occur as Diatomic Molecules

Name of Element	Formula of Basic Unit
hydrogen	H_2
nitrogen	N_2
oxygen	O_2
fluorine	F_2
chlorine	Cl_2
bromine	Br_2
iodine	I_2

Remember that nonmetals occupy the upper right side of the periodic table.

Molecular Compounds

Molecular compounds are compounds formed from two or more nonmetals. The basic units of molecular compounds are molecules composed of the constituent atoms. For example, water is composed of H_2O molecules, dry ice is composed of CO_2 molecules (▼ Figure 5.11), and acetone (finger nail-polish remover) is composed of C_3H_6O molecules.

Ionic Compounds

Ionic compounds are compounds formed from a metal and one or more nonmetals. When a metal, which has a tendency to lose electrons, combines with a nonmetal, which has a tendency to gain electrons, one or more electrons transfer from the metal to the nonmetal, creating positive and negative ions that are then attracted to each other. The basic unit of ionic compounds is the **formula unit**, the smallest electrically neutral collection of ions. Formula units are different from molecules in that they do not exist as discrete entities, but rather as part of a larger lattice. For example, salt (NaCl) is composed of Na^+ and Cl^- ions in a 1:1 ratio. In table salt, Na^+ and Cl^- ions exist in an alternating three-dimensional array (▼ Figure 5.12). However, any one Na^+ ion does

CO_2 molecules

◀ **Figure 5.11 A molecular compound** The basic units that compose dry ice, a molecular compound, are CO_2 molecules.

NaCl formula unit

▶ **Figure 5.12 An ionic compound** The basic units that compose table salt, an ionic compound, are NaCl formula units. Unlike molecular compounds, ionic compounds do not contain individual molecules but rather sodium and chloride ions in an alternating three-dimensional array.

not pair with one specific Cl^- ion. Sometimes chemists refer to formula units as molecules, but this is not strictly correct since ionic compounds do not contain distinct molecules.

EXAMPLE 5.4 **Classifying Substances as Atomic Elements, Molecular Elements, Molecular Compounds, or Ionic Compounds**

Classify each of the following substances as an atomic element, molecular element, molecular compound, or ionic compound.

(a) krypton— *Atomic*
(b) $CoCl_2$ – *Ionic Compound*
(c) nitrogen – *Molecular Element*
(d) SO_2 – *molecular compound*
(e) KNO_3 – *Ionic compound*

Solution:

(a) Krypton is an element that is not listed as diatomic in Table 5.2; therefore, it is an atomic element.

(b) $CoCl_2$ is a compound composed of a metal (left side of periodic table) and nonmetal (right side of the periodic table); therefore, it is an ionic compound.

(c) Nitrogen is an element that is listed as diatomic in Table 5.2; therefore, it is a molecular element.

(d) SO_2 is a compound composed of two nonmetals; therefore, it is a molecular compound.

(e) KNO_3 is a compound composed of a metal and two nonmetals; therefore, it is an ionic compound.

SKILLBUILDER 5.4 **Classifying Substances as Atomic Elements, Molecular Elements, Molecular Compounds, or Ionic Compounds**

Classify each of the following substances as an atomic element, molecular element, molecular compound, or ionic compound.

(a) chlorine – *molecular element*
(b) NO – *Molecular compound*
(c) Au – *Atomic Element*
(d) Na_2O – *Ionic compound*
● (e) $CrCl_3$ – *Ionic compound*

5.5   Writing Formulas for Ionic Compounds

Review Section 4.7 and Figure 4.14 to learn the elements that form ions with a predictable charge.

Since ionic compounds must be charge-neutral and since many elements form only one type of ion with a predictable charge, the formulas for many ionic compounds can be determined based on their constituent elements. For example, the formula for the ionic compound composed of sodium and chlorine must be NaCl and not anything else because in compounds Na always forms 1+ cations and Cl always forms 1− anions. In order for the compound to be charge-neutral, it must contain one Na^+ cation to every Cl^- anion. The formula for the ionic compound composed of magnesium and chlorine, however, must be $MgCl_2$ because Mg always forms 2+ cations and Cl always forms 1− anions. In order for the compound to be charge-neutral, it must contain one Mg^{2+} cation to every two Cl^- anions. In general:

TUTORIAL
Building Blocks for Naming
Ionic Compounds

- Ionic compounds always contain positive and negative ions.
- In the chemical formula, the sum of the charges of the positive ions (cations) must always equal the sum of the charges of the negative ions (anions).

To write the formula for an ionic compound, follow the procedure in the left column below. Two examples of how to apply the procedure are provided in the center and right columns.

Writing Formulas for Ionic Compounds	**EXAMPLE 5.5** Write a formula for the ionic compound that forms from aluminum and oxygen.	**EXAMPLE 5.6** Write a formula for the ionic compound that forms from magnesium and oxygen.
1. Write the symbol for the metal and its charge followed by the symbol of the nonmetal and its charge. For many elements, these charges can be determined from their group number in the periodic table (refer to Figure 4.14).	**Solution:** Al^{3+} O^{2-}	**Solution:** Mg^{2+} O^{2-}
2. Make the magnitude of the charge on each ion (without the sign) become the subscript for the other ion.	$Al^{3+}\ O^{2-}$ $\downarrow$ Al_2O_3	$Mg^{2+}\ O^{2-}$ $\downarrow$ Mg_2O_2
3. Reduce the subscripts to give a ratio with the smallest whole numbers.	In this case, the numbers cannot be reduced any further; the correct formula is Al_2O_3.	To reduce the subscripts, divide both subscripts by 2. $Mg_2O_2 \div 2 = MgO$
4. Check that the sum of the charges of the cations exactly cancels the sum of the charges of the anions.	Cations: $2(3+) = 6+$ Anions: $3(2-) = 6-$ The charges cancel.	Cations: $2+$ Anions: $2-$ The charges cancel.

SKILLBUILDER 5.5

Write a formula for the compound formed from cesium and oxygen.

$Cs\,O^{-2}$
Cs_2O

SKILLBUILDER 5.6

Write a formula for the compound formed from aluminum and nitrogen.

$Al_3\,N_3 = AlN$

EXAMPLE 5.7   Writing Formulas for Ionic Compounds

Write a formula for the compound that forms from potassium and oxygen.

Solution:

We first write the symbol for each ion along with its appropriate charge from its group number in the periodic table.

K^+ O^{2-}

We then make the magnitude of each ion's charge become the subscript for the other ion.

K^+ O^{2-} becomes K_2O

No reducing of subscripts is necessary in this case. Finally, we check to see that the sum of the charges of the cations [$2(1+) = 2+$] exactly cancels the sum of the charges of the anion ($2-$). The correct formula is K_2O.

| SKILLBUILDER 5.7 | **Writing Formulas for Ionic Compounds** |

• Write a formula for the compound that forms from calcium and bromine.

5.6 Nomenclature: Naming Compounds

Since there are so many different compounds, chemists have developed systematic ways to name them. If you learn these, you can simply examine a compound's formula to determine its name or vice versa. Many compounds, however, also have a common name. For example, H_2O has the common name *water* and the systematic name *dihydrogen monoxide*. A common name is like a nickname for a compound, used by those who are familiar with it. Since water is such a familiar compound, everyone uses its common name and not its systematic name. In the sections that follow, we learn how to systematically name simple ionic and molecular compounds. Keep in mind, however, that some compounds also have common names that are often used instead of the systematic name. Common names can be learned only through familiarity.

TUTORIAL
Chemistry Nomenclature Tools

5.7 Naming Ionic Compounds

The first step in naming an ionic compound is identifying it as one. Remember, *ionic compounds are formed from metals and nonmetals*; any time you see a metal and one or more nonmetals together in a chemical formula, it is an ionic compound. Ionic compounds can be divided into two types (▼ Figure 5.13) depending on the metal in the compound. If the metal, in all of its different compounds, always forms a cation with the same charge, then the charge is implied and the compound is a **Type I compound**. Sodium, for instance, has a 1+ charge in all of its compounds and therefore forms Type I compounds. Some examples of Type I metals are listed in Table 5.3. For most of these metals, their charge can be inferred from their group number in the periodic table (see Figure 4.14).

If, on the other hand, the metal forms compounds in which its charge is *not* always the same, then the charge is not implied and the compound is a **Type II compound**. Iron, for instance, has a 2+ charge in some of its compounds and a 3+ charge in others. Such metals are usually found in the section of the periodic table known as the **transition metals** (Figure ▶ 5.14). (Some examples of metals that form Type II ionic compounds are shown in Table 5.5.)

▶ Figure 5.13 **Classification of ionic compounds** Ionic compounds can be divided into two types, depending on the metal in the compound. If the metal, in all of its compounds, always forms an ion with the same charge, it is a Type I ionic compound. If the metal, in all of its compounds, forms ions with different charges, it is a Type II ionic compound.

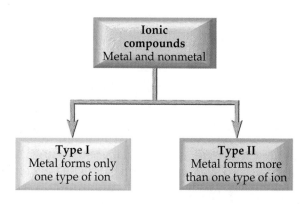

TABLE 5.3 Metals That Form Type I Ionic Compounds

Metal	Ion	Name	Group Number
Li	Li^+	lithium	1A
Na	Na^+	sodium	1A
K	K^+	potassium	1A
Rb	Rb^+	rubidium	1A
Cs	Cs^+	cesium	1A
Be	Be^{2+}	beryllium	2A
Mg	Mg^{2+}	magnesium	2A
Ca	Ca^{2+}	calcium	2A
Sr	Sr^{2+}	strontium	2A
Ba	Ba^{2+}	barium	2A
Al	Al^{3+}	aluminium	3A
Zn	Zn^{2+}	zinc	*
Ag	Ag^+	silver	*

*The charge of these metals cannot be inferred from their group number.

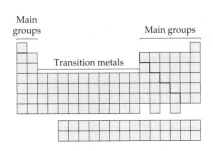

▲ **Figure 5.14   The transition metals**   The elements that form Type II ionic compounds are usually transition metals.

Naming Type I Binary Ionic Compounds

Binary compounds are those containing only two different elements. The names for binary Type I ionic compounds have the following form:

name of cation (metal)   base name of anion (nonmetal) + -*ide*

For example, the name for NaCl consists of the name of the cation, *sodium*, followed by the base name of the anion, *chlor*, with the ending -*ide*. The full name is *sodium chloride*.

NaCl   sodium chloride

The name for MgO consists of the name of the cation, *magnesium*, followed by the base name of the anion, *ox*, with the ending -*ide*. The full name is *magnesium oxide*.

MgO   magnesium oxide

> The name of the cation in ionic compounds is the same as the name of the metal.

The base names for various nonmetals and their most common charges in ionic compounds are shown in Table 5.4.

TABLE 5.4 Some Common Anions

Nonmetal	Symbol for Ion	Base Name	Anion Name
fluorine	F^-	fluor-	fluoride
chlorine	Cl^-	chlor-	chloride
bromine	Br^-	brom-	bromide
iodine	I^-	iod-	iodide
oxygen	O^{2-}	ox-	oxide
sulfur	S^{2-}	sulf-	sulfide
nitrogen	N^{3-}	nitr-	nitride

| EXAMPLE 5.8 | **Naming Type I Ionic Compounds** |

Give the name for the compound MgF_2.

Solution:

The cation is magnesium. The anion is fluorine, which becomes *fluoride*. The correct name is *magnesium fluoride.*

(handwritten) Mg

| SKILLBUILDER 5.8 | **Naming Type I Ionic Compounds** |

Give the name for the compound KBr.

(handwritten) cation anion / Potassium Bromide

| SKILLBUILDER PLUS |

Give the name for the compound Zn_3N_2.   (handwritten) zinc nitride

Naming Type II Binary Ionic Compounds

The names for binary (two-element) Type II ionic compounds have the following form:

| name of cation (metal) | charge of cation (metal) in roman numerals in parentheses | base name of anion (nonmetal) + -ide |

See Table 5.5 for some examples of metals that form Type II ionic compounds. The charge of the metal cation is obtained by inference from the sum of the charges of the nonmetal anions—remember that the sum of all the charges must be zero. For example, the name for $FeCl_3$ consists of the name of the cation, *iron*, followed by the charge of the cation in parentheses *(III)*, followed by the base name of the anion, *chlor*, with the ending *-ide*. The full name is *iron(III) chloride*.

$FeCl_3$ iron(III) chloride

TABLE 5.5 Some Metals That Form Type II Ionic Compounds and Their Common Charges

Metal	Symbol Ion	Name	Older Name*
chromium	Cr^{2+}	chromium(II)	chromous
	Cr^{3+}	chromium(III)	chromic
iron	Fe^{2+}	iron(II)	ferrous
	Fe^{3+}	iron(III)	ferric
cobalt	Co^{2+}	cobalt(II)	cobaltous
	Co^{3+}	cobalt(III)	cobaltic
copper	Cu^{+}	copper(I)	cuprous
	Cu^{2+}	copper(II)	cupric
tin	Sn^{2+}	tin(II)	stannous
	Sn^{4+}	tin(IV)	stannic
mercury	Hg_2^{2+}	mercury(I)	mercurous
	Hg^{2+}	mercury(II)	mercuric
lead	Pb^{2+}	lead(II)	plumbous
	Pb^{4+}	lead(IV)	plumbic

*An older naming system substitutes the names found in this column for the name of the metal and its charge. Under this system, chromium(II) oxide is named chromous oxide. We will *not* use this older system in this text.

The charge of iron must be 3+ in order for the compound to be charge neutral with three Cl^- anions. Likewise, the name for CrO consists of the name of the cation, *chromium*, followed by the charge of the cation in parentheses *(II)*, followed by the base name of the anion, *ox-*, with the ending *-ide*. The full name is *chromium(II) oxide*.

CrO   chromium(II) oxide

The charge of chromium must be 2+ in order for the compound to be charge-neutral with one O^{2-} anion.

EXAMPLE 5.9   Naming Type II Ionic Compounds

Give the name for the compound $PbCl_4$.

Solution:
The name for $PbCl_4$ consists of the name of the cation, *lead*, followed by the charge of the cation in parenthesis *(IV)*, followed by the base name of the anion, *chlor-*, with the ending *-ide*. The full name is *lead(IV) chloride*. We know the charge on Pb is 4+ because the charge on Cl is 1−. Since there are 4 Cl^- anions, the Pb cation must be Pb^{4+}.

PbCl₄   lead(IV) chloride

SKILLBUILDER 5.9   Naming Type II Ionic Compounds

Give the name for the compound PbO.

Naming Ionic Compounds Containing a Polyatomic Ion

Some ionic compounds contain ions that are themselves composed of a group of atoms with an overall charge. These ions are called **polyatomic ions** and are shown in Table 5.6. Ionic compounds containing polyatomic ions are named using the same procedure we apply to other ionic compounds, except that the name of the polyatomic ion is used whenever it occurs. For example, KNO_3

 TUTORIAL
Naming Polyatomic Ions

 MOLECULE
Phosphate Ion

TABLE 5.6 Some Common Polyatomic Ions

Name	Formula	Name	Formula
acetate	$C_2H_3O_2^-$	hypochlorite	ClO^-
carbonate	CO_3^{2-}	chlorite	ClO_2^-
hydrogen carbonate (or bicarbonate)	HCO_3^-	chlorate	ClO_3^-
hydroxide	OH^-	perchlorate	ClO_4^-
nitrate	NO_3^-	permanganate	MnO_4^-
nitrite	NO_2^-	sulfate	SO_4^{2-}
chromate	CrO_4^{2-}	sulfite	SO_3^{2-}
dichromate	$Cr_2O_7^{2-}$	hydrogen sulfite (or bisulfite)	HSO_3^-
phosphate	PO_4^{3-}	hydrogen sulfate (or bisulfate)	HSO_4^-
hydrogen phosphate	HPO_4^{2-}	peroxide	O_2^{2-}
ammonium	NH_4^+	cyanide	CN^-

is named according to its cation, K^+, *potassium*, and its polyatomic anion, NO_3^-, *nitrate*. The full name is *potassium nitrate*.

KNO_3 potassium nitrate

$Fe(OH)_2$ is named according to its cation, *iron*, its charge *(II)*, and its polyatomic ion, *hydroxide*. The full name is *iron(II) hydroxide*.

$Fe(OH)_2$ iron(II) hydroxide

If the compound contains both a polyatomic cation and a polyatomic anion, simply use the names of both polyatomic ions. For example, NH_4NO_3 is named *ammonium nitrate*.

NH_4NO_3 ammonium nitrate

You must be able to recognize polyatomic ions in a chemical formula, so be familiar with Table 5.6. Most polyatomic ions are **oxyanions**, anions containing oxygen. Notice that when a series of oxyanions contain different numbers of oxygen atoms, they are named systematically according to the number of oxygen atoms in the ion. If there are two ions in the series, the one with more oxygen atoms is given the ending *-ate* and the one with fewer is given the ending *-ite*. For example, NO_3^- is called *nitrate* and NO_2^- is called *nitrite*.

MOLECULES
Sulfite Ion
Sulfate Ion

NO_3^- nitrate
NO_2^- nitrite

If there are more than two ions in the series, then the prefixes *hypo-*, meaning "less than," and *per-*, meaning "more than," are used. So ClO^- is called *hypochlorite*, meaning "less oxygen than chlorite," and ClO_4^- is called *perchlorate*, meaning "more oxygen than chlorate."

MOLECULES
Perchlorate Ion
Potassium Permanganate

ClO^- hypochlorite
ClO_2^- chlorite
ClO_3^- chlorate
ClO_4^- perchlorate

EXAMPLE 5.10   **Naming Ionic Compounds That Contain a Polyatomic Ion**

Give the name for the compound K_2CrO_4.

The name for K_2CrO_4 consists of the name of the cation, *potassium*, followed by the name of the polyatomic ion, *chromate*.

Solution:

K_2CrO_4 potassium chromate

SKILLBUILDER 5.10   **Naming Ionic Compounds That Contain a Polyatomic Ion**

Give the name for the compound $Mn(NO_3)_2$.   Maganese(III) nitrate

EVERYDAY Chemistry

Polyatomic Ions

A glance at the labels of household products reveals the importance of polyatomic ions in everyday compounds. For example, the active ingredient in household bleach is sodium hypochlorite, which acts to destroy color-causing molecules in clothes (bleaching action) and to kill bacteria (disinfection). A box of baking soda contains sodium bicarbonate (sodium hydrogen carbonate), which acts as an antacid when consumed in small amounts and also as a source of carbon dioxide gas in baking. The pockets of carbon dioxide gas make baked goods fluffy rather than flat.

Calcium carbonate is the active ingredient in many antacids such as Tums and Alka-Mints. It neutralizes stomach acids, relieving the symptoms of indigestion and heartburn. Too much calcium carbonate, however, can cause constipation, so Tums should not be overused. Sodium nitrite is a common food additive used to preserve packaged meats such as ham, hot dogs, and bologna. Sodium nitrite inhibits the growth of bacteria, especially those that cause botulism, an often fatal type of food poisoning.

CAN YOU ANSWER THIS? *Write a formula for each of these compounds, which contain polyatomic ions: sodium hypochlorite, sodium bicarbonate, calcium carbonate, sodium nitrite.*

DANGER: CORROSIVE. HARMFUL IF SWALLOWED.
Ingredients: Sodium Hypochlorite, Sodium Hydroxide
May cause severe irritation or damage to eyes, skin, and mucous membranes. Avoid contact with eyes, skin and clothing. Do not ingest. For prolonged use, wear gloves.
FIRST AID: EYES–Rinse with plenty of water for 15 minutes. IF SWALLOWED–Do not induce vomiting. Drink a glassful of water. In either case, call a physician or poison control center immediately. SKIN–Remove contaminated clothing and wash skin thoroughly with water.
PHYSICAL AND CHEMICAL HAZARDS: Ultra Clorox® Fresh Wildflowers™ bleach contains a strong oxidizer. Always flush drains before and after use. **Do not use or mix with other household chemicals,** such as toilet bowl cleaners, rust removers, acids, or products containing ammonia. To do so will release hazardous gases. Prolonged contact with metal may cause pitting or discoloration. Not harmful to septic systems.

▲ The active ingredient in bleach is sodium hypochlorite.

▲ Compounds containing polyatomic ions are present in many consumer products.

5.8   Naming Molecular Compounds

The first step in naming a molecular compound is identifying it as one. Remember, molecular compounds form from two or more nonmetals. In this section, we learn how to name binary (two-element) molecular compounds. Their names have the following form:

| prefix | name of 1st element | prefix | base name of 2nd element + -ide |

When writing the name of a molecular compound, as when writing the formula, the first element is the more metal-like one (see Table 5.1). The prefixes given to each element indicate the number of atoms present.

mono- 1	*penta-* 5
di- 2	*hexa-* 6
tri- 3	*hepta-* 7
tetra- 4	*octa-* 8

If there is only one atom of the *first element* in the formula, the prefix *mono-* is normally omitted. For example, CO_2 is named according to the first element, *carbon*, with no prefix because *mono-* is omitted for the first element, followed by the prefix *di-*, to indicate two oxygen atoms, followed by the base name of the second element, *ox*, with the ending *-ide*.

carbon   di-   ox   -ide

The full name is *carbon dioxide*.

CO_2 carbon dioxide

The compound N_2O, also called laughing gas, is named according to the first element, *nitrogen*, with the prefix *di-*, to indicate that there are two of them, followed by the base name of the second element, *ox*, prefixed by *mono-*, to indicate one, and the suffix *-ide*. Since *mono-* ends with a vowel and *oxide* begins with one, an *o* is dropped and the two are combined as *monoxide*. The entire name is *dinitrogen monoxide*.

> When the prefix ends with a vowel and the base name starts with a vowel, the first vowel is normally dropped.

N_2O dinitrogen monoxide

EXAMPLE 5.11   Naming Molecular Compounds

Name each of the following: CCl_4 BCl_3 SF_6

Solution:

CCl_4 *carbon tetrachlorine*

The name of the compound is the name of the first element, *carbon*, followed by the base name of the second element, *chlor*, prefixed by *tetra-* to indicate four, and the suffix *-ide*. The entire name is *carbon tetrachloride*.

BCl_3 *boron trichloride*

The name of the compound is the name of the first element, *boron*, followed by the base name of the second element, *chlor*, prefixed by *tri-* to indicate three, and the suffix *-ide*. The entire name is *boron trichloride*.

SF_6 *sulfur hexaflouride*

The name of the compound is the name of the first element, *sulfur*, followed by the base name of the second element, *fluor*, prefixed by *hexa-* to indicate six, and the suffix *-ide*. The entire name is *sulfur hexafluoride*.

SKILLBUILDER 5.11   Naming Molecular Compounds

Name the compound N_2O_4.   *dinitrogen tetraoxide*

5.9   Naming Acids

HCl(g) refers to HCl molecules in the gas phase.

Acids are molecular compounds that dissolve in water to form H^+ ions. They are composed of hydrogen, usually written first in their formula, and one or more nonmetals, written second. Acids are characterized by their sour taste and their ability to dissolve some metals. For example, HCl is a molecular compound that, when dissolved in water, forms H^+ ions. It is an acid. To emphasize that acids occur in water solutions, HCl in water is sometimes represented as HCl(aq), where (aq) means "aqueous" or "dissolved in water." HCl has a characteristically sour taste. Since HCl is present in stomach fluids, its sour taste becomes painfully obvious during vomiting. HCl also dissolves some metals. For example, if you drop a strip of zinc into a beaker of HCl, it will slowly disappear as the HCl converts the zinc metal into Zn^{2+} cations.

Acids are present in many foods, such as lemons and limes, and they are used in some household products such as toilet bowl cleaner and Lime-A-Way. In this section, we simply learn how to name them, but in Chapter 14 we will learn more about their properties. Acids can be divided into two categories: **binary acids**, those containing only hydrogen and a nonmetal, and **oxyacids**, those containing hydrogen, a nonmetal, and oxygen (▼ Figure 5.15).

Naming Binary Acids

Binary acids are composed of hydrogen and a nonmetal. The names for binary acids have the following form:

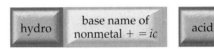

For example, HCl is named hydro*chlor*ic acid and HBr is named hydro*brom*ic acid.

HCl hydrochloric acid   HBr hydrobromic acid

▶ **Figure 5.15 Classification of acids** Acids can be divided into two types, depending on the number of elements in the acid. If the acid contains only two elements, it is a binary acid. If it contains oxygen, it is an oxyacid.

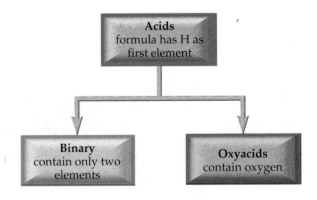

EXAMPLE 5.12   Naming Binary Acids

Give the name of H_2S.

The base name of S is *sulfur*, so the name is *hydrosulfuric acid*.

Solution:

H_2S hydrosulfuric acid

SKILLBUILDER 5.12   Naming Binary Acids

Give the name of HI.

Naming Oxyacids

Oxyacids are derived from the oxyanions found in the table of polyatomic ions (Table 5.6). For example, HNO_3 is derived from the nitrate (NO_3^-) ion, H_2SO_3 is derived from the sulfite (SO_3^{2-}) ion, and H_2SO_4 is derived from the sulfate (SO_4^{2-}) ion. Notice that these acids are simply a combination of one or more H^+ ions with an oxyanion. The number of H^+ ions depends on the charge of the oxyanion, so that the formula is always charge-neutral. The names of oxyacids depend on the ending of the oxyanion (▼ Figure 5.16) and have the following forms:

Oxyanions ending with -ate

Oxyanions ending with -ite

So HNO_3 is named *nitric acid* (oxyanion is nitrate), and H_2SO_3 is named *sulfurous acid* (oxyanion is sulfite).

HNO_3 nitric acid H_2SO_3 sulfurous acid

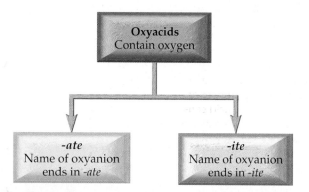

▲ Figure 5.16   **Classification of oxyacids**   Oxyacids can be divided into two types, depending on the ending of the oxyanion from which they are derived.

EXAMPLE 5.13   Naming Oxyacids

Give the name of $HC_2H_3O_2$.

The oxyanion is acetate, which ends in -ate; therefore, the name of the acid is *acetic acid*.

Solution:

$HC_2H_3O_2$ acetic acid

SKILLBUILDER 5.13   Naming Oxyacids

Give the name of HNO_2.   Nitrous Acid

5.10 Nomenclature Summary

Acids are technically a subclass of molecular compounds; that is, they are molecular compounds that form H^+ ions when dissolved in water.

Naming compounds requires several steps. The flow chart in ▼ Figure 5.17 summarizes the different categories of compounds that we have learned and how to identify and name them. The first step is to decide whether the compound is ionic, molecular, or an acid. You can recognize ionic compounds by the presence of a metal and a nonmetal, molecular compounds by two or more nonmetals, and acids by the presence of hydrogen (written first) and one or more nonmetals.

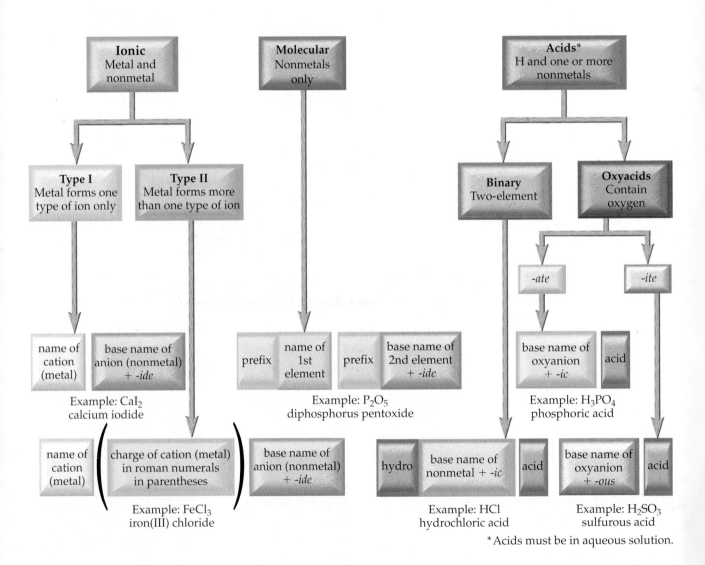

* Acids must be in aqueous solution.

▲ Figure 5.17   **Nomenclature flow chart**

Ionic Compounds

For an ionic compound, you must next decide whether it is a Type I or Type II ionic compound. Group 1A (alkali) metals, Group 2A (alkaline earth) metals, and aluminum will always form Type I ionic compounds (Figure 4.14). Most of the transition metals will form Type II ionic compounds. Once you have identified the type of ionic compound, name it according to the scheme in the chart. If the ionic compound contains a polyatomic ion—something you must recognize by familiarity—insert the name of the polyatomic ion in place of the metal (positive polyatomic ion) or the nonmetal (negative polyatomic ion).

Molecular Compounds

We have learned how to name only one type of molecular compound, the binary (two-element) compound. If you identify a compound as molecular, name it according to the scheme in Figure 5.17.

Acids

To name an acid, you must first decide whether it is a binary (two-element) acid or an oxyacid (an acid containing oxygen). Binary acids are named according to the scheme in Figure 5.17. Oxyacids must be further subdivided based on the name of their corresponding oxyanion. If the oxyanion ends in *-ate*, use one scheme; if it ends with *-ite*, use the other.

EXAMPLE 5.14   **Nomenclature Using Figure 5.17**

Name each of the following: CO, CaF_2, HF, $Fe(NO_3)_3$, $HClO_4$, H_2SO_3

Solution:

For each compound, the following table shows how to use Figure 5.17 to arrive at a name for the compound.

Formula	Flow Chart Path	Name
CO	Molecular	carbon monoxide
CaF_2	Ionic $\longrightarrow$ Type I $\longrightarrow$	calcium fluoride
HF	Acid $\longrightarrow$ Binary $\longrightarrow$	hydrofluoric acid
$Fe(NO_3)_3$	Ionic $\longrightarrow$ Type II $\longrightarrow$	iron(III) nitrate
$HClO_4$	Acid $\longrightarrow$ Oxyacid $\longrightarrow$ *-ate* $\longrightarrow$	perchloric acid
H_2SO_3	Acid $\longrightarrow$ Oxyacid $\longrightarrow$ *-ite* $\longrightarrow$	sulfurous acid

Chemistry IN THE ENVIRONMENT

Acid Rain

Acid rain occurs when rainwater mixes with air pollutants—such as NO, NO_2 and SO_2—that form acids. NO and NO_2, primarily from vehicular emissions, combine with water to form HNO_3. SO_2, primarily from coal-powered electricity generation, combines with water to form H_2SO_4. HNO_3 and H_2SO_4 both cause rainwater to become acidic. The problem is greatest in the northeastern United States, where pollutants from midwestern electrical power plants combine with rainwater to produce rain with acid levels that are up to ten times as high as normal.

When acid rain falls or flows into lakes and streams, it makes them more acidic. Some species of aquatic animals—such as trout, bass, snails, salamanders, and clams—cannot tolerate the increased acidity and die. This then disturbs the ecosystem of the lake, resulting in imbalances that may lead to the death of other aquatic species. Acid rain also weakens trees by dissolving nutrients in the soil and by damaging their leaves. Appalachian red spruce trees have been the hardest hit, with many forests showing significant acid rain damage.

▲ A forest damaged by acid rain.

Acid rain also damages building materials. Acids dissolve $CaCO_3$ (limestone), a main component of marble and concrete, and iron, the main component of steel. Consequently, many statues, buildings, and bridges in the northeastern United States show significant deterioration, and some historical gravestones made of limestone are barely legible due to acid rain damage.

▲ Acid rain harms many materials, including the limestone often used for tombstones, buildings, and statues. The problem affects many countries around the world—these damaged gargoyles are part of Notre Dame cathedral in Paris.

Although acid rain has been a problem for many years, recent legislation has offered hope for change. In 1990, Congress passed several amendments to the Clean Air Act that included provisions requiring electrical utilities to reduce SO_2 emissions. Since then, SO_2 emissions have decreased, and rain in the northeastern United States has become somewhat less acidic. With time, and continued enforcement of the acid rain program, lakes, streams, and forests damaged by acid rain should recover.

CAN YOU ANSWER THIS? *Provide the names for each of the following compounds, given here as formulas:*

NO, NO_2, SO_2, HNO_3, $CaCO_3$.

5.11 Formula Mass: The Mass of a Molecule or Formula Unit

Also in common use are the terms *molecular mass* and *molecular weight*, which have the same meaning as formula mass.

In Chapter 4, we learned about atoms and elements, and we designated the average mass of the atoms that compose an element as the atomic mass for that element. In this chapter, we learned about molecules and compounds, and so we designate the average mass of the molecules (or formula units) that compose a compound as the **formula mass**.

For any compound, the formula mass is simply the sum of the atomic masses of all the atoms in its chemical formula:

$$\text{Formula mass} = \left(\begin{array}{c}\text{\# atoms of 1st}\\ \text{element in}\\ \text{chemical formula}\end{array} \times \begin{array}{c}\text{Atomic mass}\\ \text{of}\\ \text{1st element}\end{array}\right) + \left(\begin{array}{c}\text{\# atoms of 2nd}\\ \text{element in}\\ \text{chemical formula}\end{array} \times \begin{array}{c}\text{Atomic mass}\\ \text{of}\\ \text{2nd element}\end{array}\right) + \dots$$

Like atomic mass for atoms, formula mass characterizes the average mass of a molecule or formula unit. For example, the formula mass of water, H_2O, is:

$$\text{Formula mass} = 2(1.01 \text{ amu}) + 16.00 \text{ amu}$$
$$= 18.02 \text{ amu}$$

and that of sodium chloride, NaCl, is:

$$\text{Formula mass} = 22.99 \text{ amu} + 35.45 \text{ amu}$$
$$= 58.44 \text{ amu}$$

In addition to giving a characteristic mass to the molecules or formula units of a compound, formula mass—as we will learn in Chapter 6—allows us to quantify the number of molecules or formula units in a sample of a given mass.

EXAMPLE 5.15   Calculating Formula Mass

Calculate the formula mass of carbon tetrachloride, CCl_4.

Solution:
To find the formula mass, we sum the atomic masses of each atom in the chemical formula.

$$\text{Formula mass} = 1 \times (\text{Formula mass C}) + 4 \times (\text{Formula mass Cl})$$
$$= 12.01 \text{ amu} + 4(35.45 \text{ amu})$$
$$= 153.81 \text{ amu}$$

SKILLBUILDER 5.15   Calculating Formula Masses

Calculate the formula mass of dinitrogen monoxide, N_2O, also called laughing gas.

CONCEPTUAL CHECKPOINT 5.2

Which of the following has the greatest formula mass?
(a) O_2
(b) O_3
(c) H_2O
(d) H_2O_2

CHAPTER IN REVIEW

Chemical Principles

Compounds: Matter is ultimately composed of atoms, but those atoms are often combined in compounds. The most important characteristic of a compound is its constant composition. The elements that compose a particular compound are in fixed, definite proportions in all samples of the compound.

Chemical Formulas: Compounds are represented by chemical formulas, which indicate the elements present in the compound and the relative number of atoms of each. These formulas represent the basic units that compose a compound.

Pure substances can be divided according to the basic units that compose them. Elements can be composed of atoms or molecules. Compounds can be molecular, in which case their basic units are molecules, or ionic, in which case their basic units are ions. The formulas for many ionic compounds can be written simply by knowing the elements in the compound.

Chemical Nomenclature: The names of simple ionic compounds, molecular compounds, and acids can all be written by examining their chemical formula. The nomenclature flow chart (Figure 5.17) shows the basic procedure for determining these names.

Formula Mass: The formula mass of a compound is the sum of the atomic masses of all the atoms in the chemical formula for the compound. Like atomic mass for elements, formula mass characterizes the average mass of a molecule or formula unit.

Relevance

Compounds: Most of the matter we encounter is in the form of compounds. Water, salt, and carbon dioxide are all good examples of common simple compounds. More complex compounds include caffeine, aspirin, acetone, and testosterone.

Chemical Formulas: To understand compounds we must understand their composition, which is represented by a chemical formula. The connection between the microscopic world and the macroscopic world hinges on the particles that compose matter. Since most matter is in the form of compounds, the properties of most matter depend on the molecules or ions that compose it. Molecular matter does what its molecules do; ionic matter does what its ions do. The world we see and experience is governed by what these particles are doing.

Chemical Nomenclature: Since there are so many compounds, we need a systematic way to name them. By learning these few simple rules, you will be able to name thousands of different compounds. The next time you look at the label on a consumer product, try to identify as many of the compounds as you can.

Formula Mass: Besides being the characteristic mass of a molecule or formula unit, formula mass is important in many calculations involving the composition of compounds and quantities in chemical reactions.

Chemical Skills

Constant Composition of Compounds (Section 5.2)

The law of constant composition states that all samples of a given compound should have the same ratio of their constituent elements.

To determine whether experimental data is consistent with the law of constant composition, compute the ratios of the masses of each element in all samples. When computing these ratios, it is most convenient to put the larger number in the numerator (top) and the smaller one in the denominator (bottom); that way, the ratio is greater than 1. If the ratios are the same, then the data is consistent with the law of constant composition.

Examples

EXAMPLE 5.16   Constant Composition of Compounds

Two samples said to be carbon disulfide (CS_2) are decomposed into their constituent elements. One sample produced 8.08 g S and 1.51 g C, while the other produced 31.3 g S and 3.85 g C. Are these results consistent with the law of constant composition?

Solution: Sample 1

$$\frac{\text{Mass S}}{\text{Mass C}} = \frac{8.08 \text{ g}}{1.51 \text{ g}} = 5.35$$

Sample 2

$$\frac{\text{Mass S}}{\text{Mass C}} = \frac{31.3 \text{ g}}{3.85 \text{ g}} = 8.13$$

These results are not consistent with the law of constant composition and the data given must therefore be in error.

Writing Chemical Formulas (Section 5.3)

Chemical formulas indicate the elements present in a compound and the relative number of atoms of each. When writing formulas, put the more metallic element first.

| EXAMPLE 5.17 | **Writing Chemical Formulas** |

Write a chemical formula for the compound containing one nitrogen atom for every two oxygen atoms.

Solution:

NO_2

Total Number of Each Type of Atom in a Chemical Formula (Section 5.3)

The numbers of atoms not enclosed in parentheses are given directly by their subscript.

The numbers of atoms within parentheses are found by multiplying their subscript within the parentheses by their subscript outside the parentheses.

| EXAMPLE 5.18 | **Total Number of Each Type of Atom in a Chemical Formula** |

Determine the number of each type of atom in $Pb(ClO_3)_2$.

Solution:

One Pb atom

Two Cl atoms

Six O atoms

Classifying Elements as Atomic or Molecular (Section 5.4)

Most elements exist as atomic elements, their basic units in nature being individual atoms. However, several elements (H_2, N_2, O_2, F_2, Cl_2, Br_2, and I_2) exist as molecular elements, their basic units in nature being diatomic molecules.

| EXAMPLE 5.19 | **Classifying Elements as Atomic or Molecular** |

Classify each of the following elements as atomic or molecular: Na, I, N.

Solution:

Na: atomic
I: molecular (I_2)
N: molecular (N_2)

Classifying Compounds as Ionic or Molecular (Section 5.4)

Compounds containing a metal and a nonmetal are ionic. Metals that form more than one ion, typical of transition metals, are Type II.

Compounds containing a metal and one or more nonmetals are ionic. Metals that form one type of ion—typical of Group I, Group II, and aluminum—are Type I.

Compounds composed of nonmetals are molecular.

| EXAMPLE 5.20 | **Classifying Compounds as Ionic or Molecular** |

Classify each of the following compounds as ionic or molecular. If they are ionic, classify them as Type I or Type II ionic compounds:

$FeCl_3$, K_2SO_4, CCl_4

Solution:

$FeCl_3$: ionic, Type II
        Iron (III) chloride

K_2SO_4: ionic, Type I
        potassium

CCl_4: molecular
        Carbon Chloride

Writing Formulas for Ionic Compounds (Section 5.5)

1. Write the symbol for the metal ion followed by the symbol for the nonmetal ion (or polyatomic ion) and their charges. These charges can be deduced from the group numbers in the periodic table. (In the case of polyatomic ions, the charges come from Table 5.6.)

2. Make the magnitude of the charge on each ion become the subscript for the other ion.

3. Check to see if the subscripts can be reduced to simpler whole numbers. Subscripts of 1 can be dropped, since they are normally implied.

4. Check that the sum of the charges of the cations exactly cancels the sum of the charges of the anions.

EXAMPLE 5.21 Writing Formulas for Ionic Compounds

Write a formula for the compound that forms from lithium and sulfate ions.

Solution:

$$Li^+ \quad SO_4^{2-}$$

$$Li_2(SO_4)$$

In this case, the subscripts cannot be further reduced.

$$Li_2SO_4$$

Cations: Anions:

$$2(1+) = 2+ \qquad\qquad 2-$$

Naming Type I Binary Ionic Compounds (Section 5.7)

The name of the metal is unchanged. The name of the nonmetal is its base name with the ending -ide.

EXAMPLE 5.22 Naming Type I Binary Ionic Compounds

Give the name for the compound Al_2O_3.

Solution:

aluminum oxide

Naming Type II Binary Ionic Compounds (Section 5.7)

Since the name of Type II compounds includes the charge of the metal ion, we must first find that charge. To do this, compute the total charge of the nonmetal ions.

The total charge of the metal ions must equal the total charge of the nonmetal ions, but have the opposite sign.

The name of the compound is the name of the metal ion, followed by the charge of the metal ion, followed by the base name of the nonmetal + -ide.

EXAMPLE 5.23 Naming Type II Binary Ionic Compounds

Give the name for the compound Fe_2S_3.

Solution:

$$3 \text{ sulfide ions} \times (2-) = 6-$$

$$2 \text{ iron ions} \times (?) = 6+$$
$$? = 3+$$

Charge of each iron ion $= 3+$

iron(III) sulfide

Naming Compounds Containing a Polyatomic Ion (Section 5.7)

Name Type I and Type II ionic compounds containing a polyatomic ion in the normal way, except substitute the name of the polyatomic ion (from Table 5.6) in place of the nonmetal. (This example is Type II.)

The charge on the metal ion must be equal in magnitude to the sum of the charges of the polyatomic ions but opposite in sign.

The name of the compound is the name of the metal ion, followed by the charge of the metal ion, followed by the name of the polyatomic ion.

EXAMPLE 5.24 Naming Compounds Containing a Polyatomic Ion

Give the name for the compound $Co(ClO_4)_2$.

Solution:

$$2 \text{ perchlorate ions} \times (1-) = 2-$$
$$\text{Charge of cobalt ion} = 2+$$

cobalt(II) perchlorate

Naming Molecular Compounds (Section 5.8)

The name consists of a prefix indicating the number of atoms of the first element, followed by the name of the first element, and a prefix for the number of atoms of the second element followed by the base name of the second element plus the suffix -*ide*. When *mono-* occurs on the first element, it is normally dropped.

| EXAMPLE 5.25 | Naming Molecular Compounds |

Name the compound NO_2.

Solution:
nitrogen dioxide

Naming Binary Acids (Section 5.9)

The name begins with *hydro-*, followed by the base name of the nonmetal, plus the suffix -*ic* and then the word *acid*.

| EXAMPLE 5.26 | Naming Binary Acids |

Name the acid HI.

Solution:
hydroiodic acid

Naming Oxyacids with an Oxyanion Ending in -*ate* (Section 5.9)

The name is the base name of the oxyanion + -*ic*, followed by the word *acid* (sulfate violates the rule somewhat, since in strict terms, the base name would be *sulf*).

| EXAMPLE 5.27 | Naming Oxyacids with an Oxyanion Ending in -*ate* |

Name the acid H_2SO_4.

Solution:
The oxyanion is sulfate. The name of the acid is *sulfuric acid*.

Naming Oxyacids with an Oxyanion Ending in -*ite* (Section 5.9)

The name is the base name of the oxyanion + -*ous*, followed by the word *acid*.

| EXAMPLE 5.28 | Naming Oxyacids with an Oxyanion Ending in -*ite* |

Name the acid $HClO_2$.

Solution:
The oxyanion is chlorite. The name of the acid is *chlorous acid*.

Calculating Formula Mass (Section 5.11)

The formula mass is the sum of the atomic masses of all the atoms in the chemical formula. In determining the number of each type of atom, don't forget to multiply subscripts inside parentheses by subscripts outside parentheses.

| EXAMPLE 5.29 | Calculating Formula Mass |

Calculate the formula mass of $Mg(NO_3)_2$

Solution:

$$\text{Formula mass} = 24.31 + 2(14.01) + 6(16.00)$$
$$= 148.33 \text{ amu}$$

🌑 Key Terms

acid [5.9]
atomic element [5.4]
binary acid [5.9]
binary compound [5.7]
chemical formula [5.3]

formula mass [5.11]
formula unit [5.4]
ionic compound [5.4]
law of constant
   composition [5.2]

molecular
   compound [5.4]
molecular element [5.4]
oxyacid [5.9]
oxyanion [5.7]

polyatomic ion [5.7]
transition metals [5.7]
Type I compound [5.7]
Type II compound [5.7]

Exercises

Questions

1. Do the properties of an element change when it combines with another element to form a compound? Explain.
2. How would the world be different if elements did not combine to form compounds?
3. What is the law of constant composition? Who discovered it?
4. What is a chemical formula? Give some examples.
5. In a chemical formula, which element is listed first?
6. In a chemical formula, how do you calculate the number of atoms of an element within parentheses? Give an example.
7. What is the difference between a molecular element and an atomic element? List the elements that occur as diatomic molecules.
8. What is the difference between an ionic compound and a molecular compound?
9. What is the difference between a common name for a compound and a systematic name?
10. List the metals that form Type I ionic compounds. What are the group numbers of these metals?
11. Find the block in the periodic table of elements that tend to form Type II ionic compounds. What is the name of this block?

12. What is the basic form for the names of Type I ionic compounds?
13. What is the basic form for the names of Type II ionic compounds?
14. Why are numbers needed in the names of Type II ionic compounds?
15. How are compounds containing a polyatomic ion named?
16. What polyatomic ions have a 2− charge? What polyatomic ions have a 3− charge?
17. What is the basic form for the names of molecular compounds?
18. How many atoms does each of the following prefixes specify? *mono-, di-, tri-, tetra-, penta-, hexa-.*
19. What is the basic form for the names of binary acids?
20. What is the basic form for the name of oxyacids whose oxyanions end with *-ate*?
21. What is the basic form for the name of oxyacids whose oxyanions end with *-ite*?
22. What is the formula mass of a compound?

Problems

Constant Composition of Compounds

23. Two samples of sodium chloride were decomposed into their constituent elements. One sample produced 4.65 g of sodium and 7.16 g of chlorine, and the other sample produced 7.45 g of sodium and 11.5 g of chlorine. Are these results consistent with the law of constant composition? Show why or why not.

24. Two samples of carbon tetrachloride were decomposed into their constituent elements. One sample produced 32.4 g of carbon and 373 g of chlorine, and the other sample produced 12.3 g of carbon and 112 g of chlorine. Are these results consistent with the law of constant composition? Show why or why not.

25. Upon decomposition, one sample of magnesium fluoride produced 1.65 kg of magnesium and 2.57 kg of fluorine. A second sample produced 1.32 kg of magnesium. How much fluorine (in grams) did the second sample produce?

26. The mass ratio of sodium to fluorine in sodium fluoride is 1.21:1. A sample of sodium fluoride produced 34.5 g of sodium upon decomposition. How much fluorine (in grams) was formed?

27. Use the law of constant composition to complete the following table summarizing the amounts of nitrogen and oxygen produced upon the decomposition of several samples of dinitrogen monoxide.

	Mass N_2O	Mass N	Mass O
Sample A	2.85 g	1.82 g	1.03 g
Sample B	4.55 g	____	____
Sample C	____	____	1.35 g
Sample D	____	1.11 g	____

28. Use the law of constant composition to complete the following table summarizing the amounts of iron and chlorine formed produced upon the decomposition of several samples of iron(III) chloride.

	Mass $FeCl_3$	Mass Fe	Mass Cl
Sample A	3.785 g	1.302 g	2.483 g
Sample B	2.175 g	____	____
Sample C	____	2.012 g	____
Sample D	____	____	2.329 g

Chemical Formulas

29. Write a chemical formula for the compound containing one nitrogen atom for every three bromine atoms.

30. Write a chemical formula for the compound containing one carbon atom for every four chlorine atoms.

31. Write chemical formulas for compounds containing each of the following: Fe_2Cl_3
    (a) two iron atoms for every three oxygen atoms
    (b) one phosphorus atom for every three chlorine atoms PCl_3
    (c) one phosphorus atom for every five chlorine atoms PCl_5
    (d) two silver atoms for every oxygen atom Ag_2O

32. Write chemical formulas for compounds containing each of the following:
    (a) one calcium atom for every two chlorine atoms
    (b) two nitrogen atoms for every four oxygen atoms
    (c) one silicon atom for every two oxygen atoms
    (d) one zinc atom for every two chlorine atoms

33. How many oxygen atoms are in each of the following chemical formulas?
    (a) H_3PO_4 – 4
    (b) Na_2HPO_4 – 4
    (c) $Ca(HCO_3)_2$ – 6
    (d) $Ba(C_2H_3O_2)_2$ – 4

34. How many hydrogen atoms are in each of the formulas in Problem 33?

35. Determine the number of each type of atom in each of the following formulas.
    (a) $MgCl_2$
    (b) $NaNO_3$
    (c) $Ca(NO_2)_2$
    (d) $Sr(OH)_2$

36. Determine the number of each type of atom in each of the following formulas.
    (a) NH_4Cl
    (b) $Mg_3(PO_4)_2$
    (c) $NaCN$
    (d) $Ba(HCO_3)_2$

Molecular View of Elements and Compounds

37. Classify each of the following elements as atomic or molecular.
    (a) helium – molecular
    (b) chlorine – molecular
    (c) oxygen – molecular
    (d) sodium – atomic

38. Which of the following elements have molecules as their basic units?
    (a) hydrogen
    (b) argon
    (c) bromine
    (d) mercury

39. Classify each of the following compounds as ionic or molecular.
    (a) CS_2 – molecular
    (b) CuO – ionic
    (c) KI – ionic
    (d) PCl_3 – molecular

40. Classify each of the following compounds as ionic or molecular.
    (a) PtO_2
    (b) CF_2Cl_2
    (c) CO
    (d) SO_3

41. Match the substances on the left with the basic units that compose them on the right.

    helium — molecules

    CCl_4 — formula units

    K_2SO_4 — diatomic molecules

    bromine — single atoms

42. Match the substances on the left with the basic units that compose them on the right.

    NI_3 — molecules

    copper metal — single atoms

    $SrCl_2$ — diatomic molecules

    nitrogen — formula units

43. What are the basic units—single atoms, molecules, or formula units—that compose each of the following substances?
 (a) $BaBr_2$
 (b) Ne
 (c) I_2
 (d) CO

44. What are the basic units—single atoms, molecules, or formula units—that compose each of the following substances?
 (a) Rb_2O
 (b) N_2
 (c) $Fe(NO_3)_2$
 (d) N_2F_4

45. Classify each of the following compounds as ionic or molecular. If it is ionic, classify it as a Type I or Type II ionic compound.
 (a) KCl — 1
 (b) CBr_4 — *molecular*
 (c) NO_2 — *molecular*
 (d) $Sn(SO_4)_2$ — *II*

46. Classify each of the following compounds as ionic or molecular. If it is ionic, classify it as a Type I or Type II ionic compound.
 (a) $CoCl_2$
 (b) CF_4
 (c) $BaSO_4$
 (d) NO

Writing Formulas for Ionic Compounds

47. Write a formula for the ionic compound that forms from each of the following pairs of elements.
 (a) strontium and oxygen $Sr_2O_{-2} = SrO$
 (b) sodium and oxygen $-Na\,O\cdot 2 = Na_2O$
 (c) aluminum and sulfur $Al_3\,S_{-2} = Al_2S_3$
 (d) magnesium and bromine $Mg_2\,Br = MgBr_2$.

48. Write a formula for the ionic compound that forms from each of the following pairs of elements.
 (a) aluminum and oxygen
 (b) beryllium and chlorine
 (c) calcium and sulfur
 (d) strontium and iodine

49. Write a formula for the compound that forms from potassium and
 (a) acetate
 (b) chromate
 (c) phosphate
 (d) cyanide

50. Write a formula for the compound that forms from calcium and
 (a) hydroxide
 (b) carbonate
 (c) phosphate
 (d) hydrogen phosphate

51. Write formulas for the compounds that form from the element on the left and each element on the right.
 (a) K   N, O, F
 (b) Ba   N, O, F
 (c) Al   N, O, F

52. Write formulas for the compounds that form from the element on the left and each polyatomic ion on the right.
 (a) Rb $NO_3^-, SO_4^{2-}, PO_4^{3-}$
 (b) Sr $NO_3^-, SO_4^{2-}, PO_4^{3-}$
 (c) In $NO_3^-, SO_4^{2-}, PO_4^{3-}$
 (Assume In charge is 3+).

Naming Ionic Compounds

53. Name each of the following Type I ionic compounds.
 (a) CsCl   *cesium chloride*
 (b) $SrBr_2$ *stronium bromide*
 (c) K_2O *potassium oxide*
 (d) LiF   *Lithium flouride*

54. Name each of the following Type I ionic compounds.
 (a) LiI
 (b) MgS
 (c) BaF_2
 (d) NaF

55. Name each of the following Type II ionic compounds.
 (a) $CrCl_2$ *cromium (II) chloride*
 (b) $CrCl_3$ *cromium (III) chloride*
 (c) SnO_2 *tin (II) oxide*
 (d) PbI_2 *lead (II) iodide*

56. Name each of the following Type II ionic compounds.
 (a) $HgBr_2$
 (b) Fe_2O_3
 (c) CuI_2
 (d) $SnCl_4$

57. Determine whether each of the following ionic compounds is Type I or Type II and give each an appropriate name.
    (a) Cr_2O_3
    (b) NaI
    (c) $CaBr_2$
    (d) SnO

58. Determine whether each of the following ionic compounds is Type I or Type II and give each an appropriate name.
    (a) FeI_3
    (b) $PbCl_4$
    (c) SrI_2
    (d) BaO

59. Name each of the following ionic compounds containing a polyatomic ion.
    (a) $Ba(NO_3)_2$
    (b) $Pb(C_2H_3O_2)_2$
    (c) NH_4I
    (d) $KClO_3$
    (e) $CoSO_4$
    (f) $NaClO_4$

60. Name each of the following ionic compounds containing a polyatomic ion.
    (a) $Ba(OH)_2$
    (b) $Fe(OH)_3$
    (c) $CuNO_2$
    (d) $PbSO_4$
    (e) KClO
    (f) $Mg(C_2H_3O_2)_2$

61. Provide a name for each of the following polyatomic ions.
    (a) BrO^- perbrominite
    (b) BrO_2^- brominite
    (c) BrO_3^- brominate
    (d) BrO_4^- hypobrimate

62. Provide a name for each of the following polyatomic ions.
    (a) IO^- perionite
    (b) IO_2^- ionite
    (c) IO_3^- ionate
    (d) IO_4^- hypoio

63. Write a formula for each of the following ionic compounds.
    (a) copper(II) bromide $CuBr2$
    (b) silver nitrate AgN
    (c) potassium hydroxide KOH
    (d) sodium sulfate SSu
    (e) potassium hydrogen sulfate KHS
    (f) sodium hydrogen carbonate $NaHC2$

64. Write a formula for each of the following ionic compounds.
    (a) copper(I) chlorate
    (b) potassium permanganate
    (c) lead(II) chromate
    (d) calcium fluoride
    (e) iron(II) phosphate
    (f) lithium hydrogen sulfite

Naming Molecular Compounds

65. Name each of the following molecular compounds.
    (a) SO_2 sulfur oxide
    (b) NI_3 nitrogen iodide
    (c) BrF_5 bromine flouride
    (d) NO nitrogen oxide
    (e) N_4Se_4 nitrogen selenide

66. Name each of the following molecular compounds.
    (a) XeF_4
    (b) PI_3
    (c) SO_3
    (d) $SiCl_4$
    (e) I_2O_5

67. Write a formula for each of the following molecular compounds.
    (a) carbon monoxide CaO
    (b) disulfur tetrafluoride $S4Fl3$
    (c) dichlorine monoxide $Cl2O$
    (d) phosphorus pentafluoride $PFl5$
    (e) boron tribromide $BBr3$
    (f) diphosphorus pentasulfide $P2S5$

68. Write a formula for each of the following molecular compounds.
    (a) chlorine monoxide
    (b) xenon tetroxide
    (c) xenon hexafluoride
    (d) carbon tetrabromide
    (e) diboron tetrachloride
    (f) tetraphosphorus triselenide

69. Determine whether the name shown for each of the following molecular compounds is correct. If not, give the compound the correct name.
   (a) PBr_5 phosphorus(V) pentabromide
   (b) P_2O_3 phosphorus trioxide
   (c) SF_4 monosulfur hexafluoride
   (d) NF_3 nitrogen trifluoride

70. Determine whether the name shown for each of the following molecular compounds is correct. If not, give the compound the correct name.
   (a) NCl_3 nitrogen chloride
   (b) CI_4 carbon(IV) iodide
   (c) CO carbon oxide
   (d) SCl_4 sulfur tetrachloride

Naming Acids

71. Name each of the following acids.
   (a) $HClO_2$ Hydro clonic acid
   (b) HI Hydro ionic acid
   (c) H_2SO_4 Hydro sulfunc acid
   (d) HNO_3 Hydro nitros

72. Name each of the following acids.
   (a) H_2CO_3
   (b) $HC_2H_3O_2$
   (c) HNO_2
   (d) HCl

73. Write a formula for each of the following acids.
   (a) phosphoric acid
   (b) hydrobromic acid
   (c) sulfurous acid

74. Write a formula for each of the following acids.
   (a) hydrofluoric acid
   (b) hydrocyanic acid
   (c) chlorous acid

Formula Mass

75. Calculate the formula mass for each of the following compounds.
   (a) HNO_2
   (b) $CaCl_2$
   (c) CCl_4
   (d) $Mg(NO_3)_2$

76. Calculate the formula mass for each of the following compounds.
   (a) CO_2
   (b) $C_6H_{12}O_6$
   (c) $Fe(NO_3)_3$
   (d) C_8H_{18}

77. Arrange the following compounds in order of decreasing formula mass.

$Ag_2O, PtO_2, Al(NO_3)_3, PBr_3$

78. Arrange the following compounds in order of decreasing formula mass.

$WO_2, Rb_2SO_4, Pb(C_2H_3O_2)_2, RbI$

Cumulative Problems

79. Write a chemical formula for each of the following molecular models. (White = hydrogen; red = oxygen; black = carbon; blue = nitrogen; yellow = sulfur)

(a)

(b)

(c)

80. Write a chemical formula for each of the following molecular models. (White = hydrogen; red = oxygen; black = carbon; blue = nitrogen; yellow = sulfur)

(a)

(b)

(c)

81. How many chlorine atoms are there in each of the following?
    (a) three carbon tetrachloride molecules
    (b) two calcium chloride formula units
    (c) four phosphorous trichloride molecules
    (d) seven sodium chloride formula units

82. How many oxygen atoms are there in each of the following?
    (a) four dinitrogen monoxide molecules
    (b) two calcium carbonate formula units
    (c) three sulfur dioxide molecules
    (d) five perchlorate ions

83. Specify the number of hydrogen atoms (white) represented in each of the following:

(a)   (b)   (c)

84. Specify the number of oxygen atoms (red) represented in each of the following:

(a)   (b)   (c)

85. Complete the following table:

Formula	Type of Compound (Ionic, Molecular, Acid)	Name
N_2H_4	molecular	____
____	____	potassium chloride
H_2CrO_4	____	____
____	____	cobalt(III) cyanide

86. Complete the following table:

Formula	Type of Compound (Ionic, Molecular, Acid)	Name
$K_2Cr_2O_7$	ionic	____
HBr	____	hydrobromic acid
____	____	dinitrogen pentoxide
PbO_2	____	____

87. Determine whether each of the following names is correct for the given formula. If not, give the correct name.
    (a) $Ca(NO_2)_2$ calcium nitrate
    (b) K_2O dipotassium monoxide
    (c) PCl_3 phosphorus chloride
    (d) $PbCO_3$ lead(II) carbonate
    (e) KIO_2 potassium hypoiodite

88. Determine whether each of the following names is correct for the given formula. If not, give the correct name.
    (a) HNO_3 hydrogen nitrate
    (b) $NaClO$ sodium hypochlorite
    (c) CaI_2 calcium diiodide
    (d) $SnCrO_4$ tin chromate
    (e) $NaBrO_3$ sodium bromite

89. For each of the following compounds, give the correct formula and calculate the formula mass.
    (a) tin(IV) sulfate
    (b) nitrous acid
    (c) sodium bicarbonate
    (d) phosphorus pentafluoride

90. For each of the following compounds, give the correct formula and calculate the formula mass.
    (a) barium bromide
    (b) dinitrogen trioxide
    (c) copper(I) sulfate
    (d) hydrobromic acid

91. Name each of the following compounds and calculate its formula mass.
    (a) PtO_2
    (b) N_2O_5
    (c) $Al(ClO_3)_3$
    (d) PBr_5

92. Name each of the following compounds and calculate its formula mass.
    (a) $Al_2(SO_4)_3$
    (b) P_2O_3
    (c) $HClO$
    (d) $Cr(C_2H_3O_2)_3$

Highlight Problems

93. Examine each of the following substances and their molecular views and classify each as an atomic element, a molecular element, a molecular compound, or an ionic compound.

(a)

(b)

(c)

(d)

94. Molecules can be as small as a few atoms or as large as thousands of atoms. In 1962, Max F. Perutz and John C. Kendrew were awarded the Nobel Prize for their discovery of the structure of hemoglobin, a very large molecule that transports oxygen from the lungs to cells through the bloodstream. The chemical formula of hemoglobin is $C_{2952}H_{4664}O_{832}N_{812}S_8Fe_4$. Calculate the formula mass of hemoglobin.

▲ Max F. Perutz and John C. Kendrew won a Nobel Prize in 1962 for determining the structure of hemoglobin by X-ray diffraction.

▲ A model of the hemoglobin molecule.

95. Examine each of the following consumer product labels. Write chemical formulas for as many of the compounds as possible based on what we have learned in this chapter.

(a)

(b)

(c)

(d)

Nutrition Facts
Serving Size 1/4 tsp (1g)
Servings Per Container about 340

Amount Per Serving

Calories 0

	% Daily Value*
Total Fat 0g	0%
Sodium 95mg	4%
Total Carbohydrate 0g	0%
Protein 0g	

Calcium 2%

* Percent Daily Values are based on a 2,000 calorie diet.

INGREDIENTS: CORNSTARCH, SODIUM BICARB-ONATE, CALCIUM PHOSPHATE, SODIUM ALUMINUM SULFATE.

Answers to Skillbuilder Exercises

Skillbuilder 5.1 Yes, because in both cases
$$\frac{\text{Mass O}}{\text{Mass C}} = 1.3$$

Skillbuilder 5.2 (a) Ag_2S (b) N_2O (c) TiO_2

Skillbuilder 5.3 two K atoms, one S atom, four O atoms

Skillbuilder Plus, p. 122 two Al atoms, three S atoms, twelve O atoms

Skillbuilder 5.4 (a) molecular element (b) molecular compound (c) atomic element (d) ionic compound (e) ionic compound

Skillbuilder 5.5 Cs_2O

Skillbuilder 5.6 AlN

Skillbuilder 5.7 $CaBr_2$

Skillbuilder 5.8 potassium bromide

Skillbuilder Plus, p. 129 zinc nitride

Skillbuilder 5.9 lead(II) oxide

Skillbuilder 5.10 manganese(II) nitrate

Skillbuilder 5.11 dinitrogen tetroxide

Skillbuilder 5.12 hydroiodic acid

Skillbuilder 5.13 nitrous acid

Skillbuilder 5.15 44.02 amu

Answers to Conceptual Checkpoints

5.1 (b) This formula represents 2 Al atoms + 3(2 Cr atoms + 7 O atoms) = 29 atoms.
5.2 (b)

Chemical Composition

"By definition, a chemist believes in the existence of a new substance only when he has seen the substance, touched it, weighed and examined it, confronted it with acids, bottled it, and when he has determined its 'atomic weight.'"

Eve Curie (1904–)

6.1   How Much Sodium?

Sodium is an important dietary mineral consumed primarily as sodium chloride (table salt) and involved in bodily fluid regulation. Overconsumption of dietary sodium causes elevated body fluid levels that can lead to high blood pressure. High blood pressure, in turn, increases the risk of stroke and heart attack. Consequently, people with high blood pressure should limit their sodium intake. The FDA recommends that a person consume less than 2.4 g (2400 mg) of sodium per day. However, since sodium is usually consumed as sodium chloride, it is not always easy to know how much sodium is consumed. How many grams of sodium chloride can you consume and still stay below the FDA recommendation?

To answer this question, we need to know the *chemical composition* of sodium chloride. From Chapter 5, we know its formula, NaCl, so we know that there is one sodium ion to every chloride ion. However, since the masses of sodium and chlorine are different, the relationship between the mass of sodium and the mass of sodium chloride is not clear from just the chemical formula. In this chapter, we learn how to use the information in a chemical formula, together with atomic and formula masses, to calculate the amount of a constituent element in a given amount of a compound (or vice versa).

◀ Ordinary table salt is a compound called sodium chloride. The sodium within sodium chloride is linked to high blood pressure. In this chapter, we learn how to determine how much sodium is in a given amount of sodium chloride.

▲ The mining of iron requires knowing how much iron is in a given amount of iron ore.

▲ Estimating the threat of ozone depletion from chlorofluorocarbons requires knowing how much chlorine is in a given amount of a particular chlorofluorocarbon.

Chemical composition is important not just for assessing dietary sodium, but for addressing many other issues as well. A company that mines iron, for example, wants to know how much iron it can recover from a given amount of iron ore; a company interested in developing hydrogen as a potential fuel wants to know how much hydrogen it can extract from a given amount of water. Many environmental issues also require knowledge of chemical composition. For example, an estimate of the threat of ozone depletion requires knowing how much chlorine is in a given amount of a particular chlorofluorocarbon such as freon-12 (CF_2Cl_2). Answering these questions requires understanding the relationships inherent in a chemical formula and the relationship between numbers of atoms or molecules and their masses. In this chapter, we learn these relationships.

6.2   Counting Nails by the Pound

Some hardware stores sell nails by the pound. This is easier than selling them individually because customers often need hundreds of nails and counting them takes too long. However, a customer may still want to know the number of nails contained in a given weight of nails. This problem is similar to asking how many atoms are in a given mass of an element. With atoms, however, we *must* use their mass as a way to count them because atoms are too small and too numerous to count individually. Even if you could see atoms and counted them twenty-four hours a day as long as you lived, you would barely begin to count the number of atoms in something as small as a sand grain. However, just as the hardware store customer wants to know how many nails are in a given weight, we want to know the number of atoms in a given mass. How do we do that?

Suppose the hardware store customer buys 2.60 lb of medium-sized nails. Suppose further that a dozen nails weigh 0.150 lb. How many nails did the customer buy? This calculation requires two conversions: one between pounds and dozens and another between dozens and number of nails. The conversion factor for the first part is the weight per dozen nails.

$$0.150 \text{ lb nails} = 1 \text{ doz nails}$$

The conversion factor for the second part is the number of nails in one dozen.

$$1 \text{ doz nails} = 12 \text{ nails}$$

3.4 lbs nails

The solution map for the problem is:

$$\frac{1 \text{ doz nails}}{0.150 \text{ lb nails}} \qquad \frac{12 \text{ nails}}{\text{doz nails}}$$

Beginning with 2.60 lb and using the solution map as a guide, we convert from lb to number of nails.

$$2.60 \text{ lb nails} \times \frac{1 \text{ doz nails}}{0.150 \text{ lb nails}} \times \frac{12 \text{ nails}}{1 \text{ doz nails}} = 208 \text{ nails}$$

8.25 grams carbon

▲ Asking how many nails are in a given weight of nails is similar to asking how many atoms are in a given mass of an element. In both cases, we count the objects by weighing them.

The customer who bought 2.60 lb of nails got 208 nails. He counted the nails by weighing them. If the customer purchased a different size of nail, the first conversion factor—relating pounds to dozens—would change, but the second conversion factor would not. One dozen corresponds to twelve nails, regardless of their size.

6.3 Counting Atoms by the Gram

▲ Twenty-two copper pennies contain approximately 1 mol of copper atoms.

Beginning in 1982, pennies became almost all zinc with only a copper plating. Prior to 1982, pennies were mostly copper.

The size of the mole is actually an empirically measured quantity.

Determining the number of atoms in a sample with a certain mass is similar to determining the number of nails in a sample with a certain weight, but the numbers are different. With nails, we used a dozen as a convenient number in our conversions, but a dozen is too small to use with atoms. We need a larger number because atoms are so small. The chemist's "dozen" is called the **mole (mol)** and has a value of 6.022×10^{23}.

$$1 \text{ mol} = 6.022 \times 10^{23}$$

This number is also called **Avogadro's number**, named after Amadeo Avogadro (1776–1856).

The first thing to understand about the mole is that it can specify Avogadro's number of anything. For example, one mole of marbles corresponds to 6.022×10^{23} marbles, and one mole of sand grains corresponds to 6.022×10^{23} sand grains. *One mole of anything is 6.022×10^{23} units of that thing.* One mole of atoms, ions, or molecules generally makes up objects of reasonable size. For example, twenty-two copper pennies contain approximately 1 mol of copper (Cu) atoms, and a couple of large helium balloons contain approximately 1 mol of helium (He) atoms.

The second thing to understand about the mole is how it gets its specific value. *The numerical value of the mole is defined as being equal to the number of atoms in exactly 12 g of pure carbon-12.*

This definition of the mole gives us a relationship between mass (grams of carbon) and number of atoms (Avogadro's number). This relationship, as we will see shortly, allows us to count atoms by weighing them.

Converting between Moles and Number of Atoms

Converting between moles and number of atoms is similar to converting between dozens and number of nails. To convert between moles of atoms and number of atoms we simply use the conversion factors:

$$\frac{1 \text{ mol atoms}}{6.022 \times 10^{23} \text{ atoms}} \quad \text{or} \quad \frac{6.022 \times 10^{23} \text{ atoms}}{1 \text{ mol atoms}}$$

For example, suppose we want to convert 3.5 mol of helium to the number of helium atoms. We set up the problem in the standard way.

Given: 3.5 mol He

Find: He atoms

Conversion Factor: 1 mol He = 6.022×10^{23} He atoms

Solution Map: We then draw a solution map showing the conversion from moles of He to He atoms.

$$\frac{6.022 \times 10^{23} \text{ He atoms}}{1 \text{ mol He}}$$

▲ Two large helium balloons contain approximately 1 mol of helium atoms.

Solution: Beginning with 3.5 mol He, we use the conversion factor to get to He atoms.

$$3.5 \text{ mol He} \times \frac{6.022 \times 10^{23} \text{ He atoms}}{1 \text{ mol He}} = 2.1 \times 10^{24} \text{ He atoms}$$

EXAMPLE 6.1   Converting between Moles and Number of Atoms

A silver ring contains 1.1×10^{22} silver atoms. How many moles of silver are in the ring?

Set up the problem in the normal way. You are given the number of silver atoms and asked to find the number of moles. The conversion factor is Avogadro's number.	**Given:** 1.1×10^{22} Ag atoms **Find:** mol Ag **Conversion Factor:** 1 mol Ag = 6.022×10^{23} Ag atoms
Build the solution map, beginning with silver atoms and ending at moles.	**Solution Map:** $$\frac{1 \text{ mol Ag}}{6.022 \times 10^{23} \text{ Ag atoms}}$$
Follow the solution map to solve the problem. Beginning with 1.1×10^{22} Ag atoms, use the conversion factor to get to moles of Ag.	**Solution:** $$1.1 \times 10^{22} \text{ Ag atoms} \times \frac{1 \text{ mol Ag}}{6.022 \times 10^{23} \text{ Ag atoms}} = 1.8 \times 10^{-2} \text{ mol Ag}$$

SKILLBUILDER 6.1   Converting between Moles and Number of Atoms

How many gold atoms are in a pure gold ring containing 8.83×10^{-2} mol Au?

Converting between Grams and Moles of an Element

We just learned how to convert between moles and number of atoms. As in our nail analogy, we need one more conversion factor to convert from the mass of a sample to the number of atoms in the sample. For nails, we used the weight of one dozen nails; for atoms, we need the mass of one mole of atoms.

> The mass of 1 mol of atoms of an element is called the *molar mass*. The value of an element's molar mass in grams per mole is numerically equal to the element's atomic mass in atomic mass units.

Since Avogadro's number is defined as the number of atoms in exactly 12 g of carbon-12, and since the amu is defined as 1/12 of the mass of carbon-12, it follows that the molar mass—the mass of 1 mol of atoms in grams—is numerically equal to the atomic mass in amu. For example, copper has an atomic mass of 63.55 amu; therefore, 1 mol of copper atoms has a mass of 63.55 g, and the molar mass of copper is 63.55 g/mol. Just as the weight of 1 doz nails changes for different nails, so the mass of 1 mol of atoms changes for different elements: 1 mol of sulfur atoms (sulfur atoms are lighter than copper atoms) has a mass of 32.07 g; 1 mol of carbon atoms (lighter than sulfur) has a mass of 12.01 g; and 1 mol of lithium atoms (lighter yet) has a mass of 6.94 g.

$$32.07 \text{ g sulfur} = 1 \text{ mol sulfur} = 6.022 \times 10^{23} \text{ S atoms}$$
$$12.01 \text{ g carbon} = 1 \text{ mol carbon} = 6.022 \times 10^{23} \text{ C atoms}$$
$$6.94 \text{ g lithium} = 1 \text{ mol lithium} = 6.022 \times 10^{23} \text{ Li atoms}$$

▶ Figure 6.1   **The mass of 1 mol**
(a) Each of these pictures shows the same number of nails: twelve. As you can see, twelve large nails have more weight and occupy more space than twelve small nails. The same is true for atoms. **(b)** Each of these samples has the same number of atoms: 6.022×10^{23}. Since sulfur atoms are more massive and larger than carbon atoms, 1 mol of S atoms is heavier and occupies more space than 1 mol of C atoms.

1 dozen large nails

1 dozen small nails

(a)

1 mole S (32.07 g)

1 mole C (12.01 g)

(b)

The lighter the atom, the less mass in a mole of that atom (▲ Figure 6.1).

Therefore, the molar mass of any element becomes a conversion factor between grams of that element and moles of that element. For carbon:

$$12.01 \text{ g C} = 1 \text{ mol C} \quad \text{or} \quad \frac{12.01 \text{ g C}}{1 \text{ mol C}} \quad \text{or} \quad \frac{1 \text{ mol C}}{12.01 \text{ g C}}$$

A 0.58-g diamond would be about a three-carat diamond.

Suppose we want to calculate the number of moles of carbon in a 0.58-g diamond (pure carbon). We set up the problem in the standard way.

Given: 0.58 g C

Find: mol C

Conversion Factor:

12.01 g C = 1 mol C

Solution Map: We then draw a solution map showing the conversion from grams of C to moles of C. The conversion factor is the molar mass of carbon.

$$\frac{1 \text{ mol}}{12.01 \text{ g}}$$

Solution: Beginning with 0.58 g C, we use the conversion factor to get to mol C.

$$0.58 \text{ g C} \times \frac{1 \text{ mol C}}{12.01 \text{ g C}} = 4.8 \times 10^{-2} \text{ mol C}$$

EXAMPLE 6.2	The Mole Concept—Converting between Grams and Moles

Calculate the number of moles of sulfur in 57.8 g of sulfur.

Set up the problem in the normal way. You are given the mass of sulfur and asked to find the number of moles. The conversion factor is the molar mass of sulfur.	**Given:** 57.8 g S **Find:** mol S **Conversion Factor:** 32.07 g S = 1 mol S
Draw a solution map showing the conversion from g S to mol S. The conversion factor is the molar mass of sulfur.	**Solution Map:** $$\frac{1 \text{ mol S}}{32.07 \text{ g S}}$$
Follow the solution map to solve the problem. Begin with 57.8 g S and use the conversion factor to get to mol S.	**Solution:** $$57.8 \ \cancel{\text{g S}} \times \frac{1 \text{ mol S}}{32.07 \ \cancel{\text{g S}}} = 1.80 \text{ mol S}$$

SKILLBUILDER 6.2	The Mole Concept—Converting between Grams and Moles

• Calculate the number of grams of sulfur in 2.78 mol of sulfur.

Converting between Grams of an Element and Number of Atoms

Now, suppose we want to know the number of carbon *atoms* in the 0.58-g diamond. We first convert from grams to moles and then from moles to number of atoms. The solution map is:

$$\frac{1 \text{ mol C}}{12.01 \text{ g C}} \qquad \frac{6.022 \times 10^{23} \text{ C atoms}}{\text{mol C}}$$

Notice the similarity between this solution map and the one we used for nails:

$$\frac{1 \text{ doz nails}}{0.150 \text{ lb nails}} \qquad \frac{12 \text{ nails}}{\text{doz nails}}$$

Beginning with 0.58 g carbon and using the solution map as a guide, we convert to the number of carbon atoms.

$$0.58 \ \cancel{\text{g C}} \times \frac{1 \ \cancel{\text{mol C}}}{12.01 \ \cancel{\text{g C}}} \times \frac{6.022 \times 10^{23} \text{ C atoms}}{\cancel{\text{mol C}}} = 2.9 \times 10^{22} \text{ C atoms}$$

EXAMPLE 6.3	The Mole Concept—Converting between Grams and Number of Atoms

How many aluminum atoms are in an aluminum can with a mass of 16.2 g?

Set up the problem in the normal way. You are given the mass of aluminum and asked to find the number of aluminum atoms. The required conversion factors are the molar mass of aluminum and the number of atoms in a mole.	**Given:** 16.2 g Al **Find:** Al atoms **Conversion Factors:** 26.98 g Al = 1 mol Al (molar mass of Al) $6.022 \times 10^{23} = 1$ mol

The solution map has two steps. In the first step, convert from g Al to mol Al. In the second step, convert from mol Al to the number of Al atoms.

Solution Map:

$$\dfrac{1 \text{ mol Al}}{26.98 \text{ g Al}} \qquad \dfrac{6.022 \times 10^{23} \text{ Al atoms}}{\text{mol Al}}$$

Follow the solution map to solve the problem, beginning with 16.2 g Al and multiplying by the appropriate conversion factors to arrive at Al atoms.

Solution:

$$16.2 \ \cancel{\text{g Al}} \times \dfrac{1 \ \cancel{\text{mol Al}}}{26.98 \ \cancel{\text{g Al}}} \times \dfrac{6.022 \times 10^{23} \text{ Al atoms}}{1 \ \cancel{\text{mol Al}}} = 3.62 \times 10^{23} \text{ Al atoms}$$

SKILLBUILDER 6.3   The Mole Concept—Converting between Grams and Number of Atoms

 Calculate the mass of 1.23×10^{24} helium atoms.

Before we move on, notice that numbers with large exponents, such as 6.022×10^{23}, are deceptively large. Twenty-two copper pennies contain 6.022×10^{23} or 1 mol of copper atoms, but 6.022×10^{23} pennies would cover Earth's entire surface to a depth of 300 m. Even objects small by everyday standards occupy a huge space when we have a mole of them. For example, one crystal of granulated sugar has a mass of less than 1 mg and a diameter of less than 0.1 mm, yet 1 mol of sugar crystals would cover the state of Texas to a depth of several feet. For every increase of 1 in the exponent of a number, the number increases by 10. So a number with an exponent of 23 is incredibly large. A mole has to be a large number, however, because atoms are so small.

CONCEPTUAL CHECKPOINT 6.1

Which of these statements is *always* true for samples of atomic elements, regardless of the type of element present in the samples?

(a) If two samples of different elements contain the same number of atoms, they must contain the same number of moles.

(b) If two samples of different elements have the same mass, they must contain the same number of moles.

(c) If two samples of different elements have the same mass, they must contain the same number of atoms.

6.4   Counting Molecules by the Gram

Remember, ionic compounds do not contain individual molecules. In loose language, the smallest electrically neutral collection of ions is sometimes called a molecule, but is more correctly called a formula unit.

The calculations we just performed for atoms can also be applied to molecules for covalent compounds or formula units for ionic compounds. We first look at converting between the mass of a compound and moles of the compound, then we turn to calculating the number of molecules (or formula units) from mass.

Converting between Grams and Moles of a Compound

Remember, the formula mass for a compound is simply the sum of the atomic masses of all of the atoms in a chemical formula.

For elements, the molar mass is the mass of 1 mol of atoms of that element. For compounds, the molar mass is the mass of 1 mol of molecules or formula units of that compound. The molar mass of a compound in grams per mole is numerically equal to the formula mass of the compound in atomic mass units. For example, the formula mass of CO_2 is:

$$\begin{aligned} \text{Formula mass} &= 1(\text{Atomic mass of C}) + 2(\text{Atomic mass of O}) \\ &= 1(12.01 \text{ amu}) + 2(16.00 \text{ amu}) \\ &= 44.01 \text{ amu} \end{aligned}$$

The molar mass is therefore:

Molar mass = 44.01 g/mol

Just as the molar mass of an element serves as a conversion factor between grams and moles of that element, so the molar mass of a compound serves as a conversion factor between grams and moles of that compound. For example, suppose we want to find the number of moles in a 22.5-g sample of dry ice (solid CO_2). We set up the problem in the normal way.

Given: 22.5 g CO_2

Find: mol CO_2

Conversion Factor: 44.01 g CO_2 = 1 mol CO_2 (molar mass of CO_2)

Solution Map: The solution map shows how the molar mass converts grams of the compound to moles of the compound.

$$\dfrac{1\ \text{mol CO}_2}{44.01\ \text{g CO}_2}$$

Solution:

$$22.5\ \cancel{g} \times \dfrac{1\ \text{mol CO}_2}{44.01\ \cancel{g}} = 0.511\ \text{mol CO}_2$$

EXAMPLE 6.4   The Mole Concept—Converting between Grams and Moles for Compounds

Calculate the mass (in grams) of 1.75 mol of water.

Set up the problem in the normal way. You are given moles of water and asked to find the mass. The conversion factor is the molar mass of water.

Given: 1.75 mol H_2O

Find: g H_2O

Conversion Factor:

$$\begin{aligned} H_2O\ \text{molar mass} &= 2(\text{Atomic mass H}) + 1(\text{Atomic mass O}) \\ &= 2(1.01) + 1(16.00) \\ &= 18.02\ \text{g/mol} \end{aligned}$$

Draw a solution map showing the conversion from mol H_2O to g H_2O.

Solution Map:

$$\dfrac{18.02\ \text{g H}_2O}{1\ \text{mol H}_2O}$$

Follow the solution map to solve the problem. Begin with 1.75 mol of water and use the molar mass to convert to grams of water.

Solution:

$$1.75\ \cancel{\text{mol H}_2O} \times \dfrac{18.02\ \text{g H}_2O}{\cancel{\text{mol H}_2O}} = 31.5\ \text{g H}_2O$$

SKILLBUILDER 6.4   The Mole Concept—Converting between Grams and Moles

Calculate the number of moles of NO_2 in 1.18 g of NO_2.

Converting between Grams of a Compound and Number of Molecules

Suppose that we want to find the *number of CO_2 molecules* in a sample of dry ice (solid CO_2) with a mass of 22.5 g.
The solution map for the problem is:

$$g\ CO_2 \longrightarrow mol\ CO_2 \longrightarrow CO_2\ molecules$$

$$\frac{1\ mol\ CO_2}{44.01\ g\ CO_2} \qquad \frac{6.022 \times 10^{23}\ CO_2\ molecules}{1\ mol\ CO_2}$$

Notice that the first part of the solution map is identical to computing the number of moles of CO_2 in 22.5 g of dry ice. The second part of the solution map shows the conversion from moles to number of molecules. Following the solution map, we get:

$$22.5\ \cancel{g\ CO_2} \times \frac{1\ \cancel{mol\ CO_2}}{44.01\ \cancel{g\ CO_2}} \times \frac{6.022 \times 10^{23}\ CO_2\ molecules}{1\ \cancel{mol\ CO_2}}$$
$$= 3.08 \times 10^{23}\ CO_2\ molecules$$

EXAMPLE 6.5   The Mole Concept—Converting between Mass of a Compound and Number of Molecules

Find the mass of 4.78×10^{24} NO_2 molecules.

Set up the problem in the normal way. You are given the number of NO_2 molecules and asked to find the mass. The required conversion factors are the molar mass of NO_2 and the number of molecules in a mole.

Given: 4.78×10^{24} NO_2 molecules

Find: g NO_2

Conversion Factor: $6.022 \times 10^{23} = 1$ mol

$$NO_2\ molar\ mass = 1(Atomic\ mass\ N) + 2(Atomic\ mass\ O)$$
$$= 14.01 + 2(16.00)$$
$$= 46.01\ g/mol$$

The solution map has two steps. In the first step, convert from molecules of NO_2 to moles of NO_2. In the second step, convert from moles of NO_2 to mass of NO_2.

Solution Map:

$$NO_2\ molecules \longrightarrow mol\ NO_2 \longrightarrow g\ NO_2$$

$$\frac{1\ mol\ NO_2}{6.022 \times 10^{23}\ NO_2\ molecules} \qquad \frac{46.01\ g\ NO_2}{1\ mol\ NO_2}$$

Using the solution map as a guide, begin with molecules of NO_2 and multiply by the appropriate conversion factors to arrive at g NO_2.

Solution:

$$4.78 \times 10^{24}\ \cancel{NO_2\ molecules} \times \frac{1\ \cancel{mol\ NO_2}}{6.022 \times 10^{23}\ \cancel{NO_2\ molecules}} \times$$
$$\frac{46.01\ g\ NO_2}{1\ \cancel{mol\ NO_2}} = 365\ g\ NO_2$$

SKILLBUILDER 6.5   The Mole Concept—Converting between Mass and Number of Molecules

How many H_2O molecules are in a sample of water with a mass of 3.64 g?

CONCEPTUAL CHECKPOINT 6.2

If we wanted the formula mass of a compound in amu to equal the molar mass of the compound in kilograms rather than in grams,

(a) the size of the mole would have to be larger than Avogadro's number.

(b) the size of the mole would have to be smaller than Avogadro's number.

(c) the size of the mole would not be affected.

6.5   Chemical Formulas as Conversion Factors

▲ From our knowledge of clovers, we know that each clover has three leaves. We can express that as an equivalence: 3 leaves ≡ 1 clover.

We are almost ready to address the sodium problem in our opening example. To determine how much of a particular element (such as sodium) is in a given amount of a particular compound (such as sodium chloride), we must understand the numerical relationships inherent in a chemical formula. We can understand these relationships with a simple analogy: Asking how much sodium is in a given amount of sodium chloride is much like asking how many leaves are on a given number of clovers. For example, suppose we want to know how many leaves are on 14 clovers. We need a conversion factor between leaves and clovers. For clovers, the conversion factor comes from our knowledge about them—we know that each clover has 3 leaves. We write:

$$3 \text{ leaves} \equiv 1 \text{ clover}$$

Like other conversion factors, this equivalence gives the relationship between leaves and clovers. We use the equivalence sign (≡) because while 3 leaves do not equal 1 clover, 3 leaves are equivalent to one clover, meaning that each clover must have 3 leaves to be complete. With this conversion factor, we can easily find the number of leaves in 14 clovers. The solution map is:

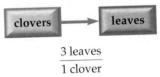

$$\frac{3 \text{ leaves}}{1 \text{ clover}}$$

We solve the problem by beginning with clovers and converting to leaves.

$$14 \text{ clovers} \times \frac{3 \text{ leaves}}{1 \text{ clover}} = 42 \text{ leaves}$$

Similarly, a chemical formula gives us equivalences between elements for a particular compound. For example, the formula for carbon dioxide (CO_2) means there are two O atoms per CO_2 molecule. We write this as:

$$2 \text{ O atoms} \equiv 1 \text{ } CO_2 \text{ molecule}$$

Just as 3 leaves ≡ 1 clover can also be written as 3 dozen leaves ≡ 1 dozen clovers, for molecules we can write:

$$2 \text{ doz O atoms} \equiv 1 \text{ doz } CO_2 \text{ molecules}$$

However, for atoms and molecules, we normally work in moles.

$$2 \text{ mol O} \equiv 1 \text{ mol } CO_2$$

With conversion factors such as these—which come directly from the chemical formula—we can determine the amounts of the constituent elements present in a given amount of a compound.

Chemical formulas are covered in Chapter 5.

► Each of these shows an equivalence.

8 legs ≡ 1 spider   4 legs ≡ 1 chair   2 H atoms ≡ 1 H$_2$O molecule

 ## Converting between Moles of a Compound and Moles of a Constituent Element

Suppose we want to know the number of moles of O in 18 mol of CO_2. Our solution map is:

$$\boxed{\text{mol } CO_2} \longrightarrow \boxed{\text{mol O}}$$

$$\frac{2 \text{ mol O}}{1 \text{ mol } CO_2}$$

We can then calculate the moles of O.

$$18 \text{ mol } CO_2 \times \frac{2 \text{ mol O}}{1 \text{ mol } CO_2} = 36 \text{ mol O}$$

EXAMPLE 6.6 **Chemical Formulas as Conversion Factors—Converting between Moles of a Compound and Moles of a Constituent Element**

Determine the number of moles of O in 1.7 mol of $CaCO_3$.

Set up the problem in the normal way. You are given the number of moles of $CaCO_3$ and asked to find the number of moles of O. The conversion factor is obtained from the chemical formula, which indicates three O atoms for every $CaCO_3$ unit.	**Given:** 1.7 mol $CaCO_3$ **Find:** mol O **Conversion Factor:** 3 mol O ≡ 1 mol $CaCO_3$
The solution map shows how the conversion factor from the chemical formula converts moles of $CaCO_3$ into moles of O.	**Solution Map:** $$\boxed{\text{mol } CaCO_3} \longrightarrow \boxed{\text{mol O}}$$ $$\frac{3 \text{ mol O}}{1 \text{ mol } CaCO_3}$$
Follow the solution map to solve the problem. The subscripts in a chemical formula are exact, so they never limit significant figures.	**Solution:** $$1.7 \text{ mol } CaCO_3 \times \frac{3 \text{ mol O}}{1 \text{ mol } CaCO_3} = 5.1 \text{ mol O}$$

SKILLBUILDER 6.6   **Chemical Formulas as Conversion Factors—Converting between Moles of a Compound and Moles of a Constituent Element**

Determine the number of moles of O in 1.4 mol of H_2SO_4.

Converting between Grams of a Compound and Grams of a Constituent Element

Now, we have everything we need to solve our sodium problem. Suppose we want to know how many grams of sodium there are in 15 g of NaCl. The chemical formula gives us the relationship between moles of Na and moles of NaCl:

$$1 \text{ mol Na} \equiv 1 \text{ mol NaCl}$$

To use this relationship, we need *mol* NaCl. But, we have *g* NaCl. We can, however, use the *molar mass* of NaCl to convert from g NaCl to mol NaCl. Then we use the conversion factor from the chemical formula to convert to mol Na. Finally, we use the molar mass of Na to convert to g Na. The solution map is:

g NaCl	mol NaCl	mol Na	g Na
	$\dfrac{1 \text{ mol NaCl}}{58.44 \text{ g NaCl}}$	$\dfrac{1 \text{ mol Na}}{1 \text{ mol NaCl}}$	$\dfrac{22.99 \text{ g Na}}{1 \text{ mol Na}}$

Notice that we must convert from g NaCl to mol NaCl *before* we can use the chemical formula as a conversion factor.

> The chemical formula gives us a relationship between moles of substances, not between grams.

We follow the solution map to solve the problem.

$$15 \text{ g NaCl} \times \frac{1 \text{ mol NaCl}}{58.44 \text{ g NaCl}} \times \frac{1 \text{ mol Na}}{1 \text{ mol NaCl}} \times \frac{22.99 \text{ g Na}}{1 \text{ mol Na}} = 5.9 \text{ g Na}$$

The general form for solving problems where you are asked to find the mass of an element present in a given mass of a compound is:

Mass compound ⟶ **Moles** compound ⟶ **Moles** element ⟶ **Mass** element

The conversions between mass and moles are accomplished using the atomic or molar mass, and the conversion between moles and moles is accomplished using the relationships inherent in the chemical formula (▼ Figure 6.2).

1 mol CCl_4 ≡ 4 mol Cl

▲ **Figure 6.2   Mole relationships from a chemical formula**   The relationships inherent in a chemical formula allow us to convert between moles of the compound and moles of a constituent element (or vice versa).

EXAMPLE 6.7   **Chemical Formulas as Conversion Factors—Converting between Grams of a Compound and Grams of a Constituent Element**

Carvone ($C_{10}H_{14}O$) is the main component of spearmint oil. It has a pleasant aroma and mint flavor. Carvone is often added to chewing gum, liqueurs, soaps, and perfumes. Find the mass of carbon in 55.4 g of carvone.

Extract the important information from the problem in the normal way. You are given the mass of carvone and asked to find the mass of one of its constituent elements.	**Given:** 55.4 g $C_{10}H_{14}O$ **MOLECULE** Carvone **Find:** g C **Conversion Factors:**

You need three conversion factors. The first is the molar mass of carvone.	Molar mass = $10(12.01) + 14(1.01) + 1(16.00)$
	          = $120.1 + 14.14 + 16.00$
	          = 150.2 g/mol

The second conversion factor is the relationship between moles of C and moles of carvone from the molecular formula.	10 mol C ≡ 1 mol $C_{10}H_{14}O$
The third conversion factor is the molar mass of carbon.	1 mol C = 12.01 g

The solution map is based on

Grams ⟶ Mole ⟶
          Mole ⟶ Grams

Remember, the conversion factor obtained from the chemical formula (10 mol C ≡ 1 mol $C_{10}H_{14}O$) applies only to moles; since we are given grams of carvone, we must first convert from g to mol.

Solution Map:

$$\dfrac{1 \text{ mol } C_{10}H_{14}O}{150.2 \text{ g } C_{10}H_{14}O} \qquad \dfrac{10 \text{ mol } C}{1 \text{ mol } C_{10}H_{14}O} \qquad \dfrac{12.01 \text{ g } C}{1 \text{ mol } C}$$

Follow the solution map to solve the problem, beginning with g $C_{10}H_{14}O$ and multiplying by the appropriate conversion factors to arrive at g C.

Solution:

$$55.4 \text{ g } \cancel{C_{10}H_{14}O} \times \dfrac{1 \text{ mol } \cancel{C_{10}H_{14}O}}{150.2 \text{ g } \cancel{C_{10}H_{14}O}} \times$$

$$\dfrac{10 \text{ mol } \cancel{C}}{1 \text{ mol } \cancel{C_{10}H_{14}O}} \times \dfrac{12.01 \text{ g C}}{1 \text{ mol } \cancel{C}} = 44.3 \text{ g C}$$

SKILLBUILDER 6.7   **Chemical Formulas as Conversion Factors—Converting between Grams of a Compound and Grams of a Constituent Element**

Determine the mass of oxygen in a 5.8-g sample of sodium bicarbonate ($NaHCO_3$).

SKILLBUILDER PLUS

Determine the mass of oxygen in a 7.20-g sample of $Al_2(SO_4)_3$.

6.6   Mass Percent Composition of Compounds

Another way to express how much of an element is in a given compound is to use the element's mass percent composition for that compound. The **mass percent composition** or simply **mass percent** of an element is the element's percentage of the total mass of the compound. For example, the mass percent composition of sodium in sodium chloride is 39%; a 100-g sample of sodium

Chemistry IN THE ENVIRONMENT

Chlorine in Chlorofluorocarbons

About twenty-five years ago, scientists began to suspect that synthetic compounds known as chlorofluorocarbons (or CFCs) were destroying a vital compound called ozone (O_3) in Earth's upper atmosphere. Upper atmospheric ozone is important because it acts as a shield to protect life on Earth from harmful ultraviolet light (▼ Figure 6.3). CFCs are chemically inert molecules—they do not readily react with other substances—used primarily as refrigerants and industrial solvents. Their inertness, however, has allowed them to leak into the atmosphere and stay there for many years. In the upper atmosphere sunlight breaks bonds within CFCs, resulting in the release of chlorine atoms. The chlorine atoms then react with ozone and destroy it, converting it into O_2.

In 1985, scientists discovered a large hole in the ozone layer over Antarctica that has since been attributed to CFCs. The amount of ozone depletion over Antarctica was a startling 50 percent. The ozone hole is transient, existing only in the Antarctic spring, from late August to November. Examination of data from previous years showed that this gradually expanding ozone hole has formed each spring since 1977 (▼ Figure 6.4), and it continues to form today. (In 2002 the ozone hole was a bit smaller than the year before, but in 2003 it again grew larger.)

A similar hole has been observed during some years over the North Pole, and a smaller, but still significant, drop in ozone has been observed over more populated areas such as the northern United States and Canada. The thinning of ozone over these areas is dangerous because ultraviolet light can harm living things and induce skin cancer in humans. Based on this evidence, most developed nations banned the production of CFCs on January 1, 1996. However, CFCs still lurk in most older refrigerators and air conditioning units and can leak into the atmosphere and destroy ozone.

▲ **Figure 6.3** **The ozone shield** Atmospheric ozone shields life on Earth from harmful ultraviolet light.

CAN YOU ANSWER THIS? *Suppose a car air conditioner contains 2.5 kg of freon-12 (CCl_2F_2), a CFC. How many kilograms of Cl are contained within the freon?*

Sep 1979   Sep 1991   Sep 2000

▲ **Figure 6.4** **Growth of the ozone hole** Antarctic ozone levels in three Septembers from 1979 to 2000. The darkest blue colors indicate the lowest ozone levels.

chloride contains 39 g of sodium. The mass percent composition can be determined from experimental data using the following formula.

$$\text{Mass percent of element } X = \frac{\text{Mass of } X \text{ in a sample of the compound}}{\text{Mass of the sample of the compound}} \times 100\%$$

For example, suppose a 0.358-g sample of chromium reacts with oxygen to form 0.523 g of the metal oxide. Then the mass percent of chromium is:

$$\text{Mass percent Cr} = \frac{\text{Mass Cr}}{\text{Mass metal oxide}} \times 100\%$$

$$= \frac{0.358 \text{ g}}{0.523 \text{ g}} \times 100\% = 68.5\%$$

Mass percent composition can be used as a conversion factor between grams of a constituent element and grams of the compound. For example, we saw that the mass percent composition of sodium in sodium chloride is 39%. This can be written as:

$$39 \text{ g sodium} \equiv 100 \text{ g sodium chloride}$$

or in fractional form:

$$\frac{39 \text{ g Na}}{100 \text{ g NaCl}} \quad \text{or} \quad \frac{100 \text{ g NaCl}}{39 \text{ g Na}}$$

These fractions are conversion factors between g Na and g NaCl.

EXAMPLE 6.8   Using Mass Percent Composition as a Conversion Factor

The FDA recommends that you consume less than 2.4 g of sodium per day. How many grams of sodium chloride can you consume and still be within the FDA guidelines? Sodium chloride is 39% sodium by mass.

Set up the problem in the normal way. The conversion factor is the mass percent of sodium in sodium chloride.	**Given:** 2.4 g Na **Find:** g NaCl **Conversion Factor:** 39 g Na $\equiv$ 100 g NaCl

The solution map starts with g Na and uses the mass percent as a conversion factor to get to g NaCl.	**Solution Map:** g Na → g NaCl $\dfrac{100 \text{ g NaCl}}{39 \text{ g Na}}$

Follow the solution map to solve the problem, beginning with grams Na and ending with grams of NaCl. You can consume 6.2 g NaCl and still be within the FDA guideline.	**Solution:** $2.4 \text{ g Na} \times \dfrac{100 \text{ g NaCl}}{39 \text{ g Na}} = 6.2 \text{ g NaCl}$

▶ Twelve and a half salt packets contain 6.2 g NaCl.

SKILLBUILDER 6.8   Using Mass Percent Composition as a Conversion Factor

If someone consumes 22 g of sodium chloride, how much sodium does that person consume? Sodium chloride is 39% sodium by mass.

$$22 \text{ g NaCl} \times \frac{100 \text{ Na}}{39 \text{ g NaCl}} =$$

6.7   Mass Percent Composition from a Chemical Formula

In the previous section, we saw how to compute mass percent composition from experimental data and how to use mass percent composition as a conversion factor. We can also compute the mass percent of any element in a compound from the chemical formula for the compound. Based on the chemical formula, the mass percent of element X in a compound is:

$$\text{Mass percent of element } X = \frac{\text{Mass of element } X \text{ in 1 mol of compound}}{\text{Mass of 1 mol of compound}} \times 100\%$$

MOLECULE
Dichlorodifluoromethane (Freon)

Suppose, for example, that we want to calculate the mass percent composition of Cl in the chlorofluorocarbon CCl_2F_2. The mass percent of Cl is given by:

CCl_2F_2

$$\text{Mass percent Cl} = \frac{2 \times \text{Molar mass Cl}}{\text{Molar mass } CCl_2F_2} \times 100\%$$

The molar mass of Cl must be multiplied by 2 because the chemical formula has a subscript of 2 for Cl, meaning that 1 mol of CCl_2F_2 contains 2 mol of Cl atoms. The molar mass of CCl_2F_2 is computed as follows:

$$\text{Molar mass} = 1(12.01) + 2(35.45) + 2(19.00)$$
$$= 120.91 \text{ g/mol}$$

So the mass percent of Cl in CCl_2F_2 is

$$\text{Mass percent Cl} = \frac{2 \times \text{Molar mass Cl}}{\text{Molar mass } CCl_2F_2} \times 100\%$$
$$= \frac{2 \times 35.45 \text{ g}}{120.91 \text{ g}} \times 100\%$$
$$= 58.64\%$$

EXAMPLE 6.9   Mass Percent Composition

Calculate the mass percent of Cl in freon-114 ($C_2Cl_4F_2$).

You are asked to find the mass percent of Cl given the molecular formula of freon-114. The required equation, given earlier, shows how to compute the mass percent of an element in a compound based on the formula for the compound.

Given: $C_2Cl_4F_2$

Find: Mass % Cl

Equation:

$$\text{Mass percent of element } X = \frac{\text{Mass of element } X \text{ in 1 mol of compound}}{\text{Mass of 1 mol of compound}}$$

The solution map simply shows how the mass of Cl in 1 mol of $C_2Cl_4F_2$ and the molar mass of $C_2Cl_4F_2$, when substituted into the mass percent equation, yield the mass percent of Cl.

Solution Map:

$$\text{Mass \% Cl} = \frac{4 \times \text{Molar mass Cl}}{\text{Molar mass } C_2Cl_4F_2} \times 100\%$$

Calculate the necessary parts of the equation and substitute the values into the equation to find mass percent Cl.

Solution:

$$4 \times \text{Molar mass Cl} = 4(35.45 \text{ g}) = 141.8 \text{ g}$$

$$\text{Molar mass } C_2Cl_4F_2 = 2(12.01) + 4(35.45) + 2(19.00)$$

$$= 24.02 + 141.8 + 38.00$$

$$= \frac{203.8 \text{ g}}{\text{mol}}$$

$$\text{Mass \% Cl} = \frac{4 \times \text{Molar mass Cl}}{\text{Molar mass } C_2Cl_4F_2} \times 100\%$$

$$= \frac{141.8 \text{ g}}{203.8 \text{ g}} \times 100\%$$

$$= 69.58\%$$

SKILLBUILDER 6.9   Mass Percent Composition

Acetic acid ($HC_2H_3O_2$) is the active ingredient in vinegar. Calculate the mass percent composition of O in acetic acid.

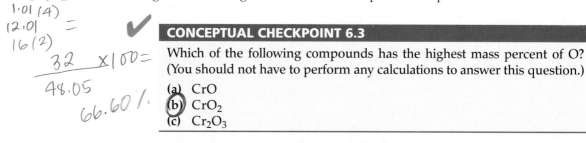

CONCEPTUAL CHECKPOINT 6.3

Which of the following compounds has the highest mass percent of O? (You should not have to perform any calculations to answer this question.)

(a) CrO
(b) CrO_2
(c) Cr_2O_3

Chemistry AND HEALTH

Fluoridation of Drinking Water

In the early 1900s, scientists discovered that people whose drinking water naturally contained fluoride (F^-) ions had fewer cavities than people whose water did not. At the proper levels, fluoride strengthens tooth enamel, which prevents tooth decay. In an effort to improve public health, fluoride has been artificially added to drinking water supplies since 1945. In the United States today, about 62% of the population drinks artificially fluoridated drinking water. The American Dental Association and public health agencies estimate that water fluoridation reduces tooth decay by 40% to 65%.

The fluoridation of public drinking water, however, is often controversial. Some opponents argue that fluoride is available from other sources—such as toothpaste, mouthwash, drops, and pills—and therefore should not be added to drinking water. Anyone who wants fluoride can get it from these optional sources, they argue, and the government should not impose fluoride on the general population. Other opponents argue that the risks associated with fluoridation are too great. Indeed, too much fluoride can cause teeth to become brown and spotted, a condition known as dental fluorosis. Extremely high levels can lead to skeletal fluorosis, a condition in which the bones become brittle and arthritic.

The scientific consensus is that, like many minerals, fluoride shows some health benefits at certain levels—about 1–4 mg/day for adults—but can have detrimental effects at higher levels. Consequently, most major cities fluoridate their drinking water at a level of about 1 mg/L. Since adults drink between 1 and 2 L of water per day, they should receive the beneficial amounts of fluoride from the water.

CAN YOU ANSWER THIS? *Fluoride is often added to water as sodium fluoride (NaF). What is the mass percent composition of F^- in NaF? How many grams of NaF should be added to 1500 L of water to fluoridate it at a level of 1.0 mg F^-/L?*

6.8   Calculating Empirical Formulas for Compounds

In the previous section we learned how to calculate mass percent composition from a chemical formula. But can we go the other way? Can we calculate a chemical formula from mass percent composition? This is important because laboratory analyses of compounds do not often give chemical formulas directly; rather, they give the relative masses of each element present in a compound. For example, if we decompose water into hydrogen and oxygen in the laboratory, we could measure the masses of hydrogen and oxygen produced. Can we get a chemical formula from this kind of data?

▶ We just learned how to go from the chemical formula of a compound to its mass percent composition. Can we also go the other way?

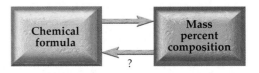

The answer is a qualified yes. We can get a chemical formula, but it is an **empirical formula**. In contrast to a **molecular formula**, which gives the specific number of each type of atom in a molecule, an empirical formula only gives the smallest whole-number ratio of each type of atom. An empirical formula *does not* necessarily represent a molecule. For example, hydrogen peroxide is a compound that contains hydrogen and oxygen with the molecular formula H_2O_2, meaning that hydrogen peroxide molecules consist of two hydrogen atoms and two oxygen atoms:

MOLECULE
Hydrogen Peroxide

H_2O_2

Hydrogen peroxide
Molecular formula H_2O_2
Empirical formula HO

However, the empirical formula of hydrogen peroxide is simply HO, the smallest whole-number ratio of hydrogen to oxygen atoms. Some other examples of empirical and molecular formulas, as well as the molecules they represent, are listed in the following table.

Empirical Formula	Molecular Formula	Common Name	molecule
CH	C_6H_6	Benzene	
CH	C_2H_2	Acetylene	
CH_2O	$C_6H_{12}O_6$	Glucose	
CO_2	CO_2	Carbon dioxide	

Notice that in some cases, different compounds with different molecular formulas can have the same empirical formula. Notice also that in some cases the empirical and molecular formula for a given compound are identical.

> The molecular formula will always be a whole-number multiple of the empirical formula.

Molecular formula = Empirical formula $\times$ n, where $n = 1, 2, 3 \ldots$

For example, H_2O_2 is HO $\times$ 2 and C_6H_6 is CH $\times$ 6.

$$HO \times 2 \longrightarrow H_2O_2 \qquad CH \times 6 \longrightarrow C_6H_6$$

Calculating an Empirical Formula from Experimental Data

A chemical formula represents a ratio of atoms or moles of atoms, not a ratio of masses.

Suppose we decompose a sample of water in the laboratory and find that it produces 3.0 g of hydrogen and 24 g of oxygen. How do we get an empirical formula from these data?

▶ Water can be decomposed by an electric current into hydrogen and oxygen. How can we find the empirical formula for water from the masses of its component elements?

We know that an empirical formula represents a ratio of atoms or a ratio of moles of atoms, but it *does not* represent a ratio of masses. So the first thing we must do is convert our data from grams to moles. How many moles of each element do we have? To convert to moles, simply divide each mass by the molar mass of that element.

$$\text{Moles H} = 3.0 \ \cancel{g \, H} \times \frac{1 \ \text{mol H}}{1.01 \ \cancel{g \, H}} = 3.0 \ \text{mol H}$$

$$\text{Moles O} = 24 \ \cancel{g \, O} \times \frac{1 \ \text{mol O}}{16.00 \ \cancel{g \, O}} = 1.5 \ \text{mol O}$$

From these data, we know there are 3 mol of H for every 1.5 mol of O. We can now write a pseudoformula for water:

$$H_3O_{1.5}$$

TUTORIAL
Empirical Formula

To get whole-number subscripts in our formula, we simply divide all the subscripts by the smallest one, in this case 1.5.

$$H_{\frac{3}{1.5}}O_{\frac{1.5}{1.5}} = H_2O$$

Our empirical formula for water, which in this case also happens to be the molecular formula, is H_2O. The procedure below can be used to obtain the empirical formula of any compound from experimental data. The left column outlines the procedure, and the center and right columns show two examples of how to apply the procedure.

Obtaining an Empirical Formula from Experimental Data

	EXAMPLE 6.10	**EXAMPLE 6.11**
	A compound containing nitrogen and oxygen is decomposed in the laboratory and produces 24.5 g of nitrogen and 70.0 g of oxygen. Calculate the empirical formula of the compound.	A laboratory analysis of aspirin determined the following mass percent composition: C 60.00% H 4.48% O 35.53% Find the empirical formula.
1. Write down (or compute) as given the masses of each element present in a sample of the compound. If you are given mass percent composition, assume a 100-g sample and compute the masses of each element from the given percentages.	**Given:** 24.5 g N 70.0 g O **Find:** empirical formula	**Given:** In a 100-g sample: 60.00 g C 4.48 g H 35.53 g O **Find:** empirical formula
2. Convert each of the masses in Step 1 to moles by using the appropriate molar mass for each element as a conversion factor.	**Solution:** $24.5 \text{ g N} \times \dfrac{1 \text{ mol N}}{14.01 \text{ g N}}$ $= 1.75 \text{ mol N}$ $70.0 \text{ g O} \times \dfrac{1 \text{ mol O}}{16.00 \text{ g O}}$ $= 4.38 \text{ mol O}$	**Solution:** $60.00 \text{ g C} \times \dfrac{1 \text{ mol C}}{12.01 \text{ g C}}$ $= 4.996 \text{ mol C}$ $4.48 \text{ g H} \times \dfrac{1 \text{ mol H}}{1.01 \text{ g H}}$ $= 4.44 \text{ mol H}$ $35.53 \text{ g O} \times \dfrac{1 \text{ mol O}}{16.00 \text{ g O}}$ $= 2.221 \text{ mol O}$
3. Write down a pseudoformula for the compound, using the moles of each element (from Step 2) as subscripts.	$N_{1.75}O_{4.38}$	$C_{4.996}H_{4.44}O_{2.221}$
4. Divide all the subscripts in the formula by the smallest subscript.	$N_{\frac{1.75}{1.75}}O_{\frac{4.38}{1.75}} \longrightarrow N_{1}O_{2.5}$	$C_{\frac{4.996}{2.221}}H_{\frac{4.44}{2.221}}O_{\frac{2.221}{2.221}} \longrightarrow C_{2.25}H_2O_1$
5. If the subscripts are not whole numbers, multiply all the subscripts by a small whole number (see the following table) to get whole-number subscripts.	$N_1O_{2.5} \times 2 \longrightarrow N_2O_5$ The correct empirical formula is N_2O_5.	$C_{2.25}H_2O_1 \times 4 \longrightarrow C_9H_8O_4$ The correct empirical formula is $C_9H_8O_4$.

Fractional Subscript	Multiply by this Number to Get Whole-Number Subscripts
_.10	10
_.20	5
_.25	4
_.33	3
_.50	2
_.66	3
_.75	4

SKILLBUILDER 6.10

A sample of a compound is decomposed in the laboratory and produces 165 g of carbon, 27.8 g of hydrogen, and 220.2 g O. Calculate the empirical formula of the compound.

SKILLBUILDER 6.11

Ibuprofen, an aspirin substitute, has the following mass percent composition:
C 75.69%; H 8.80%; O 15.51%
Calculate the empirical formula of the compound.

EXAMPLE 6.12	**Calculating an Empirical Formula from Reaction Data**

A 3.24-g sample of titanium reacts with oxygen to form 5.40 g of the metal oxide. What is the formula of the oxide?

Begin by setting up the problem in the normal way. You must recognize this problem as one requiring a special procedure.

Given:

> 3.24 g Ti
> 5.40 g oxide

Find: empirical formula

1. Write down (or compute) the masses of each element present in a sample of the compound.

   In this case, we are given the mass of the initial Ti sample and the mass of its oxide after the sample reacts with oxygen. The mass of oxygen is the difference between the mass of the oxide and the mass of titanium.

Solution:

> 3.24 g Ti
>
> Mass O = Mass oxide − Mass titanium
>
> = 5.40 g − 3.24 g
>
> = 2.16 g O

2. Convert each of the masses in Step 1 to moles by using the appropriate molar mass for each element as a conversion factor.

$$3.24 \; \cancel{g\,Ti} \times \frac{1 \; mol \; Ti}{47.88 \; \cancel{g\,Ti}} = 0.0677 \; mol \; Ti$$

$$2.16 \; \cancel{g\,O} \times \frac{1 \; mol \; O}{16.00 \; \cancel{g\,O}} = 0.135 \; mol \; O$$

3. Write down a pseudoformula for the compound, using the moles of each element obtained in Step 2 as subscripts.

$$Ti_{0.0677}O_{0.135}$$

4. Divide all the subscripts in the formula by the smallest subscript.

$$Ti_{\frac{0.0677}{0.0677}}O_{\frac{0.135}{0.0677}} \longrightarrow TiO_2$$

5. If the subscripts are not whole numbers, multiply all the subscripts by a small whole number to get whole-number subscripts.

Since the subscripts are already whole numbers, this last step is unnecessary. The correct empirical formula is TiO_2.

SKILLBUILDER 6.12	**Calculating an Empirical Formula from Reaction Data**

A 1.56-g sample of copper reacts with oxygen to form 1.95 g of the metal oxide. What is the formula of the oxide?

6.9   Calculating Molecular Formulas for Compounds

▲ Fructose, a sugar found in fruit.

MOLECULE
Fructose

You can find the molecular formula of a compound from the empirical formula if you also know the molar mass of the compound. Recall from Section 6.8 that the molecular formula is always a whole-number multiple of the empirical formula.

Molecular formula = Empirical formula × n, where n = 1, 2, 3...

Suppose we want to find the molecular formula for fructose (a sugar found in fruit) from its empirical formula, CH_2O, and its molar mass, 180.2 g/mol. We know that the molecular formula is a whole-number multiple of CH_2O.

Molecular formula = CH_2O × n

We also know that the molar mass is a whole-number multiple of the **empirical formula molar mass**, the sum of the masses of all the atoms in the empirical formula.

$$\text{Molar mass} = \text{Empirical formula molar mass} \times n$$

For a particular compound, the value of n in both cases is the same. Therefore, we can find n by computing the ratio of the molar mass to the empirical formula molar mass.

$$n = \frac{\text{Molar mass}}{\text{Empirical formula mass}}$$

For fructose, the empirical formula molar mass is:

$$\text{Empirical formula molar mass} = 1(12.01) + 2(1.01) + 16.00 = 30.03 \text{ g/mol}$$

Therefore, n is:

$$n = \frac{180.2 \text{ g/mol}}{30.03 \text{ g/mol}} = 6$$

We can then use this value of n to find the molecular formula.

$$\text{Molecular formula} = CH_2O \times 6 = C_6H_{12}O_6$$

EXAMPLE 6.13   Calculating Molecular Formula from Empirical Formula and Molar Mass

Naphthalene is a compound containing carbon and hydrogen that is often used in mothballs. Its empirical formula is C_5H_4 and its molar mass is 128.16 g/mol. Find its molecular formula.

Set up the problem in the normal way. You are given the empirical formula and the molar mass of a compound and asked to find its molecular formula.

Given:

empirical formula = C_5H_4

molar mass = 128.16 g/mol

Find: molecular formula

The molecular formula is n times the empirical formula. To find n, divide the molar mass by the empirical formula molar mass.

Solution:

$$\text{Empirical formula molar mass} = 5(12.01) + 4(1.01)$$
$$= 64.09 \text{ g/mol}$$

$$n = \frac{\text{Molar mass}}{\text{Empirical formula mass}} = \frac{128.16 \text{ g/mol}}{64.09 \text{ g/mol}} = 2$$

Therefore, the molecular formula is 2 times the empirical formula.

$$\text{Molecular formula} = C_5H_4 \times 2 = C_{10}H_8$$

SKILLBUILDER 6.13   Calculating Molecular Formula from Empirical Formula and Molar Mass

Butane is a compound containing carbon and hydrogen that is used as a fuel in butane lighters. Its empirical formula is C_2H_5 and its molar mass is 58.12 g/mol. Find its molecular formula.

SKILLBUILDER PLUS

A compound with the following mass percent composition has a molar mass of 60.10 g/mol. Find its molecular formula.

C   39.97%
H   13.41%
N   46.62%

CHAPTER IN REVIEW

Chemical Principles

The Mole Concept: The mole is a specific number (6.022×10^{23}) that is defined so as to allow us to easily count atoms or molecules by weighing them. One mole of any element has a mass equivalent to its atomic mass in grams, and a mole of any compound has a mass equivalent to its formula mass in grams. The mass of 1 mol of an element or compound is called the molar mass.

Chemical Formulas and Chemical Composition: Chemical formulas give us the relative number of each kind of element in a compound. These numbers are based on atoms or moles. By using molar masses, we can use the information in a chemical formula to determine the relative masses of each kind of element in a compound. We can then relate the mass of a sample of a compound to the masses of the elements contained in the compound.

Empirical and Molecular Formulas from Laboratory Data: The relative masses of the elements within a compound can be used to determine the empirical formula of the compound. If the chemist also knows the molar mass of the compound, he or she can also determine its molecular formula.

Relevance

The Mole Concept: The mole concept allows us to determine the number of atoms or molecules in a sample from its mass. Just as a hardware store customer wants to know the number of nails in a certain weight of nails, so we want to know the number of atoms in a certain mass of atoms. Since atoms are too small to count, we use their mass.

Chemical Formulas and Chemical Composition: The chemical composition of compounds is important because it lets us determine how much of a particular element is contained within a particular compound. For example, an assessment of the threat to the ozone from chlorofluorocarbons (CFCs) requires knowing how much chlorine is in a particular CFC.

Empirical and Molecular Formulas from Laboratory Data: The first thing a chemist wants to know about an unknown compound is its chemical formula, because the formula reveals the compound's composition. The way chemists often get formulas is by analyzing the compounds in the laboratory—either by decomposing them or by synthesizing them—to determine the relative masses of the elements they contain.

Chemical Skills

Converting between Moles and Number of Atoms (Section 6.3)

To convert between moles and number of atoms, use Avogadro's number, 6.022×10^{23} atoms = 1 mol, as a conversion factor.

Examples

EXAMPLE 6.13   Converting between Moles and Number of Atoms

Calculate the number of atoms in 4.8 mol of copper.

Given: 4.8 mol Cu

Find: Cu atoms

Conversion Factor: 1 mol Cu = 6.022×10^{23} Cu atoms

Solution Map:

$$\frac{6.022 \times 10^{23} \text{ Cu atoms}}{1 \text{ mol Cu}}$$

Solution:

$$4.8 \text{ mol Cu} \times \frac{6.022 \times 10^{23} \text{ Cu atoms}}{1 \text{ mol Cu}} =$$

$$2.9 \times 10^{24} \text{ Cu atoms}$$

Converting between Grams and Moles (Section 6.3)

To convert between grams of an element and moles of an element, use that element's molar mass. The molar mass of any element in atomic mass units is its atomic mass with the units of grams per mole. Therefore the molar mass is a conversion factor between grams and moles. To convert between grams of a *compound* and moles of a *compound*, use the compound's molar mass.

EXAMPLE 6.14   **Converting between Grams and Moles**

Calculate the mass of aluminum (in grams) of 6.73 moles of aluminum.

Given: 6.73 mol Al

Find: g Al

Conversion Factor: 26.98 g Al = 1 mol Al

Solution Map:

$$ \boxed{\text{mol Al}} \longrightarrow \boxed{\text{g Al}} $$

$$ \frac{26.98 \text{ g Al}}{1 \text{ mol Al}} $$

Solution:

$$ 6.73 \cancel{\text{ mol Al}} \times \frac{26.98 \text{ g Al}}{1 \cancel{\text{ mol Al}}} = 182 \text{ g Al} $$

Converting between Grams and Number of Atoms or Molecules (Section 6.4)

To convert from grams of an element to the number of atoms, first use the molar mass of the element to convert from grams to moles, and then use Avogadro's number to convert moles to number of atoms.

To convert from the number of atoms of an element to grams of the element, first use Avogadro's number to convert from number of atoms to moles, and then use the molar mass to convert from moles to grams.

For compounds, the molar mass is simply the formula mass with the units of grams per mole.

LIVE EXAMPLE

EXAMPLE 6.15   **Converting between Grams and Number of Atoms or Molecules**

Determine the number of atoms in a 48.3-g sample of zinc.

Given: 48.3 g Zn

Find: Zn atoms

Conversion Factors:

$$ 65.38 \text{ g Zn} = 1 \text{ mol Zn} $$
$$ 1 \text{ mol} = 6.022 \times 10^{23} \text{ atoms} $$

Solution Map:

$$ \frac{1 \text{ mol Zn}}{65.39 \text{ g Zn}} \qquad \frac{6.022 \times 10^{23} \text{ Zn atoms}}{1 \text{ mol Zn}} $$

Solution:

$$ 48.3 \cancel{\text{ g Zn}} \times \frac{1 \cancel{\text{ mol Zn}}}{65.39 \cancel{\text{ g Zn}}} \times \frac{6.022 \times 10^{23} \text{ Zn atoms}}{1 \cancel{\text{ mol Zn}}} = $$

$$ 4.45 \times 10^{23} \text{ Zn atoms} $$

Converting between Moles of a Compound and Moles of a Constituent Element (Section 6.5)

To convert between moles of a compound and moles of a constituent element, use the chemical formula of the compound as a conversion factor. The subscripts of each element in the formula specify the number of moles of that element that is equivalent to 1 mol of the compound.

EXAMPLE 6.16   **Converting between Moles of a Compound and Moles of a Constituent Element**

Determine the number of moles of oxygen in 7.20 mol of H_2SO_4.

Given: 7.20 mol H_2SO_4

Find: mol O

Conversion Factor: 4 mol O $\equiv$ 1 mol H_2SO_4

MOLECULE
Sulfuric Acid

Solution Map:

$$\boxed{\text{mol } H_2SO_4} \longrightarrow \boxed{\text{mol O}}$$

$$\frac{4 \text{ mol O}}{1 \text{ mol } H_2SO_4}$$

Solution:

$$7.20 \text{ mol } H_2SO_4 \times \frac{4 \text{ mol O}}{1 \text{ mol } H_2SO_4} = 28.8 \text{ mol O}$$

Converting between Grams of a Compound and Grams of a Constituent Element (Section 6.5)

EXAMPLE 6.17 Converting between Grams of a Compound and Grams of a Constituent Element

Find the grams of iron in 79.2 g of Fe_2O_3.

Given: 79.2 g Fe_2O_3

Find: g Fe

Conversion Factors:

Molar mass Fe_2O_3
$$= 2(55.85) + 3(16.00)$$
$$= 159.70 \text{ g/mol}$$
$$2 \text{ mol Fe} \equiv 1 \text{ mol } Fe_2O_3$$

To convert from grams of a compound to grams of a constituent element, first use the molar mass of the compound to convert from grams of the compound to moles of the compound. Then use the chemical formula to obtain a conversion factor to convert from moles of the compound to moles of the constituent element. Finally, use the molar mass of the constituent element to convert from moles of the element to grams of the element.

To convert from grams of a constituent element to grams of a compound, first use the molar mass of the constituent element to convert from grams of the element to moles of the element. Then use the chemical formula to obtain a conversion factor to convert from moles of the constituent element to moles of the compound. Finally, use the molar mass of the compound to convert from moles of the compound to grams of the compound.

Solution Map:

$$\boxed{\text{g } Fe_2O_3} \longrightarrow \boxed{\text{mol } Fe_2O_3} \longrightarrow \boxed{\text{mol Fe}} \longrightarrow \boxed{\text{g Fe}}$$

$$\frac{1 \text{ mol } Fe_2O_3}{159.70 \text{ g } Fe_2O_3} \qquad \frac{2 \text{ mol Fe}}{1 \text{ mol } Fe_2O_3} \qquad \frac{55.85 \text{ g Fe}}{1 \text{ mol Fe}}$$

Solution:

$$79.2 \text{ g } Fe_2O_3 \times \frac{1 \text{ mol } Fe_2O_3}{159.70 \text{ g } Fe_2O_3} \times \frac{2 \text{ mol Fe}}{1 \text{ mol } Fe_2O_3}$$

$$\times \frac{55.85 \text{ g Fe}}{1 \text{ mol Fe}} = 55.4 \text{ g Fe}$$

LIVE EXAMPLE

Calculating Mass Percent Composition from Experimental Data (Section 6.6)

EXAMPLE 6.18 Calculating Mass Percent Composition from Experimental Data

A 3.52-g sample of chromium reacts with fluorine to produce 7.38 g of the metal fluoride. What is the mass percent composition of chromium in the fluoride?

Given:

3.52 g Cr
7.38 g metal fluoride

Find: Cr mass percent

Solution:

The mass percent composition of an element in a compound can be determined by dividing the mass of the element within the compound by the mass of the compound and then multiplying by 100%.

$$\% \text{ Cr} = \frac{\text{Mass Cr}}{\text{Mass metal fluoride}} \times 100\%$$

$$= \frac{3.52 \text{ g}}{7.38 \text{ g}} \times 100\% = 47.7\%$$

Using Mass Percent Composition as a Conversion Factor (Section 6.6)

The mass percent composition of an element in a compound can be used as a conversion factor between grams of the element and grams of the compound. Since percent means per hundred, the mass percent composition of an element in a compound is equal to the number of grams of that element per 100 g of the compound.

LIVE EXAMPLE

EXAMPLE 6.19   Using Mass Percent Composition as a Conversion Factor

Determine the mass of titanium in 57.2 g of titanium(IV) oxide. The mass percent of titanium in titanium(IV) oxide is 59.9%.

Given: 57.2 g TiO_2

Find: g Ti

Conversion Factor: 59.9 g Ti $\equiv$ 100 g TiO_2

Solution Map:

$$\boxed{\text{g } TiO_2} \longrightarrow \boxed{\text{g Ti}}$$

$$\frac{59.9 \text{ g Ti}}{100 \text{ g } TiO_2}$$

Solution:

$$57.2 \text{ g } \cancel{TiO_2} \times \frac{59.9 \text{ g Ti}}{100 \text{ g } \cancel{TiO_2}} = 34.3 \text{ g Ti}$$

Determining Mass Percent Composition from a Chemical Formula (Section 6.7)

You are asked to find the mass percent of K given the formula of K_2O. The required equation shows how to compute the mass percent of an element in a compound based on the formula for the compound.

The solution map simply shows how the mass of K in 1 mol of K_2O and the molar mass of K_2O, when substituted into the mass percent equation, yield the mass percent of K.

Calculate the necessary parts of the equation and substitute the values into the equation to find the mass percent of K.

EXAMPLE 6.20   Determining Mass Percent Composition from a Chemical Formula

Calculate the mass percent composition of potassium in potassium oxide (K_2O).

Given: K_2O

Find: mass % K

Equation:

Mass percent of element X

$$= \frac{\text{Mass of element } X \text{ in 1 mol of compound}}{\text{Mass of 1 mol of compound}} \times 100\%$$

Solution Map:

$$\boxed{\begin{array}{c}\text{Chemical}\\\text{formula}\end{array}} \longrightarrow \boxed{\text{Mass \% K}}$$

$$\text{Mass \% K} = \frac{2 \times \text{Molar mass K}}{\text{Molar mass } K_2O} \times 100\%$$

Solution:

$$2 \times \text{Molar mass K} = 2(39.10 \text{ g}) = 78.20 \text{ g}$$

$$\text{Molar mass } K_2O = 2(39.10) + 16.00$$

$$= 94.20 \text{ g/mol}$$

$$\text{Mass \% K} = \frac{78.20 \text{ g K}}{94.20 \text{ g } K_2O} \times 100\% = 83.01\%$$

Determining an Empirical Formula from Experimental Data (Section 6.8)

To determine an empirical formula from experimental data, follow these steps.

1. Write down (or compute) as given the masses of each element present in a sample of the compound. If you are given mass percent composition, assume a 100-g sample and compute the masses of each element from the given percentages.

2. Convert each of the masses in Step 1 to moles by using the appropriate molar mass for each element as a conversion factor.

3. Write down a pseudoformula for the compound using the moles of each element (from Step 2) as subscripts.

4. Divide all the subscripts in the formula by the smallest subscript.

5. If the subscripts are not whole numbers, multiply all the subscripts by a small whole number to get whole-number subscripts.

LIVE EXAMPLE

EXAMPLE 6.21   Determining an Empirical Formula from Experimental Data

A laboratory analysis of vanillin, the flavoring agent in vanilla, determined the following mass percent composition: C, 63.15%; H, 5.30%; O, 31.55%. Determine the empirical formula of vanillin.

Given: In a 100-g sample, we have 63.15 g C, 5.30 g H, and 31.55 g O.

Find: empirical formula

Solution:

$$63.15 \text{ g C} \times \frac{1 \text{ mol C}}{12.01 \text{ g C}} = 5.258 \text{ mol C}$$

$$5.30 \text{ g H} \times \frac{1 \text{ mol H}}{1.01 \text{ g H}} = 5.25 \text{ mol H}$$

$$31.55 \text{ g O} \times \frac{1 \text{ mol O}}{16.00 \text{ g O}} = 1.972 \text{ mol O}$$

$$C_{5.258}H_{5.25}O_{1.972}$$

$$C_{\frac{5.258}{1.972}}H_{\frac{5.25}{1.972}}O_{\frac{1.972}{1.972}} \longrightarrow C_{2.67}H_{2.66}O_1$$

$$C_{2.67}H_{2.66}O_1 \times 3 \longrightarrow C_8H_8O_3$$

The correct empirical formula is $C_8H_8O_3$.

Calculating a Molecular Formula from an Empirical Formula and Molar Mass (Section 6.9)

EXAMPLE 6.22   Calculating a Molecular Formula from an Empirical Formula and Molar Mass

Acetylene, a gas often used in welding torches, has the empirical formula CH and a molar mass of 26.04 g/mol. Find its molecular formula.

Given:

empirical formula = CH
molar mass = 26.04 g/mol

Find: molecular formula

Solution:

Empirical formula molar mass
= 12.01 + 1.01
= 13.02 g/mol

To calculate the molecular formula from the empirical formula and the molar mass, first compute the empirical formula molar mass, which is the sum of the masses of the all the atoms in the empirical formula.

Next, find n, the ratio of the molar mass to empirical mass.

$$n = \frac{\text{Molar mass}}{\text{Empirical formula molar mass}}$$
$$= \frac{26.04 \text{ g/mol}}{13.02 \text{ g/mol}} = 2$$

Finally, multiply the empirical formula by n to get the molecular formula.

Molecular formula = CH × 2 $\longrightarrow C_2H_2$

Key Terms

Avogadro's number [6.3]   empirical formula molar   mass percent   molar mass [6.3]
empirical formula [6.8]   mass [6.9]   (composition) [6.6]   mole (mol) [6.3]
                                                                                      molecular formula [6.8]

Exercises

Questions

1. Why is chemical composition important?
2. How can you determine the number of atoms in a sample of an element? Why is counting them not an option?
3. How many atoms are in 1 mol of atoms?
4. How many molecules are in 1 mol of molecules?
5. What is the mass of 1 mol of atoms for an element?
6. What is the mass of 1 mol of molecules for a compound?
7. What is the mass of 1 mol of atoms of each of the following elements?
   (a) P   (b) Pt
   (c) C   (d) Cr
8. What is the mass of 1 mol of molecules of each of the following compounds?
   (a) CO_2 (b) CH_2Cl_2
   (c) $C_{12}H_{22}O_{11}$ (d) SO_2
9. The subscripts in a chemical formula give relationships between moles of the constituent elements and moles of the compound. Explain why these subscripts *do not* give relationships between grams of the constituent elements and grams of the compound.

10. Write the conversion factors between moles of each constituent element and moles of the compound for $C_{12}H_{22}O_{11}$.
11. Mass percent composition can be used as a conversion factor between grams of a constituent element and grams of the compound. Write the conversion factor (including units) inherent in each of the following mass percent compositions.
    (a) Water is 11.19% hydrogen by mass.
    (b) Fructose, also known as fruit sugar, is 53.29% oxygen by mass.
    (c) Octane, a component of gasoline, is 84.12% carbon by mass.
    (d) Ethanol, the alcohol in alcoholic beverages, is 52.14% carbon by mass.
12. What is the mathematical formula for computing mass percent composition from a chemical formula?
13. How are the empirical formula and the molecular formula of a compound related?
14. Why is it important to be able to calculate an empirical formula from experimental data?
15. What is the empirical formula mass of a compound?
16. How are the molar mass and empirical formula mass for a compound related?

Problems

The Mole Concept

17. How many mercury atoms are in 5.9 mol of mercury?

18. How many moles of gold atoms do 5.8×10^{24} gold atoms constitute?

19. How many atoms are in each of the following?
    (a) 3.4 mol Cu
    (b) 9.7×10^{-3} mol C
    (c) 22.9 mol Hg
    (d) 0.215 mol Na

20. How many moles of atoms are in each of the following?
    (a) 4.6×10^{24} Pb atoms
    (b) 2.87×10^{22} He atoms
    (c) 7.91×10^{23} K atoms
    (d) 4.41×10^{21} Ca atoms

21. Complete the following table:

Element	Moles	Number of Atoms
Ne	0.552	___
Ar	___	3.25×10^{24}
Xe	1.78	___
He	___	1.08×10^{20}

22. Complete the following table:

Element	Moles	Number of Atoms
Cr	___	9.61×10^{23}
Fe	1.52×10^{-5}	___
Ti	0.0365	___
Hg	___	1.09×10^{23}

23. Consider the following definitions.

    1 doz = 12

    1 gross = 144

    1 ream = 500

    1 mol = 6.022×10^{23}

    Suppose you have 872 sheets of paper. How many
    _____ of paper do you have?
    (a) dozens
    (b) gross
    (c) reams
    (d) moles

24. A pure copper penny contains approximately
    3.0×10^{22} copper atoms. Use the definitions in
    Problem 23 to determine how many _____ of cop-
    per atoms are in a penny.
    (a) dozens
    (b) gross
    (c) reams
    (d) moles

25. How many moles of tin atoms are in a pure tin cup
    with a mass of 42.3 g?

26. A lead fishing weight contains 0.12 mol of lead
    atoms. What is its mass?

27. A pure gold coin contains 0.145 mol of gold. What
    is the mass of the coin?

28. A helium balloon contains 0.55 g of helium. How
    many moles of helium does it contain?

29. How many moles of atoms are in each of the
    following?
    (a) 1.54 g Zn
    (b) 22.8 g Ar
    (c) 86.2 g Ta
    (d) 0.034 g Li

30. What is the mass in grams of each of the following?
    (a) 7.8 mol W
    (b) 0.943 mol Ba
    (c) 43.9 mol Xe
    (d) 1.8 mol S

31. Complete the following table:

Element	Moles	Mass
Ne	____	22.5 g
Ar	0.117	____
Xe	____	1.00 kg
He	1.44×10^{-4}	____

32. Complete the following table:

Element	Moles	Mass
Cr	0.00442	____
Fe	____	73.5 mg
Ti	1.009×10^{-3}	____
Hg	____	1.78 kg

33. A pure silver ring contains 0.0134 mmol (millimol)
    Ag. How many silver atoms does it contain?

34. A pure gold ring contains 0.0102 mmol (millimol)
    Au. How many gold atoms does it contain?

35. How many aluminum atoms are in 3.78 g of
    aluminum?

36. What is the mass of 4.91×10^{21} platinum atoms?

37. How many atoms are in each of the following?
    (a) 12.8 g Sr
    (b) 45.2 g Fe
    (c) 9.87 g Bi
    (d) 36.1 g P

38. Calculate the mass in grams of each of the following:
    (a) 7.9×10^{21} uranium atoms
    (b) 3.82×10^{22} zinc atoms
    (c) 5.8×10^{23} lead atoms
    (d) 2.1×10^{24} silicon atoms

39. How many carbon atoms are in a diamond (pure
    carbon) with a mass of 52 mg?

40. How many helium atoms are in a helium blimp
    containing 536 kg of helium?

41. How many titanium atoms are in a pure titanium
    bicycle frame with a mass of 1.28 kg?

42. How many copper atoms are in a pure copper stat-
    ue with a mass of 133 kg?

43. Complete the following table:

Element	Mass	Moles	Number of Atoms
Na	38.5 mg	___	___
C	___	1.12	___
V	___	___	214
Hg	1.44 kg	___	___

44. Complete the following table:

Element	Mass	Moles	Number of Atoms
Pt	___	0.0449	___
Fe	___	___	1.14×10^{25}
Ti	23.8 mg	___	___
Hg	___	2.05	___

45. Determine the number of moles of molecules (or formula units) in each of the following:
(a) 55.2 g sodium chloride
(b) 27.1 g nitrogen monoxide
(c) 4.81 kg carbon dioxide
(d) 1.33 mg carbon tetrachloride

46. Determine the mass of each of the following:
(a) 1.55 mol carbon tetrafluoride
(b) 0.724 mol magnesium fluoride
(c) 1.59 mmol carbon disulfide
(d) 3.87 kmol sulfur trioxide

47. Complete the following table:

Compound	Mass	Moles
H_2O	112 kg	___
N_2O	6.33 g	___
SO_2	___	2.44
CH_2Cl_2	___	0.0643

48. Complete the following table:

Compound	Mass	Moles
CO_2	___	0.0153
CO	___	0.0150
BrI	23.8 mg	___
CF_2Cl_2	1.02 kg	___

49. A mothball, composed of naphthalene ($C_{10}H_8$), has a mass of 1.32 g. How many naphthalene molecules does it contain?

50. Calculate the mass in grams of a single water molecule.

51. How many molecules are in each of the following?
(a) 3.5 g H_2O
(b) 56.1 g N_2
(c) 89 g CCl_4
(d) 19 g $C_6H_{12}O_6$

52. Calculate the mass in grams of each of the following:
(a) 5.94×10^{20} H_2O_2 molecules
(b) 2.8×10^{22} SO_2 molecules
(c) 4.5×10^{25} O_3 molecules
(d) 9.85×10^{19} CH_4 molecules

53. A sugar crystal contains approximately 1.8×10^{17} sucrose ($C_{12}H_{22}O_{11}$) molecules. What is its mass in milligrams?

54. A salt crystal has a mass of 0.12 mg. How many NaCl formula units does it contain?

Chemical Formulas as Conversion Factors

55. Determine the number of moles of Cl in 4.7 mol $CaCl_2$.

56. How many moles of O are in 14.8 mol $Fe(NO_3)_3$?

57. Which of the following contains the greatest number of moles of O?
(a) 2.3 mol H_2O
(b) 1.2 mol H_2O_2
(c) 0.9 mol $NaNO_3$
(d) 0.5 mol $Ca(NO_3)_2$

58. Which of the following contains the greatest number of moles of Cl?
(a) 3.8 mol HCl
(b) 1.7 mol CH_2Cl_2
(c) 4.2 mol $NaClO_3$
(d) 2.2 mol $Mg(ClO_4)_2$

59. Determine the number of moles of C in each of the following:
(a) 3.8 mol CH_4
(b) 0.273 mol C_2H_6
(c) 4.89 mol C_4H_{10}
(d) 22.9 mol C_8H_{18}

60. Determine the number of moles of H in each of the following:
(a) 3.15 mol H_2O
(b) 9.88 mol NH_3
(c) 0.0737 mol N_2H_4
(d) 54.1 mol $C_{10}H_{22}$

61. For each of the following, write a relationship between moles of hydrogen and moles of molecules. Then determine the total number of hydrogen atoms present. (H—white; O—red; C—black; N—blue)

(a)   (b)   (c)

62. For each of the following, write a relationship between moles of oxygen and moles of molecules. Then determine the total number of oxygen atoms present. (H—white; O—red; C—black; S—yellow)

(a)   (b)   (c)

63. How many grams of Cl are in 55 g of each of the following chlorofluorocarbons (CFCs)?
  (a) CF_2Cl_2
  (b) $CFCl_3$
  (c) $C_2F_3Cl_3$
  (d) CF_3Cl

64. Calculate the number of grams of sodium in 5.0 g of each of the following sodium-containing food additives.
  (a) $NaCl$ (table salt)
  (b) Na_3PO_4 (sodium phosphate)
  (c) $NaC_7H_5O_2$ (sodium benzoate)
  (d) $Na_2C_6H_6O_7$ (sodium hydrogen citrate)

65. Iron is found in Earth's crust as several iron compounds often called iron ores. Calculate the mass in kilograms of the amount of each of the following iron compounds that contains 1.0×10^3 kg of iron.
  (a) Fe_2O_3 (hematite)
  (b) Fe_3O_4 (magnetite)
  (c) $FeCO_3$ (siderite)

66. Lead is often found in Earth's crust as several lead compounds called lead ores. Calculate the mass in kilograms of the amount of each of the following lead compounds that contains 1.0×10^3 kg of lead.
  (a) PbS (galena)
  (b) $PbCO_3$ (cerussite)
  (c) $PbSO_4$ (anglesite)

Mass Percent Composition

67. A 2.45-g sample of strontium completely reacts with oxygen to form 2.89 g of strontium oxide. Use this data to calculate the mass percent composition of strontium in strontium oxide.

68. A 4.78-g sample of aluminum completely reacts with oxygen to form 6.67 g of aluminum oxide. Use this data to calculate the mass percent composition of aluminum in aluminum oxide.

69. A 1.912-g sample of calcium chloride is decomposed into its constituent elements and found to contain 0.690 g Ca and 1.222 g Cl. Calculate the mass percent composition of Ca and Cl in calcium chloride.

70. A 0.45-g sample of aspirin is decomposed into its constituent elements and found to contain 0.27 g C, 0.020 g H, and 0.16 g O. Calculate the mass percent composition of C, H, and O in aspirin.

71. Copper(II) fluoride contains 37.42% F by mass. Use this percentage to calculate the mass of fluorine in grams contained in 28.5 g of copper(II) fluoride.

72. Silver chloride, often used in silver plating, contains 75.27% Ag. Calculate the mass of silver chloride in grams required to make 4.8 g of silver plating.

73. In small amounts, the fluoride ion (often consumed as NaF) prevents tooth decay. According to the American Dental Association, an adult female should consume 3.0 mg of fluorine per day. Calculate the amount of sodium fluoride (45.24% F) that should be consumed to get the recommended amount of fluorine.

74. The iodide ion, usually consumed as potassium iodide, is a dietary mineral essential to good nutrition. In countries where potassium iodide is added to salt, iodine deficiency or goiter has been almost completely eliminated. The recommended daily allowance (RDA) for iodine is 150 μg/day. How much potassium iodide (76.45% I) should be consumed to meet the RDA?

Mass Percent Composition from Chemical Formula

75. Calculate the mass percent composition of nitrogen in each of the following nitrogen compounds.
  (a) N_2O
  (b) NO
  (c) NO_2
  (d) N_2O_5

76. Calculate the mass percent composition of carbon in each the following carbon compounds.
  (a) C_2H_2
  (b) C_3H_6
  (c) C_2H_6
  (d) C_2H_6O

77. Calculate the mass percent composition of each element in each of the following compounds.
(a) $C_2H_4O_2$
(b) CH_2O_2
(c) C_3H_9N
(d) $C_4H_{12}N_2$

78. Calculate the mass percent composition of each element in each of the following compounds.
(a) $FeCl_3$
(b) TiO_2
(c) H_3PO_4
(d) HNO_3

79. Iron ores have different amounts of iron per kilogram of ore. Calculate the mass percent composition of iron for the following iron ores: Fe_2O_3 (hematite), Fe_3O_4 (magnetite), $FeCO_3$ (siderite). Which ore has the highest iron content?

80. Plants need nitrogen to grow, so many fertilizers consist of nitrogen-containing compounds. Calculate the mass percent composition of nitrogen in each of the following nitrogen-containing compounds used as fertilizers: NH_3, $CO(NH_2)_2$, NH_4NO_3, $(NH_4)_2SO_4$. Which fertilizer has the highest nitrogen content?

Calculating Empirical Formulas

81. A compound containing nitrogen and oxygen is decomposed in the laboratory and produces 1.78 g of nitrogen and 4.05 g of oxygen. Calculate the empirical formula of the compound.

82. A compound containing selenium and fluorine is decomposed in the laboratory and produces 2.231 g of selenium and 3.221 g of fluorine. Calculate the empirical formula of the compound.

83. Samples of several compounds are decomposed and the following are the masses of their constituent elements. Calculate the empirical formula for each compound.
(a) 1.245 g Ni, 5.381 g I
(b) 1.443 g Se, 5.841 g Br
(c) 2.128 g Be, 7.557 g S, 15.107 g O

84. Samples of several compounds are decomposed and the following are the masses of their constituent elements. Calculate the empirical formula for each compound.
(a) 2.677 g Ba, 3.115 g Br
(b) 1.651 g Ag, 0.1224 g O
(c) 0.672 g Co, 0.569 g As, 0.486 g O

85. The rotten smell of a decaying animal carcass is partially due to a nitrogen-containing compound called putrescine. Elemental analysis of putrescine showed that it consisted of 54.50% C, 13.73% H, and 31.77% N. Calculate the empirical formula of putrescine.

86. Citric acid, the compound responsible for the sour taste of lemons, has the following elemental composition: C, 37.51%; H, 4.20%; O, 58.29%. Calculate the empirical formula of citric acid.

87. Calculate the empirical formula for each of the following compounds often found in many natural flavors and smells.
(a) ethyl butyrate (pineapple oil): C, 62.04%; H, 10.41%; O, 27.55%
(b) methyl butyrate (apple flavor): C, 58.80%; H, 9.87%; O, 31.33%
(c) benzyl acetate (oil of jasmine): C, 71.98%; H, 6.71%; O, 21.31%

88. Calculate the empirical formula for each of the following over-the-counter pain relievers.
(a) acetaminophen (Tylenol): C, 63.56%; H, 6.00%; N, 9.27%; O, 21.17%
(b) naproxen (Aleve): C, 73.03%; H, 6.13%; O, 20.84%

89. A 1.45-g sample of phosphorus burns in air and forms 2.57 g of a phosphorus oxide. Calculate the empirical formula of the oxide.

90. A 2.241-g sample of nickel reacts with oxygen to form 2.852 g of the metal oxide. Calculate the empirical formula of the oxide.

91. A 0.77-mg sample of nitrogen reacts with chlorine to form 6.61 mg of the chloride. What is the empirical formula of the nitrogen chloride?

92. A 45.2-mg sample of phosphorus reacts with selenium to form 131.6 mg of the selenide. What is the empirical formula of the phosphorus selenide?

Calculating Molecular Formulas

93. A compound containing carbon and hydrogen has a molar mass of 56.11 g/mol and an empirical formula of CH_2. Find its molecular formula.

94. A compound containing phosphorus and oxygen has a molar mass of 219.9 g/mol and an empirical formula of P_2O_3. Find its molecular formula.

95. The following are the molar masses and empirical formulas of several compounds containing carbon and chlorine. Find the molecular formula of each compound.
 (a) 284.77 g/mol, CCl
 (b) 131.39 g/mol, C_2HCl_3
 (c) 181.44 g/mol, C_2HCl

96. The following are the molar masses and empirical formulas of several compounds containing carbon and nitrogen. Find the molecular formula of each compound.
 (a) 163.26 g/mol, $C_{11}H_{17}N$
 (b) 186.24 g/mol, C_6H_7N
 (c) 312.29 g/mol, C_3H_2N

Cumulative Problems

97. A pure copper cube has an edge length of 1.42 cm. How many copper atoms does it contain? (volume of a cube = (edge length)^3; density of copper = 8.96 g/cm^3)

98. A pure silver sphere has a radius of 0.886 cm. How many silver atoms does it contain? (Volume of a sphere = $\frac{4}{3}\pi r^3$; density of silver = 10.5 g/cm^3)

99. A drop of water has a volume of approximately 0.05 mL. How many water molecules does it contain? (density of water = 1.0 g/cm^3).

100. Fingernail-polish remover is primarily acetone (C_3H_6O). How many acetone molecules are in a bottle of acetone with a volume of 325 mL? (density of acetone = 0.788 g/cm^3).

101. Complete the following table:

Substance	Mass	Moles	Number of Particles (atoms or molecules)
Ar	___	4.5×10^{-4}	___
NO_2	___	___	1.09×10^{20}
K	22.4 mg	___	___
C_8H_{18}	3.76 kg	___	___

102. Complete the following table:

Substance	Mass	Moles	Number of Particles (atoms or molecules)
$C_6H_{12}O_6$	15.8 g	___	___
Pb	___	___	9.04×10^{21}
CF_4	22.5 kg	___	___
C	___	0.0388	___

103. Determine the chemical formula of each of the following compounds and then use it to calculate the mass percent composition of each constituent element.
 (a) copper(II) iodide   (b) sodium nitrate
 (c) lead(II) sulfate   (d) calcium fluoride

104. Determine the chemical formula of each of the following compounds and then use it to calculate the mass percent composition of each constituent element.
 (a) nitrogen triiodide   (b) xenon tetrafluoride
 (c) phosphorus trichloride (d) carbon monoxide

105. The rock in a particular iron ore deposit contains 78% Fe_2O_3 by mass. How many kilograms of the rock must be processed to obtain 1.0×10^3 kg of iron?

106. The rock in a lead ore deposit contains 84% PbS by mass. How many kilograms of the rock must be processed to obtain 1.0 kg of Pb?

107. A leak in the air conditioning system of a corporate building releases 12 kg of CHF_2Cl per month. If the leak were allowed to continue, how many kilograms of Cl would be emitted into the atmosphere each year?

108. A leak in the air conditioning system of an older car releases 55 g of CF_2Cl_2 per month. How much Cl is emitted into the atmosphere each year by this car?

109. Hydrogen is a possible future fuel. However, elemental hydrogen is rare, so it must be obtained from a hydrogen-containing compound. One candidate is water. If hydrogen were obtained from water, how much hydrogen in grams could be obtained from 1.0 L of water? (density of water = 1.0 g/cm^3).

110. Hydrogen, a possible future fuel mentioned in Problem 109, can also be obtained from other compounds such as ethanol. Ethanol can be made from the fermentation of crops such as corn. How much hydrogen in grams can be obtained from 1.0 kg of ethanol (C_2H_5OH)?

111. Complete the following table consisting of compounds that contain only carbon and hydrogen.

Formula	Molar Mass	% C (by mass)	% H (by mass)
C_2H_4	___	___	___
___	58.12	82.66%	___
C_4H_8	___	___	___
___	44.09	___	18.29%

112. Complete the following table consisting of compounds that contain only chromium and oxygen

Formula	Name	Molar Mass	% Cr (by mass)	% O (by mass)
	Chromium(III) oxide	___	___	___
___	___	84.00	61.90 %	___
___	___	100.00	___	48.00%

113. Butanedione, a component of butter and body odor, has a cheesy smell. Elemental analysis of butanedione gave the following mass percent composition: C, 55.80%; H, 7.03%; O, 37.17%. The molar mass of butanedione is 86.09 g/mol. Find the molecular formula of butanedione.

114. Caffeine, a stimulant found in coffee and soda pop, has the following mass percent composition: C, 49.48%; H, 5.19%; N, 28.85%; O, 16.48%. The molar mass of caffeine is 194.19 g/mol. Find the molecular formula of caffeine.

115. Nicotine, a stimulant found in tobacco, has the following mass percent composition: C, 74.03%; H, 8.70%; N, 17.27%. The molar mass of nicotine is 162.23 g/mol. Find the molecular formula of nicotine.

116. Estradiol is a female sexual hormone that causes maturation and maintenance of the female reproductive system. Elemental analysis of estradiol gave the following mass percent composition: C, 79.37%; H, 8.88%; O, 11.75%. The molar mass of estradiol is 272.37 g/mol. Find the molecular formula of estradiol.

Highlight Problems

117. You can use the concepts in this chapter to obtain an estimate of the number of atoms in the universe. The following steps will guide you through this calculation.
     (a) Begin by calculating the number of atoms in the sun. Assume that the sun is pure hydrogen with a density of 1.4 g/cm^3. The radius of the sun is 7×10^8 m and the volume of a sphere is given by $V = \frac{4}{3}\pi r^3$.
     (b) Since the sun is an average-sized star, and since stars are believed to compose most of the mass of the visible universe (planets are so small they can be ignored), we can estimate the number of atoms in a galaxy by assuming that every star in the galaxy has the same number of atoms as our sun. The Milky Way galaxy is believed to contain 1×10^{11} stars. Use your answer from part (a) to calculate the number of atoms in the Milky Way galaxy.
     (c) The universe is estimated to contain approximately 1×10^{11} galaxies. If each of these galaxies contains the same number of atoms as the Milky Way galaxy, what is the total number of atoms in the universe?

118. Because of increasing evidence of damage to the ozone layer, chlorofluorocarbon (CFC) production was banned in 1996. However, there are about 100 million auto air conditioners that still use CFC-12 (CF_2Cl_2). These air conditioners are recharged from stockpiled supplies of CFC-12. If each of the 100 million automobiles contains 1.1 kg of CFC-12 and leaks 25% of its CFC-12 into the atmosphere per year, how much Cl in kilograms is added to the atmosphere each year due to auto air conditioners? (Assume two significant figures in your calculations.)

EP/TOMS total ozone for Oct. 1, 2001

Lowest   Highest
Ozone concentration

 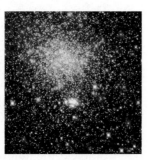

▲ Our sun is one of the 100 billion stars in the Milky Way galaxy. The universe is estimated to contain about 100 billion galaxies.

▲ The ozone hole over Antarctica, October 1, 2001. The red areas indicate the highest concentrations of ozone, while the dark green regions near the South Pole have the lowest.

119. In 1996, the media reported that possible evidence of life on Mars was found on a meteorite called Allan Hills 84001 (AH 84001). The meteorite was discovered in Antarctica in 1984 and is believed to have originated on Mars. Elemental analysis of substances within its crevices revealed carbon-containing compounds that normally derive only from living organisms. Suppose that one of those compounds had a molar mass of 202.23 g/mol and the following mass percent composition: C, 95.02%; H, 4.98%. What is the molecular formula for the carbon-containing compound?

▶ The Allan Hills 84001 meteorite. Elemental analysis of the substances within the crevices of this meteorite revealed carbon-containing compounds that normally originate from living organisms.

Answers to Skillbuilder Exercises

Skillbuilder 6.1	5.32×10^{22} Au atoms
Skillbuilder 6.2	89.2 g S
Skillbuilder 6.3	8.17 g He
Skillbuilder 6.4	2.56×10^{-2} mol NO_2
Skillbuilder 6.5	1.22×10^{23} H_2O molecules
Skillbuilder 6.6	5.6 mol O
Skillbuilder 6.7	3.3 g O
Skillbuilder Plus, p. 165	4.04 g O

Skillbuilder 6.8	8.6 g Na
Skillbuilder 6.9	53.28% O
Skillbuilder 6.10	CH_2O
Skillbuilder 6.11	$C_{13}H_{18}O_2$
Skillbuilder 6.12	CuO
Skillbuilder 6.13	C_4H_{10}
Skillbuilder Plus, p. 174	$C_2H_8N_2$

Answers to Conceptual Checkpoints

6.1 (a) The mole is a counting unit; it represents a definite number (Avogadro's number, 6.02×10^{23}). Therefore, a given number of atoms always represents a precise number of moles, regardless of what atom is involved. Atoms of different elements have different masses, so if samples of different elements have the same mass, they *cannot* contain the same number of atoms or moles.

6.2 (a) Avogadro's number was defined so as to make the molar mass of a compound (the mass of one mole, or Avogadro's number of molecules or formula units), *in grams*, numerically equal to the formula mass of the compound in amu. In order for the molar mass *in kilograms* to be numerically equal to the formula mass in amu, we would need 1000 times as many molecules or formula units in a mole. In other words, Avogadro's number would have to be 1000 times larger, or 6.02×10^{26}.

6.3 (b) This compound has the highest ratio of oxygen atoms to chromium atoms, and so must have the greatest mass percent of oxygen.

CHAPTER 7

Chemical Reactions

"Chemistry . . . is one of the broadest branches of science if for no other reason that, when we think about it, everything is chemistry."

Luciano Caglioti (1933–)

7.1   Kindergarten Volcanoes, Automobiles, and Laundry Detergents

Did you ever make a clay volcano in kindergarten that—when filled with vinegar, baking soda, and red food coloring for effect—erupted? Have you pushed the gas pedal of a car and felt the acceleration as the car moved forward? Have you wondered why laundry detergents work better than normal soap to clean your clothes? Each of these processes depends on a **chemical reaction**—the change of one or more substances into different substances.

In the classic kindergarten volcano, the baking soda (which is sodium bicarbonate) reacts with acetic acid in the vinegar to form carbon dioxide gas, water, and sodium acetate. The newly formed carbon dioxide bubbles out of the mixture, causing the eruption. Reactions that occur in liquids and form a gas are called *gas evolution reactions*. A similar reaction causes the fizzing of antacids such as Alka-Seltzer.

Hydrocarbons are covered in detail in Chapter 18.

When you drive your car, hydrocarbons such as octane (in gasoline) react with oxygen from the air to form carbon dioxide gas and water (▶ Figure 7.1). This reaction produces heat, which is used to expand the gases in the car's cylinders and accelerate the car forward. Reactions such as this one—in which a substance reacts with oxygen, emitting heat and forming one or more oxygen-containing compounds—are called *combustion reactions*. Combustion reactions are a subcategory of *oxidation–reduction reactions*, in which electrons are transferred from one substance to another. The formation of rust and the dulling of automobile paint are other examples of oxidation–reduction reactions.

◀ In the space shuttle's main engines, hydrogen molecules, H_2 (white) and oxygen molecules, O_2 (red), which are stored in the central fuel tank, react violently to form water molecules, H_2O. The reaction emits the energy that helps propel the shuttle into space.

One reason why laundry detergents work better than soap to wash clothes is that they contain substances that soften hard water. Hard water contains dissolved calcium (Ca^{2+}) and magnesium (Mg^{2+}) ions. These ions interfere with

189

▶ Figure 7.1   **A combustion reaction**   In an automobile engine, hydrocarbons such as octane (C_8H_{18}) from gasoline combine with oxygen from the air and react to form carbon dioxide and water.

Octane
(a component of gasoline)

Oxygen

Auto engine

Carbon dioxide

Water

▲ Figure 7.2   **Soap and water**
Soap forms suds with pure water (left), but reacts with the ions in hard water (right) to form a gray residue that adheres to clothes.

the action of soap by reacting with it to form a gray, slimy substance called *curd* or *soap scum* (◀ Figure 7.2). If you have ever washed your clothes in ordinary soap, you may have noticed soap scum as a gray residue on your clothes.

Laundry detergents inhibit curd formation because they contain substances such as sodium carbonate (Na_2CO_3) that remove calcium and magnesium ions from the water. When sodium carbonate dissolves in water, it *dissociates*, or separates into sodium ions (Na^+) and carbonate ions (CO_3^{2-}). The dissolved carbonate ions then react with calcium and magnesium ions in the hard water to form solid calcium carbonate ($CaCO_3$) and solid magnesium carbonate ($MgCO_3$). These solids simply settle to the bottom of the laundry mixture, resulting in the removal of the ions from the water. In other words, laundry detergents contain substances that react with the ions in hard water to immobilize them. Reactions such as these—that form solid substances in water—are called *precipitation reactions*. Precipitation reactions are also used to remove dissolved toxic metals in industrial wastes.

Chemical reactions take place all around us and even inside us. They are involved in many of the products we use daily and in many of our experiences. Chemical reactions can be relatively simple, like the combination of hydrogen and oxygen to form water, or they can be complex, like the synthesis of a protein molecule from thousands of simpler molecules. In some cases, such as the neutralization reaction that occurs in a swimming pool when acid is added to adjust the water's acidity level, chemical reactions are not noticeable to the naked eye. In other cases, such as the combustion reaction that produces a pillar of smoke and fire under the space shuttle during liftoff, chemical reactions are very obvious. In all cases, however, chemical reactions produce changes in the arrangements of the molecules and atoms that compose matter. Many times, these molecular changes cause macroscopic changes that we experience.

7.2   Evidence of a Chemical Reaction

If we could see the atoms and molecules that compose matter, we could easily identify a chemical reaction. Are atoms combining with other atoms to form compounds? Are new molecules forming? Are the original molecules decomposing? Are atoms in one molecule changing places with atoms in another? If one or more of these are happening, a chemical reaction is occurring. Of course, we don't normally see atoms and molecules, so we need other ways to identify a chemical reaction.

Fortunately, many chemical reactions produce easily detectable changes when they occur. For example, when the color-causing molecules in a brightly colored shirt decompose with repeated exposure to sunlight, the color of the shirt fades. Similarly, when the molecules imbedded in the plastic of a child's temperature-sensitive spoon transform upon warming, the color of the spoon changes. These *color changes* are evidence that a chemical reaction has occurred.

▲ Figure 7.3 **A precipitation reaction** The formation of a solid in a previously clear solution is evidence of a chemical reaction.

▲ Figure 7.4 **A gas-evolution reaction** The formation of a gas is evidence of a chemical reaction.

Other changes that identify chemical reactions include the *formation of a solid* in a previously clear solution (▲ Figure 7.3) or the *formation of a gas* (▲ Figure 7.4). Dropping Alka-Seltzer tablets into water or combining baking soda and vinegar (as in our opening example of the kindergarten volcano) are both good examples of chemical reactions that produce a gas—the gas is visible as bubbles in the liquid.

Heat absorption or *emission*, as well as *light emission*, is also evidence for reactions. For example, a natural gas flame produces heat and light. A chemical cold pack becomes cold when the plastic barrier separating two substances is broken. Both of these changes suggest that a chemical reaction is occurring.

▲ A change in temperature due to absorption or emission of heat is evidence of a chemical reaction. This chemical cold pack becomes cold when the barrier separating two substances is broken.

▲ A child's temperature-sensitive spoon changes color upon warming due to a reaction induced by the higher temperature.

In summary, each of the following provides *evidence of a chemical reaction*.

- a *color change*

- the *formation of a solid* in a previously clear solution

- the *formation of a gas* when you add a substance to a solution

- the *emission of light*

- the *emission* or *absorption of heat*

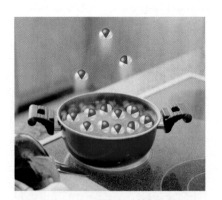

▲ Figure 7.5   **Boiling: a physical change**   When water boils, bubbles are formed and a gas is evolved. However, no chemical change has occurred because the gas, like the liquid water, is also composed of water molecules.

While these changes provide evidence of a chemical reaction, they are not *definitive* evidence. Only chemical analysis showing that the initial substances have changed into other substances conclusively proves that a chemical reaction has occurred. We can be fooled. For example, when water boils, bubbles form, but no chemical reaction has occurred. Boiling water forms gaseous steam, but both water and steam are composed of water molecules—no chemical change has occurred (◄ Figure 7.5). On the other hand, chemical reactions may occur without any obvious signs, yet chemical analysis may show that a reaction has indeed occurred. It is the changes occurring at the atomic and molecular level that determine whether a chemical reaction has occurred. Fortunately, much of the time these molecular changes also result in changes that we can perceive.

| EXAMPLE 7.1 | **Evidence of a Chemical Reaction** |

Which of the following is a chemical reaction? Why?

(a) ice melting upon warming
(b) an electric current is passed through water, resulting in the formation of hydrogen and oxygen gas which appear as bubbles rising in the water
(c) iron rusting
(d) bubbles forming when a soda can is opened

Solution:

(a) Not a chemical reaction; melting ice forms water, but both the ice and water are composed of water molecules.

(b) Chemical reaction; water decomposes into hydrogen and oxygen, as evidenced by the bubbling.

(c) Chemical reaction; iron changes into iron oxide, changing color in the process.

(d) Not a chemical reaction; even though there is bubbling, it is just carbon dioxide coming out of the liquid.

| SKILLBUILDER 7.1 | **Evidence of a Chemical Reaction** |

Which of the following is a chemical reaction? Why?

(a) butane burning in a butane lighter
(b) butane evaporating out of a butane lighter
(c) wood burning
(d) dry ice evaporating

7.3   The Chemical Equation

Chemical reactions are represented by **chemical equations**. For example, the reaction occurring in a natural-gas flame, such as the flame on your kitchen stove, is methane (CH_4) reacting with oxygen (O_2) to form carbon dioxide (CO_2) and water (H_2O). This reaction is represented by the following equation.

$$\underset{\text{reactants}}{CH_4 + O_2} \longrightarrow \underset{\text{products}}{CO_2 + H_2O}$$

The substances on the left side of the equation are called the **reactants** and the substances on the right side are called the **products**. We often specify the state of each reactant or product in parentheses next to the formula. If we add these to our equation, it becomes:

$$CH_4(g) + O_2(g) \longrightarrow CO_2(g) + H_2O(g)$$

The (g) indicates that these substances are gases in the reaction. The common states of reactants and products and their symbols used in chemical reactions are summarized in Table 7.1.

TABLE 7.1 Abbreviations Indicating the States of Reactants and Products in Chemical Equations

Abbreviation	State
(g)	gas
(l)	liquid
(s)	solid
(aq)	aqueous (water solution)*

*The (aq) designation stands for *aqueous*, which means a substance dissolved in water. When a substance dissolves in water, the mixture is called a *solution* (see Section 7.5).

Let's look more closely at our equation for the burning of natural gas. How many oxygen atoms are on each side of the equation?

$$CH_4(g) + O_2(g) \longrightarrow CO_2(g) + H_2O(g)$$

In chemical equations, atoms cannot change from one type to another—hydrogen atoms cannot change into oxygen atoms, for example. Nor can atoms disappear (recall the law of conservation of mass from Section 3.7).

There are two oxygen atoms on the left side and three on the right. Where did this additional oxygen atom on the right side come from? Since chemical equations represent real chemical reactions, atoms cannot simply appear or disappear because, as we know, atoms don't simply appear or disappear in nature. Notice also that there are four hydrogen atoms on the left and only two on the right.

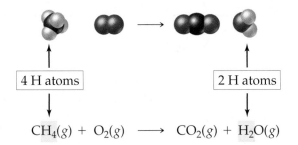

$$CH_4(g) + O_2(g) \longrightarrow CO_2(g) + H_2O(g)$$

To correct these problems, we must create a **balanced equation**; that is, we must add coefficients—not subscripts—to ensure that the number of each type of atom on both sides of the equation is equal. New atoms do not form during a reaction, nor do atoms vanish—matter must be conserved.

We balance chemical equations by adding coefficients as needed in front of the formulas of the reactants and products. This changes the number of molecules in the equation, but it does not change the *kinds* of molecules. To balance the preceding equation, for example, we put the coefficient 2 before O_2 in the reactants, and the coefficient 2 before H_2O in the products.

$$CH_4(g) + 2\,O_2(g) \longrightarrow CO_2(g) + 2\,H_2O$$

TUTORIAL
Balancing Chemical Equations

The equation is now balanced because the numbers of each type of atom on either side of the equation are equal. We can verify this by summing the number of each type of atom.

> The number of a particular type of atom within a chemical formula embedded in an equation is obtained by multiplying the subscript for the atom by the coefficient for the chemical formula.

If there is no coefficient or subscript, a 1 is implied. So, for the combustion of natural gas we have:

$$CH_4(g) + 2\,O_2(g) \longrightarrow CO_2(g) + 2\,H_2O(g)$$

Reactants	Products
1 C atom ($1 \times CH_4$)	1 C atom ($1 \times CO_2$)
4 H atoms ($1 \times CH_4$)	4 H atoms ($2 \times H_2O$)
4 O atoms ($2 \times O_2$)	4 O atoms ($1 \times CO_2 + 2 \times H_2O$)

The numbers of each type of atom on both sides of the equation are equal—the equation is balanced.

▶ A balanced chemical equation represents a chemical reaction. In this image, methane molecules combine with oxygen to form carbon dioxide and water.

$$CH_4(g) + 2\,O_2(g) \longrightarrow CO_2(g) + 2\,H_2O(g)$$

CONCEPTUAL CHECKPOINT 7.1

In photosynthesis, plants make the sugar glucose, $C_6H_{12}O_6$, from carbon dioxide and water. The equation for the reaction is

$$6\,CO_2 + 6\,H_2O \longrightarrow C_6H_{12}O_6 + x\,O_2$$

In order for this equation to be balanced, the coefficient x must be

(a) 3
(b) 6
(c) 9
(d) 12

7.4   How to Write Balanced Chemical Equations

The following procedure box details the steps for writing balanced chemical equations. As in other procedures, we show the steps in the left column and examples of applying each step in the center and right columns. Remember, change only the *coefficients* to balance a chemical equation, *never the subscripts*.

Writing Balanced Chemical Equations

	EXAMPLE 7.2	**EXAMPLE 7.3**
	Write a balanced equation for the reaction between solid silicon dioxide and solid carbon to produce solid silicon carbide and carbon monoxide gas.	Write a balanced equation for the combustion of liquid octane (C_8H_{18}), a component of gasoline, in which it combines with gaseous oxygen to form gaseous carbon dioxide and gaseous water.
1. Write a skeletal equation by writing chemical formulas for each of the reactants and products. Review Chapter 5 for nomenclature rules. (If a skeletal equation is provided, skip this step and go to Step 2.)	**Solution:** $$SiO_2(s) + C(s) \longrightarrow$$ $$SiC(s) + CO(g)$$	**Solution:** $$C_8H_{18}(l) + O_2(g) \longrightarrow$$ $$CO_2(g) + H_2O(g)$$
2. If an element occurs in only one compound on both sides of the equation, balance it first. If there is more than one such element, balance metals before nonmetals.	**Begin with Si:** $$SiO_2(s) + C(s) \longrightarrow$$ $$SiC(s) + CO(g)$$ **1 Si atom $\longrightarrow$ 1 Si atom** Si is already balanced. **Balance O next:** $$SiO_2(s) + C(s) \longrightarrow$$ $$SiC(s) + CO(g)$$ **2 O atoms $\longrightarrow$ 1 O atom** To balance O, put a 2 before $CO(g)$. $$SiO_2(s) + C(s) \longrightarrow$$ $$SiC(s) + 2 CO(g)$$ **2 O atoms $\longrightarrow$ 2 O atoms**	**Begin with C:** $$C_8H_{18}(l) + O_2(g) \longrightarrow$$ $$CO_2(g) + H_2O(g)$$ **8 C atoms $\longrightarrow$ 1 C atom** To balance C, put an 8 before $CO_2(g)$. $$C_8H_{18}(l) + O_2(g) \longrightarrow$$ $$8 CO_2(g) + H_2O(g)$$ **8 C atoms $\longrightarrow$ 8 C atoms** **Balance H next:** $$C_8H_{18}(l) + O_2(g) \longrightarrow$$ $$8 CO_2(g) + H_2O(g)$$ **18 H atoms $\longrightarrow$ 2 H atoms** To balance H, put a 9 before $H_2O(g)$. $$C_8H_{18}(l) + O_2(g) \longrightarrow$$ $$8 CO_2(g) + 9 H_2O(g)$$ **18 H atoms $\longrightarrow$ 18 H atoms**
3. If an element occurs as a free element on either side of the chemical equation, balance it last. Always balance free elements by adjusting the coefficient *on the free element*.	**Balance C:** $$SiO_2(s) + C(s) \longrightarrow$$ $$SiC(s) + 2 CO(g)$$ **1 C atom $\longrightarrow$ 1 C + 2 C** **= 3 C atoms** To balance C, put a 3 before $C(s)$. $$SiO_2(s) + 3 C(s) \longrightarrow$$ $$SiC(s) + 2 CO(g)$$ **3 C atoms $\longrightarrow$ 1 C + 2 C** **= 3 C atoms**	**Balance O:** $$C_8H_{18}(l) + O_2(g) \longrightarrow$$ $$8 CO_2(g) + 9 H_2O(g)$$ **2 O atoms $\longrightarrow$ 16 O + 9 O** **= 25 O atoms** To balance O, put a $\frac{25}{2}$ before $O_2(g)$. $$C_8H_{18}(l) + \frac{25}{2}O_2(g) \longrightarrow$$ $$8 CO_2(g) + 9 H_2O(g)$$ **25 O atoms $\longrightarrow$ 16 O + 9 O** **= 25 O atoms**
4. If the balanced equation contains coefficient fractions, clear these by multiplying the entire equation by the appropriate factor.	This step is not necessary in this example. Proceed to Step 5.	$$[C_8H_{18}(l) + \frac{25}{2}O_2(g) \longrightarrow$$ $$8 CO_2(g) + 9 H_2O(g)] \times 2$$

$$2\,C_8H_{18}(l) + 25\,O_2(g) \longrightarrow$$
$$16\,CO_2(g) + 18\,H_2O(g)$$

5. Check to make certain the equation is balanced by summing the total number of each type of atom on both sides of the equation.

$$SiO_2(s) + 3\,C(s) \longrightarrow$$
$$SiC(s) + 2\,CO(g)$$

$$2\,C_8H_{18}(l) + 25\,O_2(g) \longrightarrow$$
$$16\,CO_2(g) + 18\,H_2O(g)$$

Reactants		Products
1 Si atom	$\longrightarrow$	1 Si atom
2 O atoms	$\longrightarrow$	2 O atoms
3 C atoms	$\longrightarrow$	3 C atoms

The equation is balanced.

Reactants		Products
16 C atoms	$\longrightarrow$	16 C atoms
36 H atoms	$\longrightarrow$	36 H atoms
50 O atoms	$\longrightarrow$	50 O atoms

The equation is balanced.

SKILLBUILDER 7.2

Write a balanced equation for the reaction between solid chromium(III) oxide and solid carbon to produce solid chromium and carbon dioxide gas.

SKILLBUILDER 7.3

Write a balanced equation for the combustion of C_4H_{10} in which it combines with gaseous oxygen to form gaseous carbon dioxide and gaseous water.

EXAMPLE 7.4   Balancing Chemical Equations

Write a balanced equation for the reaction of solid aluminum with aqueous sulfuric acid to form aqueous aluminum sulfate and hydrogen gas.

Use your knowledge of chemical nomenclature from Chapter 5 to write a skeletal equation containing formulas for each of the reactants and products. The formulas for each compound MUST BE CORRECT before you begin to balance the equation.

Solution:

$$Al(s) + H_2SO_4(aq) \longrightarrow Al_2(SO_4)_3(aq) + H_2(g)$$

Since both aluminum and hydrogen occur as pure elements, balance those last. Sulfur and oxygen occur in only one compound on each side of the equation, so balance these first. Sulfur and oxygen are also part of a polyatomic ion that stays intact on both sides of the equation. *Balance polyatomic ions such as these as a unit.* There are 3 SO_4^{2-} ions on the right side of the equation, so put a 3 in front of H_2SO_4.

$$Al(s) + \mathbf{3}\,H_2SO_4(aq) \longrightarrow Al_2(SO_4)_3(aq) + H_2(g)$$

Balance Al next. Since there are 2 Al atoms on the right side of the equation, place a 2 in front of Al on the left side of the equation.

$$\mathbf{2}\,Al(s) + \mathbf{3}\,H_2SO_4(aq) \longrightarrow Al_2(SO_4)_3(aq) + H_2(g)$$

Balance H next. Since there are 6 H atoms on the left side, place a 3 in front of $H_2(g)$ on the right side.	$2\,Al(s) + 3\,H_2SO_4(aq) \longrightarrow Al_2(SO_4)_3(aq) + \mathbf{3}\,H_2(g)$

Finally, sum the number of atoms on each side to make sure that the equation is balanced.

The equation is balanced.

$2\,Al(s) + 3\,H_2SO_4(aq) \longrightarrow Al_2(SO_4)_3(aq) + 3\,H_2(g)$

Reactants		Products
2 Al atoms	$\longrightarrow$	2 Al atoms
6 H atoms	$\longrightarrow$	6 H atoms
3 S atoms	$\longrightarrow$	3 S atoms
12 O atoms	$\longrightarrow$	12 O atoms

SKILLBUILDER 7.4   Balancing Chemical Equations

Write a balanced equation for the reaction of aqueous lead(II) acetate with aqueous potassium iodide to form solid lead(II) iodide and aqueous potassium acetate.

EXAMPLE 7.5   Balancing Chemical Equations

Balance the following chemical equation.

$$Fe(s) + HCl(aq) \longrightarrow FeCl_3(aq) + H_2(g)$$

Since Cl occurs in only one compound on each side of the equation, balance it first. There is 1 Cl atom on the left side of the equation and 3 Cl atoms on the right side. Balance Cl by placing a 3 in front of HCl.	**Solution:** $Fe(s) + \mathbf{3}\,HCl(aq) \longrightarrow FeCl_3(aq) + H_2(g)$
Since H and Fe occur as free elements, balance them last. There is 1 Fe atom on the left side of the equation and 1 Fe atom on the right, so Fe is balanced. There are 3 H atoms on the left and 2 H atoms on the right. Balance H by placing a $\frac{3}{2}$ in front of H_2. (That way you don't alter other elements that are already balanced.)	$Fe(s) + \mathbf{3}\,HCl(aq) \longrightarrow FeCl_3(aq) + \dfrac{3}{2}H_2(g)$
Since the equation contains a coefficient fraction, clear it by multiplying the entire equation by 2.	$[Fe(s) + 3\,HCl(aq) \longrightarrow FeCl_3(aq) + \dfrac{3}{2}H_2(g)] \times 2$ $2\,Fe(s) + 6\,HCl(aq) \longrightarrow 2\,FeCl_3(aq) + 3\,H_2(g)$

Finally, sum the number of atoms on each side to check that the equation is balanced.

The equation is balanced.

$2\,Fe(s) + 6\,HCl(aq) \longrightarrow 2\,FeCl_3(aq) + 3\,H_2(g)$

Reactants		Products
2 Fe atoms	$\longrightarrow$	2 Fe atoms
6 Cl atoms	$\longrightarrow$	6 Cl atoms
6 H atoms	$\longrightarrow$	6 H atoms

SKILLBUILDER 7.5   Balancing Chemical Equations

Balance the following chemical equation.

$\cancel{4}HCl(g) + O_2(g) \longrightarrow \cancel{2}H_2O(l) + \cancel{2}Cl_2(g)$

$= 4\,HCl + O_2 \rightarrow 2H_2O + 2Cl_2$

7.5 Aqueous Solutions and Compounds Dissolved in Water

Reactions occurring in aqueous solution are among the most common and important. An **aqueous solution** is a homogeneous mixture of a substance with water. For example, sodium chloride (NaCl) solutions, also called saline solutions, are composed of sodium chloride dissolved in water. They are common both in the oceans and in living cells. You may have formed a NaCl solution yourself by adding table salt to water. As you stir the NaCl into the water, it seems to disappear. However, you know the NaCl is still there because you can taste its saltiness in the water. How does NaCl dissolve in water?

When ionic compounds such as NaCl dissolve in water they usually dissociate into their component ions. A NaCl solution, represented as NaCl(aq), does not contain any NaCl units, but rather dissolved Na^+ ions and Cl^- ions.

A sodium chloride solution contains independent **Na^+** and **Cl^-** ions.

Pure water

(a)

We know that NaCl is present as independent sodium and chloride ions in solution because sodium chloride solutions conduct electricity, which requires the presence of freely moving charged particles. Substances (such as NaCl) that completely dissociate into ions in solution are called *strong electrolytes* and the resultant solutions are called **strong electrolyte solutions** (◀ Figure 7.6). Similarly, a $AgNO_3$ solution, represented as $AgNO_3(aq)$, does not contain any $AgNO_3$ units, but rather dissolved Ag^+ ions and NO_3^- ions. It too is a strong electrolyte solution. When compounds containing polyatomic ions such as NO_3^- dissolve, the polyatomic ions usually dissolve as intact units.

A silver nitrate solution contains independent **Ag^+** and **NO_3^-** ions.

NaCl solution

(b)

▲ Figure 7.6   **Ions as conductors**
(a) Pure water will not conduct electricity. **(b)** Ions in a sodium chloride solution conduct electricity, causing the bulb to light. Solutions such as these are called strong electrolyte solutions.

Not all ionic compounds, however, dissolve in water. AgCl, for example, does not dissolve in water. If we add AgCl to water, it remains as solid AgCl and appears as a white solid at the bottom of the water.

When silver chloride is added to water, it remains as solid AgCl—it does not dissolve into independent ions.

Solubility

A compound is **soluble** in a particular liquid if it dissolves in that liquid. A compound is **insoluble** if it does not dissolve in the liquid. NaCl, for example, is soluble in water. If we mix solid sodium chloride into water, it dissolves and forms a strong electrolyte solution. AgCl, on the other hand, is insoluble in water. If we mix solid silver chloride into water, it remains as a solid within the liquid water.

There is no easy way to tell whether a particular compound will be soluble or insoluble in water. For ionic compounds, however, there are empirical rules that have been deduced from observations of many compounds. These are called **solubility rules** and are summarized in Table 7.2. For example, the solubility rules state that compounds containing the lithium ion are *soluble*. That means that compounds such as $LiBr$, $LiNO_3$, Li_2SO_4, $LiOH$, and Li_2CO_3 will all dissolve in water to form strong electrolyte solutions. If a compound contains Li^+, it is soluble. Similarly, the solubility rules state that compounds containing the NO_3^- ion are soluble. That means that compounds such as $AgNO_3$, $Pb(NO_3)_2$, $NaNO_3$, $Ca(NO_3)_2$ and $Sr(NO_3)_2$ all dissolve in water to form strong electrolyte solutions.

The solubility rules apply only to the solubility of the compounds in water

TABLE 7.2 Solubility Rules

Compounds Containing the Following Ions Are Mostly Soluble	Exceptions
Li^+, Na^+, K^+, NH_4^+	None
NO_3^-, $C_2H_3O_2^-$	None
Cl^-, Br^-, I^-	When any of these ions pairs with Ag^+, Hg_2^{2+}, or Pb^{2+}, the compound is insoluble
SO_4^{2-}	When SO_4^{2-} pairs with Sr^{2+}, Ba^{2+}, Pb^{2+}, or Ca^{2+}, the compound is insoluble

Compounds Containing the Following Ions Are Mostly Insoluble	Exceptions
OH^-, S^{2-}	When either of these ions pairs with Li^+, Na^+, K^+, or NH_4^+, the compound is soluble
	When S^{2-} pairs with Ca^{2+}, Sr^{2+}, or Ba^{2+}, the compound is soluble
	When OH^- pairs with Ca^{2+}, Sr^{2+}, or Ba^{2+}, the compound is slightly soluble.*
CO_3^{2-}, PO_4^{3-}	When either of these ions pairs with Li^+, Na^+, K^+, or NH_4^+, the compound is soluble

*For many purposes these can be considered insoluble.

The solubility rules also state that, with some exceptions, compounds containing the CO_3^{2-} ion are *insoluble*. Therefore, compounds such as $CuCO_3$, $CaCO_3$, $SrCO_3$, and $FeCO_3$ do not dissolve in water. Note that the solubility rules contain many exceptions. For example, compounds containing CO_3^{2-} are *soluble when paired with* Li^+, Na^+, K^+, or NH_4^+. Thus Li_2CO_3, Na_2CO_3, K_2CO_3, and $(NH_4)_2CO_3$ are all soluble.

EXAMPLE 7.6 **Determining Whether a Compound Is Soluble**

Determine whether each of the following compounds is soluble or insoluble.

(a) AgBr — In
(b) $CaCl_2$ - Soluable
(c) $Pb(NO_3)_2$ — soluable
(d) $PbSO_4$ insoluable.

Solution:

(a) Insoluble; compounds containing Br^- are normally soluble, but Ag^+ is an exception.

(b) Soluble; compounds containing Cl^- are normally soluble, and Ca^{2+} is not an exception.

(c) Soluble; compounds containing NO_3^- are always soluble.

(d) Insoluble; compounds containing SO_4^{2-} are normally soluble, but Pb^{2+} is an exception.

SKILLBUILDER 7.6 **Determining Whether a Compound Is Soluble**

Determine whether each of the following compounds is soluble or insoluble.

(a) CuS — insoluable
(b) $FeSO_4$ — soluable
(c) $PbCO_3$ - soluable
(d) NH_4Cl — soluable

7.6 Precipitation Reactions: Reactions in Aqueous Solution That Form a Solid

In Section 7.1, we learned how sodium carbonate is added to laundry detergent to react with dissolved Mg^{2+} and Ca^{2+} ions to form solids that precipitate (or come out of) solution. These reactions are examples of **precipitation reactions**, reactions that form a solid or **precipitate** upon mixing two aqueous solutions.

Precipitation reactions are common in chemistry. Potassium iodide and lead nitrate, for example, both form colorless, strong electrolyte solutions when dissolved in water (see the solubility rules). When the two solutions are combined, however, a brilliant yellow precipitate forms (▶ Figure 7.7). This precipitation reaction can be described with the following chemical equation.

$$2\,KI(aq) + Pb(NO_3)_2(aq) \longrightarrow PbI_2(s) + 2\,KNO_3(aq)$$

Precipitation reactions do not always occur when mixing two aqueous solutions. For example, if solutions of $KI(aq)$ and $NaCl(aq)$ are combined, nothing happens (▶ Figure 7.8).

$$KI(aq) + NaCl(aq) \longrightarrow \text{NO REACTION}$$

TUTORIAL
Precipitation Reactions

▲ **Figure 7.7** **Precipitation** When a potassium iodide solution is mixed with a lead(II) nitrate solution, a brilliant yellow precipitate of $PbI_2(s)$ forms.

▲ **Figure 7.8** **No reaction** When a potassium iodide solution is mixed with a sodium chloride solution, no reaction occurs.

$PbI_2(s)$ and $KNO_3(aq)$

Predicting Precipitation Reactions

The key to predicting precipitation reactions is to understand that *only insoluble compounds form precipitates*. In a precipitation reaction, two solutions containing soluble compounds combine and an insoluble compound precipitates. For example, consider the precipitation reaction from Figure 7.7.

$$2 KI(aq) + Pb(NO_3)_2(aq) \longrightarrow PbI_2(s) + 2 KNO_3(aq)$$
$$\text{soluble} \qquad \text{soluble} \qquad\qquad \text{insoluble} \qquad \text{soluble}$$

KI and $Pb(NO_3)_2$ are both soluble, but the precipitate, PbI_2, is *insoluble*. Before mixing, $KI(aq)$ and $Pb(NO_3)_2(aq)$ are both dissociated in their respective solutions.

$KI(aq)$ $Pb(NO_3)_2(aq)$

The instant that the solutions are mixed, all four ions are present.

$KI(aq)$ and $Pb(NO_3)_2(aq)$

However, new compounds—potentially insoluble ones—are now possible. Specifically, the cation from one compound can now pair with the anion from the other compound to form new (and potentially insoluble) products.

Original compounds	*Potentially insoluble products*
K I (aq)	KNO₃
Pb (NO₃) ₂(aq)	PbI₂

If the *potentially insoluble* products are both *soluble*, then no reaction occurs. If, on the other hand, one or both of the potentially insoluble products are *indeed insoluble*, a precipitation reaction occurs. In this case, KNO_3 is soluble, but PbI_2 is insoluble. Consequently, PbI_2 precipitates.

To predict whether a precipitation reaction will occur when two solutions are mixed and to write an equation for the reaction, follow the steps in the procedure box. As usual, the steps are shown in the left column, and two examples of applying the procedure are shown in the center and right column.

Writing Equations for Precipitation Reactions

	EXAMPLE 7.7	EXAMPLE 7.8
	Write an equation for the precipitation reaction that occurs (if any) when solutions of sodium carbonate and copper(II) chloride are mixed.	Write an equation for the precipitation reaction that occurs (if any) when solutions of lithium nitrate and sodium sulfate are mixed.

1. Write the formulas of the two compounds being mixed as reactants in a chemical equation.

Solution:

$$Na_2CO_3(aq) + CuCl_2(aq) \longrightarrow$$

Solution:

$$LiNO_3(aq) + Na_2SO_4(aq) \longrightarrow$$

2. Below the equation, write the formulas of the potentially insoluble products that could form from the reactants. Obtain these by combining the cation from one reactant with the anion from the other. Make sure to write correct formulas for these ionic compounds as described in Section 5.5.

$$Na_2CO_3(aq) + CuCl_2(aq) \longrightarrow$$

Potentially Insoluble Products:

NaCl $CuCO_3$

$$LiNO_3(aq) + Na_2SO_4(aq) \longrightarrow$$

Potentially Insoluble Products:

$NaNO_3$ Li_2SO_4

3. Use the solubility rules to determine whether any of the new products are indeed insoluble.

NaCl is *soluble* (compounds containing Cl^- are usually soluble and Na^+ is not an exception). $CuCO_3$ is *insoluble* (compounds containing CO_3^{2-} are usually insoluble and Cu^{2+} is not an exception).

$NaNO_3$ is *soluble* (compounds containing NO_3^- are soluble and Na^+ is not an exception). Li_2SO_4 is *soluble* (compounds containing SO_4^{2-} are soluble and Li^+ is not an exception).

4. If all of the potentially insoluble products are soluble, there will be no precipitate. Write *NO REACTION* next to the arrow.

Since this example has an insoluble product, we proceed to the next step.

$$LiNO_3(aq) + Na_2SO_4(aq) \longrightarrow$$
NO REACTION

5. If one or both of the potentially insoluble products are indeed insoluble, write their formula(s) as the product(s) of the reaction, using (s) to indicate solid. Write any soluble products with (aq) to indicate aqueous.

$$Na_2CO_3(aq) + CuCl_2(aq) \longrightarrow$$
$$CuCO_3(s) + NaCl(aq)$$

6. Balance the equation. Remember to adjust only coefficients here, not subscripts.

$$Na_2CO_3(aq) + CuCl_2(aq) \longrightarrow$$
$$CuCO_3(s) + \mathbf{2}\,NaCl(aq)$$

SKILLBUILDER 7.7

Write an equation for the precipitation reaction that occurs (if any) when solutions of potassium hydroxide and nickel(II) bromide are mixed.

SKILLBUILDER 7.8

Write an equation for the precipitation reaction that occurs (if any) when solutions of ammonium chloride and iron(III) nitrate are mixed.

EXAMPLE 7.9   **Predicting and Writing Equations for Precipitation Reactions**

Write an equation for the precipitation reaction (if any) that occurs when solutions of lead(II) acetate and sodium sulfate are mixed. If no reaction occurs, write *NO REACTION*.

1. Write the formulas of the two compounds being mixed as reactants in a chemical equation.	**Solution:** $Pb(C_2H_3O_2)_2(aq) + Na_2SO_4(aq) \longrightarrow$
2. Below the equation, write the formulas of the potentially insoluble products that could form from the reactants. These are obtained by combining the cation from one reactant with the anion from the other. Make sure to adjust the subscripts so that all formulas are charge-neutral.	$Pb(C_2H_3O_2)_2(aq) + Na_2SO_4(aq) \longrightarrow$ *Potentially insoluble products* $NaC_2H_3O_2$ $PbSO_4$
3. Use the solubility rules to determine whether any of the potentially insoluble products are indeed insoluble.	$NaC_2H_3O_2$ is *soluble* (compounds containing Na^+ are always soluble). $PbSO_4$ is *insoluble* (compounds containing SO_4^{2-} are normally soluble, but Pb^{2+} is an exception).
4. If all of the potentially insoluble products are soluble, there will be no precipitate. Write *NO REACTION* next to the arrow.	Since we have an insoluble product, we proceed to the next step.
5. If one or both of the potentially insoluble products are indeed insoluble, write their formula(s) as the product(s) of the reaction, using (s) to indicate solid. Write any soluble products with (aq) to indicate aqueous.	$Pb(C_2H_3O_2)_2(aq) + Na_2SO_4(aq) \longrightarrow PbSO_4(s) + NaC_2H_3O_2(aq)$
6. Balance the equation.	$Pb(C_2H_3O_2)_2(aq) + Na_2SO_4(aq) \longrightarrow PbSO_4(s) + 2\,NaC_2H_3O_2(aq)$

SKILLBUILDER 7.9   **Predicting and Writing Equations for Precipitation Reactions**

Write an equation for the precipitation reaction (if any) that occurs when solutions of potassium sulfate and strontium nitrate are mixed. If no reaction occurs, write *NO REACTION*.

CONCEPTUAL CHECKPOINT 7.2

Which of these reactions would result in the formation of a precipitate?
(a) $NaNO_3 + CaS$
(b) $MgSO_4 + CaS$
(c) $NaNO_3 + MgSO_4$

7.7 Writing Chemical Equations for Reactions in Solution: Molecular, Complete Ionic, and Net Ionic Equations

Consider the following equation for a precipitation reaction.

$$AgNO_3(aq) + NaCl(aq) \longrightarrow AgCl(s) + NaNO_3(aq)$$

This equation is written as a **molecular equation**, an equation showing the complete neutral formulas for every compound in the reaction. However, equations for reactions occurring in aqueous solution may be written to show that aqueous ionic compounds normally dissociate in solution. For example, the previous equation can be written as follows:

$$Ag^+(aq) + NO_3^-(aq) + Na^+(aq) + Cl^-(aq) \longrightarrow$$
$$AgCl(s) + Na^+(aq) + NO_3^-(aq)$$

When writing complete ionic equations, separate only *aqueous* ionic compounds into their constituent ions. Do NOT separate solid, liquid, or gaseous compounds.

Equations such as this one, showing the reactants and products as they are actually present in solution, are called **complete ionic equations**.

Notice that in the complete ionic equation, some of the ions in solution appear unchanged on both sides of the equation. These ions are called **spectator ions** because they do not participate in the reaction.

$$Ag^+(aq) + NO_3^-(aq) + Na^+(aq) + Cl^-(aq) \longrightarrow AgCl(s) + Na^+(aq) + NO_3^-(aq)$$

Spectator ions

To simplify the equation, and to more clearly show what is happening, spectator ions can be omitted.

$$Ag^+(aq) + Cl^-(aq) \longrightarrow AgCl(s)$$

Species refers to a kind or sort of thing. In this case, the species are all the different molecules and ions that are present during the reaction.

Equations such as this one, which show only the species that actually participate in the reaction, are called **net ionic equations**.

As another example, consider the following reaction between $HCl(aq)$ and $NaOH(aq)$.

$$HCl(aq) + NaOH(aq) \longrightarrow H_2O(l) + NaCl(aq)$$

HCl, NaOH, and NaCl exist in solution as independent ions. The *complete ionic equation* for this reaction is:

$$H^+(aq) + Cl^-(aq) + Na^+(aq) + OH^-(aq) \longrightarrow$$
$$H_2O(l) + Na^+(aq) + Cl^-(aq)$$

To write the *net ionic equation*, we remove the spectator ions, those that are unchanged on both sides of the equation.

$$H^+(aq) + Cl^-(aq) + Na^+(aq) + OH^-(aq) \longrightarrow H_2O(l) + Na^+(aq) + Cl^-(aq)$$

Spectator ions

The net ionic equation is $H^+(aq) + OH^-(aq) \longrightarrow H_2O(l)$

To summarize:
- A *molecular equation* is a chemical equation showing the complete, neutral formulas for every compound in a reaction.
- A *complete ionic equation* is a chemical equation showing all of the species as they are actually present in solution.
- A *net ionic equation* is an equation showing only the species that actually participate in the reaction.

EXAMPLE 7.10   Writing Complete Ionic and Net Ionic Equations

Consider the following precipitation reaction occurring in aqueous solution.

$$Pb(NO_3)_2(aq) + 2\,LiCl(aq) \longrightarrow PbCl_2(s) + 2\,LiNO_3(aq)$$

Write a complete ionic equation and a net ionic equation for this reaction.

Write the complete ionic equation by separating aqueous ionic compounds into their constituent ions. The $PbCl_2(s)$ remains as one unit.	**Solution:** **Complete ionic equation:** $Pb^{2+}(aq) + 2\,NO_3^-(aq) + 2\,Li^+(aq) + 2\,Cl^-(aq) \longrightarrow$ $\qquad\qquad PbCl_2(s) + 2\,Li^+(aq) + 2\,NO_3^-(aq)$
Write the net ionic equation by eliminating the spectator ions, those that are not changing during the reaction.	$Pb^{2+}(aq) + 2\,NO_3^-(aq) + 2\,Li^+(aq) + 2\,Cl^-(aq) \longrightarrow$ $\qquad\qquad PbCl_2(s) + 2\,Li^+(aq) + 2\,NO_3^-(aq)$ **Net ionic equation:** $\qquad Pb^{2+}(aq) + 2\,Cl^-(aq) \longrightarrow PbCl_2(s)$

SKILLBUILDER 7.10   Writing Complete Ionic and Net Ionic Equations

Consider the following reaction occurring in aqueous solution.

$$2\,HBr(aq) + Ca(OH)_2(aq) \longrightarrow 2\,H_2O(l) + CaBr_2(aq)$$

Write a complete ionic equation and net ionic equation for this reaction.

$2H\ 2Br^- + Ca^{+2}\,2OH^- \longrightarrow 2H_2O(L) + Ca^+\,Br_2 = 2H + 2OH^- \longrightarrow 2\,H_2O(L)$

7.8   Acid–Base and Gas Evolution Reactions

Two other kinds of reactions that occur in solution are **acid–base reactions**—reactions that form water upon mixing of an acid and a base—and **gas evolution reactions**—reactions that evolve a gas. Like precipitation reactions, these reactions occur when the cation of one reactant combines with the anion of another. As we will see in the next section, many gas evolution reactions also happen to be acid–base reactions.

▶ Foods such as lemons, limes, and vinegar contain acids.

▶ Milk of magnesia is basic and tastes bitter.

Acid–Base (Neutralization) Reactions

Even though coffee itself is acidic overall, it contains some naturally occurring bases (such as caffeine) that give it a bitter taste.

We learned in Chapter 5 that an acid is a compound characterized by its sour taste, its ability to dissolve some metals, and its tendency to form H^+ ions in solution. A base is a compound characterized by its bitter taste, its slippery feel, and its tendency to form OH^- ions in solution. Some common acids and bases are listed in Table 7.3. Acids and bases are also found in many everyday substances. Foods such as lemons, limes, and vinegar contain acids. Soap, coffee, and milk of magnesia all contain bases.

When an acid and base are mixed, the $H^+(aq)$ from the acid combines with the $OH^-(aq)$ from the base to form $H_2O(l)$. For example, consider the reaction between hydrochloric acid and sodium hydroxide mentioned earlier.

$$\text{HCl}(aq) + \text{NaOH}(aq) \longrightarrow \text{H}_2\text{O}(l) + \text{NaCl}(aq)$$
$$\quad \text{Acid} \qquad\quad \text{Base} \qquad\qquad\quad \text{Water} \qquad \text{Salt}$$

Acid–base reactions (also called **neutralization reactions**) generally form water and an ionic compound—called a **salt**—that usually remains dissolved in the solution. The net ionic equation for many acid–base reactions is:

$$\text{H}^+(aq) + \text{OH}^-(aq) \longrightarrow \text{H}_2\text{O}(l)$$

Another example of an acid–base reaction is that between sulfuric acid and potassium hydroxide.

$$\text{H}_2\text{SO}_4(aq) + 2\,\text{KOH} \longrightarrow 2\,\text{H}_2\text{O}(l) + \text{K}_2\text{SO}_4(aq)$$
$$\quad\text{acid} \qquad\qquad \text{base} \qquad\quad \text{water} \qquad\quad \text{salt}$$

TABLE 7.3 Some Common Acids and Bases

Acid	Formula	Base	Formula
hydrochloric acid	HCl	sodium hydroxide	NaOH
hydrobromic acid	HBr	lithium hydroxide	LiOH
nitric acid	HNO_3	potassium hydroxide	KOH
sulfuric acid	H_2SO_4	calcium hydroxide	$Ca(OH)_2$
perchloric acid	$HClO_4$	barium hydroxide	$Ba(OH)_2$
acetic acid	$HC_2H_3O_2$		

Again, notice the pattern of acid and base reacting to form water and a salt.

$$\text{Acid} + \text{Base} \longrightarrow \text{Water} + \text{Salt} \quad \text{(acid–base reactions)}$$

When writing equations for acid–base reactions, write the formula of the salt using the procedure for writing formulas of ionic compounds given in Section 5.5.

EXAMPLE 7.11   Writing Equations for Acid–Base Reactions

Write a molecular and net ionic equation for the reaction between aqueous HNO_3 and aqueous $Ca(OH)_2$.

You must recognize these substances as an acid and a base. First write the skeletal reaction following the general pattern of acid plus base goes to water plus salt.	**Solution:** $$\underset{\text{acid}}{HNO_3(aq)} + \underset{\text{base}}{Ca(OH)_2(aq)} \longrightarrow \underset{\text{water}}{H_2O(l)} + \underset{\text{salt}}{Ca(NO_3)_2(aq)}$$
Next, balance the equation.	$$\textbf{2}\,HNO_3(aq) + Ca(OH)_2(aq) \longrightarrow \textbf{2}\,H_2O(l) + Ca(NO_3)_2(aq)$$
Write the net ionic equation by eliminating those ions that remain the same on both sides of the equation.	$$2\,H^+(aq) + 2\,OH^-(aq) \longrightarrow 2\,H_2O(l)$$ or simply $$H^+(aq) + OH^-(aq) \longrightarrow H_2O(l)$$

SKILLBUILDER 7.11   Writing Equations for Acid–Base Reactions

● Write a molecular and net ionic equation for the reaction that occurs between aqueous H_2SO_4 and aqueous KOH.

Gas Evolution Reactions

Some aqueous reactions form a gas as a product. These reactions, as we learned in the opening section of this chapter, are called gas evolution reactions. Some gas evolution reactions form a gaseous product directly when the cation of one reactant reacts with the anion of the other. For example, when sulfuric acid reacts with lithium sulfide, dihydrogen sulfide gas is formed.

$$H_2SO_4(aq) + \overset{\frown}{Li_2S}(aq) \longrightarrow \underset{\text{Gas}}{H_2S(g)} + Li_2SO_4(aq)$$

Many gas evolution reactions such as this one are also acid–base reactions. In Chapter 14 we learn how ions such as CO_3^{2-} act as bases in aqueous solution.

Other gas evolution reactions form an intermediate product that then decomposes into a gas. For example, when aqueous hydrochloric acid is mixed with aqueous sodium bicarbonate, the following reaction occurs.

$$HCl(aq) + Na\overset{\frown}{H}CO_3(aq) \longrightarrow H_2CO_3(aq) + NaCl(aq) \longrightarrow \underset{\text{Gas}}{H_2O(l) + CO_2(g)} + NaCl(aq)$$

The intermediate product, H_2CO_3, is not stable and decomposes to form H_2O and gaseous CO_2. This reaction is almost identical to the reaction in the

▲ A gas evolution reaction: vinegar (a dilute solution of acetic acid) and baking soda (sodium bicarbonate) produce carbon dioxide.

kindergarten volcano of Section 7.1, which involves the mixing of acetic acid and sodium bicarbonate.

$$HC_2H_3O_2(aq) + NaHCO_3(aq) \longrightarrow H_2CO_3(aq) + NaC_2H_3O_2(aq) \longrightarrow$$
$$H_2O(l) + CO_2(g) + NaC_2H_3O_2(aq)$$

The bubbling is caused by the newly formed carbon dioxide gas. Other important gas evolution reactions form either H_2SO_3 or NH_4OH as intermediate products.

$$HCl(aq) + NaHSO_3(aq) \longrightarrow H_2SO_3(aq) + NaCl(aq) \longrightarrow$$
$$H_2O(l) + SO_2(g) + NaCl(aq)$$
$$NH_4Cl(aq) + NaOH(aq) \longrightarrow NH_4OH(aq) + NaCl(aq) \longrightarrow$$
$$H_2O(l) + NH_3(g) + NaCl(aq)$$

MOLECULES
Bicarbonate Ion, Carbonate Ion, Carbonic Acid

The main types of compounds that form gases in aqueous reactions, as well as the gases that they form, are listed in Table 7.4.

TABLE 7.4 Types of Compounds That Undergo Gas Evolution Reactions

Reactant Type	Intermediate Product	Gas Evolved	Example
sulfides	none	H_2S	$2\ HCl(aq) + K_2S(aq) \longrightarrow H_2S(g) + 2\ KCl(aq)$
carbonates and bicarbonates	H_2CO_3	CO_2	$2\ HCl(aq) + K_2CO_3(aq) \longrightarrow H_2O(l) + CO_2(g) + 2\ KCl(aq)$
sulfites and bisulfites	H_2SO_3	SO_2	$2\ HCl(aq) + K_2SO_3(aq) \longrightarrow H_2O(l) + SO_2(g) + 2\ KCl(aq)$
ammonium	NH_4OH	NH_3	$NH_4Cl(aq) + KOH(aq) \longrightarrow H_2O(l) + NH_3(g) + KCl(aq)$

EXAMPLE 7.12   Writing Equations for Gas Evolution Reactions

Write a molecular equation for the gas evolution reaction that occurs when you mix aqueous nitric acid and aqueous sodium carbonate.

Begin by writing a skeletal equation that includes the reactants and products that form when the cation of each reactant combines with the anion of the other.

Solution:

$$HNO_3(aq) + Na_2CO_3(aq) \longrightarrow H_2CO_3(aq) + NaNO_3(aq)$$

You must recognize that $H_2CO_3(aq)$ decomposes into $H_2O(l)$ and $CO_2(g)$ and write the corresponding equation.

$$HNO_3(aq) + Na_2CO_3(aq) \longrightarrow H_2O(l) + CO_2(g) + NaNO_3(aq)$$

Finally, balance the equation.

$$2\ HNO_3(aq) + Na_2CO_3(aq) \longrightarrow H_2O(l) + CO_2(g) + 2\ NaNO_3(aq)$$

SKILLBUILDER 7.12   Writing Equations for Gas Evolution Reactions

Write a molecular equation for the gas evolution reaction that occurs when you mix aqueous hydrobromic acid and aqueous potassium sulfite.

SKILLBUILDER PLUS

Write a net ionic equation for the previous reaction.

Chemistry AND HEALTH

Neutralizing Excess Stomach Acid

Your stomach normally contains acids that are involved in food digestion. Certain foods and stress, however, can increase the acidity of your stomach to uncomfortable levels, causing acid stomach or heartburn. Antacids are over-the-counter medicines that work by reacting with and neutralizing stomach acid. Antacids employ different bases as neutralizing agents. Tums, for example, contains $CaCO_3$; milk of magnesia contains $Mg(OH)_2$; and Mylanta contains $Al(OH)_3$. They all, however, have the same effect of neutralizing stomach acid and relieving heartburn.

CAN YOU ANSWER THIS? *Assume that stomach acid is HCl and write equations showing how each of these antacids neutralizes stomach acid.*

▲ Antacids contain bases such $Mg(OH)_2$, $Al(OH)_3$, and $NaHCO_3$.

▲ The base in an antacid neutralizes excess stomach acid, relieving heartburn and acid stomach.

7.9   Oxidation–Reduction Reactions

We cover oxidation–reduction reactions more thoroughly in Chapter 16.

Reactions involving the transfer of electrons are called **oxidation–reduction reactions** or **redox reactions**. Redox reactions are responsible for the rusting of iron, the bleaching of hair, and the production of electricity in batteries. Many redox reactions involve the reaction of a substance with oxygen.

$$2 H_2(g) + O_2(g) \longrightarrow 2 H_2O(g)$$
(reaction that powers the space shuttle)

$$4 Fe(s) + 3 O_2(g) \longrightarrow 2 Fe_2O_3(s)$$
(rusting of iron)

$$CH_4(g) + 2 O_2(g) \longrightarrow CO_2(g) + 2 H_2O(g)$$
(combustion of natural gas)

However, redox reactions need not involve oxygen. Consider, for example, the reaction between sodium and chlorine to form table salt (NaCl).

$$2 Na(s) + Cl_2(g) \longrightarrow 2 NaCl(s)$$

This reaction is similar to the reaction between sodium and oxygen to form sodium oxide.

$$4\,Na(s) + O_2(g) \longrightarrow 2\,Na_2O(s)$$

What do these two reactions have in common? In both cases, sodium (a metal with a tendency to lose electrons) reacts with a nonmetal (that has a tendency to gain electrons). In both cases, sodium atoms lose electrons to nonmetal atoms. A fundamental definition of oxidation is *the loss of electrons*, and a fundamental definition of reduction is *the gain of electrons*.

Notice that oxidation and reduction must occur together. If one substance loses electrons (oxidation), then another substance must gain electrons (reduction). For now, be able to identify redox reactions.

> Helpful mnemonics: OIL RIG—Oxidation Is Loss; Reduction Is Gain. LEO GER— Lose Electrons Oxidation; Gain Electrons Reduction

Redox reactions are those in which:
- A substance reacts with elemental oxygen.
- A metal reacts with a nonmetal.
- More generally, one substance transfers electrons to another substance.

> A reaction can be classified as a redox reaction if it meets *any one* of these requirements.

EXAMPLE 7.13   Identifying Redox Reactions

Which of the following is a redox reaction?

(a) $2\,Mg(s) + O_2(g) \longrightarrow 2\,MgO(s)$
(b) $2\,HBr(aq) + Ca(OH)_2(aq) \longrightarrow 2\,H_2O(l) + CaBr_2(aq)$
(c) $Ca(s) + Cl_2(g) \longrightarrow CaCl_2(s)$
(d) $Zn(s) + Fe^{2+}(aq) \longrightarrow Zn^{2+}(aq) + Fe(s)$

Solution:

(a) Redox reaction; Mg reacts with elemental oxygen.

(b) Not a redox reaction; it is an acid–base reaction.

(c) Redox reaction; a metal reacts with a nonmetal.

(d) Redox reaction; Zn transfers two electrons to Fe^{2+}.

SKILLBUILDER 7.13   Identifying Redox Reactions

Which of the following is a redox reaction?

(a) $2\,Li(s) + Cl_2(g) \longrightarrow 2\,LiCl(s)$
(b) $2\,Al(s) + 3\,Sn^{2+}(aq) \longrightarrow 2\,Al^{3+}(aq) + 3\,Sn(s)$
(c) $Pb(NO_3)_2(aq) + 2\,LiCl(aq) \longrightarrow PbCl_2(s) + 2\,LiNO_3(aq)$
(d) $C(s) + O_2(g) \longrightarrow CO_2(g)$

Combustion Reactions

Combustion reactions are a type of redox reaction. They are important because most of our society's energy is derived from combustion reactions. Combustion reactions are characterized by the reaction of a substance with O_2 to form one or more oxygen-containing compounds, often including water. Combustion reactions also emit heat. For example, as we saw in Section 7.3, natural gas (CH_4) reacts with oxygen to form carbon dioxide and water.

> The water formed in combustion reactions may be gaseous (*g*) or liquid (*l*) depending on the reaction conditions.

$$CH_4(g) + 2\,O_2(g) \longrightarrow CO_2(g) + 2\,H_2O(g)$$

Combustion

▲ Combustion of octane occurs in the cylinders of an automobile engine.

MOLECULES
Octane, Methanol

As we learned in the opening section of this chapter, combustion reactions power automobiles. For example, octane, a component of gasoline, reacts with oxygen to form carbon dioxide and water.

$$2\,C_8H_{18}(l) + 25\,O_2(g) \longrightarrow 16\,CO_2(g) + 18\,H_2O(g)$$

Ethanol, the alcohol in alcoholic beverages, also reacts with oxygen in a combustion reaction to form carbon dioxide and water.

$$C_2H_5OH(l) + 3\,O_2(g) \longrightarrow 2\,CO_2(g) + 3\,H_2O(g)$$

Compounds containing carbon and hydrogen—or carbon, hydrogen, and oxygen—always form carbon dioxide and water upon combustion. Other combustion reactions include the reaction of carbon with oxygen to form carbon dioxide:

$$C(s) + O_2(g) \longrightarrow CO_2(g)$$

and the reaction of hydrogen with oxygen to form water:

$$2\,H_2(g) + O_2(g) \longrightarrow 2\,H_2O(g)$$

EXAMPLE 7.14	**Writing Combustion Reactions**

Write a balanced equation for the combustion of liquid methyl alcohol (CH_3OH).

	Solution:
Begin by writing a skeletal equation showing the reaction of CH_3OH with O_2 to form CO_2 and H_2O.	$$CH_3OH(l) + O_2(g) \longrightarrow CO_2(g) + H_2O(g)$$
Balance the skeletal equation using the rules in Section 7.4.	$$\mathbf{2}\,CH_3OH(l) + \mathbf{3}\,O_2(g) \longrightarrow \mathbf{2}\,CO_2(g) + \mathbf{4}\,H_2O(g)$$

SKILLBUILDER 7.14	**Writing Combustion Reactions**

Write a balanced equation for the combustion of liquid pentane (C_5H_{12}), a component of gasoline.

SKILLBUILDER PLUS

Write a balanced equation for the combustion of liquid propanol (C_3H_7OH).

7.10   Classifying Chemical Reactions

Throughout this chapter, we have examined different types of chemical reactions. We have seen examples of precipitation reactions, acid–base reactions, gas evolution reactions, oxidation–reduction reactions, and combustion reactions. We can organize these different types of reactions with the following flow chart.

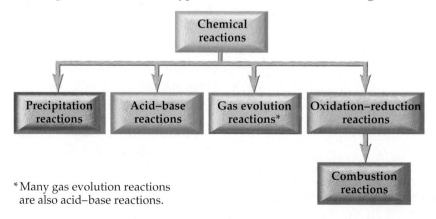

*Many gas evolution reactions are also acid–base reactions.

This classification scheme focuses on the type of chemistry or phenomenon that is occurring during the reaction (such as the formation of a precipitate or the transfer of electrons). However, another way to classify chemical reactions is by what atoms or groups of atoms do during the reaction.

Classifying Chemical Reactions by What Atoms Do

Many chemical reactions can be classified into one of the following four categories. In this classification scheme, the letters (A, B, C, D) represent atoms or groups of atoms.

Type of Reaction	Generic Equation
synthesis or combination	$A + B \longrightarrow AB$
decomposition	$AB \longrightarrow A + B$
displacement	$A + BC \longrightarrow AC + B$
double-displacement	$AB + CD \longrightarrow AD + CB$

SYNTHESIS OR COMBINATION REACTIONS. In a **synthesis** or **combination reaction**, simpler substances combine to form more complex substances. The simpler substances may be elements, such as sodium and chlorine combining to form sodium chloride.

$$2\,Na(s) + Cl_2(g) \longrightarrow 2\,NaCl(s)$$

$$2\,Na(s) + Cl_2(g) \longrightarrow 2\,NaCl(s)$$

▲ In a synthesis reaction, two simpler substances combine to make a more complex substance. In this series of photographs we see sodium metal and chlorine gas. When they combine, a chemical reaction occurs that forms sodium chloride.

The simpler substances may also be compounds, such as calcium oxide and carbon dioxide combining to form calcium carbonate.

$$CaO(s) + CO_2(g) \longrightarrow CaCO_3(s)$$

In either case, a synthesis reaction follows the general equation:

$$A + B \longrightarrow AB$$

Other examples of synthesis reactions include:

Note that the first two of these reactions are also redox reactions.

$$2\,H_2(g) + O_2(g) \longrightarrow 2\,H_2O(l)$$
$$2\,Mg(s) + O_2(g) \longrightarrow 2\,MgO(s)$$
$$SO_3(g) + H_2O(l) \longrightarrow H_2SO_4(aq)$$

DECOMPOSITION REACTIONS. In a **decomposition reaction**, a complex substance decomposes to form simpler substances. The simpler substances may be elements, such as the hydrogen and oxygen gases that form upon the decomposition of water when electrical current passes through it.

$$2\,H_2O(l) \xrightarrow{\text{electrical current}} 2\,H_2(g) + O_2(g)$$

The simpler substances may also be compounds, such as the calcium oxide and carbon dioxide that form upon heating calcium carbonate.

$$CaCO_3(s) \xrightarrow{\text{heat}} CaO(s) + CO_2(g)$$

In either case, a decomposition reaction follows the general equation:

$$AB \longrightarrow A + B$$

Other examples of decomposition reactions include:

$$2\,HgO(s) \xrightarrow{\text{heat}} 2\,Hg(l) + O_2(g)$$

$$2\,KClO_3(s) \xrightarrow{\text{heat}} 2\,KCl(s) + 3\,O_2(g)$$

$$CH_3I(g) \xrightarrow{\text{light}} CH_3(g) + I(g)$$

Notice that most decomposition reactions require energy in the form of heat, electrical current, or light to make them happen. This is because compounds are normally stable and energy must be used to decompose them. *Ultraviolet or UV light* is light in the ultraviolet region of the spectrum. UV light carries more energy than visible light and can therefore initiate the decomposition of many compounds. (Light is discussed in more detail in Chapter 9.)

DISPLACEMENT REACTIONS. In a **displacement** or **single-displacement reaction**, one element displaces another in a compound. For example, when metallic zinc is added to a solution of copper(II) chloride, the zinc replaces the copper.

$$Zn(s) + CuCl_2(aq) \longrightarrow ZnCl_2(aq) + Cu(s)$$

A displacement reaction follows the general equation:

$$A + BC \longrightarrow AC + B$$

Other examples of displacement reactions include:

$$Mg(s) + 2\,HCl(aq) \longrightarrow MgCl_2(aq) + H_2(g)$$
$$2\,Na(s) + 2\,H_2O(l) \longrightarrow 2\,NaOH(aq) + H_2(g)$$

The last reaction can be seen more easily if we write water as HOH(l).

$$2\,Na(s) + 2\,HOH(l) \longrightarrow 2\,NaOH(aq) + H_2(g)$$

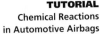

$$2\,H_2O(l) \longrightarrow 2\,H_2(g) + O_2(g)$$

▲ When electrical current is passed through water, the water undergoes a decomposition reaction to form hydrogen gas and oxygen gas.

TUTORIAL
Chemical Reactions
in Automotive Airbags

TUTORIAL
Sodium and Potassium in Water

▶ In a single-displacement reaction, one element displaces another in a compound. When zinc metal is immersed in a copper(II) chloride solution, the zinc atoms displace the copper atoms in solution.

Zn(s)

CuCl$_2$(aq)

ZnCl$_2$(aq)

Cu(s)

(a)   (b)

DOUBLE-DISPLACEMENT REACTIONS. In a **double-displacement reaction**, two elements or groups of elements in two different compounds exchange places to form two new compounds. For example, in aqueous solution, the silver in silver nitrate changes places with the sodium in sodium chloride to form solid silver chloride and aqueous sodium nitrate.

This double-displacement reaction is also a precipitation reaction.

$$AgNO_3(aq) + NaCl(aq) \longrightarrow AgCl(s) + NaNO_3(aq)$$

A double-displacement reaction follows the general form:

$$AB + CD \longrightarrow AD + CB$$

Other examples of double-displacement reactions include:

These double-displacement reactions are also acid–base reactions.

$$HCl(aq) + NaOH(aq) \longrightarrow H_2O(l) + NaCl(aq)$$
$$2\,HCl(aq) + Na_2CO_3(aq) \longrightarrow H_2CO_3(aq) + 2\,NaCl(aq)$$

As we learned in Section 7.7, $H_2CO_3(aq)$ is not stable and decomposes to form $H_2O(l) + CO_2(g)$, so the overall equation is:

This double-displacement reaction is also a gas evolution reaction and an acid–base reaction.

$$2\,HCl(aq) + Na_2CO_3(aq) \longrightarrow H_2O(l) + CO_2(g) + 2\,NaCl(aq)$$

🌐 Classification Flow Chart

A flow chart for this classification scheme of chemical reactions is as follows:

Chemical reactions

Synthesis   Decomposition   Single displacement   Double displacement

Of course no single classification scheme is perfect because all chemical reactions are unique in some sense. However, both classification schemes—one that focuses on the type of chemistry occurring and the other that focuses on what atoms or groups of atoms are doing—are helpful because they help us see differences and similarities among chemical reactions.

EXAMPLE 7.15   Classifying Chemical Reactions According to What Atoms Do

Classify each of the following reactions as a synthesis, decomposition, single-displacement, or double-displacement reaction.

(a) $Na_2O(s) + H_2O(l) \longrightarrow 2\,NaOH(aq)$ synthesis
(b) $Ba(NO_3)_2(aq) + K_2SO_4(aq) \longrightarrow BaSO_4(s) + 2\,KNO_3(aq)$ - double
(c) $2\,Al(s) + Fe_2O_3(s) \longrightarrow Al_2O_3(s) + 2\,Fe(l)$ - displacement displacement
(d) $2\,H_2O_2(aq) \longrightarrow 2\,H_2O(l) + O_2(g)$ - displacement
(e) $Ca(s) + Cl_2(g) \longrightarrow CaCl_2(s)$ - synthesis

Solution:

(a) Synthesis; a more complex substance forms from two simpler ones.

(b) Double-displacment; Ba and K switch places to form two new compounds.

(c) Single-displacement; Al displaces Fe in Al_2O_3.

(d) Decomposition; a complex substance decomposes into simpler ones.

(e) Synthesis; a more complex substance forms from two simpler ones.

SKILLBUILDER 7.15   Classifying Chemical Reactions According to What Atoms Do

Classify each of the following reactions as a synthesis, decomposition, single-displacement, or double-displacement reaction.

(a) $2\,Al(s) + 2\,H_3PO_4(aq) \longrightarrow 2\,AlPO_4(aq) + 3\,H_2(g)$
(b) $CuSO_4(aq) + 2\,KOH(aq) \longrightarrow Cu(OH)_2(s) + K_2SO_4(aq)$
(c) $2\,K(s) + Br_2(l) \longrightarrow 2\,KBr(s)$
(d) $CuCl_2(aq) \xrightarrow{\text{electrical current}} Cu(s) + Cl_2(g)$

CONCEPTUAL CHECKPOINT 7.3

Precipitation reactions and acid–base reactions can both also be classified as:

(a) synthesis reactions
(b) decomposition reactions
(c) single-displacement reactions
(d) double-displacement reactions

Chemistry IN THE ENVIRONMENT

The Reactions Involved in Ozone Depletion

In Chapter 6, *Chemistry in the Environment: Chlorine in Chlorofluorocarbons*, we learned that chlorine atoms from chlorofluorocarbons deplete the ozone layer, which normally protects life on Earth from harmful ultraviolet light. Through research, chemists have discovered the reactions by which this depletion occurs.

Ozone normally forms in the upper atmosphere according to the following reaction.

(a) $O_2(g) + O(g) \longrightarrow O_3(g)$

When chlorofluorocarbons drift to the upper atmosphere, they are exposed to ultraviolet light and undergo the following reaction.

(b) $CF_2Cl_2(g) \xrightarrow{\text{UV light}} CF_2Cl(g) + Cl(g)$

UV light

Atomic chlorine then reacts with and depletes ozone according to the following cycle of reactions.

(c) $Cl(g) + O_3(g) \longrightarrow ClO(g) + O_2(g)$

(d) $O_3(g) \xrightarrow{\text{UV light}} O_2(g) + O(g)$

UV light

(e) $O(g) + ClO(g) \longrightarrow O_2(g) + Cl(g)$

Notice that in the final reaction, atomic chlorine is regenerated and can go through the cycle again to deplete more ozone. Through this cycle of reactions, a single chlorofluorocarbon molecule can deplete thousands of ozone molecules.

CAN YOU ANSWER THIS? *Classify each of these reactions (a–e) as a synthesis, decomposition, single-displacement, or double-displacement reaction.*

CHAPTER IN REVIEW

Chemical Principles

Chemical Reactions: In a chemical reaction, one or more substances—either elements or compounds—change into different substances.

Evidence of a Chemical Reaction: The only absolute evidence for a chemical reaction is chemical analysis showing that one or more substances have changed into other substances. However, one or more of the following often accompany a chemical reaction: a color change; the formation of a solid or precipitate; the formation of a gas; the emission of light; and the emission or absorption of heat.

Chemical Equations: Chemical equations represent chemical reactions. They include formulas for the reactants (the substances present before the reaction) and for the products (the new substances formed by the reaction). Chemical equations must be balanced to reflect the conservation of matter in nature; atoms do not spontaneously appear or disappear.

Relevance

Chemical Reactions: Chemical reactions are central to many processes including transportation, energy generation, manufacture of household products, vision, and even life.

Evidence of a Chemical Reaction: We can often perceive the changes that accompany chemical reactions. In fact, we often use chemical reactions for the changes they produce. For example, we use the heat emitted by the combustion of fossil fuels to heat our homes, drive our cars, and generate electricity.

Chemical Equations: Chemical equations allow us to represent and understand chemical reactions. For example, the equations for the combustion reactions of fossil fuels let us see that carbon dioxide, a gas that contributes to global warming, is one of the products of these reactions.

Aqueous Solutions and Solubility: Aqueous solutions are mixtures of a substance dissolved in water. If a substance dissolves in water it is soluble. Otherwise, it is insoluble.

Aqueous Solutions and Solubility: Aqueous solutions are common. For example, oceans, lakes, and most of the fluids in our bodies are aqueous solutions.

Some Specific Types of Reactions:

Precipitation reaction: A solid or precipitate forms upon mixing two aqueous solutions.
Acid–base reaction: Water forms upon mixing an acid and a base.
Gas evolution reaction: A gas forms upon mixing two aqueous solutions.
Redox reaction: Electrons are transferred from one substance to another.
Combustion reaction: A substance reacts with oxygen, emitting heat, and forming an oxygen-containing compound and, many times, water.

Some Specific Types of Reactions: Many of the specific types of reactions discussed here occur in aqueous solutions and are therefore important to living organisms. Acid–base reactions, for example, constantly occur in the blood of living organisms to maintain constant blood acidity levels. In humans, a small change in blood acidity levels would result in death, so the body carries out chemical reactions to prevent this. Combustion reactions are important because they are the main energy source for our society.

Classifying Chemical Reactions: Many chemical reactions can be classified into one of the following four categories according to what atoms or groups of atoms do:

synthesis (A + B $\longrightarrow$ AB),
decomposition (AB $\longrightarrow$ A + B),
single-displacement (A + BC $\longrightarrow$ AC + B), and
double-displacement (AB + CD $\longrightarrow$ AD + CB).

Classifying Chemical Reactions: We classify chemical reactions to better understand them and to better see similarities and differences among reactions.

Chemical Skills

Examples

Identifying a Chemical Reaction (Section 7.2)

EXAMPLE 7.16   Identifying a Chemical Reaction
Which of the following is a chemical reaction?

(a) Copper turns green on exposure to air.
(b) When sodium bicarbonate is combined with hydrochloric acid, bubbling is observed.
(c) Liquid water freezes to form solid ice.
(d) A pure copper penny forms bubbles of a dark brown gas when dropped into nitric acid. The nitric acid solution turns blue.

To identify a chemical reaction, determine whether one or more of the initial substances changed into different substances. If so, a chemical reaction occurred. One or more of the following often accompanies a chemical reaction: a color change; the formation of a solid or precipitate; the formation of a gas; the emission of light; and the emission or absorption of heat.

Solution:

(a) Chemical reaction, as evidenced by the color change.
(b) Chemical reaction, as evidenced by the evolution of a gas.
(c) Not a chemical reaction; solid ice is still water.
(d) Chemical reaction, as evidenced by the evolution of a gas and by a color change.

Writing Balanced Chemical Equations (Sections 7.3, 7.4)

To write balanced chemical equations, follow these steps.

1. Write a skeletal equation by writing chemical formulas for each of the reactants and products. (If a skeletal equation is provided, proceed to Step 2.)

2. If an element occurs in only one compound on both sides of the equation, balance that element first. If there is more than one such element, and the equation contains both metals and nonmetals, balance metals before nonmetals.

3. If an element occurs as a free element on either side of the chemical equation, balance that element last.

4. If the balanced equation contains coefficient fractions, clear these by multiplying the entire equation by the appropriate factor.

5. Check to make certain the equation is balanced by summing the total number of each type of atom on both sides of the equation.

Reminders

- Change only the *coefficients* to balance a chemical equation, *never the subscripts*. Changing the subscripts would change the compound itself.

- If the equation contains polyatomic ions that stay intact on both sides of the equation, balance the polyatomic ions as a group.

LIVE EXAMPLE

EXAMPLE 7.17 Writing Balanced Chemical Equations

Write a balanced chemical equation for the reaction of solid vanadium(V) oxide with hydrogen gas to form solid vanadium(III) oxide and liquid water.

$$V_2O_5(s) + H_2(g) \longrightarrow V_2O_3(s) + H_2O(l)$$

Solution:

Vanadium occurs in only one compound on both sides of the equation. However, it is balanced, so we proceed to balance oxygen by placing a 2 in front of H_2O on the right side.

$$V_2O_5(s) + H_2(g) \longrightarrow V_2O_3(s) + \mathbf{2}\ H_2O(l)$$

Hydrogen occurs as a free element, so we balance it last by placing a 2 in front of H_2 on the left side.

$$V_2O_5(s) + \mathbf{2}\ H_2(g) \longrightarrow V_2O_3(s) + 2\ H_2O(l)$$

Finally, we check the equation.

$$V_2O_5(s) + 2\ H_2(g) \longrightarrow V_2O_3(s) + 2\ H_2O(l)$$

Reactants	Products
2 V atoms	2 V atoms
5 O atoms	5 O atoms
4 H atoms	4 H atoms

Determining Whether a Compound Is Soluble (Section 7.5)

To determine whether a compound is soluble, use the solubility rules in Table 7.2. It is easiest to begin by looking for those ions that always form soluble compounds (Li^+, Na^+, K^+, NH_4^+, NO_3^-, and $C_2H_3O_2^-$.) If a compound contains one of those, it is soluble. If it does not, look at the anion and determine whether it is mostly soluble (Cl^-, Br^-, I^-, or SO_4^{2-}) or mostly insoluble (OH^-, S^{2-}, CO_3^{2-}, or PO_4^{3-}). Look also at the cation to determine whether it is one of the exceptions.

EXAMPLE 7.18 Determining Whether a Compound Is Soluble

Determine whether each of the following compounds is soluble.

(a) $CuCO_3$
(b) $BaSO_4$
(c) $Fe(NO_3)_3$

Solution:

(a) Insoluble; compounds containing CO_3^{2-} are insoluble, and Cu^{2+} is not an exception.
(b) Insoluble; compounds containing SO_4^{2-} are usually soluble, but Ba^{2+} is an exception.
(c) Soluble; all compounds containing NO_3^- are soluble.

Predicting Precipitation Reactions (Section 7.6)

To predict whether a precipitation reaction occurs when two solutions are mixed and to write an equation for the reaction, follow these steps.

1. Write the formulas of the two compounds being mixed as reactants in a chemical equation.

2. Below the equation, write the formulas of the potentially insoluble products that could form from the reactants. These are obtained by combining the cation from one reactant with the anion from the other. Make sure to adjust the subscripts so that all formulas are charge-neutral.

3. Use the solubility rules to determine whether any of the potentially insoluble products are indeed insoluble.

4. If all of the potentially insoluble products are soluble, there will be no precipitate. Write *NO REACTION* next to the arrow.

5. If one or both of the potentially insoluble products are indeed insoluble, write their formula(s) as the product(s) of the reaction using (s) to indicate *solid*. Write any soluble products with (aq) to indicate *aqueous*.

6. Balance the equation.

LIVE EXAMPLE

EXAMPLE 7.19   Predicting Precipitation Reactions

Write an equation for the precipitation reaction that occurs, if any, when solutions of sodium phosphate and cobalt(II) chloride are mixed.

Solution:

$$Na_3PO_4(aq) + CoCl_2(aq) \longrightarrow$$

Potentially Insoluble Products:

$$NaCl \qquad Co_3(PO_4)_2$$

NaCl is soluble.
$Co_3(PO_4)_2$ is insoluble.

$$Na_3PO_4(aq) + CoCl_2(aq) \longrightarrow$$
$$Co_3(PO_4)_2(s) + NaCl(aq)$$

$$2\,Na_3PO_4(aq) + 3\,CoCl_2(aq) \longrightarrow$$
$$Co_3(PO_4)_2(s) + 6\,NaCl(aq)$$

Writing Complete Ionic and Net Ionic Equations (Section 7.7)

To write a complete ionic equation from a molecular equation, separate all aqueous ionic compounds into independent ions. Do not separate solid, liquid, or gaseous compounds.

To write a net ionic equation from a complete ionic equation, eliminate all species that do not change (spectator ions) in the course of the reaction.

EXAMPLE 7.20   Writing Complete Ionic and Net Ionic Equations

Write a complete ionic and net ionic equation for the following reaction.

$$2\,NH_4Cl(aq) + Hg_2(NO_3)_2(aq) \longrightarrow$$
$$Hg_2Cl_2(s) + 2\,NH_4NO_3(aq)$$

Solution:
Complete ionic equation:

$$2\,NH_4^+(aq) + 2\,Cl^-(aq) + Hg_2^{2+}(aq) + 2\,NO_3^-(aq) \longrightarrow$$
$$Hg_2Cl_2(s) + 2\,NH_4^-(aq) + 2\,NO_3^-(aq)$$

Net ionic equation:

$$2\,Cl^-(aq) + Hg_2^{2+}(aq) \longrightarrow Hg_2Cl_2(s)$$

Writing Equations for Acid–Base Reactions (Section 7.8)

When you see an acid and a base (see Table 7.3) as reactants in an equation, write a reaction in which the acid and the base react to form water and a salt.

EXAMPLE 7.21   Writing Equations for Acid–Base Reactions

Write an equation for the reaction that occurs when aqueous hydroiodic acid is mixed with aqueous barium hydroxide.

Solution:

$$\underset{\text{acid}}{2\,HI(aq)} + \underset{\text{base}}{Ba(OH)_2(aq)} \longrightarrow \underset{\text{water}}{2\,H_2O(l)} + \underset{\text{salt}}{BaI_2(aq)}$$

Writing Equations for Gas Evolution Reactions (Section 7.8)

See Table 7.4 to identify gas evolution reactions.

Writing Equations for Gas Evolution Reactions

Write an equation for the reaction that occurs when aqueous hydrobromic acid is mixed with aqueous potassium bisulfite.

Solution:

$$HBr(aq) + KHSO_3(aq) \longrightarrow$$
$$H_2SO_3(aq) + KBr(aq) \longrightarrow H_2O(l) + SO_2(g) + KBr(aq)$$

Identifying Redox Reactions (Section 7.9)

Redox reactions are those in which any of the following occurs:

- a substance reacts with elemental oxygen
- a metal reacts with a nonmetal
- one substance transfers electrons to another substance

Identifying Redox Reactions

Which of the following is a redox reaction?

(a) $4 Fe(s) + 3 O_2(g) \longrightarrow 2 Fe_2O_3(s)$
(b) $CaO(s) + CO_2(g) \longrightarrow CaCO_3(s)$
(c) $AgNO_3(aq) + NaCl(aq) \longrightarrow AgCl(s) + NaNO_3(aq)$

Solution:

Only (a) is a redox reaction.

Writing Equations for Combustion Reactions (Section 7.9)

In a combustion reaction, a substance reacts with O_2 to form one or more oxygen-containing compounds and, in many cases, water.

Writing Equations for Combustion Reactions

Write a balanced equation for the combustion of gaseous ethane (C_2H_6), a minority component of natural gas.

Solution:

The skeletal equation is:

$$C_2H_6(g) + O_2(g) \longrightarrow CO_2(g) + H_2O(g)$$

The balanced equation is:

$$2 C_2H_6(g) + 7 O_2(g) \longrightarrow 4 CO_2(g) + 6 H_2O(g)$$

Classifying Chemical Reactions (Section 7.10)

Chemical reactions can be classified by inspection. The four major categories are:

Synthesis or combination

$$A + B \longrightarrow AB$$

Decomposition

$$AB \longrightarrow A + B$$

Single-displacement

$$A + BC \longrightarrow AC + B$$

Double-displacement

$$AB + CD \longrightarrow AD + CB$$

Classifying Chemical Reactions

Classify each of the following chemical reactions as a synthesis, decomposition, single-displacement, or double-displacement reaction.

(a) $2 K(s) + Br_2(g) \longrightarrow 2 KBr(s)$
(b) $Fe(s) + 2 AgNO_3(aq) \longrightarrow Fe(NO_3)_2(aq) + 2 Ag(s)$
(c) $CaSO_3(s) \xrightarrow{heat} CaO(s) + SO_2(g)$
(d) $CaCl_2(aq) + Li_2SO_4(aq) \longrightarrow CaSO_4(s) + 2 LiCl(aq)$

Solution:

(a) Synthesis; KBr, a more complex substance, is formed from simpler substances.
(b) Single-displacement; Fe displaces Ag in $AgNO_3$.
(c) Decomposition; $CaSO_3$ decomposes into simpler substances.
(d) Double-displacement; Ca and Li switch places to form new compounds.

Key Terms

acid–base reaction [7.8]
aqueous solution [7.5]
balanced equation [7.3]
chemical equation [7.3]
chemical reaction [7.1]
combination
   reaction [7.10]
combustion reaction [7.9]
complete ionic
   equation [7.7]

decomposition
   reaction [7.10]
displacement
   reaction [7.10]
double-displacement
   reaction [7.10]
gas evolution reaction [7.8]
insoluble [7.5]
molecular equation [7.7]
net ionic equation [7.7]

neutralization
   reaction [7.8]
oxidation–reduction
   (redox) reaction [7.9]
precipitate [7.6]
precipitation
   reaction [7.6]
products [7.3]
reactants [7.3]
salt [7.8]

single-displacement
   reaction [7.10]
solubility rules [7.5]
soluble [7.5]
spectator ions [7.7]
strong electrolyte
   solution [7.5]
synthesis reaction [7.10]

Exercises

Questions

1. What is a chemical reaction? Give some examples.
2. If you could see atoms and molecules, what would you look for as conclusive evidence of a chemical reaction?
3. What are the main evidences of a chemical reaction?
4. What is a chemical equation? Give an example and identify the reactants and products.
5. What do each of the following abbreviations, often used in chemical equations, represent?
   (a) (g)
   (b) (l)
   (c) (s)
   (d) (aq)
6. To balance a chemical equation, adjust the _____ as necessary to make the numbers of each type of atom on both sides of the equation equal. Never adjust the _____ to balance a chemical equation.
7. List the number of each type of atom on both sides of each of the following equations. Are the equations balanced?
   (a) $2 Ag_2O(s) + C(s) \longrightarrow CO_2(g) + 4 Ag(s)$
   (b) $Pb(NO_3)_2(aq) + 2 NaCl(aq) \longrightarrow$
   $PbCl_2(s) + 2 NaNO_3(aq)$
   (c) $C_3H_8(g) + O_2(g) \longrightarrow 3 CO_2(g) + 4 H_2O(g)$
8. What is an aqueous solution? Give two examples.
9. What does it mean for a compound to be soluble? Insoluble?
10. How do ionic compounds dissolve in water?
11. How do polyatomic ions within ionic compounds dissolve in water?
12. What is a strong electrolyte solution?
13. What are the solubility rules and how are they useful?

14. What is a precipitation reaction? Give an example and identify the precipitate.
15. Will the precipitate in a precipitation reaction always be a compound that is soluble or insoluble? Explain.
16. Describe the differences between a molecular equation and a complete ionic equation. Give an example to illustrate the difference.
17. Describe the differences between a complete ionic and net ionic equation. Give an example to illustrate the difference.
18. What is an acid–base reaction? Give an example and identify the acid and the base.
19. What are the properties of acids and bases?
20. What is a gas evolution reaction? Give an example.
21. What is a redox reaction? Give an example.
22. What is a combustion reaction? Give an example.
23. What are two different ways to classify chemical reactions presented in Section 7.10? Explain the differences between them.
24. Describe each of the following general types of chemical reactions and write the generic equation for each.
   (a) synthesis
   (b) decomposition
   (c) single-displacement
   (d) double-displacement
25. Give two examples of a synthesis reaction.
26. Give two examples of a decomposition reaction.
27. Give two examples of a single-displacement reaction.
28. Give two examples of a double-displacement reaction.

Problems

Evidence of Chemical Reactions

29. Which of the following is a chemical reaction? Why?
    (a) Solid copper deposits on a piece of aluminum foil when the foil is placed in a blue copper nitrate solution. The blue color of the solution fades.
    (b) Liquid ethyl alcohol turns into a solid when placed in a low-temperature freezer.
    (c) A white precipitate forms when solutions of barium nitrate and sodium sulfate are mixed.
    (d) A mixture of sugar and water bubbles when yeasts are added. After several days, the sugar is gone and ethyl alcohol is found in the water.

30. Which of the following is a chemical reaction? Why?
    (a) Propane forms a flame and emits heat as it burns.
    (b) Acetone feels cold as it evaporates from the skin.
    (c) Bubbling is observed when potassium carbonate and hydrochloric acid solutions are mixed.
    (d) Heat is felt when a warm object is placed in your hand.

31. Vinegar forms bubbles when it is poured onto the calcium deposits on a faucet, and some of the calcium dissolves. Has a chemical reaction occurred? Why or why not?

32. When a chemical drain opener is added to a clogged sink, bubbles form and the water in the sink gets warmer. Has a chemical reaction occurred? Why or why not?

33. When a commercial hair bleaching mixture is applied to brown hair, it turns blond. Has a chemical reaction occurred? Why or why not?

34. When water is boiled in a pot, it bubbles. Has a chemical reaction occurred? Why or why not?

Writing and Balancing Chemical Equations

35. Write a balanced chemical equation for each of the following:
    (a) Solid copper reacts with solid sulfur to form solid copper(I) sulfide.
    (b) Sulfur dioxide gas reacts with oxygen gas to form sulfur trioxide gas.
    (c) Aqueous hydrochloric acid reacts with solid manganese(IV) oxide to form aqueous manganese(II) chloride, liquid water, and chlorine gas.
    (d) Liquid benzene (C_6H_6) reacts with gaseous oxygen to form carbon dioxide and liquid water.

36. Write a balanced chemical equation for each of the following:
    (a) Solid lead(II) sulfide reacts with aqueous hydrochloric acid to form solid lead(II) chloride and dihydrogen sulfide gas.
    (b) Gaseous carbon monoxide reacts with hydrogen gas to form gaseous methane (CH_4) and liquid water.
    (c) Solid iron(III) oxide reacts with hydrogen gas to form solid iron and liquid water.
    (d) Gaseous ammonia (NH_3) reacts with gaseous oxygen to form gaseous nitrogen monoxide and gaseous water.

37. Write a balanced chemical equation for each of the following:
    (a) Solid magnesium reacts with aqueous copper(I) nitrate to form aqueous magnesium nitrate and solid copper.
    (b) Gaseous dinitrogen pentoxide decomposes to form nitrogen dioxide and oxygen gas.
    (c) Solid calcium reacts with aqueous nitric acid to form aqueous calcium nitrate and hydrogen gas.
    (d) Liquid methanol (CH_3OH) reacts with oxygen gas to form gaseous carbon dioxide and gaseous water.

38. Write a balanced chemical equation for each of the following:
    (a) Gaseous acetylene (C_2H_2) reacts with oxygen gas to form gaseous carbon dioxide and gaseous water.
    (b) Chlorine gas reacts with aqueous potassium iodide to form solid iodine and aqueous potassium chloride.
    (c) Solid lithium oxide reacts with liquid water to form aqueous lithium hydroxide.
    (d) Gaseous carbon monoxide reacts with oxygen gas to form carbon dioxide gas.

39. Hydrogen has been widely suggested as a potential fuel to replace fossil fuels. Some scientists are trying to foresee any potential problems that might be associated with a hydrogen-based economy. One group of scientists have calculated that the amount of atmospheric hydrogen could increase by a factor of four due to leaks in hydrogen transport and storage. Upper atmospheric hydrogen gas reacts with oxygen gas to form liquid water. An increase in upper atmospheric water would enhance processes that release atmospheric chlorine atoms. The gaseous chlorine atoms would then react with gaseous ozone (O_3) to form gaseous chlorine monoxide and gaseous oxygen, resulting in the depletion of ozone. Write balanced chemical equations for the two reactions described here.

40. Waste water from certain industrial chemical processes contains aqueous Hg_2^{2+} ions. Since the mercury ion is toxic, it is removed from the waste water by reaction with aqueous sodium sulfide. The products of the reaction are solid mercury(I) sulfide and aqueous sodium ions. Write a balanced equation for this reaction.

41. When solid sodium is added to liquid water, it reacts with the water to produce hydrogen gas and aqueous sodium hydroxide. Write a balanced chemical equation for this reaction.

42. When iron rusts, solid iron reacts with gaseous oxygen to form solid iron(III) oxide. Write a balanced chemical equation for this reaction.

43. Sulfuric acid in acid rain forms when gaseous sulfur dioxide pollutant reacts with gaseous oxygen and liquid water to form aqueous sulfuric acid. Write a balanced chemical equation for this reaction.

44. Nitric acid in acid rain forms when gaseous nitrogen dioxide pollutant reacts with gaseous oxygen and liquid water to form aqueous nitric acid. Write a balanced chemical equation for this reaction.

45. Write a balanced chemical equation for the reaction of solid vanadium(V) oxide with hydrogen gas to form solid vanadium(III) oxide and liquid water.

46. Write a balanced chemical equation for the reaction of gaseous nitrogen dioxide with hydrogen gas to form gaseous ammonia and liquid water.

47. Write a balanced chemical equation for the fermentation of sugar ($C_{12}H_{22}O_{11}$) by yeasts in which the aqueous sugar reacts with water to form aqueous ethyl alcohol (C_2H_5OH) and carbon dioxide gas.

48. Write a balanced chemical equation for the photosynthesis reaction in which gaseous carbon dioxide and liquid water react in the presence of chlorophyll to produce aqueous glucose ($C_6H_{12}O_6$) and oxygen gas.

49. Balance each of the following chemical equations.
(a) $N_2H_4(l) \longrightarrow NH_3(g) + N_2(g)$
(b) $H_2(g) + N_2(g) \longrightarrow NH_3(g)$
(c) $Cu_2O(s) + C(s) \longrightarrow Cu(s) + CO(g)$
(d) $H_2(g) + Cl_2(g) \longrightarrow HCl(g)$

50. Balance each of the following chemical equations.
(a) $Na_2S(aq) + Cu(NO_3)_2(aq) \longrightarrow$
$NaNO_3(aq) + CuS(s)$
(b) $HCl(aq) + O_2(g) \longrightarrow H_2O(l) + Cl_2(g)$
(c) $H_2(g) + O_2(g) \longrightarrow H_2O(l)$
(d) $FeS(s) + HCl(aq) \longrightarrow FeCl_2(aq) + H_2S(g)$

51. Balance each of the following chemical equations.
(a) $BaO_2(s) + H_2SO_4(aq) \longrightarrow$
$BaSO_4(s) + H_2O_2(aq)$
(b) $Co(NO_3)_3(aq) + (NH_4)_2S(aq) \longrightarrow$
$Co_2S_3(s) + NH_4NO_3(aq)$
(c) $Li_2O(s) + H_2O(l) \longrightarrow LiOH(aq)$
(d) $Hg_2(C_2H_3O_2)_2(aq) + KCl(aq) \longrightarrow$
$Hg_2Cl_2(s) + KC_2H_3O_2(aq)$

52. Balance each of the following chemical equations.
(a) $MnO_2(s) + HCl(aq) \longrightarrow$
$Cl_2(g) + MnCl_2(aq) + H_2O(l)$
(b) $CO_2(g) + CaSiO_3(s) + H_2O(l) \longrightarrow$
$SiO_2(s) + Ca(HCO_3)_2(aq)$
(c) $Fe(s) + S(l) \longrightarrow Fe_2S_3(s)$
(d) $NO_2(g) + H_2O(l) \longrightarrow HNO_3(aq) + NO(g)$

53. Determine whether each of the following chemical equations is correctly balanced. If not, correct it.
(a) $Rb(s) + H_2O(l) \longrightarrow RbOH(aq) + H_2(g)$
(b) $2 N_2H_4(g) + N_2O_4(g) \longrightarrow$
$$3 N_2(g) + 4 H_2O(g)$$
(c) $NiS(s) + O_2(g) \longrightarrow NiO(s) + SO_2(g)$
(d) $PbO(s) + 2 NH_3(g) \longrightarrow$
$$Pb(s) + N_2(g) + H_2O(l)$$

54. Determine whether each of the following chemical equations is correctly balanced. If not, correct it.
(a) $SiO_2(s) + 4 HF(aq) \longrightarrow SiF_4(g) + 2 H_2O(l)$
(b) $2 Cr(s) + 3 O_2(g) \longrightarrow Cr_2O_3(s)$
(c) $Al_2S_3(s) + H_2O(l) \longrightarrow$
$$2 Al(OH)_3(s) + 3 H_2S(g)$$
(d) $Fe_2O_3(s) + CO(g) \longrightarrow 2 Fe(s) + CO_2(g)$

55. Human cells obtain energy from a reaction called respiration. Balance the skeletal equation for respiration.

$$C_6H_{12}O_6(aq) + O_2(g) \longrightarrow CO_2(g) + H_2O(l)$$

56. Propane camping stoves produce heat by the combustion of gaseous propane (C_3H_8). Balance the skeletal equation for the combustion of propane.

$$C_3H_8(g) + O_2(g) \longrightarrow CO_2(g) + H_2O(g)$$

57. Catalytic converters work to remove nitrogen oxides and carbon monoxide from exhaust. Balance the skeletal equation for one of the reactions that occurs in a catalytic converter.

$$NO(g) + CO(g) \longrightarrow N_2(g) + CO_2(g)$$

58. Billions of pounds of urea are produced annually for use as a fertilizer. Balance the skeletal equation for the synthesis of urea.

$$NH_3(g) + CO_2(g) \longrightarrow CO(NH_2)_2(s) + H_2O(l)$$

Solubility

59. Determine whether each of the following compounds is soluble or insoluble. For the soluble compounds, write the ions present in solution.
(a) $NaNO_3$
(b) $Pb(C_2H_3O_2)_2$
(c) $CuCO_3$
(d) $(NH_4)_2S$

60. Determine whether each of the following compounds is soluble or insoluble. For the soluble compounds, write the ions present in solution.
(a) AgI
(b) $AgNO_3$
(c) $CoPO_4$
(d) Na_3PO_4

61. Pair each cation on the left with an anion on the right that will form an *insoluble* compound and write a formula for the insoluble compound. Use each anion only once.

Ag^+ SO_4^{2-}

Ba^{2+} Cl^-

Cu^{2+} CO_3^{2-}

Fe^{3+} S^{2-}

62. Pair each cation on the left with an anion on the right that will form a *soluble* compound and write a formula for the soluble compound. Use each anion only once.

Na^+ NO_3^-

Sr^{2+} SO_4^{2-}

Co^{2+} S^{2-}

Pb^{2+} CO_3^{2-}

63. Determine whether each of the following compounds is in the correct column. If not, move it to the correct column.

Soluble	Insoluble
K_2S	K_2SO_4
$PbSO_4$	Hg_2I_2
BaS	$Cu_3(PO_4)_2$
$PbCl_2$	MgS
Hg_2Cl_2	$CaSO_4$
NH_4Cl	SrS
Na_2CO_3	Li_2S

64. Determine whether each of the following compounds is in the correct column. If not, move it to the correct column.

Soluble	Insoluble
$LiOH$	$CaCl_2$
Na_2CO_3	$Cu(OH)_2$
$AgCl$	$Ca(C_2H_3O_2)_2$
K_3PO_4	$SrSO_4$
CuI_2	Hg_2Br_2
$Pb(NO_3)_2$	$PbBr_2$
$CoCO_3$	PbI_2

Precipitation Reactions

65. Complete and balance each of the following equations. If no reaction occurs, write *NO REACTION*.
(a) $NH_4Cl(aq) + AgNO_3(aq) \longrightarrow$
(b) $NaCl(aq) + CaS(aq) \longrightarrow$
(c) $CrCl_2(aq) + Li_2CO_3(aq) \longrightarrow$
(d) $KOH(aq) + FeCl_3(aq) \longrightarrow$

66. Complete and balance each of the following equations. If no reaction occurs, write *NO REACTION*.
(a) $KNO_3(aq) + NaCl(aq) \longrightarrow$
(b) $KCl(aq) + Hg_2(C_2H_3O_2)_2(aq) \longrightarrow$
(c) $(NH_4)_2SO_4(aq) + BaCl_2(aq) \longrightarrow$
(d) $LiI(aq) + SrS(aq) \longrightarrow$

67. Write a molecular equation for the precipitation reaction (if any) that occurs when the following solutions are mixed. If no reaction occurs, write *NO REACTION*.
(a) sodium carbonate and lead(II) nitrate
(b) potassium sulfate and lead(II) acetate
(c) copper(II) nitrate and barium sulfide
(d) calcium nitrate and sodium iodide

68. Write a molecular equation for the precipitation reaction (if any) that occurs when the following solutions are mixed. If no reaction occurs, write *NO REACTION*.
(a) potassium chloride and lead(II) acetate
(b) lithium sulfate and strontium chloride
(c) potassium bromide and calcium sulfide
(d) chromium(III) nitrate and potassium phosphate

69. Determine whether each of the following equations for precipitation reactions is correct. If not, write the correct equation. If no reaction occurs, write *NO REACTION*.
(a) $Ba(NO_3)_2(aq) + (NH_4)_2SO_4(aq) \longrightarrow$ $BaSO_4(s) + 2 NH_4NO_3(aq)$
(b) $BaS(aq) + 2 KCl(aq) \longrightarrow BaCl_2(s) + K_2S(aq)$
(c) $2 KI(aq) + Pb(NO_3)_2(aq) \longrightarrow$ $PbI_2(s) + 2 KNO_3(aq)$
(d) $Pb(NO_3)_2(aq) + 2 LiCl(aq) \longrightarrow$ $2 LiNO_3(s) + PbCl_2(aq)$

70. Determine whether each of the following equations for precipitation reactions is correct. If not, write the correct equation. If no reaction occurs, write *NO REACTION*.
(a) $AgNO_3(aq) + NaCl(aq) \longrightarrow$ $NaCl(s) + AgNO_3(aq)$
(b) $K_2SO_4(aq) + Co(NO_3)_2(aq) \longrightarrow$ $CoSO_4(s) + 2 KNO_3(aq)$
(c) $Cu(NO_3)_2(aq) + (NH_4)_2S(aq) \longrightarrow$ $CuS(s) + 2 NH_4NO_3(aq)$
(d) $Hg_2(NO_3)_2(aq) + 2 LiCl(aq) \longrightarrow$ $Hg_2Cl_2(s) + 2 LiNO_3(aq)$

Ionic and Net Ionic Equations

71. Identify the spectator ions in the following complete ionic equation.

$Pb^{2+}(aq) + 2 C_2H_3O_2^-(aq) + 2 K^+(aq) + 2 Br^-(aq) \longrightarrow$ $PbBr_2(s) + 2 C_2H_3O_2^-(aq) + 2 K^+(aq)$

72. Identify the spectator ions in the following complete ionic equation.

$2 Li^+(aq) + S^{2-}(aq) + Mg^{2+}(aq) + 2 Cl^-(aq) \longrightarrow$ $MgS(s) + 2 Li^+(aq) + 2 Cl^-(aq)$

73. Write balanced complete ionic and net ionic equations for each of the following reactions.
(a) $AgNO_3(aq) + KCl(aq) \longrightarrow$ $AgCl(s) + KNO_3(aq)$
(b) $CaS(aq) + CuCl_2(aq) \longrightarrow CuS(s) + CaCl_2(aq)$
(c) $NaOH(aq) + HNO_3(aq) \longrightarrow$ $H_2O(l) + NaNO_3(aq)$
(d) $2 K_3PO_4(aq) + 3 NiCl_2(aq) \longrightarrow$ $Ni_3(PO_4)_2(s) + 6 KCl(aq)$

74. Write balanced complete ionic and net ionic equations for each of the following reactions.
(a) $HI(aq) + KOH(aq) \longrightarrow H_2O(l) + KI(aq)$
(b) $Na_2SO_4(aq) + CaI_2(aq) \longrightarrow$ $CaSO_4(s) + 2 NaI(aq)$
(c) $2 HC_2H_3O_2(aq) + Na_2CO_3(aq) \longrightarrow$ $H_2O(l) + CO_2(g) + 2 NaC_2H_3O_2(aq)$
(d) $NH_4Cl(aq) + NaOH(aq) \longrightarrow$ $H_2O(l) + NH_3(g) + NaCl(aq)$

75. Mercury (I) ions (Hg_2^{2+}) can be removed from solution by precipitation with Cl^-. Suppose a solution contains aqueous $Hg_2(NO_3)_2$. Write complete ionic and net ionic equations to show the reaction of aqueous $Hg_2(NO_3)_2$ with aqueous sodium chloride to form solid Hg_2Cl_2 and aqueous sodium nitrate.

76. Lead ions can be removed from solution by precipitation with sulfate ions. Suppose a solution contains lead(II) nitrate. Write a complete ionic and net ionic equation to show the reaction of aqueous lead(II) nitrate with aqueous potassium sulfate to form solid lead(II) sulfate and aqueous potassium nitrate.

77. Write complete ionic and net ionic equations for each of the reactions in Problem 67.

78. Write complete ionic and net ionic equations for each of the reactions in Problem 68.

Acid–Base and Gas Evolution Reactions

79. When a hydrochloric acid solution is combined with a potassium hydroxide solution, an acid–base reaction occurs. Write a balanced molecular equation and a net ionic equation for this reaction.

80. A beaker of nitric acid is neutralized with calcium hydroxide. Write a balanced molecular equation and a net ionic equation for this reaction.

81. Complete and balance each of the following equations for acid–base reactions.
(a) $HCl(aq) + Ba(OH)_2(aq) \longrightarrow$
(b) $H_2SO_4(aq) + KOH(aq) \longrightarrow$
(c) $HClO_4(aq) + NaOH(aq) \longrightarrow$

82. Complete and balance each of the following equations for acid–base reactions.
(a) $HC_2H_3O_2(aq) + Ca(OH)_2(aq) \longrightarrow$
(b) $HBr(aq) + LiOH(aq) \longrightarrow$
(c) $H_2SO_4(aq) + Ba(OH)_2(aq) \longrightarrow$

83. Complete and balance each of the following equations for gas evolution reactions.
(a) $HBr(aq) + NaHCO_3(aq) \longrightarrow$
(b) $NH_4I(aq) + KOH(aq) \longrightarrow$
(c) $HNO_3(aq) + K_2SO_3(aq) \longrightarrow$
(d) $HI(aq) + Li_2S(aq) \longrightarrow$

84. Complete and balance each of the following equations for gas evolution reactions.
(a) $HClO_4(aq) + K_2CO_3(aq) \longrightarrow$
(b) $HC_2H_3O_2(aq) + LiHSO_3(aq) \longrightarrow$
(c) $(NH_4)_2SO_4(aq) + Ca(OH)_2(aq) \longrightarrow$
(d) $HCl(aq) + ZnS(s) \longrightarrow$

Oxidation–Reduction and Combustion

85. Which of the following reactions are redox reactions?
(a) $Ba(NO_3)_2(aq) + K_2SO_4(aq) \longrightarrow$
$$BaSO_4(s) + 2\,KNO_3(aq)$$
(b) $Ca(s) + Cl_2(g) \longrightarrow CaCl_2(s)$
(c) $HCl(aq) + NaOH(aq) \longrightarrow$
$$H_2O(l) + NaCl(aq)$$
(d) $Zn(s) + Fe^{2+}(aq) \longrightarrow Zn^{2+}(aq) + Fe(s)$

86. Which of the following reactions are redox reactions?
(a) $Al(s) + 3\,Ag^+(aq) \longrightarrow Al^{3+}(aq) + 3\,Ag(s)$
(b) $4\,K(s) + O_2(g) \longrightarrow 2\,K_2O(s)$
(c) $SO_3(g) + H_2O(l) \longrightarrow H_2SO_4(aq)$
(d) $Mg(s) + Br_2(l) \longrightarrow MgBr_2(s)$

87. Complete and balance each of the following equations for combustion reactions.
(a) $C_2H_6(g) + O_2(g) \longrightarrow$
(b) $Ca(s) + O_2(g) \longrightarrow$
(c) $C_3H_8O(l) + O_2(g) \longrightarrow$
(d) $C_4H_{10}S(l) + O_2(g) \longrightarrow$

88. Complete and balance each of the following equations for combustion reactions.
(a) $S(s) + O_2(g) \longrightarrow$
(b) $C_7H_{16}(l) + O_2(g) \longrightarrow$
(c) $C_4H_{10}O(l) + O_2(g) \longrightarrow$
(d) $CS_2(l) + O_2(g) \longrightarrow$

89. Write a balanced chemical equation for the synthesis reaction of $Cl_2(g)$ with each of the following:
(a) $K(s)$
(b) $Ca(s)$
(c) $Al(s)$
(d) $Zn(s)$

90. Write a balanced chemical equation for the synthesis reaction of $F_2(g)$ with each of the following:
(a) $Sr(s)$
(b) $Ga(s)$
(c) $Li(s)$
(d) $Ag(s)$

Classifying Chemical Reactions by What Atoms Do

91. Classify each of the following chemical reactions as a synthesis, decomposition, single-displacement, or double-displacement reaction.
(a) $K_2S(aq) + Co(NO_3)_2(aq) \longrightarrow$
$$2\,KNO_3(aq) + CoS(s)$$
(b) $3\,H_2(g) + N_2(g) \longrightarrow 2\,NH_3(g)$
(c) $Zn(s) + CoCl_2(aq) \longrightarrow ZnCl_2(aq) + Co(s)$
(d) $CH_3Br(g) \longrightarrow CH_3(g) + Br(g)$
UV light

92. Classify each of the following chemical reactions as a synthesis, decomposition, single-displacement, or double-displacement reaction.
(a) $CaSO_4(s) \xrightarrow{\text{heat}} CaO(s) + SO_3(g)$
(b) $2\,Na(s) + O_2(g) \longrightarrow Na_2O_2(s)$
(c) $Pb(s) + 2\,AgNO_3(aq) \longrightarrow$
$$Pb(NO_3)_2(aq) + 2\,Ag(s)$$
(d) $HI(aq) + NaOH(aq) \longrightarrow H_2O(l) + NaI(aq)$

93. NO is a pollutant emitted by motor vehicles. It is formed by the following reaction.
    (a) $N_2(g) + O_2(g) \longrightarrow 2\,NO(g)$
    Once in the atmosphere, NO (through a series of reactions) adds one oxygen atom to form NO_2. NO_2 then interacts with UV light according to the following reaction.
    (b) $NO_2(g) \longrightarrow NO(g) + O(g)$

         UV light

    These freshly formed oxygen atoms then react with O_2 in the air to form ozone (O_3), a main component of photochemical smog.
    (c) $O(g) + O_2(g) \longrightarrow O_3(g)$
    Classify each of the preceding reactions as a synthesis, decomposition, single-displacement, or double-displacement reaction.

94. A main source of sulfur oxide pollutants are smelters where sulfide ores are converted into metals. The first step in this process is the reaction of the sulfide ore with oxygen in reactions such as:
    (a) $2\,PbS(s) + 3\,O_2(g) \longrightarrow 2\,PbO(s) + 2\,SO_2(g)$
    Sulfur dioxide can then react with oxygen in air to form sulfur trioxide.
    (b) $2\,SO_2(g) + O_2(g) \longrightarrow 2\,SO_3(g)$
    Sulfur trioxide can then react with water from rain to form sulfuric acid that falls as acid rain.
    (c) $SO_3(g) + H_2O(l) \longrightarrow H_2SO_4(aq)$
    Classify each of the preceding reactions as a synthesis, decomposition, single-displacement, or double-displacement reaction.

Cumulative Problems

95. Predict the products of each of these reactions and write balanced complete ionic and net ionic equations for each. If no reaction occurs, write *NO REACTION*.
    (a) $NaI(aq) + Hg_2(NO_3)_2(aq) \longrightarrow$
    (b) $HClO_4(aq) + Ba(OH)_2(aq) \longrightarrow$
    (c) $Li_2CO_3(aq) + NaCl(aq) \longrightarrow$
    (d) $HCl(aq) + Li_2CO_3(aq) \longrightarrow$

96. Predict the products of each of these reactions and write balanced complete ionic and net ionic equations for each. If no reaction occurs, write *NO REACTION*.
    (a) $LiCl(aq) + AgNO_3(aq) \longrightarrow$
    (b) $H_2SO_4(aq) + Li_2SO_3(aq) \longrightarrow$
    (c) $HC_2H_3O_2(aq) + Ca(OH)_2(aq) \longrightarrow$
    (d) $HCl(aq) + KBr(aq) \longrightarrow$

97. Predict the products of each of these reactions and write balanced complete ionic and net ionic equations for each. If no reaction occurs, write *NO REACTION*.
    (a) $BaS(aq) + NH_4Cl(aq) \longrightarrow$
    (b) $NaC_2H_3O_2(aq) + KCl(aq) \longrightarrow$
    (c) $KHSO_3(aq) + HNO_3(aq) \longrightarrow$
    (d) $MnCl_3(aq) + K_3PO_4(aq) \longrightarrow$

98. Predict the products of each of these reactions and write balanced complete ionic and net ionic equations for each. If no reaction occurs, write *NO REACTION*.
    (a) $H_2SO_4(aq) + HNO_3(aq) \longrightarrow$
    (b) $NaOH(aq) + LiOH(aq) \longrightarrow$
    (c) $Cr(NO_3)_3(aq) + LiOH(aq) \longrightarrow$
    (d) $HCl(aq) + Hg_2(NO_3)_2(aq) \longrightarrow$

99. Predict the type of reaction (if any) that occurs between each of the following substances. Write balanced molecular equations for each. If no reaction occurs, write *NO REACTION*.
    (a) aqueous potassium hydroxide and aqueous acetic acid
    (b) aqueous hydrobromic acid and aqueous potassium carbonate
    (c) gaseous hydrogen and gaseous oxygen
    (d) aqueous ammonium chloride and aqueous lead(II) nitrate

100. Predict the type of reaction (if any) that occurs between each of the following substances. Write balanced molecular equations for each. If no reaction occurs, write *NO REACTION*.
    (a) aqueous hydrochloric acid and aqueous copper(II) nitrate
    (b) liquid pentanol ($C_5H_{12}O$) and gaseous oxygen
    (c) aqueous ammonium chloride and aqueous calcium hydroxide
    (d) aqueous strontium sulfide and aqueous copper(II) sulfate

101. Classify each of the following reactions in as many ways as possible.
(a) $2\,Al(s) + 3\,Cu(NO_3)_2(aq) \longrightarrow$
$$2\,Al(NO_3)_3(aq) + 3\,Cu(s)$$
(b) $HBr(aq) + KHSO_3(aq) \longrightarrow$
$$H_2O(l) + SO_2(g) + NaBr(aq)$$
(c) $2\,HI(aq) + Na_2S(aq) \longrightarrow H_2S(g) + 2\,NaI(aq)$
(d) $K_2CO_3(aq) + FeBr_2(aq) \longrightarrow$
$$FeCO_3(s) + 2\,KBr(aq)$$

102. Classify each of the following reactions in as many ways as possible.
(a) $NaCl(aq) + AgNO_3(aq) \longrightarrow$
$$AgCl(s) + NaNO_3(aq)$$
(b) $2\,Rb(s) + Br_2(g) \longrightarrow 2\,RbBr(s)$
(c) $Zn(s) + NiBr_2(aq) \longrightarrow Ni(s) + ZnBr_2(aq)$
(d) $Ca(s) + 2\,H_2O(l) \longrightarrow Ca(OH)_2(aq) + H_2(g)$

103. Hard water often contains dissolved Ca^{2+} and Mg^{2+} ions. One way to soften water is to add phosphates. The phosphate ion forms insoluble precipitates with calcium and magnesium ions, removing them from solution. Suppose that a solution contains aqueous calcium chloride and aqueous magnesium nitrate. Write molecular, complete ionic, and net ionic equations showing how the addition of sodium phosphate precipitates the calcium and magnesium ions.

104. Lakes that have been acidified by acid rain (HNO_3 and H_2SO_4) can be neutralized by a process called *liming*, in which limestone ($CaCO_3$) is added to the acidified water. Write ionic and net ionic equations to show how limestone reacts with HNO_3 and H_2SO_4 to neutralize them. How would you be able to tell if the neutralization process was working?

105. What solution can you add to each of the following cation mixtures to precipitate one cation while keeping the other cation in solution? Write a net ionic equation for the precipitation reaction that occurs.
(a) $Fe^{2+}(aq)$ and $Pb^{2+}(aq)$
(b) $K^+(aq)$ and $Ca^{2+}(aq)$
(c) $Ag^+(aq)$ and $Ba^{2+}(aq)$
(d) $Cu^{2+}(aq)$ and $Hg_2^{2+}(aq)$

106. What solution can you add to each of the following cation mixtures to precipitate one cation while keeping the other cation in solution? Write a net ionic equation for the precipitation reaction that occurs.
(a) $Sr^{2+}(aq)$ and $Hg_2^{2+}(aq)$
(b) $NH_4^+(aq)$ and $Ca^{2+}(aq)$
(c) $Ba^{2+}(aq)$ and $Mg^{2+}(aq)$
(d) $Ag^+(aq)$ and $Zn^{2+}(aq)$

107. A solution contains one or more of the following ions: Ag^+, Ca^{2+}, and Cu^{2+}. When sodium chloride is added to the solution, no precipitate occurs. When sodium sulfate is added to the solution, a white precipitate occurs. The precipitate is filtered off and sodium carbonate is added to the remaining solution, producing a precipitate. Which ions were present in the original solution? Write net ionic equations for the formation of each of the precipitates observed.

108. A solution contains one or more of the following ions: Hg_2^{2+}, Ba^{2+}, and Fe^{2+}. When potassium chloride is added to the solution, a precipitate forms. The precipitate is filtered off and potassium sulfate is added to the remaining solution, producing no precipitate. When potassium carbonate is added to the remaining solution, a precipitate occurs. Which ions were present in the original solution? Write net ionic equations for the formation of each of the precipitates observed.

Highlight Problems

109. The following are molecular views of two different possible mechanisms by which an automobile air bag might function. One of these mechanisms involves a chemical reaction and the other does not. By looking at the molecular views, can you tell which mechanism operates via a chemical reaction?

110. Precipitation reactions often produce brilliant colors. Look at the photographs of each of the following precipitation reactions and write molecular, complete ionic, and net ionic equations for each one.

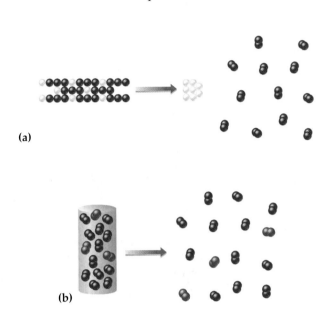

(a)

(b)

▲ When an airbag is detonated, the bag inflates. These figures show two possible ways in which the inflation may happen.

▲ **(a)** The precipitation reaction that occurs when aqueous iron(III) nitrate is added to aqueous sodium hydroxide.

▲ **(b)** The precipitation reaction that occurs when aqueous cobalt(II) chloride is added to aqueous potassium hydroxide.

▲ **(c)** The precipitation reaction that occurs when aqueous $AgNO_3$ is added to aqueous sodium iodide.

Answers to Skillbuilder Exercises

Skillbuilder 7.1   (a) Chemical reaction; heat and light are emitted.   (b) Not a chemical reaction; gaseous and liquid butane are both butane.   (c) Chemical reaction; heat and light are emitted.   (d) Not a chemical reaction; solid dry ice is made of carbon dioxide, which sublimes (evaporates) as carbon dioxide gas.

Skillbuilder 7.2
$2 \, Cr_2O_3(s) + 3 \, C(s) \longrightarrow 4 \, Cr(s) + 3 \, CO_2(g)$

Skillbuilder 7.3
$2 \, C_4H_{10}(g) + 13 \, O_2(g) \longrightarrow 8 \, CO_2(g) + 10 \, H_2O(g)$

Skillbuilder 7.4
$Pb(C_2H_3O_2)_2(aq) + 2 \, KI(aq) \longrightarrow$
$\qquad\qquad\qquad PbI_2(s) + 2 \, KC_2H_3O_2(aq)$

Skillbuilder 7.5
$4 \, HCl(g) + O_2(g) \longrightarrow 2 \, H_2O(l) + 2 \, Cl_2(g)$

Skillbuilder 7.6   (a) insoluble   (b) soluble   (c) insoluble   (d) soluble

Skillbuilder 7.7
$2 \, KOH(aq) + NiBr_2(aq) \longrightarrow Ni(OH)_2(s) + 2 \, KBr(aq)$

Skillbuilder 7.8
$NH_4Cl(aq) + Fe(NO_3)_3(aq) \longrightarrow$ NO REACTION

Skillbuilder 7.9
$K_2SO_4(aq) + Sr(NO_3)_2(aq) \longrightarrow SrSO_4(s) + 2 \, KNO_3(aq)$

Skillbuilder 7.10
Complete ionic equation:
$2 \, H^+(aq) + 2 \, Br^-(aq) + Ca^{2+}(aq) + 2 \, OH^-(aq) \longrightarrow$
$\qquad\qquad 2 \, H_2O(l) + Ca^{2+}(aq) + 2 \, Br^-(aq)$
Net ionic equation:
$2 \, H^+(aq) + 2 \, OH^-(aq) \longrightarrow 2 \, H_2O(l)$, or simply
$H^+(aq) + OH^-(aq) \longrightarrow H_2O(l)$

Skillbuilder 7.11
Molecular equation:
$H_2SO_4(aq) + 2 \, KOH(aq) \longrightarrow 2 \, H_2O(l) + K_2SO_4(aq)$
Net ionic equation:
$2 \, H^+(aq) + 2 \, OH^-(aq) \longrightarrow 2 \, H_2O(l)$

Skillbuilder 7.12
$2 \, HBr(aq) + K_2SO_3(aq) \longrightarrow$
$\qquad\qquad H_2O(l) + SO_2(g) + 2 \, KBr(aq)$

Skillbuilder Plus, p. 209
$2 \, H^+(aq) + SO_3^{2-}(aq) \longrightarrow H_2O(l) + SO_2(g)$

Skillbuilder 7.13   (a), (b), and (d) are all redox reactions; (c) is a precipitation reaction.

Skillbuilder 7.14
$C_5H_{12}(l) + 8 \, O_2(g) \longrightarrow 5 \, CO_2(g) + 6 \, H_2O(g)$

Skillbuilder Plus, p. 212
$2 \, C_3H_7OH(l) + 9 \, O_2(g) \longrightarrow 6 \, CO_2(g) + 8 \, H_2O(g)$

Skillbuilder 7.15   (a) single-displacement   (b) double-displacement   (c) synthesis   (d) decomposition

Answers to Conceptual Checkpoints

7.1 (b) There are 18 oxygen atoms on the left side of the equation, so the same number is needed on the right: $6 + 6(2) = 18$.

7.2 (b) Both of the possible products, MgS and $CaSO_4$, are insoluble. The possible products of the other reactions—Na_2S, $Ca(NO_3)_2$, Na_2SO_4, and $Mg(NO_3)_2$—are all soluble.

7.3 (d) In a precipitation reaction, cations and anions "change partners" to produce at least one insoluble product. In an acid–base reaction, H^+ and OH^- combine to form water and their partners pair off to form a salt.

CHAPTER 8

Quantities in Chemical Reactions

"Man masters nature not by force but by understanding. That is why science has succeeded where magic failed: because it has looked for no spell to cast."

Jacob Bronowski (1908–1974)

8.1 Global Warming: Too Much Carbon Dioxide

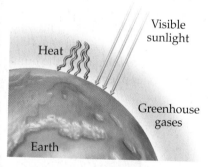

▲ **Figure 8.1   The greenhouse effect**   Greenhouse gases act like glass in a greenhouse, allowing visible-light energy to enter the atmosphere but preventing heat energy from escaping.

Average global temperatures depend on the balance between incoming sunlight, which warms Earth, and outgoing heat lost to space, which cools it. Certain gases in Earth's atmosphere, called **greenhouse gases**, affect that balance because they trap heat. These gases act like glass in a greenhouse; they allow sunlight into the atmosphere to warm Earth, but prevent heat from escaping (◄ Figure 8.1). Without greenhouse gases, more heat would escape, and Earth's average temperature would be about 60 °F colder than it is now. Caribbean tourists would freeze at an icy 21 °F, instead of baking at a tropical 81 °F. On the other hand, if the concentration of greenhouse gases in the atmosphere were to increase, Earth's average temperature would rise.

In recent years scientists have become concerned because the atmospheric concentration of carbon dioxide (CO_2)—Earth's most significant greenhouse gas in terms of its contribution to climate—is rising. This rise in CO_2 concentration enhances the atmosphere's ability to hold heat and may therefore lead to **global warming**, an increase in Earth's average temperature. Since 1860, atmospheric CO_2 levels have risen by 25%, and Earth's average temperature has increased by 0.6 °C (about 1.1 °F) (► Figure 8.2).

The primary cause of rising CO_2 concentration is the burning of fossil fuels. Fossil fuels—natural gas, petroleum, and coal—provide 90% of our society's energy. However, their combustion produces CO_2. As an example, consider the combustion of octane (C_8H_{18}), a component of gasoline.

$$2\,C_8H_{18}(l) + 25\,O_2(g) \longrightarrow 16\,CO_2(g) + 18\,H_2O(g)$$

◄ The combustion of fossil fuels such as octane (shown here) produces water and carbon dioxide as products. Carbon dioxide is a greenhouse gas that is believed to be causing global warming.

The balanced chemical equation shows that 16 mol of CO_2 are produced for every 2 mol of octane burned. Since we know the world's annual fossil fuel consumption, we can estimate the world's annual CO_2 production. A simple calculation shows that the world's annual CO_2 production—from fossil fuel combustion—matches the measured annual atmospheric CO_2 increase, implying that fossil fuel combustion is indeed responsible for increased atmospheric CO_2 levels.

▶ **Figure 8.2   Global warming**
Yearly temperature differences from
the 120-year average temperature.
Earth's average temperature has increased by about 0.6 °C since 1880.

Global temperature

The numerical relationship between chemical quantities in a balanced
chemical equation is called reaction **stoichiometry**. Stoichiometry allows us to
predict the amounts of products that form in a chemical reaction based on the
amounts of reactants. Stoichiometry also allows us to predict how much of
the reactants is necessary to form a given amount of product. These calculations are central to chemistry, allowing chemists to plan and carry out chemical reactions to obtain products in the desired quantities.

8.2   Making Pancakes: Relationships between Ingredients

The concepts of stoichiometry are similar to the concepts we use in following
a cooking recipe. Calculating the amount of carbon dioxide produced by the
combustion of a given amount of a fossil fuel is similar to calculating the number of pancakes that can be made from a given number of eggs. For example,
suppose you use the following pancake recipe.

$$1 \text{ cup flour} + 2 \text{ eggs} + \tfrac{1}{2} \text{ tsp baking powder} \longrightarrow 5 \text{ pancakes}$$

    +   + $\longrightarrow$

1 cup flour   2 eggs $\dfrac{1}{2}$ tsp baking powder   5 pancakes

▲ A recipe gives numerical relationships between the ingredients and
the number of pancakes.

The recipe shows the numerical relationships between the pancake ingredients. It says that if you have 2 eggs—and enough of everything else—you can
make 5 pancakes. We can write this relationship as an equivalence.

$$2 \text{ eggs} \equiv 5 \text{ pancakes}$$

2 eggs   5 pancakes

The $\equiv$ sign, which we first encountered in Chapter 6, means "is **equivalent to**." Therefore, 2 eggs are equivalent to 5 pancakes, meaning that for this recipe they must occur in that ratio for the pancakes to turn out right. What if you have 8 eggs? Assuming that you have enough of everything else, how many pancakes can you make? Using the preceding equivalence as a conversion factor, 8 eggs are sufficient to make 20 pancakes.

$$8 \text{ eggs} \times \frac{5 \text{ pancakes}}{2 \text{ eggs}} = 20 \text{ pancakes}$$

8 eggs   20 pancakes

The pancake recipe contains numerical conversion factors between the pancake ingredients and the number of pancakes. Other conversion factors from this recipe include:

$$1 \text{ cup flour} \equiv 5 \text{ pancakes}$$
$$\tfrac{1}{2} \text{ tsp baking powder} \equiv 5 \text{ pancakes}$$

The recipe also gives us relationships among the ingredients themselves. For example, how much baking powder is required to go with 3 cups of flour? From the recipe:

$$1 \text{ cup flour} \equiv \tfrac{1}{2} \text{ tsp baking powder}$$

With this conversion factor, we can find the appropriate amount of baking powder.

$$3 \text{ cups flour} \times \frac{\tfrac{1}{2} \text{ tsp baking powder}}{1 \text{ cup flour}} = \tfrac{3}{2} \text{ tsp baking powder}$$

8.3   Making Molecules: Mole-to-Mole Conversions

In a balanced chemical equation, we have a "recipe" for how reactants combine to form products. For example, the following equation shows how hydrogen and nitrogen combine to form ammonia (NH_3).

$$3 H_2(g) + N_2(g) \longrightarrow 2 NH_3(g)$$

The balanced equation shows that 3 H_2 molecules react with 1 N_2 molecule to form 2 NH_3 molecules. We can express this as the following equivalence.

$$3 H_2 \text{ molecules} \equiv 1 N_2 \text{ molecule} \equiv 2 NH_3 \text{ molecules}$$

Since we do not ordinarily deal with individual molecules, we can express the same equivalence in moles.

$$3 \text{ mol } H_2 \equiv 1 \text{ mol } N_2 \equiv 2 \text{ mol } NH_3$$

If we have 3 mol of N_2, and more than enough H_2, how much NH_3 can we make? We set up this problem in the standard format:

Given: 3 mol N_2

Find: mol NH_3

Conversion Factor: 1 mol N_2 ≡ 2 mol NH_3

We use this conversion factor from the balanced chemical equation in the same way that we used the conversion factors from the pancake recipe.

Solution Map: The solution map begins with mol N_2 and ends with mol NH_3. The conversion factor comes from the balanced chemical equation.

Solution:

$$\frac{2 \text{ mol } NH_3}{1 \text{ mol } N_2}$$

We can then do the conversion.

$$3 \text{ mol } N_2 \times \frac{2 \text{ mol } NH_3}{1 \text{ mol } N_2} = 6 \text{ mol } NH_3$$

We have enough N_2 for 6 mol of NH_3.

EXAMPLE 8.1   **Mole-to-Mole Conversions**

Sodium chloride, NaCl, forms by the following reaction between sodium and chlorine.

$$2 \text{ Na}(s) + Cl_2(g) \longrightarrow 2 \text{ NaCl}(s)$$

How many moles of NaCl result from the complete reaction of 3.4 mol of Cl_2? Assume that there is more than enough Na.

You are given the number of moles of a reactant (Cl_2) and asked to find how many moles of product (NaCl) will result if the reactant completely reacts. The conversion factor comes from the balanced chemical equation.	**Given:** 3.4 mol Cl_2 **Find:** mol NaCl **Conversion Factor:** 1 mol Cl_2 ≡ 2 mol NaCl
The solution map begins with moles of chlorine and uses the stoichiometric conversion factor to obtain moles of sodium chloride.	**Solution Map:** $$\frac{2 \text{ mol NaCl}}{1 \text{ mol } Cl_2}$$
Follow the solution map to solve the problem. There is enough Cl_2 to produce 6.8 mol of NaCl.	**Solution:** $$3.4 \text{ mol } Cl_2 \times \frac{2 \text{ mol NaCl}}{1 \text{ mol } Cl_2} = 6.8 \text{ mol NaCl}$$

SKILLBUILDER 8.1   **Mole-to-Mole Conversions**

Water is formed when hydrogen gas reacts explosively with oxygen gas according to the following balanced equation.

$$O_2(g) + 2 \text{ H}_2(g) \longrightarrow 2 \text{ H}_2O(g)$$

How many moles of H_2O result from the complete reaction of 24.6 mol of O_2? Assume that there is more than enough H_2.

Chemistry IN THE MEDIA

The Controversy over Oxygenated Fuels

We have seen that the balanced chemical equation for the combustion of octane, a component of gasoline, is:

$$2\,C_8H_{18}(l) + 25\,O_2(g) \longrightarrow 16\,CO_2(g) + 18\,H_2O(g)$$

We have also learned how balanced chemical equations give numerical relationships between reactants. The preceding equation shows that 25 mol of O_2 are required to completely react with 2 mol of C_8H_{18}. What if there were not enough O_2 in the cylinders of an automobile engine to fully react with the amount of octane flowing into them? For many reactions, a shortage of one reactant simply means that less product forms. We will learn about that later in this chapter. However, for some reactions, a shortage of one reactant causes other reactions—called *side reactions*—to occur along with the desired reaction. In the case of octane and the other major components of gasoline, those side reactions result in pollutants such as carbon monoxide (CO) and ozone (O_3).

In 1990, the U.S. Congress, in efforts to lower air pollution, passed amendments to the Clean Air Act requiring oil companies to add substances to gasoline that prevent these side reactions. Since these additives have the effect of increasing the amount of oxygen during combustion, the resulting gasoline is called oxygenated fuel. The additive of choice among oil companies was a compound called MTBE (methyl tertiary butyl ether). The immediate results were positive. Carbon monoxide and ozone levels in many major cities decreased significantly.

MOLECULE MTBE

▲ MTBE was the additive of choice.

Over time, however, MTBE—a compound that does not readily biodegrade—began to appear in drinking-water supplies across the nation. MTBE got into drinking water through gasoline spills at gas stations, from boat motors, and from leaking underground storage tanks. The consequences have been significant. MTBE, even at low levels, imparts a turpentine-like odor and foul taste to drinking water. It is also a suspected carcinogen.

Public response has been swift and dramatic. Several class-action lawsuits have been filed against the manufacturers of MTBE, against gas stations suspected of leaking it, and against the oil companies that put MTBE into gasoline. Several states have moved to ban MTBE from gasoline, and the U.S. Congress is in the process of imposing a federal ban on MTBE. This does raise a problem, however. MTBE was added to gasoline as a way to meet the requirements of the 1990 Clean Air Act amendments. Will the federal government temporarily suspend these requirements until a substitute for MTBE is found? Or should the government completely remove the requirements, weakening the Clean Air Act? The answers are not simple. However, ethanol, made from the fermentation of grains, is a ready substitute for MTBE that has many of the same pollution-reducing effects without the associated health hazards. Oil companies did not use ethanol originally because it was more expensive than MTBE. Now they are paying the price.

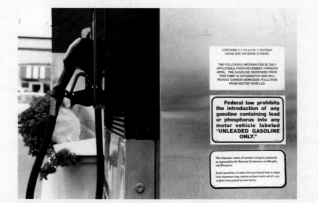

▲ The 1990 amendments to the Clean Air Act required oil companies to put additives in gasoline that increased its oxygen content.

CAN YOU ANSWER THIS? *How many moles of oxygen (O_2) are required to completely react with 425 mol of octane (approximate capacity of a 15-gal automobile gasoline tank)?*

8.4   Making Molecules: Mass-to-Mass Conversions

In Chapter 6, we learned how a chemical *formula* contains conversion factors for converting between moles of a compound and moles of its constituent elements. In this chapter, we have seen how a chemical *equation* contains conversion factors between moles of reactants and moles of products. However, we are often interested in relationships between *mass* of reactant and *mass* of product. For example, we might want to know the mass of carbon dioxide emitted by an automobile that uses a kilogram of gasoline. Or we might want to know the mass of each reactant required to obtain a certain mass of product in a synthesis reaction. These calculations are similar to calculations we learned in Section 6.5, where we converted between mass of a compound and mass of a constituent element. The general outline for these types of calculations is:

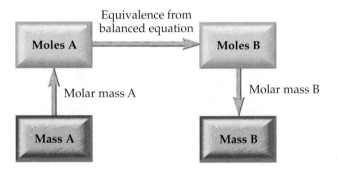

where A and B are two different substances involved in the reaction. The conversion from mass of A to moles of A is achieved using the molar mass of A. The conversion from moles of A to moles of B is achieved using conversion factors from the chemical equation, and the conversion from moles of B to mass of B is achieved using the molar mass of B. For example, suppose we want to calculate the mass of CO_2 emitted upon the combustion of 5.0×10^2 g of pure octane. The balanced chemical equation for octane combustion is:

MOLECULE
Carbon Dioxide

$$2 C_8H_{18}(l) + 25 O_2(g) \longrightarrow 16 CO_2(g) + 18 H_2O(g)$$

We set up the problem in standard format.

Given: 5.0×10^2 g C_8H_{18}

Find: g CO_2

Conversion Factors:

> 2 mol C_8H_{18} ≡ 16 mol CO_2 (from chemical equation)
> Molar mass C_8H_{18} = 114.2 g/mol
> Molar mass CO_2 = 44.01 g/mol

Notice that we are given g C_8H_{18} and asked to find g CO_2. The balanced chemical equation, however, gives us a relationship between moles of C_8H_{18} and moles of CO_2. Consequently, before using that relationship, we must convert from grams to moles.

The solution map uses the general outline

$$\text{Mass A} \longrightarrow \text{Moles A} \longrightarrow \text{Moles B} \longrightarrow \text{Mass B}$$

where A is octane and B is carbon dioxide.

Solution Map:

$$\frac{1 \text{ mol } C_8H_{18}}{114.2 \text{g } C_8H_{18}} \qquad \frac{16 \text{ mol } CO_2}{2 \text{ mol } C_8H_{18}} \qquad \frac{44.01 \text{ g } CO_2}{1 \text{ mol } CO_2}$$

Solution: We then follow the solution map to solve the problem, beginning with g C_8H_{18} and canceling units to arrive at g CO_2.

$$5.0 \times 10^2 \text{ g } C_8H_{18} \times \frac{1 \text{ mol } C_8H_{18}}{114.2 \text{ g } C_8H_{18}} \times \frac{16 \text{ mol } CO_2}{2 \text{ mol } C_8H_{18}} \times \frac{44.01 \text{ g } CO_2}{1 \text{ mol } CO_2} = 1.5 \times 10^3 \text{ g } CO_2$$

So, upon combustion, 5.0×10^2 g of octane produces 1.5×10^3 g of carbon dioxide.

EXAMPLE 8.2   Mass-to-Mass Conversions

In photosynthesis, plants convert carbon dioxide and water into glucose ($C_6H_{12}O_6$) according to the following reaction.

$$6 \text{ CO}_2(g) + 6 \text{ H}_2\text{O}(l) \xrightarrow[\text{sunlight}]{} 6 \text{ O}_2(g) + C_6H_{12}O_6(aq)$$

How many grams of glucose can be synthesized from 58.5 g of CO_2? Assume that there is more than enough water present to react with all of the CO_2.

Set up the problem in the normal way.	**Given:** 58.5 g CO_2
	Find: g $C_6H_{12}O_6$
The main conversion factor is the stoichiometric relationship between moles of carbon dioxide and moles of glucose. This conversion factor comes from the balanced equation. The other conversion factors are simply the molar masses of carbon dioxide and glucose.	**Conversion Factors:**
	6 mol CO_2 ≡ 1 mol $C_6H_{12}O_6$ (from balanced chemical equation)
	Molar mass CO_2 = 44.01 g/mol
	Molar mass $C_6H_{12}O_6$ = 180.2 g/mol

The solution map uses the general outline Mass A ⟶ Moles A ⟶ Moles B ⟶ Mass B where A is carbon dioxide and B is glucose.	**Solution Map:** $\dfrac{1 \text{ mol } CO_2}{44.01 \text{g } CO_2} \qquad \dfrac{1 \text{ mol } C_6H_{12}O_6}{6 \text{ mol } CO_2} \qquad \dfrac{180.2 \text{ g } C_6H_{12}O_6}{1 \text{ mol } C_6H_{12}O_6}$

Follow the solution map to solve the problem. Begin with grams of carbon dioxide and multiply by the appropriate factors to arrive at grams of glucose.	**Solution:** $58.5 \text{ g } CO_2 \times \dfrac{1 \text{ mol } CO_2}{44.01 \text{ g } CO_2} \times \dfrac{1 \text{ mol } C_6H_{12}O_6}{6 \text{ mol } CO_2}$ $\times \dfrac{180.2 \text{ g } C_6H_{12}O_6}{1 \text{ mol } C_6H_{12}O_6} = 39.9 \text{ g } C_6H_{12}O_6$

SKILLBUILDER 8.2   Mass-to-Mass Conversions

Magnesium hydroxide, the active ingredient in milk of magnesia, neutralizes stomach acid, primarily HCl, according to the following reaction.

$$Mg(OH)_2(aq) + 2 \text{ HCl}(aq) \longrightarrow 2 \text{ H}_2\text{O}(l) + MgCl_2(aq)$$

How much HCl in grams can be neutralized by 5.50 g of $Mg(OH)_2$?

EXAMPLE 8.3   **Mass-to-Mass Conversions**

One of the components of acid rain is nitric acid, which forms when NO_2, a pollutant, reacts with oxygen and rain-water according to the following reaction.

$$4 NO_2(g) + O_2(g) + 2 H_2O(l) \longrightarrow 4 HNO_3(aq)$$

Assuming that there is more than enough O_2 and H_2O, how much HNO_3 in kilograms forms from 1.5×10^3 kg of NO_2 pollutant?

Set up the problem in the normal way.

Given: 1.5×10^3 kg NO_2

Find: kg HNO_3

The main conversion factor is the stoichiometric relationship between moles of nitrogen dioxide and moles of nitric acid. This conversion factor comes from the balanced equation. The other conversion factors are simply the molar masses of nitrogen dioxide and nitric acid and the relationship between kilograms and grams.

Conversion Factors:

4 mol $NO_2 \equiv$ 4 mol HNO_3 (from balanced chemical equation)

Molar mass NO_2 = 46.01 g/mol

Molar mass HNO_3 = 63.02 g/ mol

1 kg = 1000 g

The solution map follows the general format of

Mass $\longrightarrow$ Moles $\longrightarrow$
            Moles $\longrightarrow$ Mass.

However, since the original quantity of NO_2 is given in kilograms, you must first convert to grams. Since the final quantity is requested in kilograms, you must convert back to kilograms at the end.

Solution Map:

Follow the solution map to solve the problem. Begin with kilograms of nitrogen dioxide and multiply by the appropriate conversion factors to arrive at kilograms of nitric acid.

Solution:

$$1.5 \times 10^3 \text{ kg NO}_2 \times \frac{1000 \text{ g}}{1 \text{ kg}} \times \frac{1 \text{ mol NO}_2}{46.01 \text{ g NO}_2} \times \frac{4 \text{ mol HNO}_3}{4 \text{ mol NO}_2}$$

$$\times \frac{63.02 \text{ g HNO}_3}{1 \text{ mol HNO}_3} \times \frac{1 \text{ kg}}{1000 \text{ g}} = 2.1 \times 10^3 \text{ kg HNO}_3$$

SKILLBUILDER 8.3   **Mass-to-Mass Conversions**

Another component of acid rain is sulfuric acid, which forms when SO_2, also a pollutant, reacts with oxygen and rainwater according to the following reaction.

$$2 SO_2(g) + O_2(g) + 2 H_2O(l) \longrightarrow 2 H_2SO_4(aq)$$

Assuming that there is plenty of O_2 and H_2O, how much H_2SO_4 in kilograms forms from 2.6×10^3 kg of SO_2?

8.5 More Pancakes: Limiting Reactant, Theoretical Yield, and Percent Yield

Let's return to our pancake analogy to understand two more concepts important in reaction stoichiometry: limiting reactant and percent yield. Recall our pancake recipe:

$$1 \text{ cup flour} + 2 \text{ eggs} + \tfrac{1}{2} \text{ tsp baking powder} \longrightarrow 5 \text{ pancakes}$$

Suppose we have 3 cups flour, 10 eggs, and 4 tsp baking powder. How many pancakes can we make? We have enough flour to make:

$$3 \text{ cups flour} \times \frac{5 \text{ pancakes}}{1 \text{ cup flour}} = 15 \text{ pancakes}$$

We have enough eggs to make:

$$10 \text{ eggs} \times \frac{5 \text{ pancakes}}{2 \text{ eggs}} = 25 \text{ pancakes}$$

We have enough baking powder to make:

$$4 \text{ tsp baking powder} \times \frac{5 \text{ pancakes}}{\tfrac{1}{2} \text{ tsp baking powder}} = 40 \text{ pancakes}$$

We have enough flour for 15 pancakes, enough eggs for 25 pancakes, and enough baking powder for 40 pancakes. Consequently, unless we get more ingredients, we can make only 15 pancakes. The flour *limits* the number of pancakes we can make. If this were a chemical reaction, the flour would be the **limiting reactant**, the reactant that limits the amount of product in a chemical reaction. Notice that the limiting reactant is simply the reactant that makes *the least amount of product*. If this were a chemical reaction, 15 pancakes would be the **theoretical yield**, the amount of product that can be made in a chemical reaction based on the amount of limiting reactant.

> The term *limiting reagent* is sometimes used in place of *limiting reactant*.

▶ If this were a chemical reaction, the flour would be the limiting reactant and 15 pancakes would be the theoretical yield.

Limiting reactant

Theoretical yield

15 pancakes   25 pancakes   40 pancakes

> The actual yield of a chemical reaction, which must be determined experimentally, often depends on the reaction conditions in various ways. We will explore some of the factors involved in Chapter 15.

Let us carry this analogy one step further. Suppose we go on to cook our pancakes. We accidentally burn three of them and one falls on the floor. So even though we had enough flour for 15 pancakes, we finished with only 11 pancakes. If this were a chemical reaction, the 11 pancakes would be our **actual yield**, the amount of product actually produced by a chemical reaction. Finally, our **percent yield**, the percentage of the theoretical yield that was actually attained, is:

$$\text{Percent yield} = \frac{11 \text{ pancakes}}{15 \text{ pancakes}} \times 100\% = 73\%$$

Since four of the pancakes were ruined, we got only 73% of our theoretical yield. In a chemical reaction, the actual yield is almost always less than 100% because at least some of the product does not form or is lost in the process of recovering it (in analogy to some of the pancakes being burned).

To summarize:

- Limiting reactant (or limiting reagent)—the reactant that is completely consumed in a chemical reaction.
- Theoretical yield—the amount of product that can be made in a chemical reaction based on the amount of limiting reactant.
- Actual yield—the amount of product actually produced by a chemical reaction.
- Percent yield $= \dfrac{\textbf{Actual yield}}{\textbf{Theoretical yield}} \times 100\%$

Now consider the following reaction.

$$Ti(s) + 2\,Cl_2(g) \longrightarrow TiCl_4(s)$$

If we begin with 1.8 mol of titanium and 3.2 mol of chlorine, what is the limiting reactant and theoretical yield of $TiCl_4$ in moles? We can set up the problem according to our standard problem-solving procedure.

Given:

1.8 mol Ti

3.2 mol Cl_2

Find:

limiting reactant
theoretical yield

Conversion Factors: The conversion factors come from the balanced chemical equation and give the relationships between moles of each of the reactants and moles of product.

1 mol Ti $\equiv$ 1 mol $TiCl_4$

2 mol Cl_2 $\equiv$ 1 mol $TiCl_4$

Like our pancake analogy, we find the limiting reactant by calculating how much product can be made from each reactant. The reactant that makes the *least amount of product* is the limiting reactant.

Solution Map:

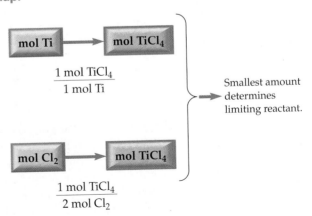

Solution:

$$1.8 \text{ mol Ti} \times \frac{1 \text{ mol TiCl}_4}{1 \text{ mol Ti}} = 1.8 \text{ mol TiCl}_4$$

$$3.2 \text{ mol Cl}_2 \times \frac{1 \text{ mol TiCl}_4}{2 \text{ mol Cl}_2} = 1.6 \text{ mol TiCl}_4$$

Limiting reactant

Least amount of product

In many industrial applications, the more costly reactant or the reactant that is most difficult to remove from the product mixture is chosen to be the limiting reactant.

Since the 3.2 mol of Cl_2 make the least amount of $TiCl_4$, Cl_2 is the limiting reactant. Notice that we began with more moles of Cl_2 than Ti, but since the reaction requires 2 Cl_2 for each Ti, Cl_2 is still the limiting reactant. The theoretical yield is 1.6 mol of $TiCl_4$.

EXAMPLE 8.4 Limiting Reactant and Theoretical Yield from Initial Moles of Reactants

Consider the following reaction.

$$2 \text{ Al}(s) + 3 \text{ Cl}_2(g) \longrightarrow 2 \text{ AlCl}_3(s)$$

If we begin with 0.552 mol of aluminum and 0.887 mol of chlorine, what is the limiting reactant and theoretical yield of $AlCl_3$ in moles?

Set up the problem in the normal way.	**Given:** 0.552 mol Al 0.887 mol Cl_2 **Find:** limiting reactant theoretical yield
The conversion factors are the stoichiometric relationships (from the balanced equation) between the moles of each reactant and the moles of product.	**Conversion Factors:** 2 mol Al ≡ 2 mol $AlCl_3$ 3 mol Cl_2 ≡ 2 mol $AlCl_3$
The solution map shows how to get from moles of each reactant to moles of $AlCl_3$. The reactant that makes the *least amount of AlCl_3* is the limiting reactant.	**Solution Map:** 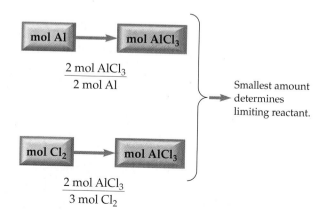

Solution:

$$0.552 \ \text{mol Al} \times \frac{2 \ \text{mol AlCl}_3}{2 \ \text{mol Al}} = 0.552 \ \text{mol AlCl}_3$$

Limiting reactant

Least amount of product

$$0.887 \ \text{mol Cl}_2 \times \frac{2 \ \text{mol AlCl}_3}{3 \ \text{mol Cl}_2} = 0.591 \ \text{mol AlCl}_3$$

Since the 0.552 mol of Al makes the least amount of $AlCl_3$, Al is the limiting reactant. The theoretical yield is 0.552 mol of $AlCl_3$.

SKILLBUILDER 8.4   **Limiting Reactant and Theoretical Yield from Initial Moles of Reactants**

Consider the following reaction.

$$2 \ Na(s) + F_2(g) \longrightarrow 2 \ NaF(s)$$

If you begin with 4.8 mol of sodium and 2.6 mol of fluorine, what is the limiting reactant and theoretical yield of NaF in moles?

CONCEPTUAL CHECKPOINT 8.1

A maker of tricycles has 17 seats, 19 bells, 37 pedals, and 49 wheels in his warehouse. The limiting component for the manufacture of new tricycles would be: (Assume that all the wheels on each tricycle are identical.)

(a) seats
(b) bells
(c) pedals
(d) wheels

8.6 Limiting Reactant, Theoretical Yield, and Percent Yield from Initial Masses of Reactants

When working in the laboratory, we normally measure the initial amounts of reactants in grams. To find limiting reactants and theoretical yields from initial masses, we must add two steps to our calculations. Consider, for example, the following synthesis reaction.

$$2 \ Na(s) + Cl_2(g) \longrightarrow 2 \ NaCl(s)$$

If we have 53.2 g of Na and 65.8 g of Cl_2, what is the limiting reactant and theoretical yield? We will approach this problem in our standard way.

Given:

53.2 g Na

65.8 g Cl_2

Find:

limiting reactant
theoretical yield

Conversion Factors: From the balanced chemical equation, we get:

2 mol Na ≡ 2 mol NaCl

1 mol Cl_2 ≡ 2 mol NaCl

We will also have to convert between grams and moles for each of the reactants and the product, so we also need the following molar masses.

$$\text{Molar mass Na} = \frac{22.99 \text{ g Na}}{1 \text{ mol Na}}$$

$$\text{Molar mass Cl}_2 = \frac{70.91 \text{ g Cl}_2}{1 \text{ mol Cl}_2}$$

$$\text{Molar mass NaCl} = \frac{58.44 \text{ g NaCl}}{1 \text{ mol NaCl}}$$

TUTORIAL
Limiting Reactant

We again find the limiting reactant by calculating how much product can be made from each reactant. Since we are given the initial amounts in grams, we must first convert to moles. After we convert to moles of product, we convert back to grams of product. The reactant that makes the *least amount of product* is the limiting reactant.

Solution Map:

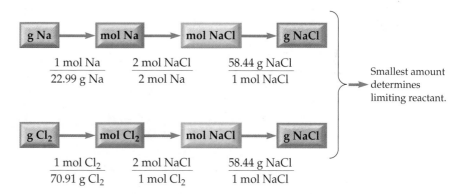

Solution: Beginning with the actual amounts of each reactant, we follow the solution map to calculate how much product can be made from each.

The limiting reactant can also be found by calculating the number of moles of NaCl (rather than grams) that can be made from each reactant. However, since theoretical yields are normally calculated in grams, we take the calculation all the way to grams to determine limiting reactant.

$$53.2 \text{ g Na} \times \frac{1 \text{ mol Na}}{22.99 \text{ g Na}} \times \frac{2 \text{ mol NaCl}}{2 \text{ mol Na}} \times \frac{58.44 \text{ g NaCl}}{1 \text{ mol NaCl}} = 135 \text{ g NaCl}$$

$$65.8 \text{ g Cl}_2 \times \frac{1 \text{ mol Cl}_2}{70.91 \text{ g Cl}_2} \times \frac{2 \text{ mol NaCl}}{1 \text{ mol Cl}_2} \times \frac{58.44 \text{ g NaCl}}{1 \text{ mol NaCl}} = 108 \text{ g NaCl}$$

Limiting
reactant

Least amount
of product

The limiting reactant is *not necessarily* the reactant with the least mass.

The actual yield is always less than the theoretical yield because at least a small amount of product is usually lost or does not form during a reaction.

Since Cl$_2$ makes the least amount of product (108 g NaCl is less than 135 g NaCl), it is the limiting reactant. Notice that the limiting reactant is not necessarily the reactant with the least mass. In this case, we had fewer grams of Na than Cl$_2$, yet Cl$_2$ was the limiting reactant because it made less NaCl. The theoretical yield is therefore 108 g of NaCl, the amount of product possible based on the limiting reactant.

Now suppose that when the synthesis was carried out, the actual yield of NaCl was 86.4 g. What is the percent yield? The percent yield is simply:

$$\text{Percent yield} = \frac{\text{Actual yield}}{\text{Theoretical yield}} \times 100\% = \frac{86.4 \text{ g}}{108 \text{ g}} \times 100\% = 80.0\%$$

EXAMPLE 8.5   Finding Limiting Reactant and Theoretical Yield

Ammonia, NH_3, can be synthesized by the following reaction.

$$2 NO(g) + 5 H_2(g) \longrightarrow 2 NH_3(g) + 2 H_2O(g)$$

What is the maximum amount of ammonia in grams that can be synthesized from 45.8 g of NO and 12.4 g of H_2?

Although this problem does not specifically ask for the limiting reactant, it must be found to determine the theoretical yield, which is the maximum amount of ammonia that can be synthesized. Begin by setting up the problem in the normal way.

The main conversion factors are the stoichiometric relationship between moles of each reactant and moles of ammonia. The other conversion factors are simply the molar masses of nitrogen monoxide, hydrogen gas, and ammonia.

Given: 45.8 g NO, 12.4 g H_2

Find: maximum amount of NH_3 (theoretical yield)

Conversion Factors:

$$2 \text{ mol NO} \equiv 2 \text{ mol NH}_3$$
$$5 \text{ mol H}_2 \equiv 2 \text{ mol NH}_3$$
$$\text{Molar mass NO} = \frac{30.01 \text{ g NO}}{1 \text{ mol NO}}$$
$$\text{Molar mass H}_2 = \frac{2.02 \text{ g H}_2}{1 \text{ mol H}_2}$$
$$\text{Molar mass NH}_3 = \frac{17.04 \text{ g NH}_3}{1 \text{ mol NH}_3}$$

Find the limiting reactant by calculating how much product can be made from each reactant. The reactant that makes the *least amount of product* is the limiting reactant.

Solution Map:

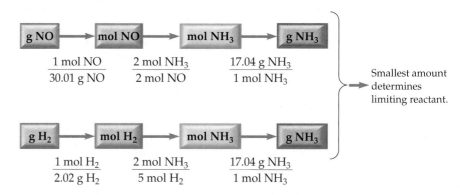

Follow the solution map, beginning with the actual amount of each reactant given, to calculate the amount of product that can be made from each reactant.

Solution:

$$45.8 \text{ g NO} \times \frac{1 \text{ mol NO}}{30.01 \text{ g NO}} \times \frac{2 \text{ mol NH}_3}{2 \text{ mol NO}} \times \frac{17.04 \text{ g NH}_3}{1 \text{ mol NH}_3} = 26.0 \text{ g NH}_3$$

Limiting reactant   Least amount of product

$$12.4 \text{ g H}_2 \times \frac{1 \text{ mol H}_2}{2.02 \text{ g H}_2} \times \frac{2 \text{ mol NH}_3}{5 \text{ mol H}_2} \times \frac{17.04 \text{ g NH}_3}{1 \text{ mol NH}_3} = 41.8 \text{ g NH}_3$$

There is enough NO to make 26.0 g of NH_3 and enough H_2 to make 41.8 g of NH_3. Therefore, NO is the limiting reactant, and the maximum amount of ammonia that can possibly be made is 26.0 g, the theoretical yield.

SKILLBUILDER 8.5   Finding Limiting Reactant and Theoretical Yield

Ammonia can also be synthesized by the following reaction.

$$3 H_2(g) + N_2(g) \longrightarrow 2 NH_3(g)$$

What is the maximum amount of ammonia in grams that can be synthesized from 25.2 g of N_2 and 8.42 g of H_2?

SKILLBUILDER PLUS

- What is the maximum amount of ammonia in kilograms that can be synthesized from 5.22 kg of H_2 and 31.5 kg of N_2?

EXAMPLE 8.6   **Finding Limiting Reactant, Theoretical Yield, and Percent Yield**

Consider the following reaction.

$$Cu_2O(s) + C(s) \longrightarrow 2\,Cu(s) + CO(g)$$

When 11.5 g of C are allowed to react with 114.5 g of Cu_2O, 87.4 g of Cu are obtained. Find the limiting reactant, theoretical yield, and percent yield.

Set up the problem in the normal way.	**Given:** 11.5 g C 114.5 g Cu_2O 87.4 g Cu produced **Find:** limiting reactant theoretical yield percent yield

The main conversion factors are the stoichiometric relationships between moles of each reactant and moles of copper. The other conversion factors are simply the molar masses of copper(I) oxide, carbon, and copper.

Conversion Factors:

1 mol Cu_2O ≡ 2 mol Cu   Molar mass Cu_2O = 143.08 g/mol
1 mol C ≡ 2 mol Cu   Molar mass C = 12.01 g/mol
                                 Molar mass Cu = 63.54 g/mol

The solution map shows how to find the mass of Cu formed by the initial masses of Cu_2O and C. The reactant that makes the *least amount of product* is the limiting reactant and determines the theoretical yield.

Solution Map:

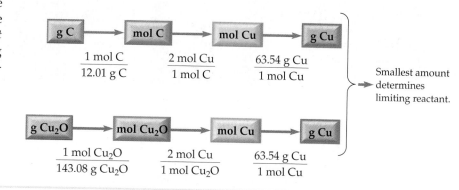

Follow the solution map, beginning with the actual amount of each reactant given, to calculate the amount of product that can be made from each reactant.

Solution:

$$11.5\;g\,C \times \frac{1\;mol\,C}{12.01\;g\,C} \times \frac{2\;mol\,Cu}{1\;mol\,C} \times \frac{63.54\;g\;Cu}{1\;mol\,Cu} = 122\;g\;Cu$$

Since Cu_2O makes the least amount of product, Cu_2O is the limiting reactant. The theoretical yield is simply the amount of product made by the limiting reactant. The percent yield is the actual yield (87.4 g Cu) divided by the theoretical yield (101.7 g Cu) multiplied by 100%.

$$114.5\;g\;Cu_2O \times \frac{1\;mol\,Cu_2O}{143.08\;g\,Cu_2O} \times \frac{2\;mol\,Cu}{1\;mol\,Cu_2O} \times \frac{63.54\;g\;Cu}{1\;mol\,Cu} = 101.7\;g\;Cu$$

Limiting reactant   Least amount of product

Theoretical yield = 101.7 g Cu

$$Percent\;yield = \frac{Actual\;yield}{Theoretical\;yield} \times 100\%$$

$$= \frac{87.4\;g}{101.7\;g} \times 100\% = 85.9\%$$

SKILLBUILDER 8.6   **Finding Limiting Reactant, Theoretical Yield, and Percent Yield**

The following reaction is used to obtain iron from iron ore:

$$Fe_2O_3(s) + 3\,CO(g) \longrightarrow 2\,Fe(s) + 3\,CO_2(g)$$

The reaction of 185 g of Fe_2O_3 with 95.3 g of CO produces 87.4 g of Fe. Find the limiting reactant, theoretical yield, and percent yield.

EVERYDAY Chemistry

Bunsen Burners

In the laboratory, we often use Bunsen burners as heat sources. These burners are normally fueled by methane. The balanced equation for methane (CH_4) combustion is:

$$CH_4(g) + 2\,O_2(g) \longrightarrow CO_2(g) + 2\,H_2O(g)$$

Most Bunsen burners have a mechanism to adjust the amount of air (and therefore of oxygen) that is mixed with the methane. If you light the burner with the air com-pletely closed off, you get a yellow, smoky flame that is not very hot. As you increase the amount of air going into the burner, the flame becomes bluer, less smoky, and hotter. When you reach the optimum adjustment, the flame has a sharp, inner blue triangle, no smoke, and is hot enough to melt glass easily. Continuing to increase the air beyond this point causes the flame to become cooler again and may actually extinguish it.

(a) No air

(b) Small amount of air

(c) Optimum

(d) Too much air

▲ Bunsen burner at various stages of air intake adjustment.

CAN YOU ANSWER THIS? *Can you use the concepts from this chapter to explain the changes in the Bunsen burner as the air intake is adjusted?*

CHAPTER IN REVIEW

Chemical Principles

Stoichiometry: A balanced chemical equation gives quantitative relationships between the amounts of reactants and products. For example, the reaction $2\,H_2 + O_2 \longrightarrow 2\,H_2O$ says that 2 mol of H_2 reacts with 1 mol of O_2 to form 2 mol of H_2O. These relationships can be used to calculate quantities such as the amount of product possible with a certain amount of reactant, or the amount of one reactant required to completely react with a certain amount of another reactant. The quantitative relationships between reactants and products in a chemical reaction are called reaction stoichiometry.

Relevance

Stoichiometry: Reaction stoichiometry is important because we often want to know numerical relationships between the reactants and products in a chemical reaction. For example, we might want to know how much carbon dioxide, a greenhouse gas, is formed upon burning a certain amount of a particular fossil fuel.

Limiting Reactant, Theoretical Yield, and Percent Yield: The limiting reactant in a chemical reaction is the reactant that, for the amounts of each reactant used in a particular instance, limits the amount of product that can be made. The theoretical yield in a chemical reaction is the amount of product that can be made based on the amount of the limiting reactant. The actual yield in a chemical reaction is the amount of product actually produced. The percent yield in a chemical reaction is the actual yield divided by theoretical yield times 100%.

Limiting Reactant, Theoretical Yield, and Percent Yield: Calculations of limiting reactant, theoretical yield, and percent yield are central to chemistry because they bring quantitative understanding to chemical reactions. Just as you need to know relationships between ingredients to follow a recipe, so you must know relationships between reactants and products to carry out a chemical reaction. The percent yield in a chemical reaction is often used as a measure of the success of the reaction. Imagine following a recipe and making only 1% of the final product—your cooking would be a failure. Similarly, low percent yields in chemical reactions are usually considered poor, and high percent yields are considered good.

Chemical Skills

Examples

Mole-to-Mole Conversions (Section 8.3)

For mole-to-mole conversions, we follow our standard problem-solving procedure, writing down the given quantities, find quantities, and conversion factors. The conversion factor comes from the balanced chemical equation.

The solution map begins with the number of moles of the given substance and then uses the conversion factor from the balanced chemical equation to get to the number of moles of the substance you are trying to find.

To compute the answer, begin with the number of moles of the given substance and follow the solution map to get to the number of moles of the substance you are trying to find.

EXAMPLE 8.7   Mole-to-Mole Conversions

How many moles of sodium oxide can be synthesized from 4.8 mol of sodium? Assume that there is more than enough oxygen present. The balanced equation is:

$$4\,Na(s) + O_2(g) \longrightarrow 2\,Na_2O(s)$$

Given: 4.8 mol Na

Find: mol Na_2O

Conversion Factor: 4 mol Na $\equiv$ 2 mol Na_2O

Solution Map:

$$\frac{2\;mol\;Na_2O}{4\;mol\;Na}$$

Solution:

$$4.8\;\cancel{mol\;Na} \times \frac{2\;mol\;Na_2O}{4\;\cancel{mol\;Na}} = 2.4\;mol\;Na_2O$$

Mole-to-Mole Conversions (Section 8.4)

For mass-to-mass conversions, we also follow our standard problem-solving procedure, writing down the given quantities, find quantities, and conversion factors. The required conversion factors include those from the balanced chemical equation as well as the molar masses of the substances involved.

LIVE EXAMPLE

EXAMPLE 8.8   Mass-to-Mass Conversions

How many grams of sodium oxide can be synthesized from 17.4 g of sodium? Assume that there is more than enough oxygen present. The balanced equation is:

$$4\,Na(s) + O_2(g) \longrightarrow 2\,Na_2O(s)$$

Given: 17.4 g Na

Find: g Na_2O

Conversion Factors:

4 mol Na = 2 mol Na_2O

Molar mass Na = 22.99 g/mol

Molar mass Na_2O = 61.98 g/mol

Draw the solution map by beginning with the mass of the given substance. Convert to moles using the molar mass and then convert to moles of the substance you are trying to find, using the conversion factor obtained from the balanced chemical equation. Finally, convert to mass of the substance you are trying to find, using its molar mass.

Solution Map:

$$\frac{1 \text{ mol Na}}{22.99 \text{ g Na}}$$ $$\frac{2 \text{ mol Na}_2\text{O}}{4 \text{ mol Na}}$$

$$\boxed{\text{mol Na}_2\text{O}} \longrightarrow \boxed{\text{g Na}_2\text{O}}$$

$$\frac{61.98 \text{ g Na}_2\text{O}}{1 \text{ mol Na}_2\text{O}}$$

Compute the answer by beginning with the amount of the given substance and multiplying by the appropriate conversion factors to get to the mass of the substance you are trying to find.

Solution:

$$17.4 \text{ g Na} \times \frac{1 \text{ mol Na}}{22.99 \text{ g Na}} \times \frac{2 \text{ mol Na}_2\text{O}}{4 \text{ mol Na}}$$

$$\times \frac{61.98 \text{ g Na}_2\text{O}}{1 \text{ mol Na}_2\text{O}} = 23.5 \text{ g Na}_2\text{O}$$

Limiting Reactant, Theoretical Yield, and Percent Yield (Sections 8.5, 8.6)

LIVE EXAMPLE

EXAMPLE 8.9 **Limiting Reactant, Theoretical Yield, and Percent Yield**

10.4 g of Fe reacts with 11.8 g of S to produce 14.2 g of Fe_2S_3. Find the limiting reactant, theoretical yield, and percent yield for this reaction. The balanced chemical equation is:

$$2 \text{ Fe}(s) + 3 \text{ S}(l) \longrightarrow \text{Fe}_2\text{S}_3(s)$$

For limiting-reactant problems, we also follow our standard problem-solving procedure, writing down the given quantities, find quantities, and conversion factors. The required conversion factors include those from the balanced chemical equation as well as the molar masses of the substances involved.

Given:

10.4 g Fe
11.8 g S
14.2 g Fe_2S_3

Find:

> limiting reactant
> theoretical yield
> percent yield

Conversion Factors:

> 2 mol Fe = 1 mol Fe_2S_3
> 3 mol S = 1 mol Fe_2S_3
> Molar mass Fe = 55.85 g/mol
> Molar mass S = 32.06 g/mol
> Molar mass Fe_2S_3 = 207.9 g/mol

The solution map for limiting-reactant problems shows how to convert from mass of each of the reactants to mass of the product for each reactant. These are mass-to-mass conversions involving the basic outline of Mass ⟶ Moles ⟶ Moles ⟶ Mass. The reactant that forms the least amount of product is the limiting reactant.

Solution Map:

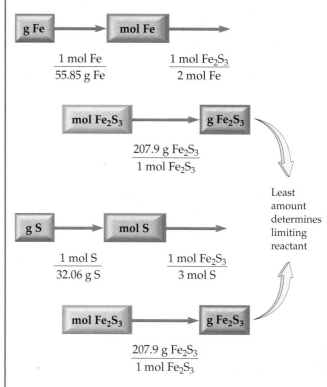

To compute the amount of product formed by each reactant, begin with the given amount of each reactant and multiply by the appropriate conversion factors, as shown in the solution map, to arrive at the mass of product for each reactant. The reactant that forms the least amount of product is the limiting reactant.

Solution:

$$10.4 \ \cancel{\text{g Fe}} \times \frac{1 \ \cancel{\text{mol Fe}}}{55.85 \ \cancel{\text{g Fe}}} \times \frac{1 \ \cancel{\text{mol Fe}_2\text{S}_3}}{2 \ \cancel{\text{mol Fe}}} \times \frac{207.9 \ \text{g Fe}_2\text{S}_3}{1 \ \cancel{\text{mol Fe}_2\text{S}_3}}$$

↑ Limiting reactant

$$= 19.4 \ \text{g Fe}_2\text{S}_3$$

Least amount of product

$$11.8 \ \cancel{\text{g S}} \times \frac{1 \ \cancel{\text{mol S}}}{32.06 \ \cancel{\text{g S}}} \times \frac{1 \ \cancel{\text{mol Fe}_2\text{S}_3}}{3 \ \cancel{\text{mol S}}} \times \frac{207.9 \ \text{g Fe}_2\text{S}_3}{1 \ \cancel{\text{mol Fe}_2\text{S}_3}}$$

$$= 25.5 \ \text{g Fe}_2\text{S}_3$$

The theoretical yield is the amount of product formed by the limiting reactant.

The limiting reactant is Fe.
The theoretical yield is 19.4 g of Fe_2S_3.

The percent yield is the actual yield divided by the theoretical yield times 100%.

$$\text{Percent yield} = \frac{\text{Actual yield}}{\text{Theoretical yield}} \times 100\%$$

$$= \frac{14.2 \ \text{g}}{19.4 \ \text{g}} \times 100\% = 73.2\%$$

● The percent yield is 73.2%.

Key Terms

actual yield [8.5]   global warming [8.1]   limiting reactant [8.5]   stoichiometry [8.1]
equivalent [8.2]   greenhouse gases [8.1]   percent yield [8.5]   theoretical yield [8.5]

Exercises

Questions

1. Why is reaction stoichiometry important? Can you give some examples?
2. What does it mean to say that two quantities in a chemical reaction are equivalent?
3. Write conversion factors showing the relationships between moles of each of the reactants and products in the following reaction.

$$N_2(g) + 3\,H_2(g) \longrightarrow 2\,NH_3(g)$$

4. For the reaction in Problem 3, how many molecules of H_2 are required to completely react with two molecules of N_2? How many moles of H_2 are required to completely react with 2 mol of N_2?
5. Write the conversion factor that you would use to convert from moles of Cl_2 to moles of NaCl in the following reaction.

$$2\,Na(s) + Cl_2(g) \longrightarrow 2\,NaCl$$

6. What is wrong with this statement in reference to the reaction in Problem 5?
"Two grams of Na react with 1 g of Cl_2 to form 2 g of NaCl."
Correct the statement to make it true.
7. What is the general form of the solution map for problems in which you are given the mass of a reactant in a chemical reaction and asked to find the mass of the product that can be made from the given amount of reactant?
8. Consider the following recipe for making tomato and garlic pasta.

2 cups noodles + 12 tomatoes
+ 3 cloves garlic $\longrightarrow$ 4 servings pasta

If you have 7 cups of noodles, 27 tomatoes, and 9 cloves of garlic, how many servings of pasta can you make? Which ingredient limits the amount of pasta that is possible?
9. In a chemical reaction, what is the limiting reactant?
10. In a chemical reaction, what is the theoretical yield?
11. In a chemical reaction, what are the actual yield and percent yield?
12. If you are given a chemical equation and specific amounts of each reactant in grams, how would you determine how much product can possibly be made?
13. Consider the following generic chemical reaction.

$$A + 2\,B \longrightarrow C + D$$

Suppose you have 12 g of A and 24 g of B. Which of the following statements are true?
   (a) A will definitely be the limiting reactant.
   (b) B will definitely be the limiting reactant.
   (c) A will be the limiting reactant if its molar mass is less than B.
   (d) A will be the limiting reactant if its molar mass is greater than B.
14. Consider the following generic chemical equation.

$$A + B \longrightarrow C$$

Suppose 25 g of A were allowed to react with 8 g of B. Analysis of the final mixture showed that A was completely used up and 4 g of B remained. What was the limiting reactant?

Problems

Mole-to-Mole Conversions

15. Consider the following generic chemical reaction.

$$A + 2\,B \longrightarrow C$$

How many moles of C are formed upon complete reaction of:
   (a) 1 mol of A
   (b) 1 mol of B
   (c) 2 mol of A
   (d) 2 mol of B

16. Consider the following generic chemical reaction.

$$2\,A + 3\,B \longrightarrow 3\,C$$

How many moles of B are required to completely react with:
   (a) 2 mol of A
   (b) 4 mol of A
   (c) 5 mol of A
   (d) 17 mol of A

17. For the reaction shown, calculate how many moles of NO_2 form when each of the following completely reacts.

$$2\,N_2O_5(g) \longrightarrow 4\,NO_2(g) + O_2(g)$$

(a) 1.3 mol N_2O_5
(b) 5.8 mol N_2O_5
(c) 4.45×10^3 mol N_2O_5
(d) 1.006×10^{-3} mol N_2O_5

18. For the reaction shown, calculate how many moles of NH_3 form when each of the following completely reacts.

$$3\,N_2H_4(l) \longrightarrow 4\,NH_3(g) + N_2(g)$$

(a) 5.3 mol N_2H_4
(b) 2.28 mol N_2H_4
(c) 5.8×10^{-2} mol N_2H_4
(d) 9.76×10^7 mol N_2H_4

19. For each reaction, calculate how many moles of the product form when 1.48 mol of the reactant in color completely reacts. Assume that there is more than enough of the other reactant.
(a) $H_2(g) + Cl_2(g) \longrightarrow 2\,HCl(g)$
(b) $2\,H_2(g) + O_2(g) \longrightarrow 2\,H_2O(l)$
(c) $2\,Na(s) + O_2(g) \longrightarrow Na_2O_2(s)$
(d) $2\,S(s) + 3\,O_2(g) \longrightarrow 2\,SO_3(g)$

20. For each reaction, calculate how many moles of the product form when 0.036 mol of the reactant in color completely reacts. Assume that there is more than enough of the other reactant.
(a) $2\,Ca(s) + O_2(g) \longrightarrow 2\,CaO(s)$
(b) $4\,Fe(s) + 3\,O_2(g) \longrightarrow 2\,Fe_2O_3(s)$
(c) $4\,K(s) + O_2(g) \longrightarrow 2\,K_2O(s)$
(d) $4\,Al(s) + 3\,O_2(g) \longrightarrow 2\,Al_2O_3(s)$

21. For the reaction shown, calculate how many moles of each product form when the following amounts of each reactant completely react to form products. Assume that there is more than enough of the other reactant.

$$2\,PbS(s) + 3\,O_2(g) \longrightarrow 2\,PbO(s) + 2\,SO_2(g)$$

(a) 1.2 mol PbS
(b) 1.2 mol O_2
(c) 7.9 mol PbS
(d) 7.9 mol O_2

22. For the reaction shown, calculate how many moles of each product form when the following amounts of each reactant completely react to form products. Assume that there is more than enough of the other reactant.

$$C_3H_8(g) + 5\,O_2(g) \longrightarrow 3\,CO_2(g) + 4\,H_2O(g)$$

(a) 8.7 mol C_3H_8
(b) 8.7 mol O_2
(c) 0.0918 mol C_3H_8
(d) 0.0918 mol O_2

23. Consider the following balanced equation.

$$2\,N_2H_4(g) + N_2O_4(g) \longrightarrow 3\,N_2(g) + 4\,H_2O(g)$$

Complete the following table, showing the appropriate number of moles of reactants and products. If the number of moles of a reactant is provided, fill in the required amount of the other reactant, as well as the moles of each product formed. If the number of moles of a product is provided, fill in the required amount of each reactant to make that amount of product, as well as the amount of the other product that is made.

mol N_2H_4	mol N_2O_4	mol N_2	mol H_2O
___	2	___	___
6	___	___	___
___	___	___	8
___	5.5	___	___
3	___	___	___
___	___	12.4	___

24. Consider the following balanced equation.

$$SiO_2(s) + 3\,C(s) \longrightarrow SiC(s) + 2\,CO(g)$$

Complete the following table, showing the appropriate number of moles of reactants and products. If the number of moles of a reactant is provided, fill in the required amount of the other reactant, as well as the moles of each product formed. If the number of moles of a product is provided, fill in the required amount of each reactant to make that amount of product, as well as the amount of the other product that is made.

mol SiO_2	mol C	mol SiC	mol CO
___	6	___	___
3	___	___	___
___	___	___	10
___	9.5	___	___
3.2	___	___	___

25. Consider the following unbalanced equation for the combustion of butane.

$$C_4H_{10}(g) + O_2(g) \longrightarrow CO_2(g) + H_2O(g)$$

Balance the equation and determine how many moles of O_2 are required to react completely with 4.9 mol of C_4H_{10}.

26. Consider the following unbalanced equation for the neutralization of acetic acid.

$$HC_2H_3O_2(aq) + Ca(OH)_2(aq) \longrightarrow H_2O(l) + Ca(C_2H_3O_2)_2(aq)$$

Balance the equation and determine how many moles of $Ca(OH)_2$ are required to completely neutralize 1.07 mol of $HC_2H_3O_2$.

27. Consider the following unbalanced equation for the reaction of solid lead with silver nitrate.

$$Pb(s) + AgNO_3(aq) \longrightarrow Pb(NO_3)_2(aq) + Ag(s)$$

(a) Balance the equation.
(b) How many moles of silver nitrate are required to completely react with 9.3 mol of lead?
(c) How many moles of $Ag(s)$ are formed by the complete reaction of 28.4 mol of Pb?

28. Consider the following unbalanced equation for the reaction of aluminum with sulfuric acid.

$$Al(s) + H_2SO_4(aq) \longrightarrow Al_2(SO_4)_3(aq) + H_2(g)$$

(a) Balance the equation.
(b) How many moles of H_2SO_4 are required to completely react with 8.3 mol of Al?
(c) How many moles of H_2 are formed by the complete reaction of 0.341 mol of Al?

Mass-to-Mass Conversions

29. For the reaction shown, calculate how many grams of oxygen form when each of the following completely reacts.

$$2 HgO(s) \longrightarrow 2 Hg(l) + O_2(g)$$

(a) 2.88 g HgO
(b) 5.21 g HgO
(c) 1.3×10^3 g HgO
(d) 4.6×10^{-3} g HgO

30. For the reaction shown, calculate how many grams of oxygen form when each of the following completely reacts.

$$2 KClO_3(s) \longrightarrow 2 KCl(s) + 3 O_2(g)$$

(a) 8.91 g $KClO_3$
(b) 0.549 g $KClO_3$
(c) 8.4×10^6 g $KClO_3$
(d) 3.3×10^{-4} g $KClO_3$

31. For each of the reactions shown, calculate how many grams of the product form when 1.8 g of the reactant in color completely reacts. Assume that there is more than enough of the other reactant.
(a) $2 Na(s) + Cl_2(g) \longrightarrow 2 NaCl(s)$
(b) $CaO(s) + CO_2(g) \longrightarrow CaCO_3(s)$
(c) $2 Mg(s) + O_2(g) \longrightarrow 2 MgO(s)$
(d) $Na_2O(s) + H_2O(l) \longrightarrow 2 NaOH(aq)$

32. For each of the reactions shown, calculate how many grams of the product form when 14.4 g of the reactant in color completely reacts. Assume that there is more than enough of the other reactant.
(a) $Ca(s) + Cl_2(g) \longrightarrow CaCl_2(s)$
(b) $2 K(s) + Br_2(l) \longrightarrow 2 KBr(s)$
(c) $4 Cr(s) + 3 O_2(g) \longrightarrow 2 Cr_2O_3(s)$
(d) $2 Sr(s) + O_2(g) \longrightarrow 2 SrO(s)$

33. For the reaction shown, calculate how many grams of each product form when the following amounts of reactant completely react to form products. Assume that there is more than enough of the other reactant.

$$2 Al(s) + Fe_2O_3(s) \longrightarrow Al_2O_3(s) + 2 Fe(l)$$

(a) 4.7 g Al
(b) 4.7 g Fe_2O_3

34. For the reaction shown, calculate how many grams of each product form when the following amounts of reactant completely react to form products. Assume that there is more than enough of the other reactant.

$$2 HCl(aq) + Na_2CO_3(aq) \longrightarrow 2 NaCl(aq) + H_2O(l) + CO_2(g)$$

(a) 10.8 g HCl
(b) 10.8 g Na_2CO_3

35. Consider the following balanced equation for the combustion of methane, a component of natural gas.

$$CH_4(g) + 2\,O_2(g) \longrightarrow CO_2(g) + 2\,H_2O(g)$$

Complete the following table, showing the appropriate masses of reactants and products. If the mass of a reactant is provided, fill in the mass of other reactant required to completely react with the given mass, as well as the mass of each product formed. If the mass of a product is provided, fill in the required masses of each reactant to make that amount of product, as well as the mass of the other product that is formed.

Mass CH_4	Mass O_2	Mass CO_2	Mass H_2O
___	2.57 g	___	___
22.32 g	___	___	___
___	___	___	11.32 g
___	___	2.94 g	___
3.18 kg	___	___	___
___	___	2.35×10^3 kg	___

36. Consider the following balanced equation for the combustion of butane, a fuel often used in lighters.

$$2\,C_4H_{10}(g) + 13\,O_2(g) \longrightarrow 8\,CO_2(g) + 10\,H_2O(g)$$

Complete the following table, showing the appropriate masses of reactants and products. If the mass of a reactant is provided, fill in the mass of other reactant required to completely react with the given mass, as well as the mass of each product formed. If the mass of a product is provided, fill in the required masses of each reactant to make that amount of product, as well as the mass of the other product that is formed.

Mass C_4H_{10}	Mass O_2	Mass CO_2	Mass H_2O
___	1.11 g	___	___
5.22 g	___	___	___
___	___	10.12 g	___
___	___	___	9.04 g
232 mg	___	___	___
___	___	118 mg	___

37. For each of the following acid–base reactions, calculate how many grams of each acid are necessary to completely react with and neutralize 2.5 g of the base.

(a) $HCl(aq) + NaOH(aq) \longrightarrow H_2O(l) + NaCl(aq)$

(b) $2\,HNO_3(aq) + Ca(OH)_2(aq) \longrightarrow$
$\qquad\qquad\qquad 2\,H_2O(l) + Ca(NO_3)_2(aq)$

(c) $H_2SO_4(aq) + 2\,KOH(aq) \longrightarrow$
$\qquad\qquad\qquad 2\,H_2O(l) + K_2SO_4(aq)$

38. For each of the following precipitation reactions, calculate how many grams of the first reactant are necessary to completely react with 17.3 g of the second reactant.

(a) $2\,KI(aq) + Pb(NO_3)_2(aq) \longrightarrow$
$\qquad\qquad\qquad PbI_2(s) + 2\,KNO_3(aq)$

(b) $Na_2CO_3(aq) + CuCl_2(aq) \longrightarrow$
$\qquad\qquad\qquad CuCO_3(s) + 2\,NaCl(aq)$

(c) $K_2SO_4(aq) + Sr(NO_3)_2(aq) \longrightarrow$
$\qquad\qquad\qquad SrSO_4(s) + 2\,KNO_3(aq)$

39. Sulfuric acid can dissolve aluminum metal according to the following reaction.

$$2\,Al(s) + 3\,H_2SO_4(aq) \longrightarrow$$
$$Al_2(SO_4)_3(aq) + 3\,H_2(g)$$

Suppose you wanted to dissolve an aluminum block with a mass of 22.5 g. What minimum amount of H_2SO_4 in grams would you need? How many grams of H_2 gas would be produced by the complete reaction of the aluminum block?

40. Hydrochloric acid can dissolve solid iron according to the following reaction.

$$Fe(s) + 2\,HCl(aq) \longrightarrow FeCl_2(aq) + H_2(g)$$

How much HCl in grams would you need to dissolve a 2.8-g iron bar on a padlock? How much H_2 would be produced by the complete reaction of the iron bar?

Limiting Reactant, Theoretical Yield, and Percent Yield

41. Consider the following generic chemical equation.

$$2\,A + 4\,B \longrightarrow 3\,C$$

What is the limiting reactant when each of the following amounts of A and B are allowed to react?
(a) 2 mol A; 5 mol B
(b) 1.8 mol A; 4 mol B
(c) 3 mol A; 4 mol B
(d) 22 mol A; 40 mol B

42. Consider the following generic chemical equation.

$$A + 3\,B \longrightarrow C$$

What is the limiting reactant when each of the following amounts of A and B are allowed to react?
(a) 1 mol A; 4 mol B
(b) 2 mol A; 3 mol B
(c) 0.5 mol A; 1.6 mol B
(d) 24 mol A; 75 mol B

43. Determine the theoretical yield of C when each of the following amounts of A and B are allowed to react in the generic reaction:

$$A + 2B \longrightarrow 3C$$

(a) 1 mol A; 1 mol B
(b) 2 mol A; 2 mol B
(c) 1 mol A; 3 mol B
(d) 32 mol A; 68 mol B

44. Determine the theoretical yield of C when each of the following amounts of A and B are allowed to react in the generic reaction:

$$2A + 3B \longrightarrow 2C$$

(a) 2 mol A; 4 mol B
(b) 3 mol A; 3 mol B
(c) 5 mol A; 6 mol B
(d) 4 mol A; 5 mol B

45. For the reaction shown, find the limiting reactant for each of the following initial amounts of reactants.

$$2K(s) + Cl_2(g) \longrightarrow 2KCl(s)$$

(a) 1 mol K; 1 mol Cl_2
(b) 1.8 mol K; 1 mol Cl_2
(c) 2.2 mol K; 1 mol Cl_2
(d) 14.6 mol K; 7.8 mol Cl_2

46. For the reaction shown, find the limiting reactant for each of the following initial amounts of reactants.

$$4Cr(s) + 3O_2(g) \longrightarrow 2Cr_2O_3(s)$$

(a) 1 mol Cr; 1 mol O_2
(b) 4 mol Cr; 2.5 mol O_2
(c) 12 mol Cr; 10 mol O_2
(d) 14.8 mol Cr; 10.3 mol O_2

47. For the reaction shown, compute the theoretical yield of product in moles for each of the following initial amounts of reactants.

$$2Mn(s) + 3O_2(g) \longrightarrow 2MnO_3(s)$$

(a) 2 mol Mn; 2 mol O_2
(b) 4.8 mol Mn; 8.5 mol O_2
(c) 0.114 mol Mn; 0.161 mol O_2
(d) 27.5 mol Mn; 43.8 mol O_2

48. For the reaction shown, compute the theoretical yield of the product in moles for each of the following initial amounts of reactants.

$$Ti(s) + 2Cl_2(g) \longrightarrow TiCl_4(s)$$

(a) 2 mol Ti; 2 mol Cl_2
(b) 5 mol Ti; 9 mol Cl_2
(c) 0.483 mol Ti; 0.911 mol Cl_2
(d) 12.4 mol Ti; 15.8 mol Cl_2

49. Consider the following reaction:

$$4HCl(g) + O_2(g) \longrightarrow 2H_2O(g) + 2Cl_2(g)$$

Each of the following molecular diagrams represents an initial mixture of the reactants. How many molecules of Cl_2 would be formed by complete reaction in each case? (Assume 100% actual yield.)

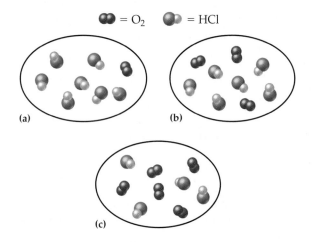

50. Consider the following reaction:

$$2CH_3OH(g) + 3O_2(g) \longrightarrow 2CO_2(g) + 4H_2O(g)$$

Each of the following molecular diagrams represents an initial mixture of the reactants. How many CO_2 molecules would be formed by complete reaction in each case? (Assume 100% actual yield.)

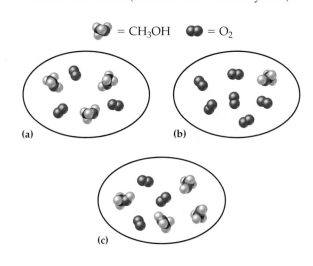

51. For the reaction shown, find the limiting reactant for each of the following initial amounts of reactants.

$$2 \text{ Li}(s) + \text{F}_2(g) \longrightarrow 2 \text{ LiF}(s)$$

(a) 1.0 g Li; 1.0 g F_2
(b) 10.5 g Li; 37.2 g F_2
(c) 2.85×10^3 g Li; 6.79×10^3 g F_2

52. For the reaction shown, find the limiting reactant for each of the following initial amounts of reactants.

$$4 \text{ Al}(s) + 3 \text{ O}_2(g) \longrightarrow 2 \text{ Al}_2\text{O}_3(s)$$

(a) 1.0 g Al; 1.0 g O_2
(b) 2.2 g Al; 1.8 g O_2
(c) 0.353 g Al; 0.482 g O_2

53. For the reaction shown, compute the theoretical yield of the product in grams for each of the following initial amounts of reactants.

$$2 \text{ Al}(s) + 3 \text{ Cl}_2(g) \longrightarrow 2 \text{ AlCl}_3(s)$$

(a) 1.0 g Al; 1.0 g Cl_2
(b) 5.5 g Al; 19.8 g Cl_2
(c) 0.439 g Al; 2.29 g Cl_2

54. For the reaction shown, compute the theoretical yield of the product in grams for each of the following initial amounts of reactants.

$$\text{Ti}(s) + 2 \text{ F}_2(g) \longrightarrow \text{TiF}_4(s)$$

(a) 1.0 g Ti; 1.0 g F_2
(b) 4.8 g Ti; 3.2 g F_2
(c) 0.388 g Ti; 0.341 g F_2

55. If the theoretical yield of a reaction is 24.8 g and the actual yield is 18.5 g, what is the percent yield?

56. If the theoretical yield of a reaction is 0.118 g and the actual yield is 0.104 g, what is the percent yield?

57. Consider the following reaction.

$$\text{CaO}(s) + \text{CO}_2(g) \longrightarrow \text{CaCO}_3(s)$$

A chemist allows 14.4 g of CaO and 13.8 g of CO_2 to react. When the reaction is finished, the chemist collects 19.4 g of CaCO_3. Determine the limiting reactant, theoretical yield, and percent yield for the reaction.

58. Consider the following reaction.

$$\text{SO}_3(g) + \text{H}_2\text{O}(l) \longrightarrow \text{H}_2\text{SO}_4(aq)$$

A chemist allows 61.5 g of SO_3 and 11.2 g of H_2O to react. When the reaction is finished, the chemist collects 54.9 g of H_2SO_4. Determine the limiting reactant, theoretical yield, and percent yield for the reaction.

59. Consider the following reaction.

$$2 \text{ NiS}_2(s) + 5 \text{ O}_2(g) \longrightarrow 2 \text{ NiO}(s) + 4 \text{ SO}_2(g)$$

When 11.2 g of NiS_2 are allowed to react with 5.43 g of O_2, 4.86 g of NiO are obtained. Determine the limiting reactant, theoretical yield of NiO, and percent yield for the reaction.

60. Consider the following reaction.

$$4 \text{ HCl}(g) + \text{O}_2(g) \longrightarrow 2 \text{ H}_2\text{O}(l) + 2 \text{ Cl}_2(g)$$

When 63.1 g of HCl are allowed to react with 17.2 g of O_2, 49.3 g of Cl_2 are collected. Determine the limiting reactant, theoretical yield of Cl_2, and percent yield for the reaction.

61. Lead ions can be precipitated from solution with NaCl according to the following reaction.

$$\text{Pb}^{2+}(aq) + 2 \text{ NaCl}(aq) \longrightarrow \text{PbCl}_2(s) + 2 \text{ Na}^+(aq)$$

When 135.8 g of NaCl are added to a solution containing 195.7 g of Pb^{2+}, a PbCl_2 precipitate forms. The precipitate is filtered and dried and found to have a mass of 252.4 g. Determine the limiting reactant, theoretical yield of PbCl_2, and percent yield for the reaction.

62. Magnesium oxide can be made by heating magnesium metal in the presence of oxygen. The balanced equation for the reaction is:

$$2 \text{ Mg}(s) + \text{O}_2(g) \longrightarrow 2 \text{ MgO}(s)$$

When 10.1 g of Mg are allowed to react with 10.5 g of O_2, 11.9 g of MgO are collected. Determine the limiting reactant, theoretical yield, and percent yield for the reaction.

Cumulative Problems

63. A solution contains an unknown mass of dissolved barium ions. When sodium sulfate is added to the solution, a white precipitate forms. The precipitate is filtered and dried and then found to have a mass of 258 mg. What mass of barium was in the original solution? (Assume that all of the barium was precipitated out of solution by the reaction.)

64. A solution contains an unknown mass of dissolved silver ions. When potassium chloride is added to the solution, a white precipitate forms. The precipitate is filtered and dried and then found to have a mass of 212 mg. What mass of silver was in the original solution? (Assume that all of the silver was precipitated out of solution by the reaction.)

65. Sodium bicarbonate is often used as an antacid to neutralize excess hydrochloric acid in an upset stomach. How much hydrochloric acid in grams can be neutralized by 3.5 g of sodium bicarbonate? (Hint: Begin by writing a balanced equation for the reaction between aqueous sodium bicarbonate and aqueous hydrochloric acid.)

66. Toilet bowl cleaners often contain hydrochloric acid to dissolve the calcium carbonate deposits that accumulate within a toilet bowl. How much calcium carbonate in grams can be dissolved by 5.8 g of HCl? (Hint: Begin by writing a balanced equation for the reaction between hydrochloric acid and calcium carbonate.)

67. The combustion of gasoline produces carbon dioxide and water. Assume gasoline to be pure octane (C_8H_{18}) and calculate how many kilograms of carbon dioxide are added to the atmosphere per 1.0 kg of octane burned. (Hint: Begin by writing a balanced equation for the combustion reaction.)

68. Many home barbecues are fueled with propane gas (C_3H_8). How much carbon dioxide in kilograms is produced upon the complete combustion of 18.9 L of propane (approximate contents of one 5-gal tank)? Assume that the density of the liquid propane in the tank is 0.621 g/mL. (Hint: Begin by writing a balanced equation for the combustion reaction.)

69. A hard water solution contains 4.8 g of calcium chloride. How much sodium phosphate in grams should be added to the solution to completely precipitate all of the calcium?

70. Magnesium ions can be precipitated from seawater by the addition of sodium hydroxide. How much sodium hydroxide in grams must be added to a sample of seawater to completely precipitate the 88.4 mg of magnesium present?

71. Hydrogen gas can be prepared in the laboratory by a single displacement reaction in which solid zinc reacts with hydrochloric acid. How much zinc in grams is required to make 14.5 g of hydrogen gas through this reaction?

72. Sodium peroxide (Na_2O_2) reacts with water to form sodium hydroxide and oxygen gas. Write a balanced equation for the reaction and determine how much oxygen in grams is formed by the complete reaction of 35.23 g of Na_2O_2.

73. Ammonium nitrate reacts explosively upon heating to form nitrogen gas, oxygen gas, and gaseous water. Write a balanced equation for this reaction and determine how much oxygen in grams is produced by the complete reaction of 1.00 kg of ammonium nitrate.

74. Pure oxygen gas can be prepared in the laboratory by the decomposition of solid potassium chlorate to form solid potassium chloride and oxygen gas. How much oxygen gas in grams can be prepared from 45.8 g of potassium chlorate?

75. Aspirin can be made in the laboratory by reacting acetic anhydride ($C_4H_6O_3$) with salicylic acid ($C_7H_6O_3$) to form aspirin ($C_9H_8O_4$) and acetic acid ($C_2H_4O_2$). The balanced equation is:

$$C_4H_6O_3 + C_7H_6O_3 \longrightarrow C_9H_8O_4 + C_2H_4O_2.$$

In a laboratory synthesis, a student begins with 5.00 mL of acetic anhydride (density = 1.08 g/mL) and 2.08 g of salicylic acid. Once the reaction is complete, the student collects 2.01 g of aspirin. Determine the limiting reactant, theoretical yield of aspirin, and percent yield for the reaction.

76. The combustion of liquid ethanol (C_2H_5OH) produces carbon dioxide and water. After 3.8 mL of ethanol (density = 0.789 g/mL) was allowed to burn in the presence of 12.5 g of oxygen gas, 3.10 mL of water (density = 1.00 g/mL) was collected. Determine the limiting reactant, theoretical yield of H_2O, and percent yield for the reaction. (Hint: Write a balanced equation for the combustion of ethanol.)

77. Urea (CH_4N_2O), a common fertilizer, can be synthesized by the reaction of ammonia (NH_3) with carbon dioxide:

$$2\,NH_3(aq) + CO_2(aq) \longrightarrow CH_4N_2O(aq) + H_2O(l)$$

An industrial synthesis of urea obtains 87.5 kg of urea upon reaction of 68.2 kg of ammonia with 105 kg of carbon dioxide. Determine the limiting reactant, theoretical yield of urea, and percent yield for the reaction.

78. Silicon, which occurs in nature as SiO_2, is the material from which most computer chips are made. If SiO_2 is heated until it melts into a liquid, it reacts with solid carbon to form liquid silicon and carbon monoxide gas. In an industrial preparation of silicon, 52.8 kg of SiO_2 reacted with 25.8 kg of carbon to produce 22.4 kg of silicon. Determine the limiting reactant, theoretical yield, and percent yield for the reaction.

79. The ingestion of lead from food, water, or other environmental sources can cause lead poisoning, a serious condition that affects the central nervous system, causing symptoms such as distractibility, lethargy, and loss of motor function. Lead poisoning is treated with chelating agents, substances that bind to lead and allow it to be eliminated in the urine. A modern chelating agent used for this purpose is succimer ($C_4H_6O_4S_2$). Suppose you are trying to determine the appropriate dose for succimer treatment of lead poisoning. What minimum mass of succimer in milligrams is needed to bind all of the lead in a patient's bloodstream? Assume that patient blood lead levels are 0.550 mg/L, that total blood volume is 5.0 L, and that 1 mol of succimer binds 1 mol of lead.

80. An emergency breathing apparatus often placed in mines or caves works via the following chemical reaction:

$$4\,KO_2(s) + 2\,CO_2(g) \longrightarrow 2\,K_2CO_3(s) + O_2(g)$$

If the oxygen supply becomes limited or if the air becomes poisoned, a worker can use the apparatus to breathe while exiting the mine. Notice that the reaction produces O_2, which can be breathed, and absorbs CO_2, a product of respiration. What minimum amount of KO_2 is required for the apparatus to produce enough oxygen to allow the user 15 minutes to exit in an emergency? Assume that an adult consumes approximately 4.4 g of oxygen in 15 minutes of normal breathing.

Highlight Problems

81. A loud classroom demonstration involves igniting a hydrogen-filled balloon. The hydrogen within the balloon explosively reacts with oxygen in the air to form water.

$$2\,H_2(g) + O_2(g) \longrightarrow 2\,H_2O(g)$$

If the balloon is filled with a mixture of hydrogen and oxygen, the explosion is even louder than if the balloon is filled with only hydrogen, and the intensity of the explosion depends on the relative amounts of oxygen and hydrogen within the balloon. Look at the following molecular views representing different amounts of hydrogen and oxygen in four different balloons. Based on the balanced chemical equation, which balloon will make the loudest explosion?

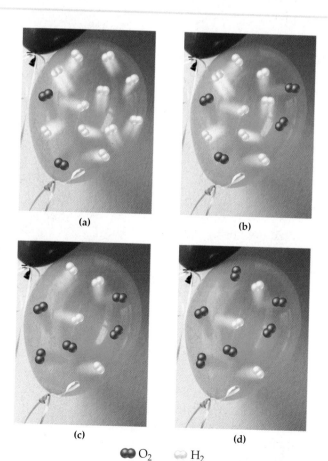

(a)

(b)

(c)

(d)

O_2 H_2

82. A hydrochloric acid solution will neutralize a sodium hydroxide solution. Look at the following molecular views showing one beaker of HCl and four beakers of NaOH. Which NaOH beaker will just neutralize the HCl beaker? Begin by writing a balanced chemical equation for the neutralization reaction.

(a)

(b)

(c)

(d)

83. As we have seen, scientists have grown increasingly worried about the potential for global warming caused by increasing atmospheric carbon dioxide levels. The world burns the fossil fuel equivalent of 7.0×10^{12} kg of petroleum per year. Assume that all of this petroleum is in the form of octane (C_8H_{18}) and calculate how much CO_2 in kilograms is produced by world fossil fuel combustion per year. (Hint: Begin by writing a balanced equation for the combustion of octane.) If the atmosphere currently contains approximately 3.0×10^{15} kg of CO_2, how long will it take for the world's fossil fuel combustion to double the amount of atmospheric carbon dioxide?

Atmospheric CO_2 levels 1860 to present

▲ Atmospheric CO_2 levels, 1860 to present.

84. Lakes that have been acidified by acid rain can be neutralized by the addition of limestone ($CaCO_3$). How much limestone in kilograms would be required to completely neutralize a 5.2×10^9–L lake containing 5.0×10^{-3} g of H_2SO_4 per liter?

Answers to Skillbuilder Exercises

Skillbuilder 8.1   49.2 mol H_2O

Skillbuilder 8.2   6.88 g HCl

Skillbuilder 8.3 4.0×10^3 kg H_2SO_4

Skillbuilder 8.4   Limiting reactant is Na; theoretical yield is 4.8 mol of NaF

Skillbuilder 8.5   30.7 g NH_3

Skillbuilder Plus, p. 246   29.4 kg NH_3

Skillbuilder 8.6   Limiting reactant is CO; theoretical yield = 127 g Fe; percent yield = 69.0%

Answers to Conceptual Checkpoints

8.1 (d) The manufacturer has enough seats for 17 tricycles, enough bells for 19 tricycles, enough pedals for 18 tricycles (with one left over), but only enough wheels for 16 tricycles (with one left over).

CHAPTER 9

Electrons in Atoms and the Periodic Table

"Anyone who is not shocked by quantum mechanics has not understood it."

Niels Bohr (1885–1962)

9.1 Blimps, Balloons, and Models of the Atom

▲ The Hindenburg was filled with hydrogen, a reactive and flammable gas. **Question:** What makes hydrogen reactive?

◀ Modern blimps are filled with helium, an inert gas. The nucleus of the helium atom (inset) has two protons, so the neutral helium atom has two electrons—a highly stable configuration. In this chapter we learn about models that explain the inertness of helium and the reactivity of other elements.

You have probably seen one of the Goodyear blimps floating in the sky. A Goodyear blimp is often present at championship sporting events such as the Rose Bowl, the Indy 500, and the U.S. Open golf tournament. It was present at the Statue of Liberty's 100th birthday party and has made appearances in countless movies and television shows. The blimp's inherent stability allows it to provide spectacular views of the world below for television and film.

The Goodyear blimp is similar to a large balloon. Unlike airplanes, which must be moving fast to stay in flight, a blimp or *airship* floats in air because it is filled with a gas that is lighter than air. The Goodyear blimp is filled with helium. Other airships in history, however, have used hydrogen for buoyancy. For example, the Hindenburg—the largest airship ever constructed—was filled with hydrogen, which turned out to be a poor choice. Hydrogen is a reactive and flammable gas. On May 6, 1937, while landing in New Jersey on its first transatlantic crossing, the Hindenburg burst into flames, destroying the airship and killing thirty-six of the ninety-seven passengers. Apparently, as the Hindenburg was landing, a leak in the hydrogen gas ignited, resulting in an explosion that destroyed the ship. (The skin of the Hindenburg, which was constructed of a flammable material, may has also been partially to blame for its demise.)

A similar accident cannot happen to the Goodyear blimp because it is filled with helium, an inert and therefore nonflammable gas. A spark or even a flame would actually be *extinguished* by helium.

Why is helium inert? What is it about helium *atoms* that makes helium *gas* inert? On the other hand, why is hydrogen reactive? Recall from Chapter 5 that elemental hydrogen exists as a diatomic element. Hydrogen atoms are so reactive that they react with each other to form hydrogen molecules. What is it about hydrogen atoms that make them so reactive? What is the difference between hydrogen and helium that accounts for their different reactivities?

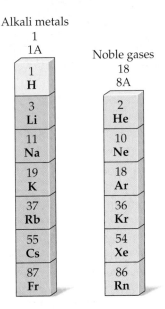

Alkali metals
1
1A

Noble gases
18
8A

The noble gases are chemically inert and the alkali metals are chemically reactive. Why?

The periodic law stated here is a modification of Mendeleev's original formulation. Mendeleev listed elements in order of increasing *mass*; today we list them in order of increasing *atomic number*.

When we examine the properties of hydrogen and helium, we make observations about nature. Mendeleev's periodic law, first discussed in Chapter 4, summarizes the results of many similar observations on the properties of elements:

When the elements are arranged in order of increasing atomic number, certain sets of properties recur periodically.

We know that hydrogen's reactivity recurs with lithium, sodium, and the other Group I metals. We also know that helium's inertness recurs with neon, argon, and the other noble gases. These are critical parts of the scientific method: observing something about nature and formulating a law that summarizes a large number of observations. Now, we need a model or theory that gives the underlying reasons for these observations and laws.

In this chapter, we examine two important models—the **Bohr model** and the **quantum-mechanical model**—that propose explanations for the inertness of helium, the reactivity of hydrogen, and the periodic law. These models explain how electrons exist in atoms and how those electrons affect the chemical and physical properties of elements. We have already learned much about the behavior of elements. We know, for example, that sodium tends to form 1+ ions and that fluorine tends to form 1− ions. We know that some elements are metals and that others are nonmetals. We know that the noble gases are chemically inert and that the alkali metals are chemically reactive. But we do not know *why*. The models in this chapter explain why.

These models were developed in the early 1900s and caused a revolution in the physical sciences, changing our fundamental view of matter at its most basic level. The scientists who devised these models—including Niels Bohr, Erwin Schrödinger, and Albert Einstein—were bewildered by their discoveries. Bohr claimed, "Anyone who is not shocked by quantum mechanics has not understood it." Schrödinger lamented, "I don't like it, and I am sorry I ever had anything to do with it." Einstein disbelieved it, insisting that, "God does not play dice with the universe." However, the quantum-mechanical model has such explanatory power that it is rarely questioned today. It forms the basis of the modern periodic table and our understanding of chemical bonding. Its applications include lasers, computers, and semiconductor devices, and it has given us new ways to design drugs that cure disease. The quantum-mechanical model for the atom is, in many ways, the foundation of modern chemistry.

▲ Niels Bohr (left) and Erwin Schrödinger (right), along with Albert Einstein, played a role in the development of quantum mechanics, yet they were bewildered by their own theory.

9.2 Light: Electromagnetic Radiation

▲ When a water surface is disturbed, waves are created that radiate outward from the site.

The Greek letter *lambda* (λ) is pronounced "lam-duh."

Helpful mnemonic: ROY G BIV—Red, Orange, Yellow, Green, Blue, Indigo, Violet

Before we explore models of the atom, we must understand a few things about light, because the interaction of light with atoms helped to shape these models. Light is familiar to all of us—we see the world by it—but we may not know much about what light is. Unlike most of what we have encountered so far in this book, light is not matter—it has no mass. Light is a form of **electromagnetic radiation**, a type of energy that travels through space at a constant speed of 3.0×10^8 m/s (186,000 mi/s). At this speed, a flash of light generated at the equator would travel around the world in one-seventh of a second. This extremely fast speed is part of the reason that you see a firework in the sky before you hear the sound of its explosion. The light from the exploding firework reaches your eye almost instantaneously. The sound, traveling much slower, takes longer.

Before the advent of quantum mechanics, light was described exclusively as a wave of electromagnetic energy traveling through space. You are probably familiar with water waves (think of the waves created by a rock dropped into a still pond) or you may have created a wave on a rope by moving the end of the rope up and down in a quick motion. In either case, the wave carries energy as it moves through the water or along the rope.

Waves are generally characterized by their **wavelength (λ),** the distance between adjacent wave crests (▼ Figure 9.1). For visible light, wavelength determines color. For example, orange light has a longer wavelength than blue light. White light, as produced by the sun or by a lightbulb, contains a spectrum of wavelengths and therefore a spectrum of color. We can see these colors—red, orange, yellow, green, blue, indigo, and violet—in a rainbow or when white light is passed through a prism (▼ Figure 9.2). Red light, with a wavelength of 750 nm (nanometers), has the longest wavelength of visible light.

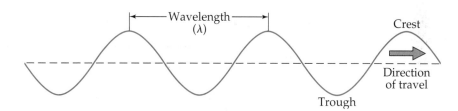

▲ **Figure 9.1 Wavelength** The wavelength of light (λ) is defined as the distance between adjacent wave crests.

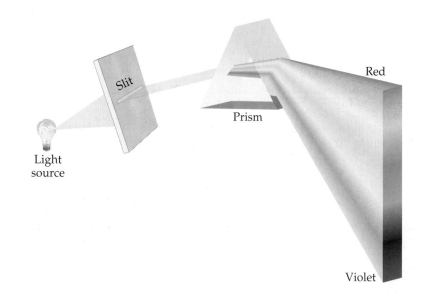

▶ **Figure 9.2 Components of white light** Light is separated into its constituent colors—red, orange, yellow, green, blue, indigo, and violet—when it is passed through a prism.

▲ **Figure 9.3   Color in objects**
A red shirt appears red because it absorbs all colors except red, which it reflects.

The Greek letter *nu* (*v*) is pronounced "noo."

Violet light, with a wavelength of 400 nm, has the shortest ($1 \text{ nm} = 10^{-9} \text{ m}$). The presence of color in white light is responsible for the colors we see in our everyday vision. For example, a red shirt is red because it reflects red light (◄ Figure 9.3). Our eyes see only the reflected light, making the shirt appear red.

Light waves are also often characterized by their **frequency (*v*),** the number of cycles or crests that pass through a stationary point in one second. Wavelength and frequency are inversely related—the shorter the wavelength, the higher the frequency. Blue light, for example, has a higher frequency than red light.

In the early twentieth century, scientists such as Albert Einstein and others discovered that the results of certain experiments could be explained only by describing light not as waves, but as particles. In this description, the light leaving a flashlight, for example, is a stream of particles. A particle of light is called a **photon,** and we can think of a photon as a single packet of light energy. The amount of energy carried in the packet depends on the wavelength of the light—the shorter the wavelength, the greater the energy. Just as water waves carry more energy if their crests are closer together—think about surf pounding a beach—light waves carry more energy if their crests are closer together. Therefore violet light (shorter wavelength) carries more energy per photon than red light (longer wavelength).

To summarize:
- Electromagnetic radiation is a form of energy that travels through space at a constant speed of 3.0×10^8 m/s and exhibits both wavelike and particle-like properties.
- The wavelength of electromagnetic radiation determines the amount of energy carried by one of its photons. The shorter the wavelength, the greater the energy of each photon.
- The frequency and energy of electromagnetic radiation are inversely related to its wavelength.

9.3   The Electromagnetic Spectrum

Electromagnetic radiation ranges in wavelength from 10^{-16} m (gamma rays) to 10^6 m (radio waves). Visible light makes up only a tiny portion of the **electromagnetic spectrum,** which includes all wavelengths of electromagnetic radiation. ▼ Figure 9.4 shows the entire electromagnetic spectrum, with short-wavelength, high-frequency radiation on the right, and long-wavelength, low-frequency radiation on the left. Visible light is only a small sliver in the middle.

▼ **Figure 9.4   The electromagnetic spectrum**

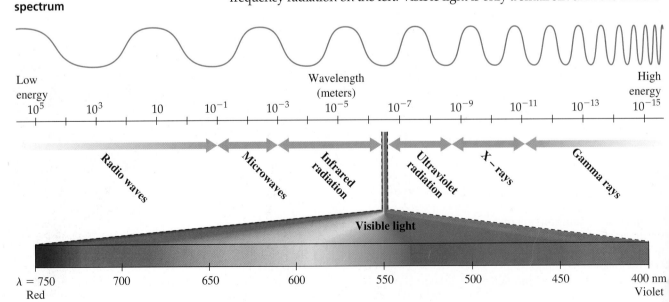

Remember that the energy carried per photon is greater for short wavelengths than for long wavelengths. Therefore, the most energetic photons are those of **gamma rays**, the form of electromagnetic radiation with the shortest wavelength. Gamma rays are produced by the sun, by stars, and by certain unstable atomic nuclei on earth. Human exposure to gamma rays is dangerous because the high energy of gamma-ray photons can damage biological molecules.

Next on the electromagnetic spectrum, at longer wavelengths than gamma rays, are **X-rays**, familiar to us from their medical use. X-rays pass through many substances that block visible light and are therefore used to image internal bones and organs. Like gamma-ray photons, X-ray photons carry enough energy to damage biological molecules. While several yearly exposures to X-rays are relatively harmless, excessive exposure to X-rays increases cancer risk.

Sandwiched between X-rays and visible light in the electromagnetic spectrum is **ultraviolet** or **UV light**, most familiar to us as the component of sunlight that produces a sunburn or suntan. While not as energetic as gamma-ray or X-ray photons, ultraviolet photons still carry enough energy to damage biological molecules. Excessive exposure to ultraviolet light increases the risk of skin cancer and cataracts and causes premature wrinkling of the skin. Next on the spectrum is **visible light**, ranging from violet (shorter wavelength, higher energy) to red (longer wavelength, lower energy). Visible photons do not damage biological molecules. They do, however, cause molecules in our eyes to rearrange and send a signal to our brain that results in vision.

Beyond visible light lies **infrared light**. The heat you feel when you place your hand near a hot object is infrared light. All warm objects, including human bodies, emit infrared light. While infrared light is invisible to our eyes, infrared sensors can detect it and are often used in night-vision technology to "see" in the dark. In the infrared region of the spectrum, warm objects—such as human bodies, for example—glow, much as a lightbulb glows in the visible region of the spectrum.

Beyond infrared light, at longer wavelengths still, are **microwaves**, used for radar and in microwave ovens. Although microwave light has longer wavelengths—and therefore lower energy per photon—than visible or infrared light, it is efficiently absorbed by water and can therefore heat substances that contain water. For this reason substances that contain water, such as food, are warmed when placed in a microwave oven, but substances that do not contain water, such as a plate, are not.

The longest wavelengths are **radio waves**, which are used to transmit the signals used by AM and FM radio, cellular telephones, television, and other forms of communication.

TUTORIAL
The Electromagnetic Spectrum

Some types of dishes contain substances that absorb microwave radiation, but most do not.

Normal photograph

Infrared photograph

▲ Warm objects, such as human or animal bodies, give off infrared light that is easily detected with an infrared camera. In the infrared photograph, the warmest areas appear as red and the coolest as dark blue. (Note that the photo confirms the familiar idea that healthy dogs have cold noses.) (*Source:* Sierra Pacific Innovations. All rights reserved. SPI CORP, www.x20.org)

EXAMPLE 9.1   Wavelength, Energy, and Frequency

Arrange the following three types of electromagnetic radiation—visible light, X-rays, and microwaves—in order of increasing:

(a) wavelength
(b) frequency
(c) energy per photon

(a) wavelength	Solution:
Examine Figure 9.4 to see that X-rays have the shortest wavelength, followed by visible light and then microwaves.	X-rays, visible light, microwaves
(b) frequency	
Since frequency and wavelength are inversely proportional—the longer the wavelength, the shorter the frequency—the ordering with respect to frequency is exactly the reverse of the ordering with respect to wavelength.	microwaves, visible light, X-rays
(c) energy per photon	
Energy per photon decreases with increasing wavelength but increases with increasing frequency; therefore the ordering with respect to energy per photon is the same as frequency.	microwaves, visible light, X-rays

SKILLBUILDER 9.1   Wavelength, Energy, and Frequency

Arrange the following colors of visible light—green, red, and blue—in order of increasing:

(a) wavelength
(b) frequency
(c) energy per photon

Chemistry AND HEALTH

Radiation Treatment for Cancer

X-rays and gamma rays are sometimes called ionizing radiation because the high energy in their photons can ionize atoms and molecules. When ionizing radiation interacts with biological molecules, it can permanently change or even destroy them. Consequently, we normally try to limit our exposure to ionizing radiation. However, doctors can use ionizing radiation to destroy molecules within unwanted cells such as cancer cells.

In radiation therapy (or radiotherapy), doctors aim X-ray or gamma-ray beams at cancerous tumors. The ionizing radiation damages the molecules within the tumor's cells that carry genetic information—information necessary for the cell to grow and divide—and the cell dies or stops dividing. Ionizing radiation also damages molecules within healthy cells; however, cancerous cells divide more quickly than healthy cells, making them more

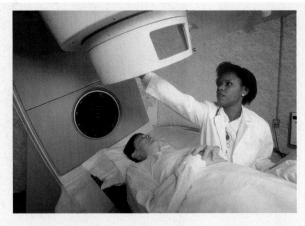

▲ Cancer patient undergoing radiation therapy.

susceptible to genetic damage. Nonetheless, healthy cells are damaged during treatments, resulting in side effects such as fatigue, skin lesions, and hair loss. Doctors try to minimize the exposure of healthy cells by appropriate shielding and by targeting the tumor from multiple directions, minimizing the exposure of healthy cells while maximizing the exposure of cancerous cells (▶ Figure 9.5).

Another side effect of exposing healthy cells to radiation is that they too may become cancerous. So a treatment for cancer may cause cancer. Why do we continue to use it? In radiation therapy, as in most other disease therapies, there is an associated risk. However, we take risks all the time, many for lesser reasons. For example, every time we drive a car, we risk injury or even death. Why? Because we perceive the benefit—such as getting to the grocery store to buy food—to be worth the risk. The situation is similar in cancer therapy or any other therapy for that matter. The benefit of cancer therapy (possibly curing a cancer that will certainly kill you) is worth the risk (a slight increase in the chance of developing a future cancer).

CAN YOU ANSWER THIS? *Why would visible light not work to destroy cancerous tumors?*

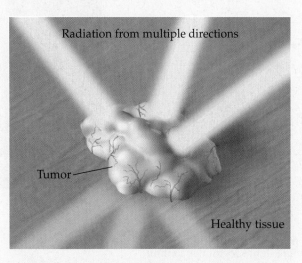

▲ **Figure 9.5 Radiation therapy** By targeting the tumor from various different directions, radiologists minimize damage to healthy tissue.

9.4   The Bohr Model: Atoms with Orbits

▲ **Figure 9.6 A neon sign** Neon atoms inside a glass tube absorb electrical energy and then re-emit the energy as light.

When an atom absorbs energy—in the form of heat, light, or electricity—it often re-emits that energy as light. For example, a neon sign is composed of one or more glass tubes filled with gaseous neon atoms. When an electrical current is passed through the tube, the neon atoms absorb some of the electrical energy and re-emit it as the familiar red light of a neon sign (◀ Figure 9.6). If the atoms in the tube are different, the emitted light is a different color. In other words, atoms of a given element emit light of unique colors (or unique wavelengths). Mercury atoms, for example, emit light that appears blue, and hydrogen atoms emit light that appears pink (▶ Figure 9.7), and helium atoms emit light that appears yellow-orange.

Closer inspection of the light emitted by hydrogen, helium, and neon atoms reveals that each contains several distinct colors or wavelengths. Just as the white light from a lightbulb can be separated into its constituent wavelengths by passing it through a prism, so the light emitted by glowing hydrogen, helium, or neon can also be separated into its constituent wavelengths (▶ Figure 9.8) by passing it through a prism. The result is called an **emission spectrum**. Notice the differences between a white-light spectrum and the emission spectra of hydrogen, helium, and neon. The white-light spectrum is *continuous*, meaning that the light intensity is uninterrupted or smooth across the entire visible range—there is some radiation at all wavelengths, with no gaps. The emission spectra of hydrogen, helium, and neon, however, are not continuous. They consist of bright spots or lines at specific wavelengths with complete darkness in between. Since the emission of light in atoms is related to the motions of electrons within the atoms, a model for how electrons exist in atoms must account for these spectra.

▶ Figure 9.7   **Light emission by different elements**   Light emitted from a mercury lamp (left) appears blue, and light emitted from a hydrogen lamp (right) appears pink.

▶ Figure 9.8   **Emission spectra**
A white-light spectrum is continuous, with some radiation emitted at every wavelength. The emission spectrum of an individual element, however, includes only certain specific wavelengths. (The different wavelengths appear as *lines* because the light from the source passes through a slit before entering the prism.) Each element produces its own unique and distinctive emission spectrum.

Slit

Prism

Photographic film

Hydrogen lamp

White light spectrum

Hydrogen light spectrum

Helium light spectrum

Neon light spectrum

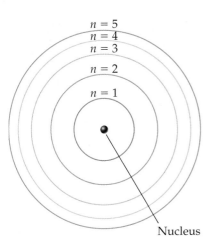

◀ Figure 9.9   **Bohr orbits**

▶ Figure 9.10   **The Bohr energy ladder**   Bohr orbits are like steps on a ladder. It is possible to stand on one step or another, but impossible to stand between steps.

A major challenge in developing a model for electrons in atoms was the discrete or bright-line nature of the emission spectra. Why did atoms, researchers wondered, emit light only at particular wavelengths when excited with energy? Why did they *not* emit a continuous spectrum? Niels Bohr developed a simple model to explain these results. In his model, now called the Bohr model, electrons travel around the nucleus in circular orbits that are similar to planetary orbits around the sun. However, unlike planets revolving around the sun—which can theoretically orbit at any distance whatsoever from the sun—electrons in the Bohr model can orbit only at *specific, fixed* distances from the nucleus (▲ Figure 9.9).

The *energy* of each Bohr orbit, specified by **quantum numbers** $n = 1, 2, 3\ldots$, was also fixed, or **quantized**. Bohr orbits are like steps of a ladder (▲ Figure 9.10), each at a specific distance from the nucleus and each at a specific energy. Just as it is impossible to stand *between steps* on a ladder, so it is impossible for an electron to exist *between orbits* in the Bohr model. An electron in an $n = 3$ orbit, for example, is farther from the nucleus and has more energy than an electron in an $n = 2$ orbit. However, an electron cannot exist at an intermediate distance or energy between the two orbits—the orbits are quantized. As long as an electron remains in a given orbit, it does not absorb or emit light, and its energy remains fixed and constant.

When an atom absorbs energy, an electron in one of these fixed orbits is *excited* or promoted to an orbit that is farther away from the nucleus (◀ Figure 9.11) and therefore higher in energy (this is analogous to moving up a step on the ladder). However, in this new configuration, the atom is less stable, and the electron quickly falls back or *relaxes* to a lower-energy orbit (this is analogous to moving down a step on the ladder). As it does so, it releases a photon of light containing the precise amount of energy—called a **quantum** of energy— that corresponds to the energy difference between the two orbits.

Since the amount of energy in a photon is directly related to its wavelength, the photon has a specific wavelength. Consequently, the light emitted by excited atoms consists of specific lines at certain wavelengths, each corresponding to a specific transition between two orbits. For example, the line at 486 nm in the hydrogen emission spectrum corresponds to an electron relaxing from the $n = 4$ orbit to the $n = 2$ orbit (▶ Figure 9.12). In the same way, the line at 657 nm (longer wavelength and therefore lower energy) corresponds to an electron relaxing from the $n = 3$ orbit to the $n = 2$ orbit. Notice that transitions between orbits that are closer together produce lower-energy (and therefore longer-wavelength) light than transitions between orbits that are farther apart.

The great success of the Bohr model of the atom was that it predicted the lines of the hydrogen emission spectrum. However, it failed to predict the emission spectra of other elements that contained more than one electron. For this, and other reasons, the Bohr model was replaced with a more sophisticated model called the quantum-mechanical or wave-mechanical model.

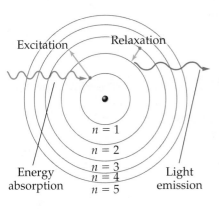

▲ Figure 9.11   **Excitation and emission**   When a hydrogen atom absorbs energy, an electron is excited to a higher-energy orbit. The electron then relaxes back to a lower-energy orbit, emitting a photon of light.

The Bohr model is still important because it provides a logical foundation to the quantum-mechanical model and reveals the historical development of scientific understanding.

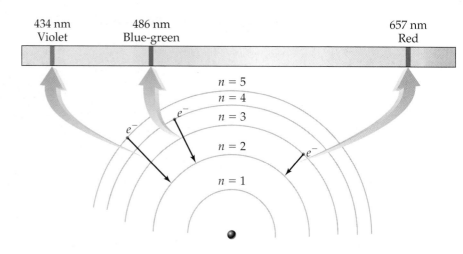

▲ Figure 9.12 **Hydrogen emission lines** The 657-nm line of the hydrogen emission spectrum corresponds to an electron relaxing from the $n = 3$ orbit to the $n = 2$ orbit. The 486-nm line corresponds to an electron relaxing from the $n = 4$ orbit to the $n = 2$ orbit, and the 434-nm line corresponds to an electron relaxing from $n = 5$ to $n = 2$.

To summarize the Bohr model:
- Electrons exist in quantized orbits at specific, fixed energies and specific, fixed distances from the nucleus.
- When energy is put into an atom, electrons are excited to higher-energy orbits.
- When an atom emits light, electrons fall from higher-energy orbits to lower-energy orbits.
- The energy (and therefore the wavelength) of the emitted light corresponds to the difference in energy between the two orbits in the transition. Since these energies are fixed and discrete, the energy (and therefore the wavelength) of the emitted light is fixed and discrete.

CONCEPTUAL CHECKPOINT 9.1

In one transition, an electron in a hydrogen atom falls from the $n = 3$ level to the $n = 2$ level. In a second transition, an electron in a hydrogen atom falls from the $n = 2$ level to the $n = 1$ level. Compared to the radiation emitted by the first of these transitions, the radiation emitted by the second will have:

(a) a lower frequency
(b) a smaller energy per photon
(c) a shorter wavelength
(d) a longer wavelength

9.5   The Quantum-Mechanical Model: Atoms with Orbitals

In the quantum-mechanical model of the atom that has supplanted the Bohr model, orbits are replaced with quantum-mechanical **orbitals**. Orbitals are different from orbits in that they represent, not specific paths that electrons follow, but probability maps that show a statistical distribution of where the electron is likely to be found. This is a nonintuitive property—one that is difficult to visualize—of electrons. A revolutionary concept in quantum mechanics is that electrons *do not* behave like particles flying through space. We cannot, in general, describe their exact paths. An orbital does not represent exactly how

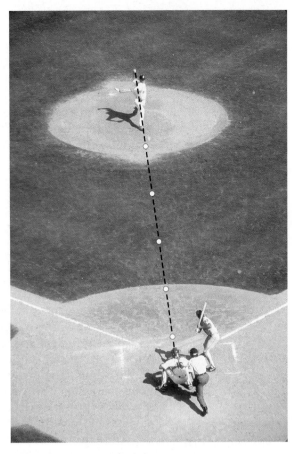

▲ **Figure 9.13** **Baseballs follow predictable paths** A baseball follows a well-defined path as it travels from the pitcher to the catcher.

an electron moves—instead, it is a probability map showing where the electron is likely to be found when the atom is probed.

Baseball Paths and Electron Probability Maps

To understand orbitals, let's contrast the behavior of a baseball with that of an electron. Imagine a baseball thrown from the pitcher's mound to a catcher at home plate (▲ Figure 9.13). The baseball's path can easily be traced as it travels from the pitcher to the catcher. The catcher can watch the baseball as it travels through the air, and she can predict exactly where the baseball will cross over home plate. She can even place her mitt in the correct place to catch it. This would be impossible for an electron. Like photons, electrons exhibit wave–particle duality. This duality leads to behavior that makes it impossible to trace an electron's path. If an electron were "thrown" from the pitcher's mound to home plate, it would land in a different place every time, *even if it were thrown in exactly the same way*. Baseballs have predictable paths—electrons do not.

In the quantum-mechanical world of the electron, the catcher could not know exactly where the electron would cross the plate for any given throw. She would have no way of putting her mitt in the right place to catch it. However, if the catcher kept track of hundreds of electron throws, she could observe a reproducible, statistical pattern of where the electron crosses the plate. She could even draw maps in the strike zone showing the probability of an electron crossing a certain area (◄ Figure 9.14). These maps are called *probability maps*.

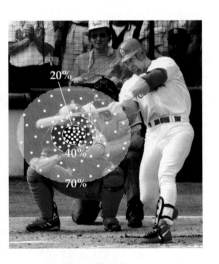

▲ **Figure 9.14** **Electrons are unpredictable** To describe the behavior of a "pitched" electron, you would have to construct a probability map of where it would cross home plate.

From Orbits to Orbitals

In the Bohr model, an *orbit* is a circular path—analogous to a baseball's path—that shows the electron's motion around an atomic nucleus. In the quantum-mechanical model, an *orbital* is a probability map, analogous to the probability map drawn by our catcher. It shows the relative likelihood of the electron being found at various locations when the atom is probed. Just as the Bohr model has different orbits with different radii, the quantum-mechanical model has different orbitals with different shapes.

9.6   Quantum-Mechanical Orbitals

Energy

▲ **Figure 9.15   Principal quantum numbers**   The principal quantum numbers ($n = 1, 2, 3, ...$) determine the energy of the hydrogen quantum-mechanical orbitals.

This analogy is purely hypothetical. It is impossible to photograph electrons in this way.

In the Bohr model of the atom, a single quantum number (n) specifies each orbit. In the quantum-mechanical model, a number and a letter are required to specify an orbital. For example, the lowest-energy orbital in the quantum-mechanical model—analogous to the $n = 1$ orbit in the Bohr model—is called the *1s orbital*. It is specified by the number 1 and the letter s. The number is called the **principal quantum number** (n) and specifies the **principal shell** of the orbital. The higher the principal quantum number, the higher the energy of the orbital. The possible principal quantum numbers are $n = 1, 2, 3...$, with energy increasing as n increases (◀ Figure 9.15). Since the 1s orbital has the lowest possible principal quantum number, it is in the lowest-energy shell and has the lowest possible energy.

The letter indicates the **subshell** of the orbital and specifies its shape. The possible letters are s, p, d, and f, each with a different shape. Orbitals within the s subshell have a spherical shape. Unlike the $n = 1$ Bohr orbit, which shows the electron's path, the 1s quantum-mechanical orbital is a three-dimensional probability map. These probability maps are best represented by dots (◀ Figure 9.16), where the dot density is proportional to the probability of finding the electron.

We can understand these probability maps and dots better with another analogy. Imagine the electron moving randomly around the nucleus. Imagine also taking a photograph of the electron every second for ten or fifteen minutes. One second the electron is very close to the nucleus; the next second it is farther away and so on. Each photo shows a dot representing the electron's position relative to the nucleus at that time. If you took hundreds of photos and superimposed all of them, you would have a probability map like Figure 9.16—a statistical representation of where the electron spends its time. Notice that the dot density for the 1s orbital is greatest near the nucleus and decreases farther away from the nucleus. This means that the electron is more likely to be found close to the nucleus than far away from it.

Orbitals can also be represented as geometric shapes that encompass most of the volume where the electron is likely to be found. For example, the 1s orbital can be represented as a sphere (▼ Figure 9.17) that encompasses the vol-

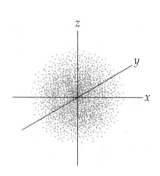

▲ **Figure 9.16   Probability map of the 1s orbital**   The dot density in this plot is proportional to the probability of finding the electron. The greater dot density near the middle represents a higher probability of finding the electron near the nucleus.

▶ **Figure 9.17   Shape representation of the 1s orbital**   Because the distribution of electron density around the nucleus in Figure 9.16 is symmetrical—the same in all directions—we can represent the 1s orbital as a sphere.

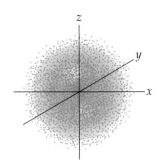

▲ **Figure 9.18 Orbital shape and electron probability for the 1s orbital** The shape representation of the 1s orbital superimposed on the dot density representation. We can see that when the electron is in the 1s orbital, it is most likely to be found within the sphere.

1s

2s

▲ **Figure 9.20 The 2s orbital** The 2s orbital is similar to the 1s orbital, but larger in size.

Shell	# of subshells	Letters specifying subshells			
n = 4	4	s	p	d	f
n = 3	3	s	p	d	
n = 2	2	s	p		
n = 1	1	s			

▲ **Figure 9.19 Subshells** The number of subshells in a given principal shell is equal to the value of n.

ume within which the electron is found 90% of the time. If we superimpose the dot density representation of the 1s orbital on the shape representation (◀ Figure 9.18), we can see that most of the dots are within the sphere, meaning that the electron is most likely to be found within the sphere when it is in the 1s orbital.

The single electron of an undisturbed hydrogen atom at room temperature is in the 1s orbital. This is called the **ground state**, or lowest energy state, of the hydrogen atom. However, like the Bohr model, the quantum-mechanical model allows transitions to higher-energy orbitals upon the absorption of energy. What are these higher-energy orbitals? What do they look like?

The next orbitals are those with principal quantum number n = 2. Unlike the n = 1 principal shell, which contains only one subshell (specified by s), the n = 2 principal shell contains two subshells, specified by s and p.

The number of subshells in a given principal shell is equal to the value of n.

Therefore the n = 1 principal shell has one subshell, the n = 2 principal shell has two subshells, and so on (▲ Figure 9.19). The s subshell contains the 2s orbital, higher in energy than the 1s orbital and slightly larger (◀ Figure 9.20), but otherwise similar in shape. The p subshell contains three 2p orbitals (▼ Figure 9.21), all with the same dumbbell-like shape but with different orientations.

The next principal shell, n = 3, contains three subshells specified by s, p, and d. The s and p subshells contain the 3s and 3p orbitals, similar in shape to the 2s and 2p orbitals, but slightly larger and higher in energy. The d subshell contains the five d orbitals shown in ▶ Figure 9.22. The next principal shell, n = 4, contains four subshells specified by s, p, d, and f. The s, p, and d subshells are similar to those in n = 3. The f subshell contains seven orbitals (called the 4f orbitals), whose shape we do not consider in this book.

As we have already discussed, hydrogen's single electron is usually in the 1s orbital because electrons seek out the lowest-energy orbital available. In hydrogen, the rest of the orbitals are normally empty. However, the absorption of

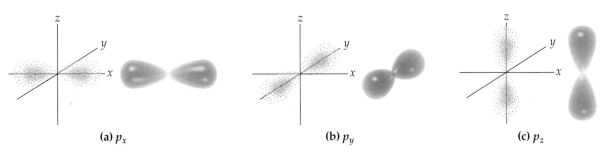

(a) p_x (b) p_y (c) p_z

▲ **Figure 9.21 The 2p orbitals**

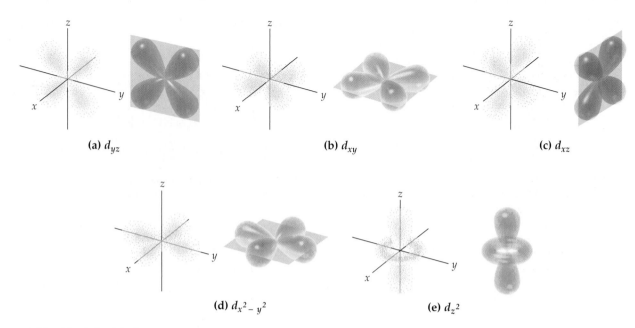

(a) d_{yz}

(b) d_{xy}

(c) d_{xz}

(d) $d_{x^2-y^2}$

(e) d_{z^2}

▲ Figure 9.22   **The 3d orbitals**

energy by a hydrogen atom can cause the electron to jump (or make a transition) from the 1s orbital to a higher-energy orbital. When the electron is in a higher-energy orbital, the hydrogen atom is said to be in an **excited state**.

Because of their higher energy, excited states are unstable, and the electron will usually fall (or relax) back to a lower-energy orbital. In the process the electron emits energy, often in the form of light. As in the Bohr model, the energy difference between the two orbitals involved in the transition determines the wavelength of the emitted light (the greater the energy difference, the shorter the wavelength). The quantum-mechanical model predicts the bright-line spectrum of hydrogen as well as the Bohr model. However, it can also predict the bright-line spectra of other elements as well.

Chemistry AND HEALTH

Magnetic Resonance Imaging

We have just learned that atoms emit radiation of a particular wavelength when one of their electrons makes a transition from a higher-energy orbital to a lower-energy one. The study of these transitions and the associated radiation is called *spectroscopy*. Spectroscopy is an important tool for chemists, allowing them to analyze atoms and molecules by observing how they interact with radiation. Spectroscopy, especially in magnetic resonance imaging or *MRI*, has also become an important tool in medicine.

MRI is based on a type of spectroscopy called *nuclear magnetic resonance* or *NMR spectroscopy*. Unlike the emission spectra discussed earlier, which involve electrons making transitions between energy levels, NMR involves atomic nuclei making transitions between energy levels.

The best way to understand NMR is to think of atomic nuclei as tiny magnets (▶ Figure 9.23). When these magnets are placed in an external magnetic field, they align themselves with this external field to minimize

▲ Figure 9.23   **The nucleus as a magnet**   A nucleus is like a small magnet that aligns itself with an external magnetic field.

their energy (just as the needle of a compass aligns itself with Earth's magnetic field). However, just as the energies of an electron in an atom are quantized, so the energies of nuclei in an external field are quantized—only certain, fixed energies are allowed. These fixed energies correspond to fixed orientations relative to the external magnetic field. In the simplest case, only two orientations are allowed, one lower in energy than the other (▼ Figure 9.24).

Electromagnetic radiation of the correct energy will cause a transition between the two orientations of the nucleus. The energy of the radiation that causes the transition depends on the energy separation between the two orientations, which in turn depends on the strength of the external magnetic field. In normal NMR spectroscopy, a sample is placed in a uniform magnetic field. The wavelength of electromagnetic radiation striking the sample is then varied to find the wavelength or frequency that causes the transition between the two allowed orientations. This frequency is called the *resonance frequency*.

In MRI, the sample is the patient. The nuclei are those of hydrogen atoms within water molecules contained in the patient's tissues. However, instead of putting the patient in a uniform magnetic field, he or she is put in a magnetic field that varies in space. For example, the magnetic field may be strongest on the left side of the patient and weaker on the right. Then the nuclei on the left side of the patient will have a resonance frequency of higher energy than those on the right side. By mapping these resonance frequencies—each resonance frequency corresponding to a different position in space—MRI can obtain a remarkably clear and detailed image of the patient's internal tissues (▼ Figure 9.25).

CAN YOU ANSWER THIS? *Will the wavelength of electromagnetic radiation required to cause a transition in the preceding example (stronger magnetic field on the left side of the person than the right side) be longer or shorter on the left side versus the right? Explain.*

▲ Figure 9.24   **Nuclear energy levels**   The energies of a nucleus in an external magnetic field, which correspond to different orientations, are quantized. Light of the correct energy causes a transition from one orientation to the other.

Higher energy orientation

Transition caused by electromagnetic radiation of the correct energy

Lower energy orientation

Energy

▲ Figure 9.25   **Magnetic resonance imaging**   MRI produces remarkably clear images of a patient's internal tissues.

Electron Configurations: How Electrons Occupy Orbitals

An **electron configuration** simply shows the occupation of orbitals by electrons for a particular atom. For example, the electron configuration for a ground-state hydrogen atom is:

H $1s^1$ ◀—— Number of electrons in orbital

Orbital

The electron configuration tells us that hydrogen's single electron is in the $1s$ orbital.

Another way to represent this information is with an **orbital diagram**, which gives similar information but shows the electrons as arrows in a box representing the orbital. The orbital diagram for a ground-state hydrogen atom is:

H | ↑ |

1s

The box represents the 1s orbital and the arrow within the box represents the electron in the 1s orbital. In orbital diagrams, the direction of the arrow (pointing up or pointing down) represents **electron spin**, a fundamental property of electrons. All electrons have spin. The **Pauli exclusion principle** states that orbitals may hold no more than two electrons with opposing spins. We symbolize this as two arrows pointing in opposite directions ↑↓. Helium atoms, for example, have two electrons. The electron configuration and orbital diagram for helium are:

Electron configuration   **Orbital diagram**

He $1s^2$ | ↑↓ |

1s

Since we know that electrons occupy the lowest-energy orbitals available, and since we know that only two electrons (with opposing spins) are allowed in each orbital, we can continue to build ground-state electron configurations for the rest of the elements as long as we know the energy ordering of the orbitals. ▼ Figure 9.26 shows the energy ordering of a number of orbitals for multi-electron atoms.

Notice that, for multi-electron atoms, the subshells within a principal shell *do not* have the same energy. Thus in elements other than hydrogen, the energy ordering is not determined by the principal quantum number alone. For example, the 4s subshell is lower in energy than the 3d subshell, even though its principal quantum number is higher. Using this relative energy ordering, we can write ground-state electron configurations and orbital diagrams for other elements. For lithium, which has three electrons, the electron configuration and orbital diagram are:

> The subshells within a principal shell do not have the same energy because of electron–electron interactions.

Electron configuration   **Orbital diagram**

Li $1s^22s^1$ | ↑↓ | | ↑ |

1s   2s

> Remember that the number of electrons in an atom is equal to its atomic number.

For carbon, which has six electrons, the electron configuration and orbital diagram are:

Electron configuration   **Orbital diagram**

C $1s^22s^22p^2$ | ↑↓ | | ↑↓ | | ↑ | ↑ | |

1s   2s   2p

▶ **Figure 9.26 Energy ordering of orbitals for multi-electron atoms** Different subshells within the same principal shell have different energies.

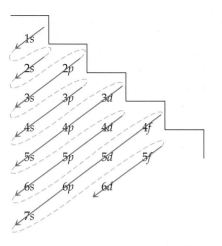

▲ Figure 9.27 Orbital filling order
The arrows indicate the order in
which orbitals fill.

Notice that the 2p electrons occupy the p orbitals (of equal energy) singly, rather than pairing in one orbital. This is a result of **Hund's rule**, which states that when filling orbitals of equal energy, electrons fill them singly first, with parallel spins.

Before we write electron configurations for other elements, let us summarize what we have learned so far:
- Electrons occupy orbitals so as to minimize the energy of the atom; therefore, lower-energy orbitals fill before higher-energy orbitals. Orbitals fill in the following order: 1s 2s 2p 3s 3p 4s 3d 4p 5s 4d 5p 6s (◄ Figure 9.27).
- Orbitals can hold no more than two electrons each. When two electrons occupy the same orbital, they must have opposing spins. This is known as the Pauli exclusion principle.
- When orbitals of identical energy are available, these are first occupied singly with parallel spins rather than in pairs. This is known as Hund's rule.

Consider the electron configurations and orbital diagrams for elements with atomic numbers 3 through 10.

Symbol (#e⁻)	Electron configuration	Orbital diagram
Li (3)	$1s^22s^1$	
Be (4)	$1s^22s^2$	
B (5)	$1s^22s^22p^1$	
C (6)	$1s^22s^22p^2$	
N (7)	$1s^22s^22p^3$	
O (8)	$1s^22s^22p^4$	
F (9)	$1s^22s^22p^5$	
Ne (10)	$1s^22s^22p^6$	

Notice how the p orbitals fill. As a result of Hund's rule, the p orbitals fill with single electrons before they fill with paired electrons. The electron configuration of neon represents the complete filling of the $n = 2$ principal shell. When writing electron configurations for elements beyond neon—or beyond any other noble gas—the electron configuration of the previous noble gas is often abbreviated by the symbol for the noble gas in brackets. For example, the electron configuration of sodium is:

$$\text{Na} \quad 1s^2 2s^2 2p^6 3s^1$$

This can also be written as:

$$\text{Na} \quad [\text{Ne}]3s^1$$

where [Ne] represents $1s^2 2s^2 2p^6$, the electron configuration for neon.

To write an electron configuration for an element, first find its atomic number from the periodic table—this number equals the number of electrons in the neutral atom. Then use the order of filling from Figure 9.26 or 9.27 to distribute the electrons in the appropriate orbitals. Remember that each orbital can hold a maximum of 2 electrons. Consequently:

- the s subshell has only 1 orbital and therefore can hold only 2 electrons.
- the p subshell has 3 orbitals and therefore can hold 6 electrons.
- the d subshell has 5 orbitals and therefore can hold 10 electrons.
- the f subshell has 7 orbitals and therefore can hold 14 electrons.

EXAMPLE 9.2   Electron Configurations

Write electron configurations for each of the following elements.

(a) Mg
(b) S
(c) Ga

(a) Magnesium has 12 electrons. Distribute two of these into the $1s$ orbital, two into the $2s$ orbital, six into the $2p$ orbitals, and two into the $3s$ orbital.

You can also write the electron configuration more compactly using the noble gas core notation. For magnesium, we use [Ne] to represent $1s^2 2s^2 2p^6$.

Solution:

$$\text{Mg} \quad 1s^2 2s^2 2p^6 3s^2$$

$$or$$

$$\text{Mg} \quad [\text{Ne}]3s^2$$

(b) Sulfur has 16 electrons. Distribute two of these into the $1s$ orbital, two into the $2s$ orbital, six into the $2p$ orbitals, two into the $3s$ orbital, and four into the $3p$ orbitals.

You can write the electron configuration more compactly by using [Ne] to represent $1s^2 2s^2 2p^6$.

$$\text{S} \quad 1s^2 2s^2 2p^6 3s^2 3p^4$$

$$or$$

$$\text{S} \quad [\text{Ne}]3s^2 3p^4$$

(c) Gallium has 31 electrons. Distribute two of these into the 1s orbital, two into the 2s orbital, six into the 2p orbitals, two into the 3s orbital, six into the 3p orbitals, two into the 4s orbital, ten into the 3d orbitals, and one into the 4p orbitals. Notice that the d subshell has five orbitals and can therefore hold 10 electrons.

Ga $1s^2 2s^2 2p^6 3s^2 3p^6 4s^2 3d^{10} 4p^1$

or

You can write the electron configuration more compactly by using [Ar] to represent $1s^2 2s^2 2p^6 3s^2 3p^6$.

Ga $[Ar]4s^2 3d^{10} 4p^1$

SKILLBUILDER 9.2   **Electron Configurations**

Write electron configurations for each of the following elements.

(a) Al $^{-13}$
(b) Br - 35
(c) Sr - 38

SKILLBUILDER PLUS

Write electron configurations for each of the following ions.

(a) Al^{3+}
(b) Cl^-
(c) O^{2-}

EXAMPLE 9.3   **Writing Orbital Diagrams**

Write an orbital diagram for silicon.

Solution:
Since silicon is atomic number 14, it has 14 electrons. Draw a box for each orbital, putting the lowest-energy orbital (1s) on the far left and proceeding to orbitals of higher energy to the right.

1s   2s   2p   3s   3p

Distribute the 14 electrons into the orbitals, allowing a maximum of 2 electrons per orbital and remembering Hund's rule. The complete orbital diagram is:

Si $1s$ $2s$ $2p$ $3s$ $3p$

SKILLBUILDER 9.3   **Writing Orbital Diagrams** – 18

• Write an orbital diagram for argon.

CONCEPTUAL CHECKPOINT 9.2

Which of the following pairs of elements have the same *total* number of electrons in p orbitals?

(a) Na and K
(b) K and Kr
(c) P and N
(d) Ar and Ca

9.7   Electron Configurations and the Periodic Table

Valence Electrons

Valence electrons are the electrons in the outermost principal shell (the principal shell with the highest principal quantum number, n). These electrons are important because, as we will see in the next chapter, they are involved in chemical bonding. Electrons that are *not* in the outermost principal shell are called **core electrons**. For example, silicon, with the electron configuration of $1s^2 2s^2 2p^6 3s^2 3p^2$, has 4 valence electrons (those in the $n = 3$ principal shell) and 10 core electrons.

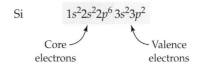

Si $1s^2 2s^2 2p^6\ 3s^2 3p^2$

Core — electrons   Valence — electrons

EXAMPLE 9.4   **Valence Electrons and Core Electrons**

Write an electron configuraton for selenium and identify the valence electrons and the core electrons.

Solution:

Write the electron configuration for selenium by determining the total number of electrons from selenium's atomic number (34) and then distributing them into the appropriate orbitals.

Se $1s^2 2s^2 2p^6 3s^2 3p^6 4s^2 3d^{10} 4p^4$

The valence electrons are those in the outermost principal shell. For selenium, the outermost principal shell is the $n = 4$ shell, which contains 6 electrons (2 in the $4s$ orbital and 4 in the three $4p$ orbitals). All other electrons, including those in the $3d$ orbitals, are core electrons.

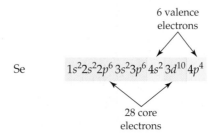

6 valence electrons

Se $1s^2 2s^2 2p^6\ 3s^2 3p^6\ 4s^2\ 3d^{10}\ 4p^4$

28 core electrons

SKILLBUILDER 9.4   **Valence Electrons and Core Electrons**

Write an electron configuration for chlorine and identify the valence electrons and core electrons.

► Figure 9.28 **Outer electron configurations of the first eighteen elements**

1A							8A
1 **H** $1s^1$	2A	3A	4A	5A	6A	7A	2 **He** $1s^2$
3 **Li** $2s^1$	4 **Be** $2s^2$	5 **B** $2s^22p^1$	6 **C** $2s^22p^2$	7 **N** $2s^22p^3$	8 **O** $2s^22p^4$	9 **F** $2s^22p^5$	10 **Ne** $2s^22p^6$
11 **Na** $3s^1$	12 **Mg** $3s^2$	13 **Al** $3s^23p^1$	14 **Si** $3s^23p^2$	15 **P** $3s^23p^3$	16 **S** $3s^23p^4$	17 **Cl** $3s^23p^5$	18 **Ar** $3s^23p^6$

▲ Figure 9.28 shows the first eighteen elements in the periodic table with their outer electron configurations listed below each one. As you move across a row, the orbitals are simply filling in the correct order. As you move down a column, the highest principal quantum number increases, but the number of electrons in each subshell remains the same. Consequently, the elements within a column (or family) all have the same number of valence electrons and similar outer electron configurations.

A similar pattern exists for the entire periodic table (▼ Figure 9.29). Notice that, because of the filling order of orbitals, the periodic table can be divided into blocks representing the filling of particular subshells.

- The first two columns on the left side of the periodic table are the *s* block with outer electron configurations of ns^1 (first column) and ns^2 (second column).
- The six columns on the right side of the periodic table are the *p* block with outer electron configurations of: ns^2np^1, ns^2np^2, ns^2np^3, ns^2np^4, ns^2np^5 (halogens), and ns^2np^6 (noble gases).
- The transition metals are the *d* block.
- The lanthanides and actinides (also called the inner transition metals) are the *f* block.

▲ Figure 9.29 **Outer electron configurations of the elements**

Remember that main-group elements are those in the two far left columns (1A, 2A) and the six far right columns (3A–8A) of the periodic table.

Notice that, except for helium, the number of valence electrons for any main-group element is equal to the group number of its column. For example, we can tell that chlorine has 7 valence electrons because it is in the column with group number 7A. The row number in the periodic table is equal to the number of the highest principal shell (n value). For example, since chlorine is in row 3, its highest principal shell is the $n = 3$ shell.

The transition metals have electron configurations with trends that differ somewhat from main-group elements. As you move across a row in the d block, the d orbitals are filling (Figure 9.29). However, the principal quantum number of the d orbital being filled across each row in the transition series is equal to the row number minus one (in the fourth row, the $3d$ orbitals fill; in the fifth row, the $4d$ orbitals fill; and so on). For the first transition series, the outer configuration is $4s^2 3d^x$ (x = number of d electrons) with two exceptions: Cr is $4s^1 3d^5$ and Cu is $4s^1 3d^{10}$. There is a special stability associated with a half-filled d subshell and a completely filled d subshell that causes these exceptions. Otherwise, the number of outer-shell electrons in a transition series does not change as you move across a period. In other words, *the transition series represents the filling of core orbitals and the number of valence electrons is mostly constant.*

We can now see that the organization of the periodic table allows us to write the electron configuration for any element simply based on its position in the periodic table. For example, suppose we want to write an electron configuration for P. The inner electrons of P are simply those of the noble gas that precedes P in the periodic table, Ne. So we can represent the inner electrons with [Ne]. We obtain the outer electron configuration by tracing the elements between Ne and P and assigning electrons to the appropriate orbitals (◄ Figure 9.30). Remember that the highest n value is given by the row number (3 for phosphorus). So we begin with [Ne], then add in the two $3s$ electrons as we trace across the s block, followed by three $3p$ electrons as we trace across the p block to P, which is in the third column of the p block. The electron configuration is:

$$\text{P} \quad [\text{Ne}]3s^2 3p^3$$

Notice that P is in column 5A and therefore has 5 valence electrons and an outer electron configuration of $ns^2 np^3$.

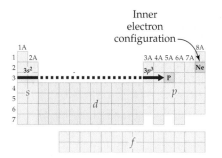

▲ **Figure 9.30   Electron configuration of phosphorus**   Determining the electron configuration for P from its position in the periodic table.

To summarize, follow these steps to write an electron configuration for an element based on its position in the periodic table.

- The inner electron configuration for any element is the electron configuration of the noble gas that immediately precedes that element in the periodic table. Represent the inner configuration with the symbol for the noble gas in brackets.
- The outer electrons can be deduced from the element's position within a particular block (*s*, *p*, *d*, or *f*) in the periodic table. Trace the elements between the preceding noble gas and the element of interest, and assign electrons to the appropriate orbitals.
- The highest principal quantum number (highest *n* value) is equal to the row number of the element in the periodic table.
- For any element containing *d* electrons, the principal quantum number (*n* value) of the outermost *d* electrons is equal to the row number of the element minus 1.

EXAMPLE 9.5	**Writing Electron Configurations from the Periodic Table**

Use the periodic table to write an electron configuration for arsenic.

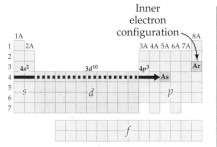

▲ Figure 9.31   **Electron configuration of arsenic**   Determining the electron configuration for As from its position in the periodic table.

Solution:

The noble gas that precedes arsenic in the periodic table is argon, so the inner electron configuration is [Ar]. Obtain the outer electron configuration by tracing the elements between Ar and As and assigning electrons to the appropriate orbitals. Remember that the highest n value is given by the row number (4 for arsenic). So, we begin with [Ar], then add in the two 4s electrons as we trace across the s block, followed by ten 3d electrons as we trace across the d block (the n value for d subshells is equal to the row number minus one), and finally the three 4p electrons as we trace across the p block to As, which is in the third column of the p block (◀ Figure 9.31).

The electron configuration is:

$$\text{As} \qquad [Ar]4s^2 3d^{10} 4p^3$$

SKILLBUILDER 9.5 **Writing Electron Configurations from the Periodic Table**

Use the periodic table to determine the electron configuration for tin.

 CONCEPTUAL CHECKPOINT 9.3

Which element has the *fewest* valence electrons?

(a) B
(b) Ca
(c) V
(d) Cr
(e) Ga

9.8   The Explanatory Power of the Quantum-Mechanical Model

▲ Figure 9.32   **Electron configurations of the noble gases**   The noble gases (except for helium) all have 8 valence electrons and completely full outer principal shells.

At the beginning of this chapter, we learned that the quantum-mechanical model explained the chemical properties of the elements such as the inertness of helium, the reactivity of hydrogen, and the periodic law. We can now see how. *The chemical properties of elements are largely determined by the number of valence electrons they contain.* Their properties vary in a periodic fashion because the number of valence electrons is periodic.

Since elements within a column in the periodic table have the same number of valence electrons, they also have similar chemical properties. The noble gases, for example, all have 8 valence electrons, except for helium, which has 2 (◀ Figure 9.32). Although we don't get into the quantitative (or numerical) aspects of the quantum-mechanical model in this book, calculations show that atoms with 8 valence electrons (or 2 for helium) are particularly low in energy, and therefore stable. Consequently, the noble gases are chemically stable, and thus relatively inert or nonreactive.

Elements with electron configurations close to the noble gases are the most reactive because they can attain noble gas electron configurations by losing or gaining a small number of electrons. Alkali metals (Group 1) are among the most reactive metals since their outer electron configuration (ns^1) is 1 electron beyond a noble gas configuration (▶ Figure 9.33). If they can react to lose the ns^1 electron, they attain a noble gas configuration. This explains why—as we learned in Chapter 4—the Group 1 metals tend to form 1+ cations. As an example, consider the electron configuration of sodium:

$$\text{Na} \qquad 1s^2 2s^2 2p^6 3s^1$$

Alkali
metals
1
1A

| 3 |
| **Li** |
| $2s^1$ |

| 11 |
| **Na** |
| $3s^1$ |

| 19 |
| **K** |
| $4s^1$ |

| 37 |
| **Rb** |
| $5s^1$ |

| 55 |
| **Cs** |
| $6s^1$ |

| 87 |
| **Fr** |
| $7s^1$ |

▲ **Figure 9.33 Electron configurations of the alkali metals** The alkali metals all have ns^1 electron configurations and are therefore 1 electron beyond a noble gas configuration. In their reactions, they tend to lose that electron, forming 1+ ions and attaining a noble gas configuration.

Alkaline earth
metals
2
2A

| 4 |
| **Be** |
| $2s^2$ |

| 12 |
| **Mg** |
| $3s^2$ |

| 20 |
| **Ca** |
| $4s^2$ |

| 38 |
| **Sr** |
| $5s^2$ |

| 56 |
| **Ba** |
| $6s^2$ |

| 88 |
| **Ra** |
| $7s^2$ |

▲ **Figure 9.34 Electron configurations of the alkaline earth metals** The alkaline earth metals all have ns^2 electron configurations and are therefore 2 electrons beyond a noble gas configuration. In their reactions, they tend to lose 2 electrons, forming 2+ ions and attaining a noble gas configuration.

Halogens
17
7A

| 9 |
| **F** |
| $2s^2 2p^5$ |

| 17 |
| **Cl** |
| $3s^2 3p^5$ |

| 35 |
| **Br** |
| $4s^2 4p^5$ |

| 53 |
| **I** |
| $5s^2 5p^5$ |

| 85 |
| **At** |
| $6s^2 6p^5$ |

▲ **Figure 9.35 Electron configurations of the halogens** The halogens all have $ns^2 np^5$ electron configurations and are therefore 1 electron short of a noble gas configuration. In their reactions, they tend to gain 1 electron, forming 1− ions and attaining a noble gas configuration.

Atoms and/or ions that have the same electron configuration are termed *isoelectronic*.

In reactions, sodium loses its $3s$ electron, forming a 1+ ion with the electron configuration of neon.

$$\text{Na}^+ \quad 1s^2 2s^2 2p^6$$
$$\text{Ne} \quad 1s^2 2s^2 2p^6$$

Similarly, alkaline earth metals, with an outer electron configuration of ns^2, also tend to be reactive metals, losing their ns^2 electrons to form 2+ cations (▲ Figure 9.34). For example, consider magnesium:

$$\text{Mg} \quad 1s^2 2s^2 2p^6 3s^2$$

In reactions, magnesium loses its two $3s$ electrons, forming a 2+ ion with the electron configuration of neon.

$$\text{Mg}^{2+} \quad 1s^2 2s^2 2p^6$$

On the other side of the periodic table, halogens are among the most reactive nonmetals because of their $ns^2 np^5$ electron configurations (▲ Figure 9.35). They are only one electron away from a noble gas configuration and tend to react to gain that one electron, forming 1− ions. For example, consider fluorine:

$$\text{F} \quad 1s^2 2s^2 2p^5$$

In reactions, fluorine gains an additional $2p$ electron, forming a 1− ion with the electron configuration of neon.

$$\text{F}^- \quad 1s^2 2s^2 2p^6$$

1	2														3	4	5	6	7	8
Li^+	Be^{2+}																	O^{2-}	F^-	
Na^+	Mg^{2+}														Al^{3+}			S^{2-}	Cl^-	
K^+	Ca^{2+}														Ga^{3+}			Se^{2-}	Br^-	
Rb^+	Sr^{2+}					Transition metals form cations				with various charges					In^{3+}			Te^{2-}	I^-	
Cs^+	Ba^{2+}																			

▲ Figure 9.36 **Elements that form predictable ions**

The elements that form predictable ions are shown in ▲ Figure 9.36 (first introduced in Chapter 4). Notice how the charge of these ions reflects their electron configuration—these elements form ions with noble gas electron configurations.

9.9 Periodic Trends: Atomic Size, Ionization Energy, and Metallic Character

The quantum-mechanical model also explains other periodic trends such as atomic size, ionization energy, and metallic character. We will examine these one at a time.

Atomic Size

The **atomic size** of an atom is determined by how far the outermost electrons are from the nucleus. As we move across a period in the periodic table, we know that electrons are going into orbitals with the same principal quantum number, n. Since the principal quantum number largely determines the size of an orbital, electrons are therefore filling orbitals of approximately the same size, and we might expect atomic size to remain constant across a period. However, with each step across a period, the number of protons in the nucleus is also increasing. This increase in the number of protons results in a greater pull on the electrons, causing atomic size to actually decrease. Therefore:

> As you move across a period, or row, to the right in the periodic table, atomic size decreases, as shown in ▶ Figure 9.37.

As you move down a column in the periodic table, the highest principal quantum number, n, increases. Since the size of an orbital increases with increasing principal quantum number, the electrons that occupy the outermost orbitals are farther from the nucleus as you move down a column. Therefore:

TUTORIAL
Atomic Radii Movie

> As you move down a column, or family, in the periodic table, atomic size increases, as shown in Figure 9.37.

▶ **Figure 9.37 Periodic properties: Atomic size** Atomic size decreases as you move to the right across a period and increases as you move down a column in the periodic table.

Relative atomic sizes of the representative elements

1A							8A
H	2A	3A	4A	5A	6A	7A	He
Li	Be	B	C	N	O	F	Ne
Na	Mg	Al	Si	P	S	Cl	Ar
K	Ca	Ga	Ge	As	Se	Br	Kr
Rb	Sr	In	Sn	Sb	Te	I	Xe
Cs	Ba	Tl	Pb	Bi	Po	At	Rn

Sizes of atoms tend to increase down a column

Sizes of atoms tend to decrease across a period

(a)

(b)

(c)

(d)

EXAMPLE 9.6   Atomic Size

Choose the larger atom from each of the following pairs.

(a) C or O
(b) Li or K
(c) C or Al
(d) Se or I

Solution

(a) C or O

Carbon atoms are larger than O atoms because, as we trace the path between C and O on the periodic table (see margin), we move to the right within the same period. Atomic size decreases as you go to the right.

(b) Li or K

Potassium atoms are larger than Li atoms because, as we trace the path between Li and K on the periodic table (see margin), we move down a column. Atomic size increases as you go down a column.

(c) C or Al

Aluminum atoms are larger than C atoms because, as we trace the path between C and Al on the periodic table (see margin), we move down a column (atomic size increases) and then to the left across a period (atomic size increases). These effects add together for an overall increase.

(d) Se or I

Based on periodic properties alone, we cannot tell which atom is larger, because as we trace the path between Se and I (see margin) we go down a column (atomic size increases) and then to the right across a period (atomic size decreases). These effects tend to cancel one another.

Chemistry AND HEALTH

Pumping Ions: Atomic Size and Nerve Impulses

No matter what you are doing at this moment, tiny pumps in each of the trillions of cells that make up your body are hard at work. These pumps, located in the cell membrane, move a number of different ions into and out of the cell. The most important such ions are sodium (Na^+) and potassium (K^+). However, these ions are pumped in opposite directions. Sodium ions are pumped *out of cells*, while potassium ions are pumped *into cells*. The result is a *chemical gradient* for each ion: The concentration of sodium is higher outside the cell than within, while exactly the opposite is true for potassium.

The ion pumps within the cell membrane are analogous to water pumps in a high-rise building that pump water against the force of gravity to a tank on the roof. Other structures within the membrane, called ion channels, are like the building's faucets. When they open momentarily, bursts of sodium and potassium ions, driven by their concentration gradients, flow back across the membrane—sodium flowing in and potassium flowing out. These ion pulses are the basis for the transmission of nerve signals in the brain, heart, and throughout the body. Consequently, every move you make or every thought you have is mediated by the flow of these ions.

How do the pumps and channels differentiate between sodium and potassium ions? How do the ion pumps selectively move sodium out of the cell and potassium into the cell? To answer this question, we must examine the sodium and potassium ions more closely. In what way do they differ? Both are cations of group I metals. All group I metals tend to lose one electron to form cations with 1+ charge, so that cannot be the decisive factor. But potassium (atomic number 19) lies directly below sodium in the periodic table (atomic number 11), and based on periodic properties is therefore larger than sodium. The potassium ion has a radius of 133 pm while the sodium ion has a radius of 95 pm. (Recall from Chapter 2 that $1 \text{ pm} = 10^{-12}$ m.) The pumps and channels within cell membranes are so sensitive that they can distinguish between the sizes of these two ions and selectively allow only one or the other to pass. The result is the transmission of nerve signals that allows you to read this page.

Na^+ K^+

CAN YOU ANSWER THIS? *Other ions, including calcium and magnesium, are also important to nerve signal transmission. Arrange the following four ions in order of increasing size: K^+, Na^+, Mg^{2+}, and Ca^{2+}.*

SKILLBUILDER 9.6 **Atomic Size**

Choose the larger atom from each of the following pairs.

(a) Pb or Po
(b) Rb or Na
(c) Sn or Bi
(d) F or Se

Ionization Energy

The **ionization energy** of an atom is the energy required to remove an electron from the atom in the gaseous state. For example, the ionization of sodium can be represented with the following equation.

$$Na + \text{Ionization energy} \longrightarrow Na^+ + 1e^-$$

Based on what you know about electron configurations, what would you predict about ionization energy trends? Would it take more or less energy to remove an electron from Na than from Cl? We know that Na has an outer electron configuration of $3s^1$ and Cl has an outer electron configuration of $3s^2 3p^5$. Since removing an electron from sodium gives it a noble gas configuration—and removing an electron from Cl does not—we would expect

Ionization energy increases

▲ Figure 9.38   **Periodic properties: Ionization energy**   Ionization energy increases as you move to the right across a period and decreases as you move down a column in the periodic table.

sodium to have a lower ionization energy, and that is the case. We can generalize this idea in the following statement:

> As you move across a period, or row, to the right in the periodic table, ionization energy increases (▲ Figure 9.38).

What happens to ionization energy as you move down a column? As we have learned, the principal quantum number, n, increases as you move down a column. Within a given subshell, orbitals with higher principal quantum numbers are larger than orbitals with smaller principal quantum numbers. Consequently, electrons in the outermost principal shell are farther away from the positively charged nucleus—and therefore held less tightly—as you move down a column. This results in a lower ionization energy (if the electron is held less tightly, it is easier to pull away) as you move down a column. Therefore:

> As you move down a column, or family, in the periodic table, ionization energy decreases (Figure 9.38).

Notice that the trends in ionization energy are consistent with the trends in atomic size. As an atom gets smaller, it is more difficult to ionize because the electrons are held more tightly. Therefore, as you go across a period, atomic size decreases and ionization energy increases. Similarly, as you go down a column, atomic size increases and ionization energy decreases since electrons are farther from the nucleus and therefore less tightly held.

EXAMPLE 9.7   Ionization Energy

Choose the element with the higher ionization energy from each of the following pairs.

(a) Mg or P
(b) As or Sb
(c) N or Si
(d) O or Cl

(a)

(b)

(c)

(d)

Solution:

(a) Mg or P

P has a higher ionization than Mg because, as we trace the path between Mg and P on the periodic table (see margin), we move to the right within the same period. Ionization energy increases as you go to the right.

(b) As or Sb

As has a higher ionization energy than Sb because, as we trace the path between As and Sb on the periodic table (see margin), we move down a column. Ionization energy decreases as you go down a column.

(c) N or Si

N has a higher ionization energy than Si because, as we trace the path between N and Si on the periodic table (see margin), we move down a column (ionization energy decreases) and then to the left across a period (ionization energy decreases). These effects sum together for an overall decrease.

(d) O or Cl

Based on periodic properties alone, we cannot tell which has a higher ionization energy because, as we trace the path between O and Cl (see margin) we go down a column (ionization energy decreases) and then to the right across a period (ionization energy increases). These effects tend to cancel.

SKILLBUILDER 9.7   Ionization Energy

Choose the element with the higher ionization energy from each of the following pairs.

(a) Mg or Sr
(b) In or Te
(c) C or P
(d) F or S

Metallic Character

As we learned in Chapter 4, metals tend to lose electrons in their chemical reactions, while nonmetals tend to gain electrons. As you move across a period in the periodic table, ionization energy increases, which means that electrons are less likely to be lost in chemical reactions. Consequently:

As you move across a period, or row, to the right in the periodic table, **metallic character** decreases (▼ Figure 9.39).

▶ **Figure 9.39 Periodic properties: metallic character**   Metallic character decreases as you move to the right across a period and increases as you move down a column in the periodic table.

As you move down a column in the periodic table, ionization energy decreases, making electrons more likely to be lost in chemical reactions. Consequently:

As you move down a column, or family, in the periodic table, metallic character increases (Figure 9.39).

TUTORIAL
Interactive Periodic Table

These trends, based on the quantum-mechanical model, explain the distribution of metals and nonmetals that we learned in Chapter 4. Metals are found toward the left side of the periodic table and nonmetals (with the exception of hydrogen) toward the upper right.

EXAMPLE 9.8   Metallic Character

Choose the more metallic element from each of the following pairs.

(a) Sn or Te

(b) Si or Sn

(c) Br or Te

(d) Se or I

(a)

(b)

(c)

Solution:

(a) Sn or Te

Sn is more metallic than Te because, as we trace the path between Sn and Te on the periodic table (see margin), we move to the right within the same period. Metallic character decreases as you go to the right.

(b) Si or Sn

Sn is more metallic than Si because, as we trace the path between Si and Sn on the periodic table (see margin), we move down a column. Metallic character increases as you go down a column.

(c) Br or Te

Te is more metallic than Br because, as we trace the path between Br and Te on the periodic table (see margin), we move down a column (metallic character increases) and then to the left across a period (metallic character increases). These effects add together for an overall increase.

(d) Se or I

Based on periodic properties alone, we cannot tell which is more metallic because as we trace the path between Se and I (see margin), we go down a column (metallic character increases) and then to the right across a period (metallic character decreases). These effects tend to cancel.

SKILLBUILDER 9.8   Metallic Character

Choose the more metallic element from each of the following pairs.

(a) Ge or In

(b) Ga or Sn

(c) P or Bi

(d) B or N

(d)

CHAPTER IN REVIEW

Chemical Principles

Relevance

Light: Light is electromagnetic radiation, a kind of energy that travels through space at a constant speed of 3.0×10^8 m/s (186,000 mi/s) and exhibits both wavelike and particle-like behavior. Particles of light are called photons. The wave nature of light is characterized by its wavelength, the distance between adjacent crests in the wave. The wavelength of light is inversely proportional to both the frequency—the number of cycles that pass a stationary point in one second—and the energy of a photon. Electromagnetic radiation ranges in wavelength from 10^{-16} m (gamma rays) to 10^6 m (radio waves). In between these lie X-rays, ultraviolet light, visible light, infrared light, and microwaves.

Light: Light enables us to see the world. However, we see only visible light, a small sliver in the center of the electromagnetic spectrum. Other forms of electromagnetic radiation are used for cancer therapy, X-ray imaging, night vision, microwave cooking, and communications. Light is also important to many chemical problems. We can learn about the electronic structure of atoms, for example, by examining their interaction with light.

The Bohr Model: The emission spectrum of hydrogen, consisting of bright lines at specific wavelengths, can be explained by the Bohr model for the hydrogen atom. In this model, electrons occupy circular orbits at specific fixed distances from the nucleus. Each orbit is specified by a quantum number (n), which also specifies the orbit's energy. While an electron is in a given orbit, its energy remains constant. When it jumps between orbits, a quantum of energy is absorbed or emitted. Since the difference in energy between orbits is fixed, the energy emitted or absorbed is also fixed. Emitted energy is carried away by a photon of specific wavelength.

The Bohr Model: The Bohr model was a first attempt to explain the bright-line spectra of atoms. While it did predict the spectrum of the hydrogen atom, it failed at predicting the spectra of other atoms. Consequently, it was replaced by the quantum-mechanical model.

The Quantum-Mechanical Model: The quantum-mechanical model for the atom replaces orbits with orbitals, which are electron probability maps. Orbitals show the relative probability of the electron's being found in various places when the atom is probed. Orbitals are specified with a number (n), called the principal quantum number, and a letter. The principal quantum number, which must be an integer ($1, 2, 3 \ldots$), specifies the principal shell, and the letter (s, p, d, or f) specifies the subshell of the orbital. In the hydrogen atom, the energy of orbitals depends only on n. In multi-electron atoms, the energy ordering is $1s$ $2s$ $2p$ $3s$ $3p$ $4s$ $3d$ $4p$ $5s$ $4d$ $5p$ $6s$.

An electron configuration shows the occupation of orbitals for a particular atom. These are written by filling the orbitals in order of increasing energy while keeping in mind the Pauli exclusion principle (each orbital can hold a maximum of two electrons with opposing spins) and Hund's rule (electrons occupy orbitals of identical energy singly before pairing).

The Quantum-Mechanical Model: The quantum-mechanical model changed the way we view nature. Before the quantum-mechanical model, electrons were viewed as small particles, much like any other particle. Electrons were supposed to follow the normal laws of motion, just as a baseball does. However, the electron, with its wavelike properties, does not follow these laws. Instead, electron motion is describable only through probabilistic predictions. Quantum theory single-handedly changed the predictability of nature at its most fundamental level.

The quantum-mechanical model of the atom predicts and explains many of the chemical properties we have learned in earlier chapters.

The Periodic Table: Elements within the same column of the periodic table have similar outer electron configurations and the same number of valence electrons (electrons in the outermost principal shell). Consequently, they have similar chemical properties. The periodic table is divisible into blocks (s block, p block, d block, and f block) in which particular sublevels are filled. As you move across a period to the right in the periodic table, atomic size decreases, ionization energy increases, and metallic character decreases. As you move down a column in the periodic table, atomic size increases, ionization energy decreases, and metallic character increases.

The Periodic Table: The periodic law exists because the number of valence electrons is periodic, and valence electrons determine chemical properties. Quantum theory also predicts that atoms with 8 outer shell electrons (or 2 for helium) are particularly stable, thus explaining the inertness of the noble gases. Atoms without noble gas configurations undergo chemical reactions to attain them, explaining the reactivity of the alkali metals and the halogens as well as the tendency of several families to form ions with certain charges.

Chemical Skills

Examples

Predicting Relative Wavelength, Energy, and Frequency of Light (Section 9.3)

EXAMPLE 9.9   Predicting Relative Wavelength, Energy, and Frequency of Light

Which of the following types of light—infrared or ultraviolet—has the longer wavelength? Higher frequency? Higher energy per photon?

Solution:
Infrared light has the longer wavelength (Figure 9.4). Ultraviolet light has the higher frequency and the higher energy per photon.

- Relative wavelengths can be obtained from Figure 9.4.
- Energy per photon increases with decreasing (shorter) wavelength.
- Frequency increases with decreasing (shorter) wavelength.

Writing Electron Configurations and Orbital Diagrams (Sections 9.6, 9.7)

LIVE EXAMPLE

EXAMPLE 9.10   Writing Electron Configurations and Orbital Diagrams

Write an electron configuration and orbital diagram (outer electrons only) for germanium.

Solution:
Germanium is atomic number number 32; therefore, it has 32 electrons.

To write electron configurations, determine the number of electrons in the atom from the element's atomic number and then follow these rules:

Electron Configuration

- Electrons occupy orbitals so as to minimize the energy of the atom; therefore, lower-energy orbitals fill before higher-energy orbitals. Orbitals fill in the following order: $1s\ 2s\ 2p\ 3s\ 3p\ 4s\ 3d\ 4p\ 5s\ 4d\ 5p\ 6s$ (Figure 9.27). The s subshells hold up to 2 electrons, p subshells hold up to 6, d subshells hold up to 10, and f subshells hold up to 14.

Ge $1s^2 2s^2 2p^6 3s^2 3p^6 4s^2 3d^{10} 4p^2$

or

Ge $[Ar]4s^2 3d^{10} 4p^2$

- Orbitals can hold no more than 2 electrons each. When 2 electrons occupy the same orbital, they must have opposing spins.
- When orbitals of identical energy are available, these are first occupied singly with parallel spins rather than in pairs.

Orbital Diagram (Outer Electrons)

$\uparrow\downarrow$		$\uparrow\downarrow$	$\uparrow\downarrow$	$\uparrow\downarrow$	$\uparrow\downarrow$	$\uparrow\downarrow$		$\uparrow$	$\uparrow$	

$4s$ $3d$ $4p$

Key Terms

atomic size [9.9]
Bohr model [9.1]
core electrons [9.7]
electromagnetic
   radiation [9.2]
electromagnetic
   spectrum [9.3]
electron
   configuration [9.6]
electron spin [9.6]
emission spectrum [9.4]
excited state [9.4]

frequency (ν) [9.2]
gamma rays [9.3]
ground state [9.6]
Hund's rule [9.6]
infrared light [9.3]
ionization energy [9.9]
metallic character [9.9]
microwaves [9.3]
orbital diagram [9.6]
orbitals [9.5]
Pauli exclusion
   principle [9.6]

photon [9.2]
principal quantum
   number [9.6]
principal shell [9.6]
quantized [9.4]
quantum (plural,
   quanta) [9.4]
quantum-mechanical
   model [9.1]
quantum numbers [9.4]
radio waves [9.3]
subshell [9.6]

ultraviolet (UV) light [9.3]
valence electrons [9.7]
visible light [9.3]
wavelength (λ) [9.2]
X-rays [9.3]

Exercises

Questions

1. When were the Bohr model and the quantum-mechanical model for the atom developed? What is their purpose?
2. What is light?
3. How fast does light travel? What are some examples of its fast speed?
4. What is white light? Colored light?
5. Explain, in terms of absorbed and reflected light, why a blue object appears blue.
6. What is the relationship between the wavelength of light and the amount of energy carried by its photons?
7. How are wavelength and frequency related?
8. What produces gamma rays?
9. How are X-rays used?
10. Why should excess exposure to gamma rays and X-rays be avoided?
11. Why should excess exposure to ultraviolet light be avoided?
12. What objects emit infrared light? What technology exploits this?
13. Why do microwave ovens heat food but seldom heat the dish the food is on?
14. What type of electromagnetic radiation is used in communications devices such as cellular telephones?
15. Describe the Bohr model for the hydrogen atom.
16. What is an emission spectrum? Use the Bohr model to explain why the emission spectra of atoms consist of distinct lines at specific wavelengths.
17. Explain the difference between a Bohr orbit and a quantum-mechanical orbital.
18. What is the difference between the ground state of an atom and an excited state of an atom?
19. Explain how the motion of an electron is different from the motion of a baseball. What is a probability map?

20. Explain why quantum-mechanical orbitals have "fuzzy" boundaries.
21. List the four possible subshells in the quantum-mechanical model, the number of orbitals in each subshell, and the maximum number of electrons that can be contained in each subshell.
22. List all of the quantum-mechanical orbitals, in the correct energy order for atoms other than hydrogen, through $5s$.
23. What is the Pauli exclusion principle? Why is it important when writing electron configurations?
24. What is Hund's rule? Why is it important when writing orbital diagrams?
25. Within an electron configuration, what do symbols such as [Ne] and [Kr] represent?
26. Explain the difference between valence electrons and core electrons.
27. Identify each block in the following blank periodic table.
   (a) s block
   (b) p block
   (c) d block
   (d) f block

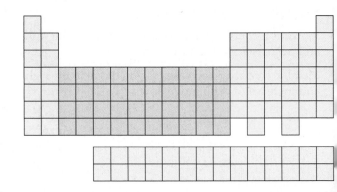

28. Give some examples of the explanatory power of the quantum-mechanical model.
29. Explain why Group 1 elements tend to form 1+ ions and Group 7 elements tend to form 1− ions.

30. Explain the periodic trends in each of the following:
    (a) ionization energy
    (b) atomic size
    (c) metallic character

Problems

Wavelength, Energy, and Frequency of Electromagnetic Radiation

31. Which one of these types of electromagnetic radiation has the longest wavelength?
    (a) visible
    (b) ultraviolet
    (c) infrared
    (d) X-ray

32. Which one of these types of electromagnetic radiation has the shortest wavelength?
    (a) radio waves
    (b) microwaves
    (c) infrared
    (d) ultraviolet

33. Write the following types of electromagnetic radiation in order of increasing energy per photon.
    (a) radio waves
    (b) microwaves
    (c) infrared
    (d) ultraviolet

34. Write the following types of electromagnetic radiation in order of decreasing energy per photon.
    (a) gamma rays
    (b) radio waves
    (c) microwaves
    (d) visible light

35. List two types of electromagnetic radiation with frequencies higher than visible light.

36. List two types of electromagnetic radiation with frequencies lower than infrared light.

37. List the following three types of radiation—X-rays, gamma rays, and microwaves—in order of:
    (a) increasing energy per photon
    (b) increasing frequency
    (c) increasing wavelength

38. List the following three types of electromagnetic radiation—visible, infrared, and radio waves—in order of:
    (a) decreasing energy per photon
    (b) decreasing frequency
    (c) decreasing wavelength

The Bohr Model

39. Bohr orbits have fixed _____ and fixed _____.

40. In the Bohr model, what happens when an electron makes transitions between orbits?

41. Two of the emission wavelengths in the hydrogen emission spectrum are 410 nm and 434 nm. One of these is due to the $n = 6$ to $n = 2$ transition and the other is due to the $n = 5$ to $n = 2$ transition. Which wavelength goes with which transition?

42. Two of the emission wavelengths in the hydrogen emission spectrum are 656 nm and 486 nm. One of these is due to the $n = 4$ to $n = 2$ transition and the other is due to the $n = 3$ to $n = 2$ transition. Which wavelength goes with which transition?

The Quantum-Mechanical Model

43. Make a sketch of the $1s$ and $2p$ orbitals. How would the $2s$ and $3p$ orbitals differ from the $1s$ and $2p$ orbitals?

44. Make a sketch of the $3d$ orbitals. How would the $4d$ orbitals differ from the $3d$ orbitals?

45. Which electron is, on average, closer to the nucleus: an electron in a $2s$ orbital or an electron in a $3s$ orbital?

46. Which electron is, on average, farther from the nucleus: an electron in a $3p$ orbital or an electron in a $4p$ orbital?

47. According to the quantum-mechanical model for the hydrogen atom, which of the following electron transitions would produce light with longer wavelength: $2p$ to $1s$ or $3p$ to $1s$?

48. According to the quantum-mechanical model for the hydrogen atom, which of the following transitions would produce light with longer wavelength: $3p$ to $2s$ or $4p$ to $2s$?

Electron Configurations

49. Write full electron configurations for each of the following elements.
(a) C
(b) Na
(c) Ar
(d) Si

50. Write full electron configurations for each of the following elements.
(a) N
(b) S
(c) Ne
(d) K

51. Write full orbital diagrams for each of the following elements and indicate the number of unpaired electrons in each.
(a) Be
(b) C
(c) F
(d) Ne

52. Write full orbital diagrams for each of the following elements and indicate the number of unpaired electrons in each.
(a) B
(b) N
(c) Li
(d) He

53. Write electron configurations for each of the following elements. Use the symbol of the previous noble gas in brackets to represent the core electrons.
(a) Ga
(b) As
(c) Rb
(d) Sn

54. Write electron configurations for each of the following elements. Use the symbol of the previous noble gas in brackets to represent the core electrons.
(a) Te
(b) Br
(c) I
(d) Cs

55. Write electron configurations for each of the following transition metals.
(a) Ti
(b) V
(c) Cr
(d) Mn

56. Write electron configurations for each of the following transition metals.
(a) Co
(b) Ni
(c) Cu
(d) Zn

Valence Electrons and Core Electrons

57. Write full electron configurations for each of the following elements and indicate the valence electrons and the core electrons.
(a) B
(b) N
(c) Sb
(d) K

58. Write full electron configurations for each of the following elements and indicate the valence electrons and the core electrons.
(a) Sr
(b) Cl
(c) Kr
(d) Ge

59. Write orbital diagrams for the valence electrons of each of the following elements and indicate the number of unpaired electrons in each.
(a) Si
(b) Ca
(c) Cl
(d) Ar

60. Write orbital diagrams for the valence electrons of each of the following elements and indicate the number of unpaired electrons in each.
(a) Ga
(b) K
(c) Kr
(d) Br

61. How many valence electrons are in each of the following:
(a) O
(b) S
(c) Br
(d) Rb

62. How many valence electrons are in each of the following:
(a) Ba
(b) Al
(c) Be
(d) Se

Electron Configurations and the Periodic Table

63. Give the outer electron configuration for each of the following columns in the periodic table.
    (a) 1A
    (b) 2A
    (c) 5A
    (d) 7A

64. Give the outer electron configuration for each of the following columns in the periodic table.
    (a) 3A
    (b) 4A
    (c) 6A
    (d) 8A

65. Use the periodic table to write electron configurations for each of the following elements.
    (a) Al
    (b) Be
    (c) In
    (d) Zr

66. Use the periodic table to write electron configurations for each of the following elements.
    (a) Xe
    (b) Sc
    (c) Zr
    (d) Ba

67. Use the periodic table to write electron configurations for each of the following elements.
    (a) As
    (b) Ba
    (c) Ni
    (d) Bi

68. Use the periodic table to write electron configurations for each of the following elements.
    (a) Se
    (b) Sn
    (c) Pb
    (d) Cd

69. How many $2p$ electrons are in each of the following elements?
    (a) C
    (b) N
    (c) F
    (d) P

70. How many $3d$ electrons are in each of the following elements?
    (a) Fe
    (b) Zn
    (c) K
    (d) As

71. Give the number of elements in periods 1 and 2 of the periodic table. Explain why they are different.

72. Give the number of elements in periods 3 and 4 of the periodic table. Explain why they are different.

73. Name an element in the third period (row) of the periodic table with:
    (a) 3 valence electrons
    (b) a total of 4 $3p$ electrons
    (c) 6 $3p$ electrons
    (d) 2 $3s$ electrons and no $3p$ electrons

74. Name an element in the fourth period of the periodic table with:
    (a) 5 valence electrons
    (b) a total of 4 $4p$ electrons
    (c) a total of 3 $3d$ electrons
    (d) a complete outer shell

75. Use the periodic table to identify the element with the following electron configuration.
    (a) $[Ne]3s^2 3p^5$
    (b) $[Ar]4s^2 3d^{10} 4p^1$
    (c) $[Ar]4s^2 3d^6$
    (d) $[Kr]5s^1$

76. Use the periodic table to identify the element with the following electron configuration.
    (a) $[Ne]3s^1$
    (b) $[Kr]5s^2 4d^{10}$
    (c) $[Xe]6s^2$
    (d) $[Kr]5s^2 4d^{10} 5p^3$

Periodic Trends

77. Choose the element with the higher ionization energy from each of the following pairs.
    (a) Na or Rb
    (b) Ga or Ge
    (c) P or I
    (d) P or Sn

78. Choose the element with the higher ionization energy from each of the following pairs.
    (a) As or At
    (b) Br or Bi
    (c) Si or Cl
    (d) P or Sb

79. Arrange the following elements in order of increasing ionization energy: Te, Pb, Cl, S, Sn

80. Arrange the following elements in order of increasing ionization energy: Ga, In, F, Si, N

81. Choose the element with the larger atoms from each of the following pairs.
(a) Al or In
(b) Si or N
(c) P or Pb
(d) C or F

82. Choose the element with the larger atoms from each of the following pairs.
(a) Sn or Si
(b) Br or Ga
(c) Sn or Bi
(d) Se or Sn

83. Arrange the following elements in order of increasing atomic size: Ca, Rb, S, Si, Ge, F

84. Arrange the following elements in order of increasing atomic size: Cs, Sb, S, Pb, Se

85. Choose the more metallic element from each of the following pairs.
(a) Sr or Sb
(b) As or Bi
(c) Cl or O
(d) S or As

86. Choose the more metallic element from each of the following pairs.
(a) Sb or Pb
(b) K or Ge
(c) Ge or Sb
(d) As or Sn

87. Arrange the following elements in order of increasing metallic character: Fr, Sb, In, S, Ba, Se

88. Arrange the following elements in order of increasing metallic character: Sr, N, Si, P, Ga, Al

Cumulative Problems

89. What is the maximum number of electrons that can occupy the $n = 3$ quantum shell?

90. What is the maximum number of electrons that can occupy the $n = 4$ quantum shell?

91. Use the electron configurations of the alkali metals to explain why they tend to form 1+ ions.

92. Use the electron configurations of the halogens to explain why they tend to form 1− ions.

93. Write electron configurations for each of the following ions.
(a) Ca^{2+}
(b) K^+
(c) S^{2-}
(d) Br^-

94. Write electron configurations for each of the following ions.
(a) F^-
(b) P^{3-}
(c) Li^+
(d) Al^{3+}

95. Examine Figure 4.12, which shows the division of the periodic table into metals, nonmetals, and metalloids. Use what you know about electron configurations to explain these divisions.

96. Examine Figure 4.14, which shows the elements that form predictable ions. Use what you know about electron configurations to explain these trends.

97. Explain what is wrong with each of the following electron configurations and write the correct configuration based on the number of electrons.
    (a) $1s^3 2s^3 2p^9$
    (b) $1s^2 2s^2 2p^6 2d^4$
    (c) $1s^2 1p^5$
    (d) $1s^2 2s^2 2p^8 3s^2 3p^1$

98. Explain what is wrong with each of the following electron configurations and write the correct configuration based on the number of electrons.
    (a) $1s^4 2s^4 2p^{12}$
    (b) $1s^2 2s^2 2p^6 3s^2 3p^6 3d^{10}$
    (c) $1s^2 2p^6 3s^2$
    (d) $1s^2 2s^2 2p^6 3s^2 3p^6 4s^2 4d^{10} 4p^3$

99. Bromine is a highly reactive liquid while krypton is an inert gas. Explain the difference based on their electron configurations.

100. Potassium is a highly reactive metal while argon is an inert gas. Explain the difference based on their electron configurations.

101. Based on periodic trends, which one of the following elements do you expect to be most easily oxidized: Ge, K, S, or N?

102. Based on periodic trends, which one of the following elements do you expect to be most easily reduced: Ca, Sr, P, or Cl?

103. When an electron makes a transition from the $n = 3$ to the $n = 2$ hydrogen atom Bohr orbit, the energy difference between these two orbits (3.0×10^{-19} J) is given off in a photon of light. The relationship between the energy of a photon and its wavelength is given by $E = hc/\lambda$, where E is the energy of the photon in J, h is Planck's constant (6.626×10^{-34} J·s), and c is the speed of light (3.00×10^8 m/s). Find the wavelength of light emitted by hydrogen atoms when an electron makes this transition.

104. When an electron makes a transition from the $n = 4$ to the $n = 2$ hydrogen atom Bohr orbit, the energy difference between these two orbits (4.1×10^{-19} J) is given off in a photon of light. The relationship between the energy of a photon and its wavelength is given by $E = hc/\lambda$, where E is the energy of the photon in J, h is Planck's constant (6.626×10^{-34} J·s), and c is the speed of light (3.00×10^8 m/s). Find the wavelength of light emitted by hydrogen atoms when an electron makes this transition.

105. The distance from the sun to Earth is 1.496×10^8 km. How long does it take light to travel from the sun to Earth?

106. The nearest star is Alpha Centauri, at a distance of 4.3 light-years from Earth. A light-year is the distance that light travels in one year (365 days). How far away, in kilometers, is Alpha Centauri from Earth?

107. In the beginning of this chapter, we learned that the quantum-mechanical model for the atom is the foundation for modern chemical understanding. Explain why this is so.

108. Niels Bohr said, "Anyone who is not shocked by quantum mechanics has not understood it." What did he mean by this?

109. The wave nature of matter was first proposed by Louis de Broglie, who suggested that the wavelength (λ) of a particle was related to its mass (m) and its velocity (v) by the following equation: $\lambda = h/mv$, where h is Planck's constant (6.626×10^{-34} J·s). Calculate the de Broglie wavelength of each of the following: (a) a 0.0459-kg golf ball traveling at 95 m/s; (b) an electron traveling at 3.88×10^6 m/s. Can you explain why the wave nature of matter is significant for the electron, but not for the golf ball? (Hint: Express mass in kilograms.)

110. The particle nature of light was first proposed by Albert Einstein, who suggested that light could be described as a stream of particles called photons. A photon of wavelength λ has an energy (E) given by the following equation: $E = hc/\lambda$, where E is the energy of the photon in J, h is Planck's constant (6.626×10^{-34} J·s), and c is the speed of light (3.00×10^8 m/s). Calculate the energy of 1 mol of photons with a wavelength of 632 nm.

Highlight Problems

111. Excessive exposure to sunlight increases the risk of skin cancer because some of the photons have enough energy to break chemical bonds in biological molecules. These bonds require approximately 250–800 kJ/mol of energy to break. The energy of a single photon is given by $E = hc/\lambda$, where E is the energy of the photon in J, h is Planck's constant $(6.626 \times 10^{-34}\,\text{J} \cdot \text{s})$, and c is the speed of light $(3.00 \times 10^8\,\text{m/s})$. Determine which of the following kinds of light contain enough energy to break chemical bonds in biological molecules by calculating the total energy in 1 mol of photons for light of each wavelength.

    (a) infrared light (1500 nm)
    (b) visible light (500 nm)
    (c) ultraviolet light (150 nm)

112. The quantum-mechanical model, besides revolutionizing chemistry, shook the philosophical world because of its implications regarding determinism. Determinism is the idea that the outcomes of future events are determined by preceding events. The trajectory of a baseball, for example, is deterministic; that is, its trajectory—and therefore its landing place—is determined by its position, speed, and direction of travel. Before quantum mechanics, most scientists thought that fundamental particles—such as electrons and protons—also behaved deterministically. The implication of this was that the entire universe must behave deterministically—its future must be determined by preceding events. Quantum mechanics challenged this reasoning because fundamental particles did not behave deterministically—their future paths were not determined by preceding events. Some scientists struggled with this idea. Einstein himself refused to believe it, stating, "God does not play dice with the universe." Explain what Einstein meant by this statement.

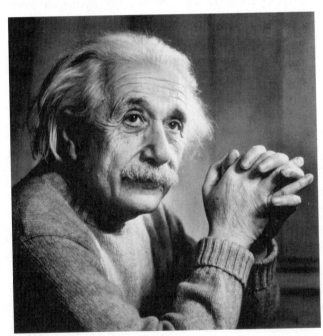

▲ "God does not play dice with the universe."

Answers to Skillbuilder Exercises

Skillbuilder 9.1   **(a)** blue, green, red   **(b)** red, green, blue   **(c)** red, green, blue

Skillbuilder 9.2   **(a)** Al $1s^22s^22p^63s^23p^1$ or $[Ne]3s^23p^1$

(b) Br $1s^22s^22p^63s^23p^64s^23d^{10}4p^5$ or $[Ar]4s^23d^{10}4p^5$

(c) Sr $1s^22s^22p^63s^23p^64s^23d^{10}4p^65s^2$ or $[Kr]5s^2$

Skillbuilder Plus, p. 281   Subtract 1 electron for each unit of positive charge. Add 1 electron for each unit of negative charge.

(a) Al^{3+} $1s^22s^22p^6$

(b) Cl^- $1s^22s^22p^63s^23p^6$

(c) O^{2-} $1s^22s^22p^6$

Skillbuilder 9.3

Ar

   1s   2s   2p   3s   3p

Skillbuilder 9.4

Cl $1s^22s^22p^6\ 3s^23p^5$

10 core electrons   7 valence electrons

Skillbuilder 9.5 $[Kr]5s^24d^{10}5p^2$

Skillbuilder 9.6   **(a)** Pb   **(b)** Rb   **(c)** cannot tell based on periodic properties   **(d)** Se

Skillbuilder 9.7   **(a)** Mg   **(b)** Te   **(c)** cannot tell based on periodic properties   **(d)** F

Skillbuilder 9.8   **(a)** In   **(b)** cannot tell based on periodic properties   **(c)** Bi   **(d)** B

Answers to Conceptual Checkpoints

9.1 (c) The higher energy levels are more closely spaced then the lower ones, so the difference in energy between $n = 2$ and $n = 1$ is greater than the difference in energy between $n = 3$ and $n = 2$. The photon emitted when an electron falls from $n = 2$ to $n = 1$ therefore carries more energy, corresponding to radiation with a shorter wavelength and higher frequency.

9.2 (d) Both have six electrons in $2p$ orbitals and six electrons in $3p$ orbitals.

9.3 (d) The outermost principal shell for Cr is $n = 4$, which contains only a single valence electron, $4s^1$. (The five d electrons are in the $n = 3$ shell, and so are core electrons.)

CHAPTER 10

Chemical Bonding

"The fascination of a growing science lies in the work of the pioneers at the very borderland of the unknown, but to reach this frontier one must pass over well traveled roads ..."

Gilbert N. Lewis (1875–1946)

10.1   Bonding Models and AIDS Drugs

Proteins are discussed in more detail in Chapter 19.

In 1989, researchers discovered the structure of a molecule called HIV-protease. HIV-protease is a protein (a class of biological molecules) synthesized by the human immunodeficiency virus (HIV), which causes AIDS. HIV-protease is crucial to the virus's ability to replicate itself. Without HIV-protease, HIV could not spread in the human body because the virus could not copy itself, and AIDS would not develop.

With knowledge of the HIV-protease structure, drug companies set out to design a molecule that would disable protease by sticking to the working part of the molecule (called the *active site*). To design such a molecule, researchers used **bonding theories**—models that predict how atoms bond together to form molecules—to simulate how potential drug molecules would interact with the protease molecule. By the early 1990s, these companies had developed several drug molecules that seemed to work. Since these molecules inhibit the action of HIV-protease, they are called *protease inhibitors*. In human trials, protease inhibitors in combination with other drugs have decreased the viral count in HIV-infected individuals to undetectable levels. Many AIDS patients are still alive today because of the development of these drugs.

Bonding theories are central to chemistry because they predict how atoms bond together to form compounds. They predict what combinations of atoms form compounds and what combinations do not. For example, bonding theories predict why salt is NaCl and not $NaCl_2$ and why water is H_2O and not H_3O. Bonding theories also explain the shapes of molecules, which in turn determine many of their physical and chemical properties. The bonding theory you will learn in this chapter is called **Lewis theory,** named after the American chemist who developed it, G. N. Lewis (1875–1946). It involves representing electrons as dots and drawing what are called *dot structures* or *Lewis structures* to represent molecules. These structures, which are fairly simple to draw, have tremendous predictive power. It takes just a few minutes to

◀ The gold-colored structure on the computer screen is a representation of HIV-protease. The molecule shown in the center is Indinavir, a protease inhibitor.

use Lewis theory to determine whether a particular set of atoms will form a stable molecule and what that molecule might look like. Although modern chemists also use more advanced bonding theories to better predict molecular properties, Lewis theory remains the simplest method for making quick, everyday predictions about molecules.

10.2   Representing Valence Electrons with Dots

In the previous chapter, we learned that valence electrons are the electrons in the outermost principal shell. Since valence electrons are most important in bonding, Lewis theory focuses on these. In Lewis theory, the valence electrons of an element are represented as dots surrounding the symbol of the element. The result is called a **Lewis structure**, or **dot structure**. For example, the electron configuration of O is:

and the Lewis structure is:

Each dot represents a valence electron. The dots are placed around the element's symbol with a maximum of two dots per side. While the exact location of dots is not critical, in this book we fill in the dots singly first and then pair them.

The Lewis structures for all of the period 2 elements are:

Remember, the number of valence electrons for any main-group element (except helium, which has 2 valence electrons but is in Group 8A) is equal to the group number of the element.

$$Li\cdot \quad \cdot Be\cdot \quad \cdot \overset{\cdot}{B}\cdot \quad \cdot \overset{\cdot}{\underset{\cdot}{C}}\cdot \quad \cdot \overset{\cdot}{\underset{\cdot}{N}}: \quad \cdot \overset{\cdot\cdot}{\underset{\cdot}{O}}: \quad :\overset{\cdot\cdot}{\underset{\cdot}{F}}: \quad :\overset{\cdot\cdot}{\underset{\cdot\cdot}{Ne}}:$$

Lewis structures allow us to easily see the number of valence electrons in an atom. Atoms with 8 valence electrons—which are particularly stable—are easily identified because they have eight dots, an **octet**.

Helium is somewhat of an exception. Its electron configuration and Lewis structure are:

$$1s^2 \quad He:$$

The Lewis structure of helium contains only two dots (a **duet**). For helium, a duet represents a stable electron configuration.

In Lewis theory, a **chemical bond** involves the sharing or transfer of electrons to attain stable electron configurations for the bonding atoms. If the electrons are transferred, the bond is an **ionic bond**. If the electrons are shared, the bond is a **covalent bond**. In either case, the bonding atoms get stable electron configurations. As we have seen, a stable configuration usually consists of eight electrons in the outermost or valence shell. This observation leads to the **octet rule**:

In chemical bonding, atoms transfer or share electrons so that all obtain outer shells with eight electrons.

Hydrogen, lithium, and beryllium are exceptions: Each of these achieves stability when it has two electrons in its outermost shell.

| EXAMPLE 10.1 | **Writing Lewis Structures for Elements** |

Write a Lewis structure for phosphorus.

| Since phosphorus is in Group 5A in the periodic table, it has 5 valence electrons. Represent these as five dots surrounding the symbol for phosphorus. | **Solution:** $\cdot \dot{P} \colon$ |

| SKILLBUILDER 10.1 | **Writing Lewis Structures for Elements** |

Write a Lewis structure for Mg.

10.3   Lewis Structures for Ionic Compounds: Electrons Transferred

Recall from Chapter 5 that when metals bond with nonmetals, electrons are transferred from the metal to the nonmetal. The metal becomes a cation and the nonmetal becomes an anion. The attraction between the cation and the anion results in an ionic compound. In Lewis theory, we represent this by moving electron dots from the metal to the nonmetal. For example, potassium and chlorine have the following Lewis structures.

$$K\cdot \quad :\ddot{C}l:$$

When potassium and chlorine bond, potassium transfers its valence electron to chlorine.

$$K\cdot \quad :\ddot{C}l: \quad \longrightarrow \quad K^+ \; [:\ddot{C}l:]^-$$

Recall from Section 4.7 that atoms that lose electrons become positively charged and atoms that gain electrons become negatively charged.

The transfer of the electron gives chlorine an octet (shown as eight dots around chlorine), and leaves potassium with an octet in the previous principal shell, which is now the valence shell. The potassium, because it lost an electron, becomes positively charged, while the chlorine, which gained an electron, becomes negatively charged. The Lewis structure of an anion is usually written within brackets with the charge in the upper right corner (outside the brackets). The positive and negative charges attract one another, which then results in the compound KCl.

| EXAMPLE 10.2 | **Writing Ionic Lewis Structures** |

Write a Lewis structure for the compound MgO.

| Draw the Lewis structures of magnesium and oxygen by drawing two dots around the symbol for magnesium and six dots around the symbol for oxygen. | **Solution:** $\cdot Mg\cdot \quad \cdot \ddot{O}\colon$ |
| In MgO, magnesium loses its 2 valence electrons, forming a 2+ charge, and oxygen gains two electrons, forming a 2− charge and acquiring an octet. | $Mg^{2+} \; [:\ddot{O}\!:]^{2-}$ |

| SKILLBUILDER 10.2 | **Writing Ionic Lewis Structures** |

Write a Lewis structure for the compound NaBr.

Recall from Section 5.4 that ionic
compounds do not exist as distinct molecules, but rather as part of a large lattice of alternating cations and anions.

Lewis theory predicts the correct chemical formulas for ionic compounds.
For the compound that forms between K and Cl, for example, Lewis theory
predicts one potassium cation to every chlorine anion, KCl. As another example, consider the ionic compound formed between sodium and sulfur. The
Lewis structures for sodium and sulfur are:

$$\text{Na} \cdot \quad \cdot \ddot{\underset{\cdot\cdot}{\text{S}}} \colon$$

Notice that sodium must lose its 1 valence electron to get an octet (in the previous principal shell), while sulfur must gain 2 electrons to get an octet. Consequently, the compound that forms between sodium and sulfur requires two
sodium atoms to every one sulfur atom. The Lewis structure is:

$$\text{Na}^+ \; [\colon\!\ddot{\underset{\cdot\cdot}{\text{S}}}\!\colon]^{2-} \; \text{Na}^+$$

The two sodium atoms each lose their 1 valence electron, while the sulfur
atom gains 2 electrons and gets an octet. The correct chemical formula is Na_2S.

EXAMPLE 10.3   **Using Lewis Theory to Predict the Chemical Formula of an Ionic Compound**

Use Lewis theory to predict the formula for the compound that forms between calcium and chlorine.

Draw the Lewis structures of cal-cium and chlorine by drawing two dots around the symbol for calcium and seven dots around the symbol for chlorine.	**Solution:** $\cdot\text{Ca}\cdot \quad \colon\!\ddot{\underset{\cdot\cdot}{\text{Cl}}}\!\colon$
Calcium must lose its 2 valence elec-trons (to effectively get an octet in its previous principal shell), while chlorine needs to gain only 1 elec-tron to get an octet. Consequently, the compound that forms between Ca and Cl must have two chlorine atoms to every one calcium atom.	$[\colon\!\ddot{\underset{\cdot\cdot}{\text{Cl}}}\!\colon]^- \; \text{Ca}^{2+} \; [\colon\!\ddot{\underset{\cdot\cdot}{\text{Cl}}}\!\colon]^-$ The formula is therefore $CaCl_2$.

 SKILLBUILDER 10.3   **Using Lewis Theory to Predict the Chemical Formula of an Ionic Compound**

Use Lewis theory to predict the formula for the compound that forms between magnesium and nitrogen.

CONCEPTUAL CHECKPOINT 10.1

Which of the following nonmetals forms an ionic compound with aluminum with the formula Al_2X_3 (where X represents the nonmetal)?

(a) Cl
(b) S
(c) N
(d) C

10.4   Covalent Lewis Structures: Electrons Shared

Recall from Chapter 5 that when nonmetals bond with other nonmetals, a
molecular compound results. Molecular compounds contain covalent bonds,
in which electrons are shared between atoms rather than transferred. In Lewis
theory, we represent covalent bonding by allowing neighboring atoms to share
some of their valence electrons in order to attain octets (or duets for hydrogen).
For example, hydrogen and oxygen have the following Lewis structures.

$$\text{H}\cdot \quad \cdot\ddot{\underset{\cdot\cdot}{\text{O}}}\!\colon$$

In water, hydrogen and oxygen share their electrons so that each hydrogen atom gets a duet and the oxygen atom gets an octet.

$$H:\ddot{O}:H$$

The shared electrons—those that appear in the space between the two atoms— count toward the octets (or duets) of *both of the atoms.*

Duet   Octet   Duet

Electrons that are shared between two atoms are called **bonding pair** electrons, while those that are only on one atom are called **lone pair** electrons.

Sometimes lone pair electrons are also called nonbonding electrons.

Bonding
pair $H:\ddot{O}:H$

Lone
pair

Bonding pair electrons are often represented by dashes to emphasize that they are a chemical bond.

Remember that each dash represents a *pair* of shared electrons.

$$H—\ddot{O}—H$$

Lewis theory also explains why the halogens form diatomic molecules. Consider the Lewis structure of chlorine.

$$:\ddot{Cl}:$$

If two Cl atoms pair together, they can each get an octet.

$$:\ddot{Cl}:\ddot{Cl}: \quad or \quad :\ddot{Cl}—\ddot{Cl}:$$

When we examine elemental chlorine, it indeed exists as a diatomic molecule, just as Lewis theory predicts. The same is true for the other halogens.

Similarly, Lewis theory predicts that hydrogen, which has the following Lewis structure:

$$H\cdot$$

should exist as H_2. When two hydrogen atoms share their valence electrons, they each get a duet, a stable configuration for hydrogen.

$$H:H \quad or \quad H$$

TUTORIAL
H_2 Bond Formation

Again, Lewis theory is correct. In nature, elemental hydrogen exists as H_2 molecules.

Double and Triple Bonds

In Lewis theory, two atoms may share more than one electron pair to get octets. For example, we know from Chapter 5 that oxygen exists as the diatomic molecule, O_2. The Lewis structure of an oxygen atom is:

$$\cdot\ddot{O}:$$

If we pair two oxygen atoms together and then try to write a Lewis structure, we do not have enough electrons to give each O atom an octet.

$$:\ddot{O}:\ddot{O}:$$

However, we can convert a lone pair into an additional bonding pair by moving it into the bonding region.

$$:\ddot{O}:\ddot{O}: \quad \longrightarrow \quad :\ddot{O}::\ddot{O}: \quad or \quad :\ddot{O}=\ddot{O}:$$

Each oxygen atom now has an octet because the additional bonding pair counts toward the octet of both oxygen atoms.

Octet ———→ :Ö:::Ö: ←——— Octet

When two electron pairs are shared between two atoms, the resulting bond is a **double bond**. In general, double bonds are shorter and stronger than single bonds. For example, the distance between oxygen nuclei in an oxygen–oxygen double bond is 121 pm. In a single bond, it is 148 pm.

Atoms can also share three electron pairs. Consider the Lewis structure of N_2. Since each N atom has 5 valence electrons, the Lewis structure for N_2 has 10 electrons. A first attempt at writing the Lewis structure gives:

$$:\ddot{N}:\ddot{N}:$$

As with O_2, we do not have enough electrons to satisfy the octet rule for both N atoms. However, if we convert two additional lone pairs into bonding pairs, each nitrogen atom can get an octet.

$$:\ddot{N}:\ddot{N}: \quad \longrightarrow \quad :N:::N: \quad or \quad :N\equiv N:$$

The resulting bond is called a **triple bond**. Triple bonds are even shorter and stronger than double bonds. For example, the distance between nitrogen nuclei in a nitrogen–nitrogen triple bond is 110 pm. In a double bond, the distance is 124 pm. When we examine nitrogen in nature, we find that it indeed exists as a diatomic molecule with a very strong short bond between the two nitrogen atoms. The bond is so strong that it is difficult to break, making N_2 a relatively unreactive molecule.

| 10.5 | Writing Lewis Structures for Covalent Compounds |

To write a Lewis structure for a covalent compound, follow these steps:

1. **Write the correct skeletal structure for the molecule.** The Lewis structure of a molecule must have the atoms in the correct positions. For example, you could *not* write a Lewis structure for water if you started with the hydrogen atoms next to each other and the oxygen atom at the end (H H O). In nature, oxygen is the central atom and the hydrogens are **terminal atoms** (at the ends). The correct skeletal structure is H O H.

   The only way to absolutely know the correct skeletal structure for any molecule is by examining its structure in nature. However, we can write likely skeletal structures by remembering two guidelines. First, *hydrogen atoms will always be terminal*. Since hydrogen requires only a duet, it will never be a central atom because central atoms must form at least two bonds and hydrogen can form only one. Second, *many molecules tend to be symmetrical*, so when a molecule contains several atoms of the same type, these tend to be in terminal positions. This second guideline, however, has many exceptions. In cases where the skeletal structure is unclear, this text will provide you with the correct skeletal structure.

When guessing at skeletal structures, put the less metallic elements in terminal positions and the more metallic elements in central positions. Halogens, being among the least metallic elements, are nearly always terminal.

2. **Calculate the total number of electrons for the Lewis structure by summing the valence electrons of each atom in the molecule.** Remember that the number of valence electrons for any main-group element is equal to its group number in the periodic table. **If you are writing a Lewis structure for a polyatomic ion, the charge of the ion must be considered when calculating the total number of electrons.** Add 1 electron for each negative charge and subtract 1 electron for each positive charge.

1 pm = 10^{-12} m

3. **Distribute the electrons among the atoms, giving octets (or duets for hydrogen) to as many atoms as possible.** Begin by placing 2 electrons between each pair of atoms. These are the minimal number of bonding electrons. Then distribute the remaining electrons, first to terminal atoms, and then to the central atom, giving octets to as many atoms as possible.

4. **If any atoms lack an octet, form double or triple bonds as necessary to give them octets.** Do this by moving lone electron pairs from terminal atoms into the bonding region with the central atom.

TUTORIAL
Learning Lewis Dot Structures

A brief version of this procedure is shown in the left column below. Two examples of applying it are shown in the center and right columns.

Writing Lewis Structures for Covalent Compounds	EXAMPLE 10.4	EXAMPLE 10.5
	Write a Lewis structure for CO_2.	Write a Lewis structure for CCl_4.
1. Write the correct skeletal structure for the molecule.	**Solution:** Following the symmetry guideline, we write: O C O	**Solution:** Following the symmetry guideline, we write: Cl Cl C Cl Cl
2. Calculate the total number of electrons for the Lewis structure by summing the valence electrons of each atom in the molecule.	Total number of electrons for Lewis structure = $$\left(\begin{array}{c}\text{\# valence}\\ \text{e}^- \text{ for C}\end{array}\right) + 2\left(\begin{array}{c}\text{\# valence}\\ \text{e}^- \text{ for O}\end{array}\right)$$ $$= 4 + 2(6)$$ $$= 16$$	Total number of electrons for Lewis structure = $$\left(\begin{array}{c}\text{\# valence}\\ \text{e}^- \text{ for C}\end{array}\right) + 4\left(\begin{array}{c}\text{\# valence}\\ \text{e}^- \text{ for Cl}\end{array}\right)$$ $$= 4 + 4(7)$$ $$= 32$$
3. Distribute the electrons among the atoms, giving octets (or duets for hydrogen) to as many atoms as possible. Begin with the bonding electrons, and then proceed to lone pairs on terminal atoms, and finally to lone pairs on the central atom.	Bonding electrons first. O:C:O (4 of 16 electrons used) Lone pairs on terminal atoms next. :Ö:C:Ö: (16 of 16 electrons used)	Bonding electrons first. Cl Cl:C:Cl Cl (8 of 32 electrons used) Lone pairs on terminal atoms next. :C̈l: :C̈l:C:C̈l: :C̈l: (32 of 32 electrons used)
4. If any atoms lack an octet, form double or triple bonds as necessary to give them octets.	Move lone pairs from the oxygen atoms to bonding regions to form double bonds. :Ö:C:Ö: ⟶ :O::C::O:	Since all of the atoms have octets, the Lewis structure is complete.

SKILLBUILDER 10.4
Write a Lewis structure for CO.

SKILLBUILDER 10.5
Write a Lewis structure for H_2CO.

Writing Lewis Structures for Polyatomic Ions

We write Lewis structures for polyatomic ions by following the same procedure, but we pay special attention to the charge of the ion when calculating the number of electrons for the Lewis structure. Add 1 electron for each negative charge and subtract 1 electron for each positive charge. We normally show the Lewis structure for a polyatomic ion within brackets and write the charge of the ion in the upper right corner. For example, suppose we want to write a Lewis structure for the CN^- ion. We begin by writing the skeletal structure.

CN

We next calculate the total number of electrons for the Lewis structure by summing the number of valence electrons for each atom and adding one for the negative charge.

Total number of electrons
for Lewis structure = (# valence e^- in C) + (# valence e^- in N) + 1

= 4 + 5 + 1   Add one e^- to account
                            for −1 charge of ion.

= 10

We then place two electrons between each pair of atoms

C:N   (2 of 10 electrons used)

and then distribute the remaining electrons.

$:\ddot{C}:\ddot{N}:$ (10 of 10 electrons used)

Since neither of the atoms has octets, we move two lone pairs into the bonding region to form a triple bond, giving both atoms octets. We also enclose the Lewis structure in brackets and write the charge of the ion in the upper right corner.

$[:C:::N:]^-$ or $[:C\equiv N:]^-$

EXAMPLE 10.6   Writing Lewis Structures for Polyatomic Ions

Write the Lewis structure for the NH_4^+ ion.

Begin by writing the skeletal structure. Since hydrogen atoms must be terminal, and following the guideline of symmetry, put the nitrogen atom in the middle surrounded by four hydrogen atoms.

Solution:

          H
H   N   H
          H

Calculate the total number of electrons for the Lewis structure by summing the number of valence electrons for each atom and subtracting 1 for the positive charge.

Total number of
electrons for Lewis structure = 5 + 4 − 1 = 8

4 × (# valence e^- in H)

valence e^- in N

Subtract 1 e^- to account
for +1 charge of ion.

Next, place 2 electrons between each pair of atoms.

$$\begin{array}{c} H \\ H\!:\!\ddot{N}\!:\!H \quad \text{(8 of 8 electrons used)} \\ H \end{array}$$

Since the nitrogen atom has an octet and since all of the hydrogen atoms have duets, the placement of electrons is complete. Write the entire Lewis structure in brackets and write the charge of the ion in the upper right corner.

$$\left[\begin{array}{c} H \\ H\!:\!\ddot{N}\!:\!H \\ H \end{array}\right]^{+} \quad or \quad \left[\begin{array}{c} H \\ | \\ H\!-\!N\!-\!H \\ | \\ H \end{array}\right]^{+}$$

SKILLBUILDER 10.6 **Writing Lewis Structures for Polyatomic Ions**

Write a Lewis structure for the ClO⁻ ion.

Exceptions to the Octet Rule

Lewis theory is often correct in its predictions; however, there are some exceptions. For example, if we try to write a Lewis structure for NO, which has 11 electrons, the best we can do is:

$$:\dot{N}::\ddot{O}: \quad or \quad :\dot{N}\!=\!\ddot{O}:$$

The nitrogen atom does not have an octet, so this is not a great Lewis structure. However, NO exists in nature. Why? As with any simple theory, Lewis theory is not sophisticated enough to be correct every time. It is impossible to write good Lewis structures for molecules with odd numbers of electrons, yet some of these molecules exist in nature. In such cases, we simply write the best Lewis structure that we can. Another significant exception to the octet rule is boron, which tends to form compounds with only 6 electrons around B, rather than 8. For example, BF_3 and BH_3—both of which exist in nature—lack an octet for B.

MOLECULE
Boron Trifluoride

$$:\ddot{F}: \qquad H \\ :\ddot{F}\!:\!B\!:\!\ddot{F}: \qquad H\!:\!\ddot{B}\!:\!H$$

A third type of exception to the octet rule is also common. A number of molecules, such as SF_6 and PCl_5, have more than 8 electrons around a central atom in their Lewis structure.

These are often referred to as expanded octets. Beyond mentioning them, we do not cover expanded octets in this book. In spite of these exceptions, which can largely be accommodated within the theory, Lewis theory remains a powerful and simple way to understand chemical bonding.

CONCEPTUAL CHECKPOINT 10.2

Which two species have the same number of lone electron pairs in their Lewis structures?

(a) H_2O and H_3O^+
(b) NH_3 and H_3O^+
(c) NH_3 and CH_4
(d) NH_3 and NH_4^+

10.6 Resonance: Equivalent Lewis Structures for the Same Molecule

When writing Lewis structures, we may find that, for some molecules, we can write more than one good Lewis structure. For example, consider writing a Lewis structure for SO_2. We begin with the skeletal structure:

O S O

We then sum the valence electrons.

Total number of electrons for Lewis structure
$= (\text{\# valence } e^- \text{ in S}) + 2(\text{\# valence } e^- \text{ in O})$
$= 6 + 2(6)$
$= 18$

We next place two electrons between each pair of atoms

O:S:O   (4 of 18 electrons used)

and then distribute the remaining electrons, first to terminal atoms

:Ö:S:Ö: (16 of 18 electrons used)

and finally to the central atom.

:Ö:S̈:Ö: (18 of 18 electrons used)

Since the central atom lacks an octet, we move one lone pair from an oxygen atom into the bonding region to form a double bond, giving all of the atoms octets.

:Ö::S̈:Ö: *or*   :Ö=S̈—Ö:

However, we could have formed the double bond with the other oxygen atom.

:Ö—S̈=Ö:

These two Lewis structures are equally correct. In cases such as this—where we can write two or more equivalent (or nearly equivalent) Lewis structures for the same molecule—we find that the molecule exists in nature as an average or intermediate between the two Lewis structures. Any *one* of the two Lewis structures for SO_2 would predict that SO_2 should contain two different kinds of bonds (one double bond and one single bond). However, when we examine SO_2 in nature, we find that both of the bonds are equivalent and intermediate in strength and length between a double bond and single bond. We account for this in Lewis theory by representing the molecule with both structures, called **resonance structures**, with a double-headed arrow between them.

$$:\ddot{O}{=}\ddot{S}{-}\ddot{O}: \longleftrightarrow :\ddot{O}{-}\ddot{S}{=}\ddot{O}:$$

The true structure of SO_2 is intermediate between these two resonance structures.

EXAMPLE 10.7   **Writing Resonance Structures**

Write a Lewis structure for the NO_3^- ion. Include resonance structures.

Begin by writing the skeletal structure. Using the guideline of symmetry, make the three oxygen atoms terminal.	**Solution:** O O N O
Sum the valence electrons (adding 1 electron to account for the -1 charge) to determine the total number of electrons in the Lewis structure.	Total number of electrons for Lewis structure $= 5 + 3(6) + 1 = 24$ $3 \times$ (# valence e^- in O) # valence e^- in N Add one e^- to account for negative charge of ion.
Place 2 electrons between each pair of atoms.	O O:N:O (6 of 24 electrons used)
Distribute the remaining electrons, first to terminal atoms.	:Ö: :Ö:N:Ö: (24 of 24 electrons used)
Since there are no electrons remaining to complete the octet of the central atom, form a double bond by moving a lone pair from one of the oxygen atoms into the bonding region with nitrogen. Enclose the structure in brackets and write the charge at the upper right.	$\left[\begin{array}{c}:\ddot{O}:\\:\ddot{O}:N::\ddot{O}:\end{array}\right]^-$ *or* $\left[\begin{array}{c}:\ddot{O}:\\ \| \\:\ddot{O}{-}N{=}\ddot{O}:\end{array}\right]^-$
Notice that you could have formed the double bond with either of the other two oxygen atoms.	$\left[\begin{array}{c}:\ddot{O}:\\ \| \\:\ddot{O}{=}N{-}\ddot{O}:\end{array}\right]^-$ *or* $\left[\begin{array}{c}:\ddot{O}\\ \| \\:\ddot{O}{-}N{-}\ddot{O}:\end{array}\right]^-$
Since the three Lewis structures are equally correct, write the three structures as resonance structures.	$\left[\begin{array}{c}:\ddot{O}:\\ \| \\:\ddot{O}{=}N{-}\ddot{O}:\end{array}\right]^- \longleftrightarrow \left[\begin{array}{c}:\ddot{O}\\ \| \\:\ddot{O}{-}N{-}\ddot{O}:\end{array}\right]^- \longleftrightarrow \left[\begin{array}{c}:\ddot{O}:\\ \| \\:\ddot{O}{-}N{=}\ddot{O}:\end{array}\right]^-$

SKILLBUILDER 10.7   **Writing Resonance Structures**

Write a Lewis structure for the NO_2^- ion. Include resonance structures.

Chemistry IN THE ENVIRONMENT

The Lewis Structure of Ozone

Ozone is a form of oxygen in which three oxygen atoms bond together. Its Lewis structure consists of the following two resonance structures:

$$:\ddot{O}=\ddot{O}-\ddot{\underset{..}{O}}: \quad \longleftrightarrow \quad :\ddot{\underset{..}{O}}-\ddot{O}=\ddot{O}:$$

Compare the Lewis structure of ozone to the Lewis structure of O_2:

$$:\ddot{O}=\ddot{O}:$$

Which molecule, O_3 or O_2, do you think has the stronger oxygen–oxygen bond? If you deduced O_2, you are correct. O_2 has a stronger bond because it is a pure double bond. Ozone, on the other hand, has bonds that are intermediate between single and double, so O_3 has weaker bonds. The effects of this are significant. As we learned in the *Chemistry in the Environment* box in Chapter 6, O_3 shields us from harmful ultraviolet light entering Earth's atmosphere. O_3 is ideally suited to do this because pho-

tons at wavelengths of 280–320 nm (the most dangerous components of sunlight to humans) are just strong enough to break ozone's bonds. In the process, the photons are absorbed.

$$:\ddot{\underset{..}{O}}-\ddot{O}=\ddot{O}: + \text{UV light} \longrightarrow :\ddot{O}=\ddot{O}: + \cdot\ddot{\underset{..}{O}}\cdot$$

The same wavelengths of UV light, however, do not have sufficient energy to break the stronger double bond of O_2, which is therefore transparent to UV. As the ozone layer continues to thin, no other molecules in our atmosphere can do the job that ozone does. Consequently, it is important that we continue, and even strengthen, the ban on ozone-depleting compounds.

CAN YOU ANSWER THIS? *Why are the following Lewis structures for ozone incorrect?*

$$:\ddot{\underset{..}{O}}-\ddot{\underset{..}{O}}-\ddot{\underset{..}{O}}: \qquad :\ddot{\underset{..}{O}}=O=\ddot{\underset{..}{O}}:$$

10.7 Predicting the Shapes of Molecules

Lewis theory, in combination with **valence shell electron pair repulsion (VSEPR) theory**, can be used to predict the shapes of molecules. VSEPR is based on the simple idea that **electron groups**—lone pairs, single bonds, or multiple bonds—repel each other. This repulsion between the negative charge of electron groups on the central atom determines the geometry of the molecule. For example, consider CO_2, which has the following Lewis structure:

$$:\ddot{O}=C=\ddot{O}:$$

The geometry of CO_2 is determined by the repulsion between the two electron groups (or double bonds) on the central carbon atom. These two electron groups get as far away from each other as possible, resulting in a bond angle of 180° and a **linear** geometry for CO_2.

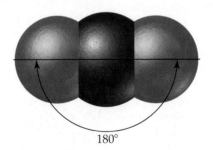

180°

As another example, consider the molecule H_2CO. Its Lewis structure is:

$$\overset{\displaystyle :O:}{\underset{\displaystyle H-C-H}{\parallel}}$$

This molecule has three electron groups around the central atom. These three electron groups get as far away from each other as possible, resulting in a bond angle of 120° and a **trigonal planar** geometry.

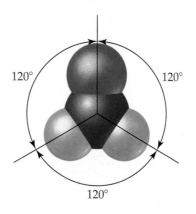

A tetrahedron is a geometric shape with four triangular faces.

If a molecule has four electron groups around the central atom, as in CH_4, it has a **tetrahedral** geometry with bond angles of 109.5°.

CH_4 is shown here with both a ball-and-stick model (above) and a space-filling model (below). Although space-filling models more closely portray molecules, ball-and-stick models are often used to clearly illustrate molecular geometries.

The electron groups repelling each other cause the tetrahedral shape—the tetrahedron allows the maximum separation among the four groups. When we write the structure of CH_4 on paper, it may seem that the molecule should be square planar, with bond angles of 90°. However, in three dimensions the electron groups can get farther away from each other by forming the tetrahedral geometry.

MOLECULE
Methane

Each of the preceding examples has only bonding groups of electrons around the central atom. What happens in molecules with lone pairs around the central atom? These lone pairs also repel other electron groups. For example, consider NH_3:

$$H-\underset{\underset{\textstyle ..}{\overset{\textstyle |}{N}}}{}-H$$
$$\overset{\textstyle |}{\underset{}{H}}$$

The four electron groups (one lone pair and three bonding pairs) get as far away from each other possible. If we look only at the electrons, we find that the **electron geometry**—the geometrical arrangement of the electron groups—is tetrahedral.

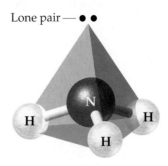

Lone pair — ● ●

However, the **molecular geometry**—the geometrical arrangement of the atoms—is **trigonal pyramidal**.

Trigonal pyramidal
structure

Notice that, although the electron geometry and the molecular geometry are different, the electron geometry is relevant to the molecular geometry. In other words, the lone pair exerts its influence on the bonding pairs.

Consider one last example, H_2O. Its Lewis structure is:

$$H-\overset{\cdot\cdot}{\underset{\cdot\cdot}{O}}-H$$

Since it has four electron groups, its electron geometry is also tetrahedral.

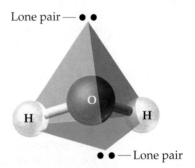

Lone pair — ● ●

● ● — Lone pair

However, its molecular geometry is **bent.**

For reasons we don't cover here, the bond angles in NH_3 and H_2O are actually a few degrees smaller than the ideal tetrahedral angles.

Bent structure

Table 10.1 summarizes the electron and molecular geometry of a molecule based on the total number of electron groups, the number of bonding groups, and the number of lone pairs.

To determine the geometry of any molecule, use the following procedure. As usual, we give the steps in the left column and two examples of applying the steps in the center and right columns.

TUTORIAL
VSEPR Movie

TABLE 10.1 Electron and Molecular Geometries

Electron Groups*	Bonding Groups	Lone Pairs	Electron Geometry	Angle between Electron Groups**	Molecular Geometry	Example
2	2	0	linear	180°	linear	$:\ddot{O}=C=\ddot{O}:$
3	3	0	trigonal planar	120°	trigonal planar	(H—C—H with double-bonded O)
3	2	1	trigonal planar	120°	bent	$:\ddot{O}=\ddot{S}—\ddot{O}:$
4	4	0	tetrahedral	109.5°	tetrahedral	(H—C—H with four H)
4	3	1	tetrahedral	109.5°	trigonal pyramidal	$H—\ddot{N}—H$ (with H)
4	2	2	tetrahedral	109.5°	bent	$H—\ddot{O}—H$

*Count only electron groups around the *central* atom. Each of the following is considered one electron group: a lone pair, a single bond, a double bond, and a triple bond.
**Angles listed here are idealized. Actual angles in specific molecules may vary by several degrees.

LIVE EXAMPLE

Predicting Geometry Using VSEPR	EXAMPLE 10.8	EXAMPLE 10.9
	Predict the electron and molecular geometry of PCl_3.	Predict the electron and molecular geometry of the $[NO_3]^-$ ion.
1. *Draw a Lewis structure for the molecule.*	Solution: PCl_3 has 26 electrons. $:\ddot{Cl}:\ddot{P}:\ddot{Cl}:$ (with $:\ddot{Cl}:$ above)	Solution: $[NO_3]^-$ has 24 electrons. $[:\ddot{O}:\ddot{N}::\ddot{O}:]^-$ (with $:\ddot{O}:$ above)
2. *Determine the total number of electron groups around the central atom.* Lone pairs, single bonds, double bonds, and triple bonds each count as one group.	The central atom (P) has four electron groups.	The central atom (N) has three electron groups (the double bond counts as one group).
3. *Determine the number of bonding groups and the number of lone pairs around the central atom.* These should sum to the result from Step 2. Bonding groups include single bonds, double bonds, and triple bonds.	$:\ddot{Cl}:\ddot{P}:\ddot{Cl}:$ (with $:\ddot{Cl}:$ above) — Lone pair Three of the four electron groups around P are bonding groups and one is a lone pair.	$[:\ddot{O}:\ddot{N}::\ddot{O}:]^-$ (with $:\ddot{O}:$ above) — No lone pairs All three of the electron groups around N are bonding groups.

4. *Use Table 10.1 to determine the electron geometry and molecular geometry.*

The electron geometry is tetrahedral (four electron groups) and the molecular geometry—the shape of the molecule—is trigonal pyramidal (four electron groups, three bonding groups, and one lone pair).

SKILLBUILDER 10.8

Predict the molecular geometry of ClNO (N is the central atom).

The electron geometry is trigonal planar (three electron groups) and the molecular geometry—the shape of the molecule—is trigonal planar (three electron groups, three bonding groups, and no lone pairs).

SKILLBUILDER 10.9

Predict the molecular geometry of the SO_3^{2-} ion.

CONCEPTUAL CHECKPOINT 10.3

Which of the following conditions necessarily leads to a molecular geometry that is identical to the electron geometry?

(a) The presence of a double bond between the central atom and a terminal atom.
(b) The presence of two or more identical terminal atoms bonded to the central atom.
(c) The presence of one or more lone pairs on the central atom.
(d) The absence of any lone pairs on the central atom.

Representing Molecular Geometries on Paper

Since molecular geometries are three-dimensional, they are often difficult to represent on two-dimensional paper. Many chemists use the following notation for bonds to indicate three-dimensional structures on two-dimensional paper.

—	‖····	◄
Straight line	*Hashed lines*	*Wedge*
Bond in plane of paper	Bond going into the paper	Bond coming out of the paper

The major molecular geometries used in this book are shown here using this notation:

X—A—X
Linear

Trigonal planar

Bent

Tetrahedral

Trigonal pyramidal

Chemistry AND HEALTH

Fooled by Molecular Shape

Artificial sweeteners, such as aspartame (Nutrasweet™), taste sweet but have few or no calories. Why? Because taste and caloric value are entirely separate properties of foods. The caloric value of a food depends on the amount of energy released when the food is metabolized. For example, sucrose (table sugar) is metabolized by oxidation to carbon dioxide and water:

$$C_{12}H_{22}O_{11} + 6\,O_2 \longrightarrow 12\,CO_2 + 11\,H_2O + 5644\ kJ$$

When your body metabolizes one mole of sucrose, it obtains 5644 kJ of energy. Some artificial sweeteners, such as saccharin, are not metabolized at all—they just pass through the body unchanged—and therefore have no caloric value. Other artificial sweeteners, such as aspartame, are metabolized, but have a much lower caloric content (for a given amount of sweetness) than sucrose.

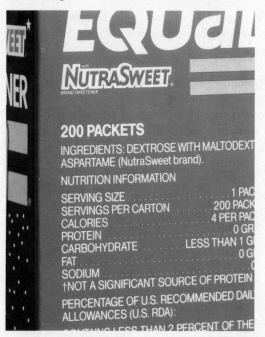

The *taste* of a food, however, is independent of its metabolism. The sensation of taste originates in the tongue, where specialized cells called taste cells act as highly sensitive and specific molecular detectors. These cells can detect sugar molecules out of the thousands of different types of molecules present in a mouthful of food. The main basis for this discrimination is the molecule's *shape*.

The surface of a taste cell contains specialized protein molecules called taste receptors. A particular *tastant*— a molecule that we can taste—fits snugly into a special pocket on the taste receptor protein called the *active site*, just as a key fits into a lock (see Section 15.12). For example, a sugar molecule just fits into the active site of the sugar receptor protein called Tlr3. When the sugar molecule (the key) enters the active site (the lock), the different subunits of the Tlr3 protein split apart. This split causes a series of events that result in transmission of a nerve signal, which reaches the brain and registers a sweet taste.

Artificial sweeteners taste sweet because they fit into the receptor pocket that normally binds sucrose. In fact, both aspartame and saccharin actually bind to the active site in the Tlr3 protein more strongly than sugar does! For this reason, artificial sweeteners are "sweeter than sugar." It takes 200 times as much sucrose as aspartame to trigger the same amount of nerve signal transmission from taste cells.

This type of lock-and-key fit between the active site of a protein and a particular molecule is important not only to taste but to many other biological functions as well. For example, immune response, the sense of smell, and many types of drug action all depend on shape-specific interactions between molecules and proteins. In fact, the ability of scientists to determine the shapes of key biological molecules is largely responsible for the revolution in biology that has occurred over the last 50 years.

CAN YOU ANSWER THIS? *Proteins are long-chain molecules in which each link is an amino acid. The simplest amino acid is glycine, which has the following structure:*

$$\text{H}-\overset{\displaystyle \text{H}}{\underset{\displaystyle \text{H}}{\text{N}}}-\overset{\displaystyle \text{H}}{\underset{\displaystyle \text{H}}{\text{C}}}-\overset{\displaystyle :\!\text{O}:}{\text{C}}-\overset{..}{\underset{..}{\text{O}}}-\text{H}$$

Determine the geometry about each interior atom in the glycine structure and make a three-dimensional sketch of the molecule.

10.8   Electronegativity and Polarity: Why Oil and Water Don't Mix

If you combine oil and water in a container, they separate into distinct regions (▶ Figure 10.1). Why? Something about water molecules causes them to bunch together into one region, expelling the oil molecules into a separate region. What is that something? We can begin to understand the answer by examining the Lewis structure of water.

$$\text{H}-\overset{..}{\underset{..}{\text{O}}}-\text{H}$$

▲ Figure 10.1   **Oil and water don't mix** Question: Why not?

The two bonds between O and H each consist of an electron pair—2 electrons shared between the oxygen atom and the hydrogen atom. The oxygen and hydrogen atoms each donate 1 electron to this electron pair; however, like unruly children, they don't share them equally. The oxygen atom takes more than its fair share of the electron pair.

Electronegativity

The ability of an element to attract electrons within a covalent bond is called **electronegativity**. Oxygen is more electronegative than hydrogen, which means that, on average, the shared electrons are more likely to be found near the oxygen atom than near the hydrogen atom. Consider one of the two OH bonds:

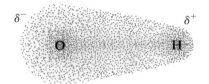

Dipole moment

The representation for depicting electron density in this figure is introduced in Section 9.6.

Since the electron pair is unequally shared (with oxygen getting the larger share), the oxygen atom has a partial negative charge, symbolized by $\delta-$ (delta minus). The hydrogen atom (getting the smaller share) has a partial positive charge, symbolized by $\delta+$ (delta plus). The result of this is uneven electron sharing is a **dipole moment**, a separation of charge within the bond. Covalent bonds that have a dipole moment are called **polar covalent bonds.** The magnitude of the dipole moment, and therefore the degree of polarity of the bond, depends on the electronegativity difference between the two elements in the bond and the length of the bond. For a fixed bond length, the greater the electronegativity difference, the greater the dipole moment and the more polar the bond.

The value of electronegativity is assigned using a relative scale on which fluorine, the most electronegative element, has an electronegativity of 4.0. All other electronegativities are defined relative to fluorine.

▼ Figure 10.2 shows the relative electronegativities of the elements. Notice that electronegativity increases as you go toward the right across a period in the periodic table and decreases as you go down a column in the periodic table. If two elements with identical electronegativities form a covalent bond,

▲ Figure 10.2   **Electronegativity of the elements**   Linus Pauling introduced the scale shown here. He arbitrarily set the electronegativity of fluorine at 4.0 and computed all other values relative to fluorine.

◀ **Figure 10.3 Pure covalent bonding** In Cl_2, the two Cl atoms share the electrons evenly. This is a pure covalent bond.

they equally share the electrons, and there is no dipole moment. For example, the chlorine molecule, composed of two chlorine atoms (which of course have identical electronegativities), has a covalent bond in which electrons are evenly shared (▲ Figure 10.3). The bond has no dipole moment and the molecule is **nonpolar**.

If there is a large electronegativity difference between the two elements in a bond, such as normally occurs between a metal and a nonmetal, the electron is completely transferred and the bond is ionic. For example, sodium and chlorine form an ionic bond (▼ Figure 10.4).

◀ **Figure 10.4 Ionic bonding** In NaCl, Na completely transfers an electron to Cl. This is an ionic bond.

If there is an intermediate electronegativity difference between the two elements, such as between two different nonmetals, then the bond is polar covalent. For example, HF forms a polar covalent bond (▼ Figure 10.5).

TUTORIAL
Electronegativity and Bonding

◀ **Figure 10.5 Polar covalent bonding** In HF, the electrons are shared, but the shared electrons are more likely to be found on F than on H. The bond is polar covalent.

These concepts are summarized in Table 10.2 and ▼ Figure 10.6.

TABLE 10.2 The Effect of Electronegativity Difference on Bond Type

Electronegativity Difference (ΔEN)	Bond Type	Example
zero (0–0.4)	pure covalent	Cl_2
intermediate (0.4–2.0)	polar covalent	HF
large (2.0+)	ionic	NaCl

The degree of bond polarity is a continuous function. The guidelines given here are only approximate.

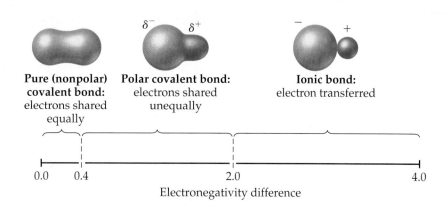

Pure (nonpolar) covalent bond: electrons shared equally

Polar covalent bond: electrons shared unequally

Ionic bond: electron transferred

0.0   0.4   2.0   4.0
Electronegativity difference

▶ **Figure 10.6 The continuum of bond types** The type of bond (pure covalent, polar covalent, or ionic) is related to the electronegativity difference between the bonded atoms.

EXAMPLE 10.10 **Classifying Bonds as Pure Covalent, Polar Covalent, or Ionic**

Determine whether the bond formed between each of the following pairs of atoms is pure covalent, polar covalent, or ionic.

(a) Sr and F
(b) N and Cl
(c) N and O

Solution:

(a) From Figure 10.2, we find the electronegativity of Sr (1.0) and of F (4.0). The electronegativity difference (ΔEN) is:

$$\Delta EN = 4.0 - 1.0 = 3.0$$

Using Table 10.2, we classify this bond as ionic.

(b) From Figure 10.2, we find the electronegativity of N (3.0) and of Cl (3.0). The electronegativity difference (ΔEN) is:

$$\Delta EN = 3.0 - 3.0 = 0$$

Using Table 10.2, we classify this bond as pure covalent.

(c) From Figure 10.2, we find the electronegativity of N (3.0) and of O (3.5). The electronegativity difference (ΔEN) is:

$$\Delta EN = 3.5 - 3.0 = 0.5$$

Using Table 10.2, we classify this bond as polar covalent.

SKILLBUILDER 10.10 **Classifying Bonds as Pure Covalent, Polar Covalent, or Ionic**

Determine whether the bond formed between each of the following pairs of atoms is pure covalent, polar covalent, or ionic.

(a) I and I
(b) Cs and Br
(c) P and O

Polar Bonds and Polar Molecules

We just learned how to identify polar bonds. Does the presence of one or more polar bonds in a molecule always result in a polar molecule? The answer is no. A **polar molecule** is one with polar bonds that add together—they do not cancel each other—to form a net dipole moment. For diatomic molecules, you can easily tell polar molecules from nonpolar ones. If a diatomic molecule contains a polar bond, then the molecule is polar. However, for molecules with more than two atoms, it is more difficult to tell polar molecules from nonpolar ones because two or more polar bonds may cancel one another. For example, consider carbon dioxide:

$$:\ddot{O}=C=\ddot{O}:$$

Each C=O *bond* is polar because oxygen and carbon have different electronegativities (3.5 and 2.5). However, since CO_2 has a linear geometry, the dipole moment of one bond completely cancels the dipole moment of the other and the *molecule* is nonpolar. We can understand this with a simple analogy. Consider each polar bond as a rope pulling on the central atom. In CO_2, we can see how the two ropes pulling in opposing directions cancel each other:

We can also represent polar bonds with arrows (or vectors) that point in the direction of the negative pole and have a plus sign at the positive pole (as shown above for carbon dioxide.) If the arrows (or vectors) point in exactly opposing directions as in carbon dioxide, the dipole moments cancel.

Water, on the other hand, has two dipole moments that do not cancel. If we imagine each bond as a rope pulling on oxygen, we see that, because of the angle between the bonds, the pulls of the two ropes do not cancel:

Consequently, water is a polar molecule. We can use symmetry as a guide to determine whether a molecule containing polar bonds is indeed polar. Highly symmetric molecules will tend to be nonpolar even if they have polar bonds because the bond dipole moments (or the pulls of the ropes) tend to cancel. Asymmetric molecules that contain polar bonds will tend to be polar because the bond dipole moments (or the pulls of the ropes) tend not to cancel. Table 10.3 summarizes various common cases.

In summary, to determine whether a molecule is polar:
- **Determine whether the molecule contains polar bonds**. A bond is polar if the two bonding atoms have different electronegativities. If there are no polar bonds, the molecule is nonpolar.
- **Determine whether the polar bonds add together to form a net dipole moment**. You must first use VSEPR to determine the geometry of the molecule. Then visualize each bond as a rope pulling on the central atom. Is the molecule highly symmetrical? Do the pulls of the ropes cancel? If so, there is no net dipole moment and the molecule is nonpolar. If the molecule is asymmetrical and the pulls of the rope do not cancel, the molecule is polar.

δ^+ δ^-

In the vector representation of a dipole moment, the vector points in the direction of the atom with the partial negative charge.

TUTORIAL
Bond Polarity and Geometry

TABLE 10.3 Common Cases of Adding Dipole Moments to Determine whether a Molecule Is Polar

Nonpolar

Two identical polar bonds pointing in opposite directions will cancel. The molecule is nonpolar.

Polar

Two polar bonds with an angle of less than 180° between them will not cancel. The molecule is polar.

Nonpolar

Three identical polar bonds at 120° from each other will cancel. The molecule is nonpolar.

Nonpolar

Four identical polar bonds in a tetrahedral arrangement (109.5° from each other) will cancel. The molecule is nonpolar.

Polar

Three polar bonds in a trigonal pyramidal arrangement (109.5°) will not cancel. The molecule is polar.

> *Note: In all cases where the polar bonds cancel, the bonds are assumed to be identical. If one or more of the bonds are different than the other(s), the bonds will not cancel and the molecule is polar.*

EXAMPLE 10.11   Determining whether a Molecule Is Polar

Determine whether NH_3 is polar.

Begin by drawing the Lewis structure of NH_3. Since N and H have different electronegativities, the bonds are polar.	**Solution:** $$H-\underset{\cdot\cdot}{N}-H$$ with H above N
The geometry of NH_3 is trigonal pyramidal (four electron groups, three bonding groups, one lone pair). Draw a three-dimensional picture of NH_3 and imagine each bond as a rope that is being pulled. The pulls of the ropes do not cancel and the molecule is polar.	 NH_3 is polar

SKILLBUILDER 10.11   Determining whether a Molecule Is Polar

Determine whether CH_4 is polar.

Whether or not a molecule is polar is important because polar molecules tend to behave differently than nonpolar molecules. Water and oil do not mix, for example, because water molecules are polar and the molecules that compose oil are generally nonpolar. Polar molecules interact strongly with other polar molecules because the positive end of one molecule is attracted to the negative end of another, just as the south pole of a magnet is attracted to the north pole of another magnet (▼ Figure 10.7). A mixture of polar and nonpolar molecules is similar to a mixture of small magnetic and nonmagnetic particles. The magnetic particles clump together, excluding the nonmagnetic ones and separating into distinct regions (▼ Figure 10.8). Similarly, the polar molecules attract one another, forming regions from which the nonpolar molecules are excluded (▼ Figure 10.9).

▲ Figure 10.7   **Dipole–dipole attraction**   Just as the north pole of one magnet is attracted to the south pole of another, so the positive end of one molecule with a dipole is attracted to the negative end of another molecule with a dipole.

▲ Figure 10.8   **Magnetic and nonmagnetic particles**   Magnetic particles attract one another, excluding nonmagnetic particles. This behavior is analogous to that of polar and nonpolar molecules.

▶ Figure 10.9   **Polar and nonpolar molecules**   A mixture of polar and nonpolar molecules, like a mixture of magnetic and nonmagnetic particles, separates into distinct regions because the polar molecules attract one another, excluding the nonpolar ones.
Question: Can you think of some examples of this behavior?

EVERYDAY Chemistry

How Soap Works

Imagine eating a greasy cheeseburger with both hands and no napkins. By the end of the meal, your hands are coated with grease and oil. If you try to wash them with only water, they remain greasy. However, if you add a little soap, the grease washes away. Why? As we learned previously, water molecules are polar and the molecules that compose grease and oil are nonpolar. As a result, water and grease repel each other.

The molecules that compose soap, however, have a special structure that allows them to interact strongly with both water and grease. One end of a soap molecule is polar while the other end is nonpolar.

Soap molecule

Polar head   Nonpolar tail
attracts water   attracts grease

The polar head of a soap molecule strongly attracts water molecules, while the nonpolar tail strongly attracts grease and oil molecules. Soap is a sort of molecular liaison, one end interacting with water and the other end interacting with grease. Soap therefore allows water and grease to mix, removing the grease from your hands and washing it down the drain.

CAN YOU ANSWER THIS? *Consider the following detergent molecule. Which end do you think is polar? Which end is nonpolar?*

$$CH_3(CH_2)_{11}OCH_2CH_2OH$$

CHAPTER IN REVIEW

Chemical Principles

Lewis Theory: Lewis theory is a model for chemical bonding. In Lewis theory, chemical bonds are formed when atoms transfer valence electrons (ionic bonding) or share valence electrons (covalent bonding) to attain noble gas electron configurations. In Lewis theory, valence electrons are represented as dots surrounding the symbol for an element. When two or more elements bond together, the dots are transferred or shared so that every atom gets eight dots (an octet), or two dots (a duet) in the case of hydrogen.

Molecular Shapes: The shapes of molecules can be predicted by combining Lewis theory with valence shell electron pair repulsion (VSEPR) theory. In this model, electron groups—lone pairs, single bonds, double bonds, and triple bonds—around the central atom repel one another and determine the geometry of the molecule.

Relevance

Lewis Theory: Bonding theories predict what combinations of elements will form stable compounds. They can also be used to predict the properties of those compounds. For example, bonding theories are used by pharmaceutical companies when they are designing drug molecules that must interact with a specific part of a protein molecule.

Molecular Shapes: Molecular shapes determine many of the properties of compounds. Water's bent geometry, for example, causes it to be a liquid at room temperature instead of a gas. It also causes ice to float on water and is responsible for the hexagonal patterns in snowflakes.

Electronegativity and Polarity: Electronegativity refers to the relative ability of elements to attract electrons within a chemical bond. Electronegativity increases as you move to the right across a period in the periodic table and decreases as you move down a column. When two non-metal atoms of different electronegativities form a covalent bond, the electrons in the bond are not evenly shared and the bond is polar. In diatomic molecules, a polar bond results in a polar molecule. In multi-atom molecules, polar bonds may cancel, forming a nonpolar molecule, or they may sum, forming a polar molecule.

Electronegativity and Polarity: The polarity of a molecule influences many of its properties such as whether it will be a solid, liquid, or gas at room temperature and whether it will mix with other compounds. Oil and water, for example, do not mix because water is polar while oil is nonpolar.

Chemical Skills

Examples

Lewis Structures for Elements (Section 10.2)

The Lewis structure of any element is simply the symbol for the element with the valence electrons represented as dots drawn around the element. The number of valence electrons is equal to the group number of the element (for main-group elements).

EXAMPLE 10.12   Lewis Structures for Elements

What is the Lewis structure of sulfur?

Solution:
Since S is in Group 6, it has 6 valence electrons. We draw these as dots surrounding its symbol, S.

$$\cdot \ddot{\underset{\cdot\cdot}{S}} \colon$$

Writing Lewis Structures for Ionic Compounds (Section 10.3)

In an ionic Lewis structure, the metal loses all of its valence electrons to the nonmetal, which gets an octet. The nonmetal, with its octet, is normally written in brackets with the charge in the upper right corner.

EXAMPLE 10.13   Writing Lewis Structures for Ionic Compounds

Write a Lewis structure for lithium bromide.

Solution:

$$Li^+ \; [\colon \ddot{\underset{\cdot\cdot}{Br}} \colon]^-$$

Using Lewis Theory to Predict the Chemical Formula of an Ionic Compound (Section 10.3)

To determine the chemical formula of an ionic compound, write the Lewis structures of each of the elements. Then choose the correct number of each type of atom so that the metal atom(s) lose all of their valence electrons and the nonmetal atom(s) get an octet.

EXAMPLE 10.14   Using Lewis Theory to Predict the Chemical Formula of an Ionic Compound

Use Lewis theory to predict the formula for the compound that forms between potassium and sulfur.

Solution:
The Lewis structures of K and S are:

$$K\cdot \qquad \cdot \ddot{\underset{\cdot\cdot}{S}} \colon$$

Potassium must lose 1 electron and sulfur must gain 2. Consequently, we need two potassium atoms to every sulfur atom. The Lewis structure is:

$$K^+ [\colon \ddot{\underset{\cdot\cdot}{S}} \colon]^{2-} K^+$$

The correct formula is K_2S.

Writing Lewis Structures for Covalent Compounds (Sections 10.4, 10.5)

To write covalent Lewis structures, follow these steps:

1. *Write the correct skeletal structure for the molecule.* Hydrogen atoms will always be terminal, halogens will usually be terminal, and many molecules tend to be symmetrical.

2. *Calculate the total number of electrons for the Lewis structure by summing the valence electrons of each atom in the molecule.* Remember that the number of valence electrons for any main-group element is equal to its group number in the periodic table. For poly-atomic ions, add 1 electron for each negative charge and subtract 1 electron for each positive charge.

3. *Distribute the electrons among the atoms, giving octets (or duets for hydrogen) to as many atoms as possible.* Begin by placing 2 electrons between each pair of atoms. These are the bonding electrons. Then distribute the remaining electrons, first to terminal atoms and then to the central atom.

4. *If any atoms lack an octet, form double or triple bonds as necessary to give them octets.* Do this by moving lone electron pairs from terminal atoms into the bonding region with the central atom.

LIVE EXAMPLE

EXAMPLE 10.15   Writing Lewis Structures for Covalent Compounds

Write a Lewis structure for CS_2.

Solution:

SCS

$$\text{Total \# e}^- = 1 \times (\text{\# valence e}^- \text{ in C})$$
$$+ 2 \times (\text{\# valence e}^- \text{ in S})$$
$$= 4 + 2(6)$$
$$= 16$$

S:C:S   (4 of 16 e⁻ used)

:S̈:C:S̈:   (16 of 16 e⁻ used)

:S̈::C::S̈:   or   :S̈=C=S̈:

Writing Resonance Structures (Section 10.6)

When two or more equivalent (or nearly equivalent) Lewis structures can be written for a molecule, the true structure is an average between these. Represent this by writing all of the correct structures (called resonance structures) with double-headed arrows between them.

EXAMPLE 10.16   Writing Resonance Structures

Write resonance structures for SeO_2.

Solution:

We can write a Lewis structure for SeO_2 by following the steps for writing covalent Lewis structures. We find that we can write two equally correct structures, so we draw them both as resonance structures.

:Ö—S̈e=Ö: ⟷   :Ö=S̈e—Ö:

Predicting the Shapes of Molecules (Section 10.7)

To determine the shape of a molecule, follow these steps:

1. *Draw a Lewis structure for the molecule.*

2. *Determine the total number of electron groups around the central atom.* Lone pairs, single bonds, double bonds, and triple bonds each count as one group.

3. *Determine the number of bonding groups and the number of lone pairs around the central atom.* These should sum to the result from Step 2. Bonding groups include single bonds, double bonds, and triple bonds.

4. *Use Table 10.1 to determine the electron geometry and molecular geometry.*

| EXAMPLE 10.17 | Predicting the Shapes of Molecules |

Predict the geometry of SeO_2.

Solution:
The Lewis structure for SeO_2 (as we saw in Example 10.16) is composed of the following two resonance structures.

$$:\ddot{O}-\ddot{S}e=\ddot{O}: \quad \longleftrightarrow \quad :\ddot{O}=\ddot{S}e-\ddot{O}:$$

Either of the resonance structures will give the same geometry.
Total number of electron groups = 3

Number of bonding groups = 2
Number of lone pairs = 1

Electron geometry = Trigonal planar
Molecular geometry = Bent

Determining whether a Molecule Is Polar (Section 10.8)

• *Determine whether the molecule contains polar bonds.* A bond is polar if the two bonding atoms have different electronegativities. If there are no polar bonds, the molecule is nonpolar.

• *Determine whether the polar bonds add together to form a net dipole moment.* Use VSEPR to determine the geometry of the molecule. Then visualize each bond as a rope pulling on the central atom. Is the molecule highly symmetrical? Do the pulls of the ropes cancel? If so, there is no net dipole moment and the molecule is nonpolar. If the molecule is asymmetrical and the pulls of the rope do not cancel, the molecule is polar.

LIVE EXAMPLE

| EXAMPLE 10.18 | Determining whether a Molecule Is Polar |

Determine whether SeO_2 is polar.

Solution:
Se and O are nonmetals with different electronegativities (2.4 for Se and 3.5 for O). Therefore, the Se–O bonds are polar.

As we saw in Example 10.17, the geometry of SeO_2 is bent.

The polar bonds do not cancel but rather sum to give a net dipole moment. Therefore the molecule is polar.

Key Terms

bent [10.7]
bonding pair [10.4]
bonding theory [10.1]
chemical bond [10.2]
covalent bond [10.2]
dipole moment [10.8]
dot structure [10.2]
double bond [10.4]
duet [10.2]

electron geometry [10.7]
electron group [10.7]
electronegativity [10.8]
ionic bond [10.2]
Lewis structure [10.2]
Lewis theory [10.1]
linear [10.7]
lone pair [10.4]

molecular
  geometry [10.7]
nonpolar [10.8]
octet [10.2]
octet rule [10.2]
polar covalent bond [10.8]
polar molecule [10.8]
resonance
  structures [10.6]

terminal atom [10.5]
tetrahedral [10.7]
trigonal planar [10.7]
trigonal pyramidal [10.7]
triple bond [10.4]
valence shell electron
  pair repulsion theory
  (VSEPR) [10.7]

Exercises

Questions

1. Why are bonding theories important?
2. Give some examples of what bonding theories can predict.
3. Write the electron configurations for Ne and Ar. How many valence electrons do they each have?
4. In Lewis theory, what is an octet? What is a duet?
5. According to Lewis theory, what is a chemical bond?
6. What is the difference between ionic bonding and covalent bonding?
7. How can Lewis theory be used to determine the formula of ionic compounds? You may explain this with an example.
8. What is the difference between lone pair and bonding pair electrons?
9. How are double and triple bonds physically different from single bonds?
10. What is the procedure for writing a covalent Lewis structure?
11. How do you determine the number of electrons that go into the Lewis structure of a molecule?
12. How do you determine the number of electrons that go into the Lewis structure of a polyatomic ion?

13. Why does the octet rule have exceptions? Give some examples.
14. What are resonance structures? Why are they necessary?
15. Explain how VSEPR predicts the shapes of molecules.
16. If all of the electron groups around a central atom are bonding groups (that is, there are no lone pairs), what is the molecular geometry for:
    (a) two electron groups
    (b) three electron groups
    (c) four electron groups
17. Give the bond angles for each of the geometries in Question 16.
18. What is the difference between electron geometry and molecular geometry in VSEPR?
19. What is electronegativity?
20. What is the most electronegative element on the periodic table?
21. What is a polar covalent bond?
22. What is a dipole moment?
23. Why is it important to know if a molecule is polar or nonpolar?
24. If a molecule has polar bonds, will the molecule itself be polar? Why or why not?

Problems

Writing Lewis Structures for Elements

25. Write an electron configuration for each of the following elements and the corresponding Lewis structure. Indicate which electrons in the electron configuration are included in the Lewis structure.
    (a) N
    (b) C
    (c) Cl
    (d) Ar

26. Write an electron configuration for each of the following elements and the corresponding Lewis structure. Indicate which electrons in the electron configuration are included in the Lewis structure.
    (a) Li
    (b) P
    (c) F
    (d) Ne

27. Write Lewis structures for each of the following elements.
    (a) K
    (b) Al
    (c) P
    (d) Ar

28. Write Lewis structures for each of the following elements.
    (a) Mg
    (b) Si
    (c) S
    (d) Br

29. Write a generic Lewis structure for the halogens. Do the halogens tend to gain or lose electrons in chemical reactions? How many?

30. Write a generic Lewis structure for the alkali metals. Do the alkali metals tend to gain or lose electrons in chemical reactions? How many?

31. Write a generic Lewis structure for the alkaline earth metals. Do the alkaline earth metals tend to gain or lose electrons in chemical reactions? How many?

32. Write a generic Lewis structure for the elements in the oxygen family (Group 6). Do the elements in the oxygen family tend to gain or lose electrons in chemical reactions? How many?

33. Write a Lewis structure for each of the following ions.
    (a) Cl^-
    (b) Se^{2-}
    (c) Na^+
    (d) Mg^{2+}

34. Write a Lewis structure for each of the following ions.
    (a) N^{3-}
    (b) S^{2-}
    (c) Ca^{2+}
    (d) Al^{3+}

35. For each of the following ions, indicate the noble gas that has the same Lewis structure as the ion.
    (a) Br^-
    (b) O^{2-}
    (c) Rb^+
    (d) Ba^{2+}

36. For each of the following ions, indicate the noble gas that has the same Lewis structure as the ion.
    (a) Se^{2-}
    (b) I^-
    (c) Sr^{2+}
    (d) F^-

Lewis Structures for Ionic Compounds

37. Determine whether each of the following compounds would be best represented by an ionic or a covalent Lewis structure.
    (a) Rb_2O
    (b) CO_2
    (c) Al_2S_3
    (d) NO

38. Determine whether each of the following compounds would be best represented by an ionic or a covalent Lewis structure.
    (a) $MgCl_2$
    (b) K_2S
    (c) BrCl
    (d) SF_6

39. Write a Lewis structure for each of the following ionic compounds.
    (a) NaF
    (b) CaO
    (c) $SrBr_2$
    (d) K_2O

40. Write a Lewis structure for each of the following ionic compounds.
    (a) SrO
    (b) Li_2S
    (c) CaI_2
    (d) RbF

41. Use Lewis theory to determine the formula for the compound that forms from:
    (a) Sr and Se
    (b) Ba and Cl
    (c) Na and S
    (d) Al and O

42. Use Lewis theory to determine the formula for the compound that forms from:
    (a) Ca and N
    (b) Mg and I
    (c) Ca and S
    (d) Cs and F

43. Draw the Lewis structure for the ionic compound that forms from Li and:
    (a) F
    (b) O
    (c) N

44. Draw the Lewis structure for the ionic compound that forms from Ba and:
    (a) F
    (b) O
    (c) N

45. Determine what is wrong with each of the following ionic Lewis structures and write the correct structure.

(a) $[Cs:]^+$ $[:\ddot{C}l:]^-$

(b) Ba^+ $[:\ddot{O}:]^-$

(c) Ca^{2+} $[:\ddot{\underset{..}{I}}:]^-$

46. Determine what is wrong with each of the following ionic Lewis structures and write the correct structure.

(a) $[:\ddot{O}:]^{2-}$ Na^+ $[:\ddot{O}:]^{2-}$

(b) $Mg:\ddot{O}:$

(c) $[Li:]^+[:\ddot{\underset{..}{S}}:]^-$

Lewis Structures for Covalent Compounds

47. Write a Lewis structure for each of the following molecules.
(a) PH_3
(b) SCl_2
(c) F_2
(d) HI

48. Write a Lewis structure for each of the following molecules.
(a) CH_4
(b) NF_3
(c) OF_2
(d) H_2O

49. Write a Lewis structure for each of the following molecules.
(a) O_2
(b) CO
(c) $HONO$ (N is central)
(d) SO_2

50. Write a Lewis structure for each of the following molecules.
(a) N_2O (oxygen is terminal)
(b) SiH_4
(c) CI_4
(d) Cl_2CO (carbon is central)

51. Write a Lewis structure for each of the following molecules.
(a) C_2H_2
(b) C_2H_4
(c) N_2H_2
(d) N_2H_4

52. Write a Lewis structure for each of the following molecules.
(a) H_2CO (carbon is central)
(b) H_3COH (carbon and oxygen are both central)
(c) H_3COCH_3 (oxygen is between the two carbon atoms)
(d) H_2O_2

53. Determine what is wrong with each of the following Lewis structures and write the correct structure.

(a) $:\ddot{N}=\ddot{N}:$

(b) $:\ddot{S}-Si-\ddot{S}:$

(c) $H-H-\ddot{O}:$

(d) $:\ddot{\underset{..}{I}}-N-\ddot{\underset{..}{I}}:$ with $:\ddot{\underset{..}{I}}:$ below N

54. Determine what is wrong with each of the following Lewis structures and write the correct structure.

(a) $H-H-H-\ddot{N}:$

(b) $:\ddot{C}l=O=\ddot{C}l:$

(c) $H-\underset{\underset{..}{\overset{:\ddot{O}:}{|}}}{C}-\ddot{O}-H$

(d) $H=\ddot{B}r:$

55. Write a Lewis structure for each of the following molecules or ions. Include resonance structures if necessary.
(a) SeO_2
(b) CO_3^{2-}
(c) ClO^-
(d) ClO_2^-

56. Write a Lewis structure for each of the following molecules or ions. Include resonance structures if necessary.
(a) ClO_3^-
(b) ClO_4^-
(c) NO_3^-
(d) SO_3

57. Write a Lewis structure for each of the following ions. Include resonance structures if necessary.
    (a) PO_4^{3-}
    (b) CN^-
    (c) NO_2^-
    (d) SO_3^{2-}

58. Write a Lewis structure for each of the following ions. Include resonance structures if necessary.
    (a) SO_4^{2-}
    (b) HSO_4^- (S is central; H is attached to one of the O atoms)
    (c) NH_4^+
    (d) BrO_2^- (Br is central)

59. Write a Lewis structure for each of the following molecules that are exceptions to the octet rule.
    (a) BCl_3
    (b) NO_2
    (c) BH_3

60. Write a Lewis structure for each of the following molecules that are exceptions to the octet rule.
    (a) BBr_3
    (b) NO

Predicting the Shapes of Molecules

61. Determine the number of electron groups around the central atom for each of the following molecules.
    (a) PCl_3
    (b) SBr_2
    (c) CH_2Cl_2
    (d) CS_2

62. Determine the number of electron groups around the central atom for each of the following molecules.
    (a) CH_4
    (b) NF_3
    (c) OF_2
    (d) H_2S

63. Determine the number of bonding groups and the number of lone pairs for each of the molecules in Problem 61. The sum of these should equal your answer to Problem 61.

64. Determine the number of bonding groups and the number of lone pairs for each of the molecules in Problem 62. The sum of these should equal your answer to Problem 62.

65. Determine the molecular geometry of each of the following molecules.
    (a) CBr_4
    (b) H_2CO
    (c) CS_2
    (d) BH_3

66. Determine the molecular geometry of each of the following molecules.
    (a) SiO_2
    (b) BF_3
    (c) $CFCl_3$ (carbon is central)
    (d) H_2CS (carbon is central)

67. Determine the bond angles for each molecule in Problem 65.

68. Determine the bond angles for each molecule in Problem 66.

69. Determine the electron and molecular geometries of each of the following molecules.
    (a) N_2O (oxygen is terminal)
    (b) SO_2
    (c) H_2S
    (d) PF_3

70. Determine the electron and molecular geometries of each of the following molecules. (Hint: Determine the geometry around each of the two central atoms.)
    (a) C_2H_2 (skeletal structure HCCH)
    (b) C_2H_4 (skeletal structure H_2CCH_2)
    (c) C_2H_6 (skeletal structure H_3CCH_3)

71. Determine the bond angles for each molecule in Problem 69.

72. Determine the bond angles for each molecule in Problem 70.

73. Determine the electron and molecular geometries of each of the following molecules. For those with two central atoms, indicate the geometry about each central atom.
    (a) N_2
    (b) N_2H_2 (skeletal structure HNNH)
    (c) N_2H_4 (skeletal structure H_2NNH_2)

74. Determine the electron and molecular geometries of each of the following molecules. For those with more than one central atom, indicate the geometry about each central atom.
    (a) CH_3OH (skeletal structure H_3COH)
    (b) H_3COCH_3 (skeletal structure H_3COCH_3)
    (c) H_2O_2 (skeletal structure HOOH)

75. Determine the molecular geometry of each of the following polyatomic ions.
    (a) CO_3^{2-}
    (b) ClO_2^-
    (c) NO_3^-
    (d) NH_4^+

76. Determine the molecular geometry of each of the following polyatomic ions.
    (a) ClO_4^-
    (b) BrO_2^-
    (c) NO_2^-
    (d) SO_4^{2-}

Electronegativity and Polarity

77. Use Figure 10.2 to determine the electronegativity of each of the following elements.
    (a) Mg
    (b) Si
    (c) Br

78. Use Figure 10.2 to determine the electronegativity of each of the following elements.
    (a) F
    (b) C
    (c) S

79. List the following elements in order of increasing electronegativity: Rb, Si, Cl, Ca, Ga

80. List the following elements in order of decreasing electronegativity: Ba, N, F, Si, Cs

81. Use Figure 10.2 to find the electronegativity difference between each of the following pairs of elements and then use Table 10.2 to classify the bonds that occur between them as pure covalent, polar covalent, or ionic.
    (a) Mg and Br
    (b) Cr and F
    (c) Br and Br
    (d) Si and O

82. Use Figure 10.2 to find the electronegativity difference between each of the following pairs of elements and then use Table 10.2 to classify the bonds that occur between them as pure covalent, polar covalent, or ionic.
    (a) K and Cl
    (b) N and N
    (c) C and S
    (d) C and Cl

83. Arrange the following diatomic molecules in order of increasing bond polarity:

    ICl, HBr, H_2, CO

84. Arrange the following diatomic molecules in order of decreasing bond polarity:

    HCl, NO, F_2, HI

85. Classify each of the following diatomic molecules as polar or nonpolar.
    (a) CO
    (b) O_2
    (c) F_2
    (d) HBr

86. Classify each of the following diatomic molecules as polar or nonpolar.
    (a) I_2
    (b) NO
    (c) HCl
    (d) N_2

87. For each polar molecule in Problem 85, draw the molecule and indicate the positive and negative ends of the dipole moment.

88. For each polar molecule in Problem 86, draw the molecule and indicate the positive and negative ends of the dipole moment.

89. Classify each of the following molecules as polar or nonpolar.
    (a) CS_2
    (b) SO_2
    (c) CH_4
    (d) CH_3Cl

90. Classify each of the following molecules as polar or nonpolar.
    (a) H_2CO
    (b) CH_3OH
    (c) CH_2Cl_2
    (d) SiO_2

91. Classify each of the following molecules as polar or nonpolar.
    (a) BH_3
    (b) $CHCl_3$
    (c) C_2H_2
    (d) NH_3

92. Classify each of the following molecules as polar or nonpolar.
    (a) N_2H_2
    (b) H_2O_2
    (c) CF_4
    (d) NO_2

Cumulative Problems

93. Write electron configurations and Lewis structures for each of the following elements. Indicate which of the electrons in the electron configuration are shown in the Lewis structure.
(a) Ca
(b) Ga
(c) As
(d) I

94. Write electron configurations and Lewis structures for each of the following elements. Indicate which of the electrons in the electron configuration are shown in the Lewis structure.
(a) Rb
(b) Ge
(c) Kr
(d) Se

95. Determine whether each of the following compounds is ionic or covalent and write an appropriate Lewis structure.
(a) K_2S
(b) CHFO (carbon is central)
(c) MgSe
(d) PBr_3

96. Determine whether each of the following compounds is ionic or covalent and write an appropriate Lewis structure.
(a) HCN
(b) ClF
(c) MgI_2
(d) CaS

97. Write a Lewis structure for $OCCl_2$ (carbon is central) and determine whether the molecule is polar. Draw a three-dimensional structure for the molecule.

98. Write a Lewis structure for CH_3COH and determine whether the molecule is polar. Draw a three-dimensional structure for the molecule. The skeletal structure is:

$$
\begin{array}{ccc}
& H & O \\
H & C & C & H \\
& H &
\end{array}
$$

99. Write a Lewis structure for acetic acid (a component of vinegar), CH_3COOH, and draw a three-dimensional sketch of the molecule. The skeletal structure is:

$$
\begin{array}{ccccc}
& H & O & & \\
H & C & C & O & H \\
& H & & &
\end{array}
$$

100. Write a Lewis structure for benzene, C_6H_6, and draw a three-dimensional sketch of the molecule. The skeletal structure is the ring shown here. (Hint: Include two resonance structures.)

$$
\begin{array}{ccc}
& H & \\
& C & \\
HC & & CH \\
HC & & CH \\
& C & \\
& H &
\end{array}
$$

101. Consider the following neutralization reaction.

$$HCl(aq) + NaOH(aq) \longrightarrow H_2O(l) + NaCl(aq)$$

Write the reaction showing the Lewis structures of each of the reactants and products.

102. Consider the following precipitation reaction.

$$Ba(NO_3)_2(aq) + 2\,LiCl(aq) \longrightarrow BaCl_2(s) + 2\,LiNO_3(aq)$$

Write the reaction showing the Lewis structures of each of the reactants and products.

103. Consider the following redox reaction:

$$2\,K(s) + Cl_2(g) \longrightarrow 2\,KCl(s)$$

Draw Lewis structures for each reactant and product and determine which reactant was oxidized and which one was reduced.

104. Consider the following redox reaction:

$$Ca(s) + Br_2(g) \longrightarrow CaBr_2(s)$$

Draw Lewis structures for each reactant and product and determine which reactant was oxidized and which one was reduced.

105. Each of the following compounds contains both ionic and covalent bonds. Write an ionic Lewis structure for each one, including the covalent structure for the ion in brackets. Write resonance structures if necessary.
  (a) KOH
  (b) KNO_3
  (c) LiIO
  (d) $BaCO_3$

106. Each of the following compounds contains both ionic and covalent bonds. Write an ionic Lewis structure for each one, including the covalent structure for the ion in brackets. Write resonance structures if necessary.
  (a) $RbIO_2$
  (b) $Ca(OH)_2$
  (c) NH_4Cl
  (d) $Sr(CN)_2$

107. Each of the following molecules contains an expanded octet (10 or 12 electrons) around the central atom. Write a Lewis structure for each molecule.
  (a) PF_5
  (b) SF_4
  (c) SeF_4

108. Each of the following molecules contains an expanded octet (10 or 12 electrons) around the central atom. Write a Lewis structure for each molecule.
  (a) ClF_5
  (b) SF_6
  (c) IF_5

109. Formic acid is responsible for the sting in biting ants. By mass, formic acid is 26.10% C, 4.38% H, and 69.52% O. The molar mass of formic acid is 46.02 g/mol. Find the molecular formula of formic acid and draw its Lewis structure.

110. Diazomethane has the following composition by mass: 28.57% C, 4.80% H, and 66.64% N. The molar mass of diazomethane is 42.04 g/mol. Find the molecular formula of diazomethane and draw its Lewis structure.

Highlight Problems

111. Some theories on aging suggest that a class of molecules and ions called *free radicals* cause some diseases and aging. Free radicals are molecules or ions containing an unpaired electron. As you know from Lewis theory, such molecules are not chemically stable and quickly react with other molecules. Free radicals may attack molecules within the cell, such as DNA, changing them and causing cancer or other diseases. Free radicals may also attack molecules on the surfaces of cells, making them appear foreign to the body's immune system. The immune system then attacks the cell and destroys it, weakening the body. Draw a Lewis structure for each of the following free radicals implicated in this theory of aging.
  (a) O_2^-
  (b) O^-
  (c) OH
  (d) CH_3OO (unpaired electron on terminal oxygen)

▲ Free radicals, molecules containing unpaired electrons (represented here as X·), may attack biological molecules such as the DNA molecule depicted here.

112. Free radicals (see Problem 111) are also important in many environmentally significant reactions. For example, photochemical smog, which forms as a result of the action of sunlight on air pollutants, is formed in part by the following two steps.

$$NO_2 \xrightarrow{\text{UV light}} NO + O$$

$$O + O_2 \longrightarrow O_3$$

The product of this reaction, ozone, is a pollutant in the lower atmosphere. Ozone is an eye and lung irritant and also accelerates the weathering of rubber products. Write Lewis structures for each of the reactants and products in the preceding reactions.

▲ Ozone damages rubber products.

113. The following are formulas of several molecules along with a space-filling model of their structure. Determine whether the structure is correct and if not, make a sketch of the correct structure.

(a) H_2Se

(b) CSe_2

(c) PCl_3

(d) CF_2Cl_2

Answers to Skillbuilder Exercises

Skillbuilder 10.1 $\cdot Mg \cdot$

Skillbuilder 10.2

$Na^+\ [:\ddot{\underset{..}{B}}r:]^-$

Skillbuilder 10.3 Mg_3N_2

Skillbuilder 10.4

$:C\equiv O:$

Skillbuilder 10.5

$$\underset{H-\overset{\|}{C}-H}{\overset{\ddot{O}:}{\,}}$$

Skillbuilder 10.6

$$[:\ddot{\underset{..}{C}}l - \ddot{\underset{..}{O}}:]^-$$

Skillbuilder 10.7

$$[:\ddot{O}=\ddot{N}-\ddot{\underset{..}{O}}:]^- \longleftrightarrow [:\ddot{\underset{..}{O}}-\ddot{N}=\ddot{O}:]^-$$

Skillbuilder 10.8   bent

Skillbuilder 10.9   trigonal pyramidal

Skillbuilder 10.10   **(a)** pure covalent
(b) ionic
(c) polar covalent

Skillbuilder 10.11 CH_4 is nonpolar

Answers to Conceptual Checkpoints

10.1 (b) Aluminum must lose its 3 valence electrons to get an octet. Sulfur must gain 2 electrons to get an octet. Therefore, 2 Al atoms are required for every 3 S atoms.

10.2 (b) Both NH_3 and H_3O^+ have 1 lone electron pair.

10.3 (d) If there are no lone pairs on the central atom, all of its valence electrons are involved in bonds, so the molecular geometry must be the same as the electron geometry.

Solutions

"Life can be thought of as water kept at the right temperature in the right atmosphere in the right light for a long enough period of time."

N. J. Berrill (1903–1996)

13.1 Tragedy in Cameroon

Carbon dioxide, a colorless and odorless gas, displaced the air in low-lying regions surrounding the lake, leaving no oxygen for the inhabitants to breathe. The rotten-egg smell indicates the presence of some additional sulfur-containing gases.

Most people living near Lake Nyos in Cameroon, West Africa, had an ordinary day on August 22, 1986. Unfortunately, the day ended in tragedy. On that evening, a large cloud of carbon dioxide gas, burped up from the depths of Lake Nyos, killed more than 1700 people and about 3000 head of cattle. Survivors tell of smelling rotten eggs, feeling a warm sensation, and then losing consciousness. Two years before that, a similar tragedy had occurred in Lake Monoun, just 60 miles away, killing thirty-seven people. Today, scientists are taking steps to prevent these lakes, both of which are in danger of burping again, from accumulating the carbon dioxide that caused the disaster.

◄ Carbon dioxide bubbled out of Lake Nyos and flowed into the adjacent valley. The carbon dioxide came from the bottom of the lake, where it was held in solution by the pressure of the water above it. When the layers in the lake were disturbed, the carbon dioxide came out of solution due to the decrease in pressure—with lethal consequences.

▲ Cameroon is in West Africa.

▲ Engineers watch as carbon dioxide vented from the bottom of Lake Nyos creates a geyser. The controlled release of carbon dioxide from the lake bed is designed to prevent future catastrophes like the one that killed more than 1700 people in 1986.

Lake Nyos is a water-filled volcanic crater. Some 50 miles beneath the surface of the lake, molten volcanic rock (magma) produces carbon dioxide gas that seeps into the lake through the volcano's plumbing system. The carbon dioxide mixes with the lake water, and the great pressure at the bottom of the deep lake allows the concentration of carbon dioxide to become very high (just as the pressure in a beer can allows the concentration of carbon dioxide in beer to be very high). Over time, the carbon dioxide and water mixture at the bottom of the lake became so concentrated that—either because of the high concentration itself or because of some other natural trigger such as a landslide—some gaseous carbon dioxide escaped. The rising bubbles disrupted the stratified layers of lake water, causing the highly concentrated carbon dioxide and water mixture at the bottom of the lake to rise, lowering the pressure on it. The drop in pressure on the mixture released more carbon dioxide bubbles just as the drop in pressure upon opening a beer can releases carbon dioxide bubbles. This in turn caused more churning and more carbon dioxide release. Since carbon dioxide is heavier than air, it traveled down the sides of the volcano and into the nearby valley, displacing air and asphyxiating many of the local residents.

In efforts to prevent these events from occurring again—by 2001, carbon dioxide concentrations had already returned to dangerously high levels—scientists built a piping system that slowly vents carbon dioxide from the lake bottom. This system gradually releases the carbon dioxide into the atmosphere, preventing a repeat of the tragedy.

13.2   Solutions: Homogenous Mixtures

The carbon dioxide and water mixture at the bottom of Lake Nyos is an example of a **solution**, a homogenous mixture of two or more substances. Solutions are all around us—most of the liquids and gases that we encounter every day are actually solutions. When most people think of a solution, they think of a solid dissolved in water. The ocean, for example, is a solution of salt and other solids dissolved in water, and our blood is a solution of several solids (as well as some gases) dissolved in water. However, many other kinds of solutions exist. A solution may be composed of a gas and a liquid (like the carbon dioxide and water of Lake Nyos), a liquid and another liquid, a solid and a gas, or other combinations (see Table 13.1).

The most common solutions, however, are those containing a solid, a liquid, or a gas and water. These are called *aqueous solutions*—they are critical to life and are the main focus of this chapter. Common examples of aqueous solutions include sugar water and salt water, both solutions of solids and water. Similarly, ethyl alcohol—the alcohol in alcoholic beverages—readily

Aqueous comes from the Latin word *aqua*, meaning "water."

TABLE 13.1 Common Types of Solutions

Solution Phase	Solute Phase	Solvent Phase	Example
gaseous solutions	gas	gas	air (mainly oxygen and nitrogen)
liquid solutions	gas	liquid	soda water (CO_2 and water)
	liquid	liquid	vodka (ethanol and water)
	solid	liquid	seawater (salt and water)
solid solutions	solid	solid	brass (copper and zinc) and other alloys

TABLE 13.2 Common Laboratory Solvents

Common Polar Solvents	Common Nonpolar Solvents
water (H_2O)	hexane (C_6H_{12})
acetone (CH_3COCH_3)	ethyl ether ($CH_3CH_2OCH_2CH_3$)
methyl alcohol (CH_3OH)	toluene (C_7H_8)

mixes with water to form a solution of a liquid with water, and we have already seen an example of a gas-and-water solution in Lake Nyos.

A solution has at least two components. The majority component is usually called the **solvent**, and the minority component is called the **solute**. In our carbon-dioxide-and-water solution, carbon dioxide is the solute and water is the solvent. In a salt-and-water solution, salt is the solute and water is the solvent. Because water is so abundant on Earth, it is a common solvent. However, other solvents are often used in the laboratory and even in the home, especially to form solutions with nonpolar solutes. For example, you may use paint thinner, a nonpolar solvent, to remove grease from a dirty bicycle chain or from ball bearings. The paint thinner dissolves (or forms a solution with) the grease, removing it from the metal. In general, polar solvents dissolve polar or ionic solutes and nonpolar solvents dissolve nonpolar solutes. This tendency is described by the rule *like dissolves like*. Thus, similar kinds of solvents dissolve similar kinds of solutes. Table 13.2 lists some common polar and nonpolar laboratory solvents.

> In a solid/liquid solution, the liquid is usually considered the solvent, regardless of the relative proportions of the components.

> See Sections 10.8 and 12.6 to review the concept of polarity.

> Like dissolves like—polar solvents dissolve polar solutes and nonpolar solvents dissolve nonpolar solutes.

CONCEPTUAL CHECKPOINT 13.1

Which of these compounds would you expect to be *least* soluble in water?

(a) CCl_4
(b) CH_3Cl
(c) H_2S
(d) KF

13.3 Solutions of Solids Dissolved in Water: How to Make Rock Candy

We have already seen several examples of solutions of a solid dissolved in water. The ocean, for example, is a solution of salt and other solids dissolved in water. A sweetened cup of coffee is a solution of sugar and other solids dissolved in water. Our blood is a solution of several solids (and some gases) dissolved in water. Not all solids, however, dissolve in water. We already know that nonpolar solids—such as lard and shortening, for example—do not dissolve in water. However, solids such as calcium carbonate and sand do not dissolve either.

When a solid is put into water, there is a competition between the attractive forces that hold the solid together (the solute–solute interactions) and the attractive forces occurring between the water molecules and the particles that compose the solid (the solvent–solute interactions). For example, when sodium chloride is put into water, there is a competition between the attraction of Na^+ cations and Cl^- anions to each other and the attraction of Na^+

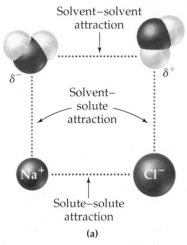

Solvent–solvent attraction

δ^- δ^+

Solvent–solute attraction

Na$^+$ Cl$^-$

Solute–solute attraction

(a)

▲ **Figure 13.1   How a solid dissolves in water   (a)** When NaCl is put into water, the attraction between water molecules and Na$^+$ and Cl$^-$ ions (solvent–solute attraction) overcomes the attraction between Na$^+$ and Cl$^-$ ions (solute–solute attraction). **(b)** The positive ends of the water dipoles are attracted to the negatively charged Cl$^-$ ions and the negative ends of the water dipoles are attracted to the positively charged Na$^+$ ions. The result is that water molecules surround the ions of NaCl and disperse them in the solution.

(b)

and Cl$^-$ to water molecules (▲ Figure 13.1a). For sodium ions, the attraction is between the positive charge of the sodium ion and the negative side of water's dipole moment (▲ Figure 13.1b). For chloride ions, the attraction is between the negative charge of the chloride ion and the positive side of water's dipole moment. In the case of NaCl, the attraction to water wins, and sodium chloride dissolves (▼ Figure 13.2). In the case of calcium carbonate (CaCO$_3$), the attraction between Ca^{2+} ions and CO$_3{}^{2-}$ ions wins and calcium carbonate does not dissolve in water.

▶ **Figure 13.2   A sodium chloride solution**   In a solution of NaCl, the Na$^+$ and Cl$^-$ ions are dispersed in the water.

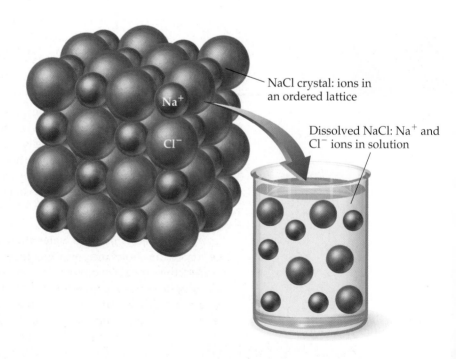

NaCl crystal: ions in an ordered lattice

Dissolved NaCl: Na$^+$ and Cl$^-$ ions in solution

Solubility and Saturation

The **solubility** of a compound is defined as the amount of the compound, usually in grams, that will dissolve in a certain amount of liquid. For example, the solubility of sodium chloride at 25 °C is 36 g NaCl per 100 g water, while the solubility of calcium carbonate is close to zero. A solution that has 36 g of NaCl per 100 g water is called a saturated sodium chloride solution. A **saturated solution** is one that holds the maximum amount of solute under the solution conditions. If additional solute is added to a saturated solution, it will not dissolve. An **unsaturated solution** is one holding less than the maximum amount of solute. If additional solute is added to an unsaturated solution, it will dissolve. A **supersaturated solution** is one holding more than the normal maximum amount of solute. The solute will normally precipitate from (or come out of) a supersaturated solution. As the carbon dioxide and water solution rose from the bottom of Lake Nyos, for example, it became supersaturated because of the drop in pressure. The excess gas came out of the solution and rose to the surface of the lake, where it was emitted into the surrounding air.

Supersaturated solutions can form under special circumstances, such as the sudden release in pressure that occurs in a soda can when it is opened.

(a)   (b)   (c)

▲ A supersaturated solution holds more than the normal maximum amount of solute. In some cases, such as the sodium acetate solution pictured here, a supersaturated solution may be temporarily stable. Any disturbance however, such as dropping in a small piece of solid sodium acetate **(a)**, will cause the solid to come out of solution **(b, c)**.

Table 7.2 lists the solubility rules for ionic compounds.

In Chapter 7 we learned the solubility rules, which give us a qualitative description of the solubility of ionic solids. Molecular solids may also be soluble in water depending on whether the solid is polar. Table sugar ($C_{12}H_{22}O_{11}$), for example, is polar and soluble in water. Nonpolar solids, such as lard and vegetable shortening, are usually insoluble in water.

Electrolyte Solutions: Dissolved Ionic Solids

There is an important difference, however, between a sugar solution (containing a molecular solid) and a salt solution (containing an ionic solid) (▶ Figure 13.3). In a salt solution the dissolved particles are ions, while in a sugar solution the dissolved particles are molecules. The ions in the salt solution are mobile charged particles and can therefore conduct electricity. As we learned in Section 7.5, a solution containing a solute that dissociates into ions is called an **electrolyte solution**. The sugar solution contains dissolved sugar molecules and cannot conduct electricity; it is called a **nonelectrolyte solution**. In general, soluble ionic solids form electrolyte solutions, while soluble molecular solids form nonelectrolyte solutions.

NaCl forms a strong electrolyte solution (Section 7.5). Weak electrolyte solutions will be covered in Chapter 14.

▶ Figure 13.3 **Electrolyte and non-electrolyte solutions** Electrolyte solutions contain dissolved ions (charged particles) and therefore conduct electricity. Nonelectrolyte solutions contain dissolved molecules (neutral particles) and so do not conduct electricity.

Dissolved ions (NaCl)

Dissolved molecules (sugar)

Electrolyte solution   Nonelectrolyte solution

How Solubility Varies with Temperature

The solubility of solids in water can be highly dependent on temperature. Have you ever noticed how much easier it is to dissolve sugar in hot tea than in cold tea? In general, the solubility of *solids* in water increases with increasing temperature (▼ Figure 13.4). For example, the solubility of potassium nitrate (KNO_3) at 20 °C is about 37 g KNO_3 per 100 g of water. However, at 50 °C, the solubility rises to 88 g KNO_3 per 100 g of water. A common way to purify a solid is a technique called **recrystallization**. In this technique, the solid is put into water (or some other solvent) at an elevated temperature. Enough solid is added to the solvent to create a saturated solution at the elevated temperature. As the solution cools, the solubility decreases, causing some of the solid to precipitate from solution. If the solution cools slowly, the solid will form crystals as it comes out. The crystalline structure tends to reject impurities, resulting in a purer solid.

Rock Candy

A similar effect can be seen if you make rock candy. To make rock candy, a saturated sucrose (table sugar) solution is prepared at an elevated temperature. A string is left to dangle in the solution, and the solution is allowed to cool and stand for several days. As the solution cools, it becomes supersaturated and sugar crystals grow on the string. After several days, beautiful and delicious crystals, or "rocks," of sugar cover the string, ready to be admired and eaten.

▲ Rock candy is composed of sugar crystals that have been grown through recrystallization.

▶ Figure 13.4 **Solubility of some ionic solids as a function of temperature**

13.4 Solutions of Gases in Water: How Soda Pop Gets Its Fizz

The water at the bottom of Lake Nyos and a can of soda pop are both examples of a gas dissolved in a liquid. They are solutions of carbon dioxide and water. Most liquids exposed to air contain some dissolved gases. Lake water and seawater, for example, contain dissolved oxygen necessary for the survival of fish. Our blood contains dissolved nitrogen, oxygen, and carbon dioxide. Even tap water contains dissolved nitrogen and oxygen.

You can see the dissolved gases in ordinary tap water by heating it on a stove. Before the water reaches its boiling point, you will see small bubbles develop in the water. These bubbles are dissolved air (mostly nitrogen and oxygen) coming out of solution. Once the water boils, the bubbling becomes more vigorous—these larger bubbles are composed of water vapor. The dissolved air comes out of solution because—unlike solids, whose solubility *increases* with increasing temperature—the solubility of gases in water *decreases* with increasing temperature. As the temperature of the water rises, the solubility of the dissolved nitrogen and oxygen decreases and these gases come out of solution, forming small bubbles around the bottom of the pot. The decrease in the solubility of gases with increasing temperature is the reason that warm soda pop bubbles more than cold soda pop and also the reason that warm beer goes flat faster than cold beer. The carbon dioxide comes out of solution faster (bubbles more) at room temperature than at lower temperature because it is less soluble at room temperature.

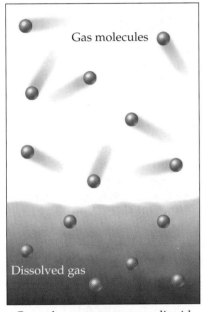

Gas at low pressure over a liquid

Gas molecules

Dissolved gas

Cold soda pop   Warm soda pop

▲ Warm soda pop fizzes more than cold soda pop because the solubility of the dissolved carbon dioxide decreases with increasing temperature.

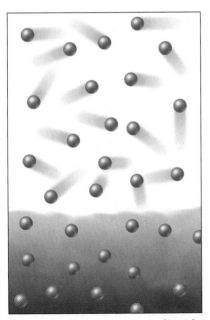

Gas at high pressure over a liquid

▲ **Figure 13.5 Pressure and solubility** The higher the pressure above a liquid, the more soluble the gas is in the liquid.

The solubility of gases also depends on pressure. The higher the pressure above a liquid, the more soluble the gas is in the liquid (◀ Figure 13.5). In a can of soda pop and in Lake Nyos, carbon dioxide is maintained in solution by high pressure. In soda pop, the pressure is provided by a large amount of carbon dioxide gas that is pumped into the can before sealing it.

▶ **Figure 13.6** **Pop! Fizz!** A can of soda pop is pressurized with carbon dioxide. When the can is opened the pressure is released, lowering the solubility of carbon dioxide in the solution and causing it to come out of solution as bubbles.

CO_2 pressure released

CO_2 under pressure

CO_2 bubbles out of solution

CO_2 dissolved in solution

The increase in solubility of a gas with increasing pressure is known as *Henry's law*.

When the can is opened, the pressure is released and the solubility of carbon dioxide decreases, resulting in bubbling (▲ Figure 13.6). In Lake Nyos, the pressure is provided by the mass of the lake water itself pushing down on the carbon-dioxide-rich water at the bottom of the lake. When the stratification (or layering) of the lake is disturbed, the pressure on the carbon dioxide solution is lowered and the solubility of carbon dioxide decreases, resulting in the release of excess carbon dioxide gas.

13.5   Specifying Solution Concentration: Mass Percent

As we have seen, the amount of solute in a solution is an important property of the solution. For example, the amount of carbon dioxide in the water at the bottom of Lake Nyos is an important predictor of when the deadly event may repeat itself. A **dilute solution** is one containing small amounts of solute relative to solvent. If the water at the bottom of Lake Nyos were a dilute carbon dioxide solution, it would pose little threat. A **concentrated solution** is one containing large amounts of solute relative to solvent. If the water at the bottom of Lake Nyos becomes concentrated in carbon dioxide (through the continual feeding of carbon dioxide from magma into the lake), it becomes a large threat. A common way to report solution concentration is *mass percent*.

Mass Percent

Also in common use are *parts per million (ppm)*, the number of grams of solute per 1 million g of solution, and *parts per billion (ppb)*, the number of grams of solute per 1 billion g of solution.

Mass percent is simply the number of grams of solute per 100 g of solution. So a solution with a concentration of 14% by mass, for example, contains 14 g of solute per 100 g of solution. To calculate mass percent, simply divide the mass of the solute by the mass of the solution (solute *and* solvent) and multiply by 100%.

Note that the denominator is the mass of *solution*, not the mass of solvent.

$$\text{Mass percent} = \frac{\text{Mass solute}}{\text{Mass solution}} \times 100\%$$

For example, suppose you wanted to calculate the mass percent of NaCl in a solution containing 15.3 g of NaCl and 155.0 g of water. Set up the problem as you normally would.

Given:

15.3 g NaCl

155.0 g H_2O

Find: mass percent

Equation: This problem requires the use of the equation that defines mass percent.

$$\text{Mass percent} = \frac{\text{Mass solute}}{\text{Mass solution}} \times 100\%$$

Solution: The mass of solution is simply the mass of NaCl plus the mass of H_2O.

$$\text{Mass solution} = \text{Mass NaCl} + \text{Mass } H_2O$$
$$= 15.3 \text{ g} + 155.0 \text{ g}$$
$$= 170.3 \text{ g}$$

We then substitute the correct quantities into the equation.

$$\text{Mass percent} = \frac{\text{Mass solute}}{\text{Mass solution}} \times 100\%$$
$$= \frac{15.3 \text{ g}}{170.3 \text{ g}} \times 100\%$$
$$= 8.98\%$$

The solution is 8.98% NaCl by mass.

EXAMPLE 13.1   **Calculating Mass Percent**

Calculate the mass percent of a solution containing 27.5 g of ethanol (C_2H_6O) and 175 mL of H_2O. (Assume that the density of water is 1.00 g/mL.)

Begin by setting up the problem. You are given the mass of ethanol and the volume of water and asked to find the mass percent of the solution.

Given:

27.5 g C_2H_6O
175 mL H_2O

Find: mass percent

You will need the equation that defines mass percent and the density of water

Equation and Conversion Factor:

$$\text{Mass percent} = \frac{\text{Mass solute}}{\text{Mass solution}} \times 100\%$$

$$d(H_2O) = \frac{1.00 \text{ g}}{\text{mL}}$$

To find the mass percent, substitute into the equation for mass percent. You need the mass of the solution, which is simply the mass of ethanol plus the mass of water. The mass of water is obtained from the volume of water by using the density as a conversion factor.

Solution:

$$\text{Mass } H_2O = 175 \text{ mL } H_2O \times \frac{1.00 \text{ g}}{\text{mL}} = 175 \text{ g}$$

$$\text{Mass solution} = \text{Mass } C_2H_6O + \text{Mass } H_2O$$
$$= 27.5 \text{ g} + 175 \text{ g}$$
$$= 202.5 \text{ g}$$

Finally, substitute the correct quantities into the equation and calculate the mass percent.

$$\text{Mass percent} = \frac{\text{Mass solute}}{\text{Mass solution}} \times 100\%$$

$$= \frac{27.5 \text{ g}}{202.5 \text{ g}} \times 100\%$$

$$= 13.6\%$$

SKILLBUILDER 13.1   **Calculating Mass Percent**

Calculate the mass percent of a sucrose solution containing 11.3 g of sucrose and 412.1 mL of water. (Assume that the density of water is 1.00 g/mL.)

Using Mass Percent in Calculations

The mass percent of a solution can be used as a conversion factor between mass of the solute and mass of the solution. The key to using mass percent in this way is to write it as a fraction.

$$\text{Mass percent} = \frac{\text{g solute}}{100 \text{ g solution}}$$

A solution containing 3.5% sodium chloride, for example, has the following conversion factor.

$$\frac{3.5 \text{ g NaCl}}{100 \text{ g solution}} \qquad \text{converts g solution} \longrightarrow \text{g NaCl}$$

This conversion factor converts from grams of solution to grams of NaCl. If you want to go the other way, simply invert the conversion factor.

$$\frac{100 \text{ g solution}}{3.5 \text{ g NaCl}} \qquad \text{converts g NaCl} \longrightarrow \text{g solution}$$

As an example of using mass percent as a conversion factor, consider a water sample from the bottom of Lake Nyos containing 8.5% carbon dioxide by mass. How much carbon dioxide in grams is contained in 28.6 L of the water solution? (Assume that the density of the solution is 1.03 g/mL.) We set up the problem in the normal way.

Given:

8.5% CO_2 by mass

28.6 L solution

Find: g CO_2

Conversion Factors: The main conversion factor is the mass percent of the solution. We write it as g CO_2 per 100 g solution.

$$\frac{8.5 \text{ g } CO_2}{100 \text{ g solution}}$$

We will also need the density of the solution and the conversion factor between L and mL.

$$\frac{1.03 \text{ g}}{\text{mL}}$$

$$1000 \text{ mL} = 1 \text{ L}$$

Solution Map: The solution map begins with L solution and shows the conversion to mL solution and then to g solution using the density. The map then proceeds from g solution to g CO_2, using the mass percent (expressed as a fraction) as a conversion factor.

Solution: Finally, we follow the solution map to compute the answer.

$$28.6 \text{ L solution} \times \frac{1000 \text{ mL}}{\text{L}} \times \frac{1.03 \text{ g}}{\text{mL}}$$

$$\times \frac{8.5 \text{ g CO}_2}{100 \text{ g solution}} = 2.5 \times 10^3 \text{ g CO}_2$$

In this example, we used mass percent to convert from a given amount of *solution* to the amount of *solute* present in the solution. In Example 13.2, we use mass percent to convert from a given amount of *solute* to the amount of *solution* containing that solute.

EXAMPLE 13.2   Using Mass Percent in Calculations

A soft drink contains 11.5% sucrose ($C_{12}H_{22}O_{11}$) by mass. What volume of the soft drink solution in milliliters contains 85.2 g of sucrose? (Assume a density of 1.00 g/mL).

You are given the concentration of sucrose in a soft drink and a mass of sucrose. You are asked to find the volume of the soft drink that contains the given mass of sucrose. Write the mass percent concentration of sucrose as a conversion factor, remembering that percent means *per hundred*. You will also need the density to use as a conversion factor between mass and volume of the soft drink.	**Given:** 11.5% $C_{12}H_{22}O_{11}$ by mass 85.2 g $C_{12}H_{22}O_{11}$ **Find:** mL solution (soft drink) **Conversion Factors:** $\dfrac{11.5 \text{ g } C_{12}H_{22}O_{11}}{100 \text{ g solution}}$ $d = \dfrac{1.00 \text{ g}}{\text{mL}}$
Convert from g solute ($C_{12}H_{22}O_{11}$) to g solution using the mass percent in fractional form as the conversion factor. Convert to mL using the density.	**Solution Map:** g $C_{12}H_{22}O_{11}$ → g solution → mL solution $\dfrac{100 \text{ g solution}}{11.5 \text{ g } C_{12}H_{22}O_{11}}$ $\dfrac{1 \text{ mL}}{1.00 \text{ g}}$
Follow the solution map to solve the problem.	**Solution:** $85.2 \text{ g } C_{12}H_{22}O_{11} \times \dfrac{100 \text{ g solution}}{11.5 \text{ g } C_{12}H_{22}O_{11}}$ $\times \dfrac{1 \text{ mL solution}}{1.00 \text{ g}} = 741 \text{ mL solution}$

SKILLBUILDER 13.2   Using Mass Percent in Calculations

How much sucrose ($C_{12}H_{22}O_{11}$) in grams is contained in 355 mL (12 oz) of the soft drink in Example 13.2?

Chemistry IN THE ENVIRONMENT

The Dirty Dozen

▲ Potentially dangerous chemicals can leak into the environment and contaminate water and food supplies.

A number of potentially harmful chemicals—such as DDT, dioxin, and polychlorinated biphenyls (PCBs)—can make their way into our water sources from industrial dumping, atmospheric emissions, agriculture, and household dumping. Since crops, livestock, and fish all rely on water, they too can accumulate these chemicals from water. Human consumption of food or water contaminated with these chemicals can lead to a number of diseases and adverse health effects such as increased cancer risk, liver damage, or central nervous system damage. Governments around the world have joined forces to ban a number of these kinds of chemicals—called persistent organic pollutants or POPs—from production. The original treaty targeted twelve such substances called the dirty dozen (Table 13.3).

One difficult problem with all of these chemicals is their persistence. Once they get into the environment, they stay there for a long time. A second problem is a process called *bioamplification*. Because these chemicals are nonpolar, they are stored and concentrated in the fatty tissues of the organisms that consume them. As larger organisms eat smaller ones they consume more of the stored chemicals. The result is an increase in the concentrations of these chemicals as they move up the food chain. Under the draft treaty, nearly all intentional production of these chemicals will be banned.

TABLE 13.3 The Dirty Dozen

1. aldrin (insecticide)
2. chlordane (insecticide by-product)
3. DDT (insecticide)
4. dieldrin (insecticide)
5. dioxin (industrial by-product)
6. eldrin (insecticide)
7. furan (industrial by-product)
8. heptachlor (insecticide)
9. hexachlorobenzene (fungicide, industrial by-product)
10. mirex (insecticide, fire retardant)
11. polychlorinated biphenyls (PCBs) (electrical insulators)
12. toxaphene (insecticide)

In the United States, the presence of these contaminants in water supplies is monitored under supervision of the Environmental Protection Agency (EPA). The EPA has set limits, called maximum contaminant levels (MCLs), for each of these in food and drinking water. Some MCLs for selected compounds in water supplies are listed in Table 13.4.

TABLE 13.4 EPA Maximum Contaminant Level (MCL) for Several "Dirty Dozen" Chemicals

chlordane	0.002 mg/L
dioxin	0.00000003 mg/L
heptachlor	0.0004 mg/L
hexachlorobenzene	0.001 mg/L

Notice the units that the EPA uses to express the concentration of the contaminants: milligrams per liter. This unit is a conversion factor between liters of water consumed and the mass in milligrams of the pollutant. According to the EPA, as long as the contaminant concentrations are below these levels, the water is safe to drink.

CAN YOU ANSWER THIS? *Using what you know about conversion factors, calculate how much of each of the chemicals in Table 13.4 (at their MCL) would be present in 715 L of water, the approximate amount of water consumed by an adult in one year.*

13.6 Specifying Solution Concentration: Molarity

A second way to express solution concentration is **molarity (M)**, defined as the number of moles of solute per liter of solution. We calculate the molarity of a solution as follows:

$$\text{Molarity (M)} = \frac{\text{Moles solute}}{\text{Liters solution}}$$

◀ Figure 13.7 **Making a solution of specific molarity**   To make 1.00 L of a 1.00 M NaCl solution, you add 1.00 mol (58.44 g) of sodium chloride to a flask and then dilute to 1.00 L of total volume.   **Question:** What would happen if you added 1 L of water to 1 mol of sodium chloride? Would the resulting solution be 1 M?

How to prepare a 1.00 molar NaCl solution.

1.00 mole NaCl
(58.44 g)

Water

Add water until solid is dissolved. Then add additional water until the 1-liter mark is reached.

Mix

First add 1.00 mole of NaCl.

A 1.00 molar NaCl solution

TUTORIAL
Solution Formation from a Solid

Note that molarity is moles of solute per liter of *solution*, not per liter of solvent. To make a solution of a specified molarity, you usually put the solute into a flask and then add water to the desired volume of solution. For example, to make 1.00 L of a 1.00 M NaCl solution, you add 1.00 mol of NaCl to a flask and then add water to make 1.00 L of solution (▲ Figure 13.7). You *do not* combine 1.00 mol of NaCl with 1.00 L of water because that would result in a total volume exceeding 1.00 L and therefore a molarity of less than 1.00 M. Molarity is moles of solute per liter of *solution*.

To calculate molarity, simply divide the number of moles of the solute by the volume of the solution (solute *and* solvent) in liters. For example, calculate the molarity of a sucrose ($C_{12}H_{22}O_{11}$) solution made with 1.58 mol of sucrose diluted to a total volume of 5.0 L of solution. Set up the problem in the normal way.

Given:

1.58 mol $C_{12}H_{22}O_{11}$
5.0 L solution

Find: molarity (M)

Equation: This problem requires the use of the equation that defines molarity.

$$\text{Molarity (M)} = \frac{\text{Moles solute}}{\text{Liters solution}}$$

Solution: Simply substitute the correct values into the equation and compute the answer.

$$\text{Molarity (M)} = \frac{\text{Moles solute}}{\text{Liters solution}}$$
$$= \frac{1.58 \text{ mol } C_{12}H_{22}O_{11}}{5.0 \text{ L solution}}$$
$$= 0.32 \text{ M}$$

Calculating Molarity

Calculate the molarity of a solution made by putting 15.5 g NaCl into a beaker and adding water to make 1.50 L of NaCl solution.

You are given the mass of sodium chloride (the solute) and the volume of solution. You are asked to find the molarity of the solution.	**Given:** 15.5 g NaCl 1.50 L solution **Find:** molarity (M)
You will need the equation that defines molarity and the molar mass of NaCl.	**Equation and Conversion Factor:** $$\text{Molarity (M)} = \frac{\text{Moles solute}}{\text{Liters solution}}$$ $$\text{Molar mass of NaCl} = \frac{58.44 \text{ g}}{1 \text{ mol}}$$
To calculate molarity, substitute the correct values into the equation and compute the answer. However, you must first convert the amount of NaCl from grams to moles using the molar mass of NaCl.	**Solution:** $$\text{mol NaCl} = 15.5 \text{ g NaCl} \times \frac{1 \text{ mol NaCl}}{58.44 \text{ g NaCl}} = 0.2652 \text{ mol NaCl}$$ $$\text{Molarity (M)} = \frac{\text{Moles solute}}{\text{Liters solution}}$$ $$= \frac{0.2652 \text{ mol NaCl}}{1.50 \text{ L solution}}$$ $$= 0.177 \text{ M}$$

Calculating Molarity

Calculate the molarity of a solution made by putting 55.8 g of $NaNO_3$ into a beaker and diluting to 2.50 L.

Using Molarity in Calculations

The molarity of a solution can be used as a conversion factor between moles of the solute and liters of the solution. For example, a 0.500 M NaCl solution contains 0.500 mol NaCl for every liter of solution.

$$\frac{0.500 \text{ mol NaCl}}{\text{L solution}}$$ converts L solution $\longrightarrow$ mol NaCl

This conversion factor converts from liters of solution to moles of NaCl. If you want to go the other way, simply invert the conversion factor.

$$\frac{\text{L solution}}{0.500 \text{ mol NaCl}}$$ converts mol NaCl $\longrightarrow$ L solution

For example, how many grams of sucrose ($C_{12}H_{22}O_{11}$) are contained in 1.72 L of 0.758 M sucrose solution? We set up the problem in the normal way.

Given:

0.758 M $C_{12}H_{22}O_{11}$

1.72 L solution

Find: g $C_{12}H_{22}O_{11}$

Conversion Factors: The main conversion factor is the molarity of the solution. We write it as mol $C_{12}H_{22}O_{11}$ per L solution.

$$\frac{0.758 \text{ mol } C_{12}H_{22}O_{11}}{\text{L solution}}$$

We will also need the molar mass of sucrose.

$$\text{Molar mass of } C_{12}H_{22}O_{11} = \frac{342.34 \text{ g}}{\text{mol}}$$

Solution Map: The solution map begins with L solution and shows the conversion to mol $C_{12}H_{22}O_{11}$ using the molarity and then the conversion to g using the molar mass.

$$\frac{0.758 \text{ mol } C_{12}H_{22}O_{11}}{\text{L solution}} \qquad \frac{342.34 \text{ g}}{\text{mol}}$$

Solution: We then follow the solution map to compute the answer.

$$1.72 \text{ L solution} \times \frac{0.758 \text{ mol } C_{12}H_{22}O_{11}}{\text{L solution}}$$

$$\times \frac{342.34 \text{ g } C_{12}H_{22}O_{11}}{\text{mol } C_{12}H_{22}O_{11}} = 446 \text{ g } C_{12}H_{22}O_{11}$$

In this example, we used molarity to convert from a given amount of *solution* to the amount of *solute* in that solution. In the example that follows, we use molarity to convert from a given amount of *solute* to the amount of *solution* containing that solute.

EXAMPLE 13.4 **Using Molarity in Calculations**

How many liters of a 0.114 M NaOH solution contains 1.24 mol of NaOH?

You are given the molarity of an NaOH solution and the number of moles of NaOH. You are asked to find the volume of solution that contains the given number of moles.

Given:

0.114 M NaOH

1.24 mol NaOH

Find: L solution

You will need to use the molarity of the solution (that is given) as a conversion factor.

Conversion Factor:

$$\frac{0.114 \text{ mol NaOH}}{\text{L solution}}$$

The solution map begins with mol NaOH and shows the conversion to liters of solution using the molarity.

Solution Map:

$$\frac{1 \text{ L solution}}{0.114 \text{ mol NaOH}}$$

Solve the problem by following the solution map.

Solution:

$$1.24 \; \cancel{\text{mol NaOH}} \times \frac{1 \text{ L solution}}{0.114 \; \cancel{\text{mol NaOH}}} = 10.9 \text{ L solution}$$

SKILLBUILDER 13.4   Using Molarity in Calculations

How much of a 0.225 M KCl solution contains 55.8 g of KCl?

Ion Concentrations

The reported concentration of a solution containing a molecular compound usually reflects the concentration of the solute as it actually exists in solution. For example, a 1.0 M glucose ($C_6H_{12}O_6$) solution indicates that the solution contains 1.0 mol of $C_6H_{12}O_6$ per liter of solution. However, the reported concentration of solution containing an ionic compound reflects the concentration of the solute *before it is dissolved in solution*. For example, a 1.0 M $CaCl_2$ solution contains 1.0 mol of Ca^{2+} per liter and 2.0 mol of Cl^- per liter. The concentration of the individual ions present in a solution containing an ionic compound can usually be deduced from the overall concentration, as shown by the following example.

EXAMPLE 13.5   Ion Concentration

Determine the molar concentrations of Na^+ and PO_4^{3-} in a 1.50 M Na_3PO_4 solution.

You are given the concentration of an ionic solution and asked to find the concentrations of the component ions.

Given: 1.50 M Na_3PO_4

Find: molarity (M) of Na^+ and PO_4^{3-}

Since a formula unit of Na_3PO_4 contains 3 Na^+ ions (as indicated by the subscript), the concentration of Na^+ is three times the concentration of Na_3PO_4. Since the same formula unit contains one PO_4^{3-} ion, the concentration of PO_4^{3-} is equal to the concentration of Na_3PO_4.

Solution:

molarity of Na^+ = 3(1.50 M) = 4.50 M

molarity of PO_4^{3-} = 1.50 M

SKILLBUILDER 13.5   Ion Concentration

Determine the molar concentrations of Ca^{2+} and Cl^- in a 0.75 M $CaCl_2$ solution.

13.7 Solution Dilution

When diluting acids, always add the concentrated acid to the water. *Never add water to concentrated acid solutions.*

To save space in laboratory storerooms, solutions are often stored in concentrated forms called **stock solutions**. For example, hydrochloric acid is often stored as a 12 M stock solution. However, many lab procedures call for much less concentrated hydrochloric acid solutions, so chemists must dilute the stock solution to the required concentration. This is normally done by diluting a certain amount of the stock solution with water. How do we know how much of the stock solution to use? The easiest way to solve these problems is to use the following dilution equation:

$$M_1 V_1 = M_2 V_2$$

where M_1 and V_1 are the molarity and volume of the initial concentrated solution and M_2 and V_2 are the molarity and volume of the final diluted solution. This equation works because the molarity multiplied by the volume gives the number of moles of solute ($M \times V = \text{mol}$), which is the same in both solutions. For example, suppose a laboratory procedure calls for 5.00 L of a 1.50 M KCl solution. How should you prepare this solution from a 12.0 M stock solution? Set up the problem in the normal way.

TUTORIAL
Solution Formation by Dilution

Given: $M_1 = 12.0$ M
$M_2 = 1.50$ M
$V_2 = 5.00$ L

Find: V_1

Equation: $M_1 V_1 = M_2 V_2$

Solution: We solve the equation for V_1, the volume of the stock solution required for the dilution, and then substitute in the correct values to compute it.

$$M_1 V_1 = M_2 V_2$$

$$V_1 = \frac{M_2 V_2}{M_1}$$

$$= \frac{1.50\,\frac{\text{mol}}{\text{L}} \times 5.00\ \text{L}}{12.0\,\frac{\text{mol}}{\text{L}}}$$

$$= 0.625\ \text{L}$$

Consequently, we make the solution by diluting 0.625 L of the stock solution to a total volume of 5.00 L (V_2). The resulting solution will be 1.50 M in KCl (▼ Figure 13.8).

▶ Figure 13.8 **Making a solution by dilution of a more concentrated solution**

How to make 5.00 L of a 1.50 M KCl solution from a 12.0 M stock solution.

Dilute with water to total volume of 5.00 L

0.625 L of 12.0 M stock solution

1.50 M KCl

$$M_1 V_1 = M_2 V_2$$

$$\frac{12.0\ \text{mol}}{\text{L}} \times 0.625\ \text{L} = \frac{1.50\ \text{mol}}{\text{L}} \times 5.00\ \text{L}$$

$$7.50\ \text{mol} = 7.50\ \text{mol}$$

EXAMPLE 13.6   **Solution Dilution**

To what volume should you dilute 0.100 L of a 15 M NaOH solution to obtain a 1.0 M NaOH solution?

Your are given the initial volume and concentration of an NaOH solution and a final concentration. You are asked to find the volume required to dilute the initial solution to the given final concentration.	**Given:** $V_1 = 0.100$ L $M_1 = 15$ M $M_2 = 1.0$ M **Find:** V_2
The necessary equation is the solution dilution equation given previously in this section.	**Equation:** $M_1 V_1 = M_2 V_2$

Solve the equation for V_2, the volume of the final solution, and substitute the required quantities to compute V_2. You would make the solution by diluting 0.100 L of the stock solution to a total volume of 1.5 L (V_2). The resulting solution will have a concentration of 1.0 M.

Solution:

$$M_1 V_1 = M_2 V_2$$

$$V_2 = \frac{M_1 V_1}{M_2}$$

$$= \frac{15\,\frac{\text{mol}}{\text{L}} \times 0.100\text{ L}}{1.0\,\frac{\text{mol}}{\text{L}}}$$

$$= 1.5\text{ L}$$

SKILLBUILDER 13.6   **Solution Dilution**

● How much 6.0 M NaNO$_3$ solution should be used to make 0.585 L of a 1.2 M NaNO$_3$ solution?

● 13.8   Solution Stoichiometry

See Sections 8.2 through 8.4 for a review of reaction stoichiometry.

As we discussed in Chapter 7, many chemical reactions take place in aqueous solutions. Precipitation reactions, neutralization reactions, and gas evolution reactions, for example, all occur in aqueous solutions. In Chapter 8, we learned how the coefficients in chemical equations are used as conversion factors between moles of reactants and moles of products in stoichiometric calculations. These conversion factors are often used to determine, for example, the amount of product obtained in a chemical reaction based on a given amount of reactant or the amount of one reactant needed to completely react with a given amount of another reactant. The general solution map for these kinds of calculations is

where A and B are two different substances involved in the reaction and the conversion factor between them comes from the stoichiometric coefficients in the balanced chemical equation.

In reactions involving aqueous reactant and products, it is often convenient to specify the amount of reactants or products in terms of their volume and concentration. We can then use the volume and concentration to calculate the number of moles of reactants or products, and then use the stoichiometric coefficients to convert to other quantities in the reaction. The general solution map for these kinds of calculations is where the conversions between volume and moles are achieved using the molarities of the solutions. For example, consider the following reaction for the neutralization of sulfuric acid.

$$H_2SO_4(aq) + 2\,NaOH(aq) \longrightarrow Na_2SO_4(aq) + 2\,H_2O(l)$$

How much 0.125 M NaOH solution is required to completely neutralize 0.225 L of 0.175 M H_2SO_4 solution?

We set up the problem in the normal way.

Given:

0.225 L H_2SO_4 solution

0.175 M H_2SO_4

0.125 M NaOH

Find: L NaOH solution

Conversion Factors: The conversion factors for this problem are the molarities of the two solutions expressed in mol of solute per L of solution and the stoichiometric relationship (from the balanced equation) between mol of H_2SO_4 and mol of NaOH.

$$M\,(H_2SO_4) = \frac{0.175\ \text{mol}\ H_2SO_4}{L\ H_2SO_4\ \text{solution}}$$

$$M\,(NaOH) = \frac{0.125\ \text{mol}\ NaOH}{L\ NaOH\ \text{solution}}$$

$$1\ \text{mol}\ H_2SO_4 \equiv 2\ \text{mol}\ NaOH$$

Solution Map: The solution map for this problem is similar to the solution maps for other stoichiometric problems. We first use the volume and molarity of H_2SO_4 solution to get mol H_2SO_4. Then we use the stoichiometric coefficients from the equation to convert mol H_2SO_4 to mol NaOH. Finally, we use the molarity of NaOH to get to L NaOH solution.

$$
\begin{array}{ccc}
\dfrac{0.175\ \text{mol}\ H_2SO_4}{L\ H_2SO_4\ \text{solution}} & \dfrac{2\ \text{mol}\ NaOH}{1\ \text{mol}\ H_2SO_4} & \dfrac{1\ L\ NaOH\ \text{solution}}{0.125\ \text{mol}\ NaOH}
\end{array}
$$

Solution: To solve the problem, we follow the solution map and compute the answer.

$$0.225\ \text{L}\ H_2SO_4\ \text{solution} \times \frac{0.175\ \text{mol}\ H_2SO_4}{L\ H_2SO_4\ \text{solution}} \times \frac{2\ \text{mol}\ NaOH}{1\ \text{mol}\ H_2SO_4}$$

$$\times \frac{1\ L\ NaOH\ \text{solution}}{0.125\ \text{mol}\ NaOH} = 0.630\ \text{L}\ NaOH\ \text{solution}$$

It will take 0.630 L of the NaOH solution to completely neutralize the H_2SO_4.

EXAMPLE 13.7   **Solution Stoichiometry**

Consider the following precipitation reaction:

$$2\,KI(aq) + Pb(NO_3)_2(aq) \longrightarrow PbI_2(s) + 2\,KNO_3(aq)$$

How much 0.115 M KI solution in liters is required to completely precipitate the Pb^{2+} in 0.104 L of 0.225 M $Pb(NO_3)_2$ solution?

You are given the concentration of a reactant, KI, in a chemical reaction. You are also given the volume and concentration of a second reactant, $Pb(NO_3)_2$. You are asked to find the volume of the first reactant that completely reacts with the given amount of the second.

The conversion factors for this problem are the molarities of the two solutions expressed in mol of solute per L of solution and the stoichiometric relationship (from the balanced equation) between mol KI and mol $Pb(NO_3)_2$.

The solution map for this problem is similar to the solution maps for other stoichiometric problems. First use the volume and molarity of $Pb(NO_3)_2$ solution to get mol $Pb(NO_3)_2$. Then use the stoichiometric coefficients from the equation to convert mol $Pb(NO_3)_2$ to mol KI. Finally, use mol KI to find L KI solution.

Follow the solution map to solve the problem. Begin with volume of $Pb(NO_3)_2$ solution and cancel units to arrive at volume of KI solution.

Given:

0.115 M KI

0.104 L $Pb(NO_3)_2$ solution

0.225 M $Pb(NO_3)_2$

Find: L KI solution

Conversion Factors:

$$M\ KI = \frac{0.115\ mol\ KI}{L\ KI\ solution}$$

$$M\ Pb(NO_3)_2 = \frac{0.225\ mol\ Pb(NO_3)_2}{L\ Pb(NO_3)_2\ solution}$$

$$2\ mol\ KI \equiv 1\ mol\ Pb(NO_3)_2$$

Solution Map:

$$\frac{0.225\ mol\ Pb(NO_3)_2}{L\ Pb(NO_3)_2\ solution} \qquad \frac{2\ mol\ KI}{1\ mol\ Pb(NO_3)_2} \qquad \frac{1\ L\ KI\ solution}{0.115\ mol\ KI}$$

Solution:

$$0.104\ \cancel{L\ Pb(NO_3)_2\ solution} \times \frac{0.225\ \cancel{mol\ Pb(NO_3)_2}}{\cancel{L\ Pb(NO_3)_2\ solution}} \times \frac{2\ \cancel{mol\ KI}}{\cancel{mol\ Pb(NO_3)_2}}$$

$$\times \frac{L\ KI\ solution}{0.115\ \cancel{mol\ KI}} = 0.407\ L\ KI\ solution$$

SKILLBUILDER 13.7   **Solution Stoichiometry**

How many milliliters of 0.112 M Na_2CO_3 are necessary to completely react with 27.2 mL of 0.135 M HNO_3 according to the following reaction?

$$2\ HNO_3(aq) + Na_2CO_3(aq) \longrightarrow H_2O(l) + CO_2(g) + 2\ NaNO_3(aq)$$

SKILLBUILDER PLUS

A 25.0-mL sample of HNO_3 solution requires 35.7 mL of 0.108 M Na_2CO_3 to completely react with all of the HNO_3 in the solution. What was the concentration of the HNO_3 solution?

APPENDIX: MATHEMATICS REVIEW

⬤ Basic Algebra

In chemistry, you often have to solve an equation for a particular variable. For example, suppose you want to solve the following equation for V.

$$PV = nRT$$

To solve an equation for a particular variable, you must isolate that variable on one side of the equation. The rest of the variables or numbers will then be on the other side of the equation. To solve the above equation for V, simply divide both sides by P.

$$\frac{\cancel{P}V}{\cancel{P}} = \frac{nRT}{P}$$

$$V = \frac{nRT}{P}$$

The Ps cancel and we are left with an expression for V. For another example, consider solving the following equation for °F.

$$°C = \frac{(°F - 32)}{1.8}$$

First, eliminate the 1.8 in the denominator of the right side by multiplying both sides by 1.8.

$$(1.8)\,°C = \frac{(°F - 32)}{\cancel{1.8}}(\cancel{1.8})$$

$$(1.8)\,°C = (°F - 32)$$

Then eliminate the -32 on the right by adding 32 to both sides.

$$(1.8)\,°C + 32 = (°F - 32) + 32$$

$$(1.8)\,°C + 32 = °F$$

We are now left with an expression for °F.

In general, solve equations by following these guidelines:

- Cancel numbers or symbols in the denominator (bottom part of a fraction) by multiplying by the number or symbol to be canceled.
- Cancel numbers or symbols in the numerator (upper part of a fraction) by dividing by the number or symbol to be canceled.
- Eliminate numbers or symbols that are added by subtracting the same number or symbol.
- Eliminate numbers or symbols that are subtracted by adding the same number or symbol.

- Whether you add, subtract, multiply, or divide, **always perform the same operation for both sides of a mathematical equation**. (Otherwise, the two sides will no longer be equal.)

For a final example, solve the following equation for x.

$$\frac{67x - y + 3}{6} = 2z$$

Cancel the 6 in the denominator by multiplying both sides by 6.

$$(6)\frac{67x - y + 3}{6} = (6)2z$$

$$67x - y + 3 = 12z$$

Eliminate the $+3$ by subtracting 3 from both sides.

$$67x - y + 3 - 3 = 12z - 3$$

$$67x - y = 12z - 3$$

Eliminate the $-y$ by adding y to both sides.

$$67x - y + y = 12z - 3 + y$$

$$67x = 12z - 3 + y$$

Cancel the 67 by dividing both sides by 67.

$$\frac{67x}{67} = \frac{12z - 3 + y}{67}$$

$$x = \frac{12z - 3 + y}{67}$$

FOR PRACTICE   Using Algebra to Solve Equations

Solve each of the following for the indicated variable.

(a) $P_1V_1 = P_2V_2$; solve for V_2

(b) $\frac{V_1}{T_1} = \frac{V_2}{T_2}$; solve for T_1

(c) $PV = nRT$; solve for n

(d) $K = °C + 273$; solve for $°C$

(e) $\frac{3x + 7}{2} = y$; solve for x

(f) $\frac{32}{y + 3} = 8$; solve for y

Answers:

(a) $V_2 = \frac{P_1V_1}{P_2}$

(b) $T_1 = \frac{V_1T_2}{V_2}$

(c) $n = \frac{PV}{RT}$

(d) $°C = K - 273$

(e) $x = \frac{2y - 7}{3}$

(f) $y = 1$

Mathematical Operations with Scientific Notation

Writing numbers in scientific notation is covered in detail in Section 2.2. Briefly, a number written in scientific notation consists of a **decimal part**, a number that is usually between 1 and 10, and an **exponential part**, 10 raised to an **exponent**, n.

Each of the following numbers is written in both scientific and decimal notation.

$$1.0 \times 10^5 = 100{,}000 \qquad 1.0 \times 10^{-6} = 0.000001$$
$$6.7 \times 10^3 = 6700 \qquad 6.7 \times 10^{-3} = 0.0067$$

Multiplication and Division

To multiply numbers expressed in scientific notation, multiply the decimal parts and add the exponents.

$$(A \times 10^m)(B \times 10^n) = (A \times B) \times 10^{m+n}$$

To divide numbers expressed in scientific notation, divide the decimal parts and subtract the exponent in the denominator from the exponent in the numerator.

$$\frac{(A \times 10^m)}{(B \times 10^n)} = \left(\frac{A}{B}\right) \times 10^{m-n}$$

Consider the following example involving multiplication.

$$(3.5 \times 10^4)(1.8 \times 10^6) = (3.5 \times 1.8) \times 10^{4+6}$$
$$= 6.3 \times 10^{10}$$

Consider the following example involving division.

$$\frac{(5.6 \times 10^7)}{(1.4 \times 10^3)} = \left(\frac{5.6}{1.4}\right) \times 10^{7-3}$$
$$= 4.0 \times 10^4$$

Addition and Subtraction

To add or subtract numbers expressed in scientific notation, rewrite all the numbers so that they have the same exponent, then add or subtract the decimal parts of the numbers. The exponents remained unchanged.

$$\begin{array}{r} A \times 10^n \\ \pm B \times 10^n \\ \hline (A \pm B) \times 10^n \end{array}$$

Notice that the numbers *must have* the same exponent.

Consider the following example involving addition.

$$4.82 \times 10^7$$
$$+3.4 \quad \times 10^6$$

First, express both numbers with the same exponent. In this case, we rewrite the lower number and perform the addition as follows:

$$4.82 \times 10^7$$
$$+0.34 \times 10^7$$
$$\overline{5.16 \times 10^7}$$

Consider the following example involving subtraction.

$$7.33 \times 10^5$$
$$-1.9 \quad \times 10^4$$

First, express both numbers with the same exponent. In this case, we rewrite the lower number and perform the subtraction as follows:

$$7.33 \times 10^5$$
$$-0.19 \times 10^5$$
$$\overline{7.14 \times 10^5}$$

FOR PRACTICE   Mathematical Operations with Scientific Notation

Perform each of the following operations.

(a) $(2.1 \times 10^7)(9.3 \times 10^5)$

(b) $(5.58 \times 10^{12})(7.84 \times 10^{-8})$

(c) $\dfrac{(1.5 \times 10^{14})}{(5.9 \times 10^8)}$

(d) $\dfrac{(2.69 \times 10^7)}{(8.44 \times 10^{11})}$

(e) $\begin{array}{r} 1.823 \times 10^9 \\ +1.11 \times 10^7 \end{array}$

(f) $\begin{array}{r} 3.32 \times 10^{-5} \\ +3.400 \times 10^{-7} \end{array}$

(g) $\begin{array}{r} 6.893 \times 10^9 \\ -2.44 \times 10^8 \end{array}$

(h) $\begin{array}{r} 1.74 \times 10^4 \\ -2.9 \times 10^3 \end{array}$

Answers:

(a) 2.0×10^{13}

(b) 4.37×10^5

(c) 2.5×10^5

(d) 3.19×10^{-5}

(e) 1.834×10^9

(f) 3.35×10^{-5}

(g) 6.649×10^9

(h) 1.45×10^4

Logarithms

The log of a number is the exponent to which 10 must be raised to obtain that number. For example, the log of 100 is 2 because 10 must be raised to the 2nd power to get 100. Similarly, the log of 1000 is 3 because 10 must be raised to the 3rd power to get 1000. The logs of several multiples of 10 are shown on the following page.

$$\log 10 = 1$$
$$\log 100 = 2$$
$$\log 1000 = 3$$
$$\log 10{,}000 = 4$$

Because $10^0 = 1$ by definition, $\log 1 = 0$.

The log of a number smaller than 1 is negative because 10 must be raised to a negative exponent to get a number smaller than 1. For example, the log of 0.01 is -2 because 10 must be raised to the power of -2 to get 0.01. Similarly, the log of 0.001 is -3 because 10 must be raised to the power of -3 to get 0.001. The logs of several fractional numbers are shown below.

$$\log 0.1 = -1$$
$$\log 0.01 = -2$$
$$\log 0.001 = -3$$
$$\log 0.0001 = -4$$

The logs of numbers that are not multiples of 10 can be computed on your calculator. See your calculator manual for specific instructions.

Inverse Logarithms

The inverse logarithm or invlog function (sometimes called antilog) is exactly the opposite of the log function. For example, the log of 100 is 2 and the inverse log of 2 is 100. The log function and the invlog function undo one another.

$$\log 1000 = 3$$
$$\text{invlog } 3 = 1000$$
$$\text{invlog } (\log 1000) = 1000$$

The inverse log of a number is simply 10 raised to that number.

$$\text{invlog } x = 10^x$$
$$\text{invlog } 3 = 10^3 = 1000$$

The inverse logs of numbers can be computed on your calculator. See your calculator manual for specific instructions.

| FOR PRACTICE | **Logarithms and Inverse Logarithms** |

Perform each of the following operations.

(a) $\log 1.0 \times 10^5$ (f) invlog 1.44

(b) $\log 59$ (g) invlog -6.0

(c) $\log 1.0 \times 10^{-5}$ (h) invlog -0.250

(d) $\log 0.068$ (i) invlog $(\log 88)$

(e) invlog 7.0

Answers:

(a) 5.00   (f) 28

(b) 1.77   (g) 1×10^{-6}

(c) -5.00 (h) 0.56

(d) -1.17 (i) 88

(e) 1×10^7

GLOSSARY

absolute zero The coldest temperature possible. Absolute zero (0 K or $-273\,°C$ or $-459\,°F$) is the temperature at which molecular motion stops. Lower temperatures do not exist.

acid A molecular compound that dissolves in solution to form H^+ ions. Acids have the ability to dissolve some metals and will turn litmus paper red.

acid rain Acidic precipitation in the form of rain; created when fossil fuels are burned, releasing SO_2 and NO_2, which then react with water in the atmosphere to form sulfuric acid and nitric acid.

acid–base reaction A reaction that forms water and typically a salt.

acidic solution A solution containing a concentration of H_3O^+ ions greater than 1.0×10^{-7} (pH < 7).

activation energy The amount of energy that must be absorbed by reactants before a reaction can occur; an energy hump that normally exists between the reactants and products.

activity series of metals A listing of metals (and hydrogen) in order of decreasing activity, decreasing ability to oxidize, and decreasing tendency to lose electrons.

actual yield The amount of product actually produced by a chemical reaction.

addition polymer A polymer formed by addition of monomers to one another without elimination of any atoms.

alcohol An organic compound containing an —OH functional group bonded to a carbon atom and having the general formula ROH.

aldehyde An organic compound with the general formula $RCHO$.

alkali metals The Group 1A elements, which are highly reactive metals.

alkaline battery A dry cell employing half-reactions that use a base.

alkaline earth metals The Group 2A elements, which are fairly reactive metals.

alkaloids Organic bases found in plants.

alkanes Hydrocarbons in which all carbon atoms are connected by single bonds. Noncyclic alkanes have the general formula C_nH_{2n+2}.

alkene A hydrocarbon that contains at least one double bond between carbon atoms. Noncyclic alkenes have the general formula C_nH_{2n}.

alkyl group In an organic molecule, any group containing only singly bonded carbon atoms and hydrogen atoms.

alkyne A hydrocarbon that contains at least one triple bond between carbon atoms. Noncylclic alkynes have the general formula C_nH_{2n-2}.

alpha particle A particle consisting of two protons and two neutrons (a helium nucleus), represented by the symbol ^4_2He.

alpha (α) radiation Radiation emitted by an unstable nucleus, consisting of alpha particles.

alpha (α)-helix The most common secondary protein structure. The amino acid chain is wrapped into a tight coil from which the side chains extend outward. The structure is maintained by hydrogen bonding interactions between NH and CO groups along the peptide backbone of the protein.

amine An organic compound that contains nitrogen and has the general formula NR_3, where R may be an alkyl group or a hydrogen atom.

amino acid A molecule containing an amine group, a carboxylic acid group, and an R group (also called a side chain). Amino acids are the building blocks of proteins.

amorphous A type of solid matter in which atoms or molecules do not have long-range order (e.g., glass and plastic).

amphoteric In Brønsted–Lowry terminology, able to act as either an acid or a base.

anion A negatively charged ion.

anode The electrode where oxidation occurs in an electrochemical cell.

aqueous solution A homogeneous mixture of a substance with water.

aromatic ring A ring of carbon atoms containing alternating single and double bonds. Another name for the benzene ring.

Arrhenius acid A substance that produces H^+ ions in aqueous solution.

Arrhenius base A substance that produces OH^- ions in aqueous solution.

atmosphere (atm) The average pressure at sea level, 101,325 Pa.

atom The smallest identifiable unit of an element.

atomic element An element that exists in nature with single atoms as the basic unit.

atomic mass A weighted average of the masses of each naturally occurring isotope of an element; atomic mass is the average mass of the atoms of an element.

atomic mass unit (amu) The unit commonly used to express the masses of protons, neutrons, and nuclei. 1 amu = 1.66×10^{-24} g.

atomic number (Z) The number of protons in the nucleus of an atom.

atomic size The atomic size of an atom is determined by how far the outermost electrons are from the nucleus.

atomic solid A solid whose component units are individual atoms (e.g., diamond, C; iron, Fe).

atomic theory   A theory that states that all matter is composed of tiny particles called atoms.

Avogadro's law   The volume (V) of a gas and the amount of the gas in moles (n) are directly proportional.

Avogadro's number   The number of entities in a mole, 6.022×10^{23}.

balanced equation   A chemical equation in which the numbers of each type of atom on both sides of the equation are equal.

base   A molecular compound that dissolves in solution to form OH^- ions. Bases have a slippery feel and turn litmus paper blue.

base chain   The longest continuous chain of carbon atoms in an organic compound.

basic solution   A solution containing a concentration of OH^- ions greater than 1.0×10^{-7} (pH $>$ 7).

bent   The molecular geometry in which 3 atoms are not in a straight line. This geometry occurs when the central atoms contain 4 electron groups (2 bonding and 2 nonbonding) or 3 electron groups (2 bonding and 1 nonbonding).

benzene (C_6H_6)   A particularly stable organic compound consisting of six carbon atoms joined by alternating single and double bonds in a ring structure.

beta particle   A form of radiation consisting of an energetic electron and represented by the symbol $_{-1}^{0}e$.

beta (β) radiation   Energetic electrons emitted by an unstable nucleus.

beta (β)-pleated sheet   A common pattern in the secondary structure of proteins. The protein chain is extended in a zigzag pattern, and the peptide backbones of neighboring chains interact with one another through hydrogen bonding to form sheets.

binary acid   An acid containing only hydrogen and a nonmetal.

binary compound   A compound containing only two different kinds of elements.

biochemistry   The study of the chemical substances and processes that occur in living organisms.

Bohr model   A model for the atom in which electrons travel around the nucleus in circular orbits at specific, fixed distances from the nucleus.

boiling point   The temperature at which the vapor pressure of a liquid is equal to the pressure above it.

boiling point elevation   The increase in the boiling point of a solution caused by the presence of the solute.

bonding pair   Electrons that are shared between two atoms in a chemical bond.

bonding theory   A model that predicts how atoms bond together to form molecules.

Boyle's law   The volume (V) of a gas and its pressure (P) are inversely proportional.

branched alkane   An alkane composed of carbon atoms bonded in chains containing branches.

Brønsted–Lowry acid   A proton (H^+ ion) donor.

Brønsted–Lowry base   A proton (H^+ ion) acceptor.

buffer   A solution that resists pH change by neutralizing added acid or added base.

Calorie (Cal)   An energy unit equivalent to 1000 little-c calories.

calorie (cal)   The amount of energy required to raise the temperature of 1 g of water by 1 °C.

carbohydrates   Polyhydroxyl aldehydes or ketones or their derivatives, containing multiple —OH groups and often having the general formula $(CH_2O)_n$.

carbonyl group   A carbon atom double bonded to an oxygen atom.

carboxylic acid   An organic compound with the general formula RCOOH.

catalyst   A substance that increases the rate of a chemical reaction but is not consumed by the reaction.

cathode   The electrode where reduction occurs in an electrochemical cell.

cation   A positively charged ion.

cell   The smallest structural unit of living organisms that has the properties associated with life.

cell membrane   The structure that bounds the cell and holds the contents of the cell together.

cellulose   A common polysaccharide composed of repeating glucose units linked together.

Celsius (°C) scale   A temperature scale often used by scientists. On this scale, water freezes at 0 °C and boils at 100 °C. Room temperature is approximately 25 °C.

chain reaction   A self-sustaining chemical or nuclear reaction yielding energy or products that cause further reactions of the same kind.

charge   A fundamental property of protons and electrons. Charged particles experience forces such that like charges repel and unlike charges attract.

Charles's law   The volume (V) of a gas and its temperature (T) expressed in kelvins are directly proportional.

chemical bond   The sharing or transfer of electrons to attain stable electron configurations among the bonding atoms.

chemical change   A change in which matter changes its composition.

chemical energy   Energy associated with chemical changes.

chemical equation   An equation that represents a chemical reaction; the reactants are on the left side of the equation and the products are on the right side.

chemical formula   A way to represent a compound. At a minimum, the chemical formula indicates the elements present in the compound and the relative number of atoms of each element.

chemical properties   Properties that a substance can display only through changing its composition.

chemical reaction   The process by which one or more substances transform into different substances via a chemical change. Chemical reactions often emit or absorb energy.

chemical symbol   A one- or two-letter abbreviation for an element. Chemical symbols are listed directly below the atomic number in the periodic table.

chemistry   The science that seeks to understand what matter does by studying what atoms and molecules do.

chromosome A biological structure containing genes, located within the nucleus of a cell.

codon A sequence of three bases in a nucleic acid that codes for one amino acid.

colligative properties Physical properties of solutions that depend on the number of solute particles present but not the type of solute particles.

collision theory A theory of reaction rates stating that effective collisions between reactant molecules must take place in order for the reaction to occur.

color change One type of evidence of a chemical reaction, involving the change in color of a substance after a reaction.

combined gas law A law that combines Boyle's law and Charles's law; it is used to calculate how a property of a gas (P, V, or T) changes when two other properties are changed at the same time.

combustion reaction A reaction in which a substance reacts with oxygen, emitting heat and forming one or more oxygen-containing compound.

complementary base In DNA, a base capable of precise pairing with a specific other DNA base.

complete ionic equation A chemical equation showing all the species as they are actually present in solution.

complex carbohydrate A carbohydrate composed of many repeating saccharide units.

compound A substance composed of two or more elements in fixed, definite proportions.

compressible Able to occupy a smaller volume when subjected to increased pressure. Gases are compressible because, in the gas phase, atoms or molecules are widely separated.

concentrated solution A solution containing large amounts of solute.

condensation A physical change in which a substance is converted from its gaseous form to its liquid form.

condensation polymer A class of polymers that expel atoms, usually water, during their formation or polymerization.

condensed structural formula A shorthand way of writing a structural formula.

conjugate acid–base pair In Brønsted–Lowry terminology, two substances related to each other by the transfer of a proton.

conservation of energy, law of A law stating that energy can be neither created nor destroyed. The total amount of energy is constant and cannot change; it can only be transferred from one object to another or converted from one form to another.

conservation of mass, law of A law stating that in a chemical reaction, matter is neither created nor destroyed.

constant composition, law of A law stating that all samples of a given compound have the same proportions of their constituent elements.

conversion factor A factor used to convert between two separate units; a conversion factor is constructed from any two quantities known to be equivalent.

copolymers Polymers that are composed of two different kinds of monomers and result in chains composed of alternating units rather than a single repeating unit.

core electrons The electrons that are not in the outermost principal shell of an atom.

corrosion The oxidation of metals (e.g., rusting of iron).

covalent atomic solid An atomic solid, such as diamond, that is held together by covalent bonds.

covalent bond The bond that results when two nonmetals combine in a chemical reaction. In a covalent bond, the atoms share their electrons.

critical mass The mass of uranium or plutonium required for a nuclear reaction to be self-sustaining.

crystalline A type of solid matter with atoms or molecules arranged in a well-ordered, three-dimensional array with long-range, repeating order (e.g., salt and diamond).

cytoplasm In a cell, the region between the nucleus and the cell membrane.

Dalton's law of partial pressure A law stating that the sum of the partial pressures of each of the components in a gas mixture equals the total pressure.

daughter nuclide The nuclide product of a nuclear decay.

decimal part One part of a number expressed in scientific notation.

decomposition A reaction in which a complex substance decomposes to form simpler substances; $AB \longrightarrow A + B$.

density (d) A fundamental property of materials that differs from one substance to another. The units of density are those of mass divided by volume, most commonly expressed in g/cm^3, g/mL, or g/L.

derived unit A unit formed from the combination of other units.

dilute solution A solution containing small amounts of solute.

dimer A molecule formed by the joining together of two smaller molecules.

dipeptide Two amino acids linked together via a peptide bond.

dipole moment A measure of the separation of charge in a bond or in a molecule.

diprotic acid An acid containing two ionizable protons.

disaccharide A carbohydrate that can be decomposed into two simpler carbohydrates.

dispersion force The intermolecular force present in all molecules and atoms. Dispersion forces are caused by fluctuations in the electron distribution within molecules or atoms.

displacement A reaction in which one element displaces another in a compound; $A + BC \longrightarrow AC + B$.

dissociation In aqueous solution, the process by which a solid ionic compound separates into its ions.

disubstituted benzene A benzene in which two hydrogen atoms have been replaced by an atom or group of atoms.

DNA (deoxyribonucleic acid) Long chainlike molecules that occur in the nucleus of cells and act as blueprints for the construction of proteins.

dot structure A drawing that represents the valence electrons in atoms as dots; it shows a chemical bond as the sharing or transfer of electron dots.

double bond The bond that exists when two electron pairs are shared between two atoms. In general, double bonds are shorter and stronger than single bonds.

double displacement A reaction in which two elements or groups of elements in two different compounds exchange places to form two new compounds; $AB + CD \longrightarrow AD + CB$.

dry cell   An ordinary battery (voltaic cell); it does not contain large amounts of liquid water.

duet   The name for the two electrons corresponding to a stable Lewis structure in hydrogen and helium.

dynamic equilibrium   In a chemical reaction, the condition in which the rate of the forward reaction equals the rate of the reverse reaction.

electrical current   The flow of electric charge — for example, electrons flowing through a wire or ions through a solution.

electrical energy   Energy associated with the flow of electric charge.

electrochemical cell   A device that creates electrical current from a redox reaction.

electrolysis   A process in which electrical current is used to drive an otherwise nonspontaneous redox reaction.

electrolytic cell   An electrochemical cell used for electrolysis.

electromagnetic radiation   A type of energy that travels through space at a constant speed of 3.0×10^8 m/s (186,000 miles/s) and exhibits both wavelike and particlelike behavior. Light is a form of electromagnetic radiation.

electromagnetic spectrum   A spectrum that includes all wavelengths of electromagnetic radiation.

electron   A negatively charged particle that occupies most of the atom's volume but contributes almost none of its mass.

electron configuration   A representation that shows the occupation of orbitals by electrons for a particular element.

electron geometry   The geometrical arrangement of the electron groups in a molecule.

electron group   A general term for a lone pair, single bond, or multiple bond in a molecule.

electron spin   A fundamental property of all electrons that causes them to have magnetic fields associated with them. The spin of an electron can either be oriented up $\left(+\frac{1}{2}\right)$ or down $\left(-\frac{1}{2}\right)$.

electronegativity   The ability of an element to attract electrons within a covalent bond.

element   A substance that cannot be broken down into simpler substances.

emission spectrum   A spectrum associated with the emission of electromagnetic radiation by elements or compounds.

empirical formula   A formula for a compound that gives the smallest whole-number ratio of each type of atom.

empirical formula molar mass   The sum of the molar masses of all the atoms in an empirical formula.

endothermic   Describes a process that absorbs heat energy.

endothermic reaction   A chemical reaction that absorbs energy from the surroundings.

endpoint   The point in a reaction at which the reactants are in exact stoichiometric proportions.

energy   The capacity to do work.

English system   A unit system commonly used in the United States.

enzymes   Biological catalysts that increase the rates of biochemical reactions; enzymes are abundant in living organisms.

equilibrium constant (K_{eq})   The ratio, at equilibrium, of the concentrations of the products raised to their stoichiometric coefficients divided by the concentrations of the reactants raised to their stoichiometric coefficients.

equivalent   The stoichiometric proportions of elements and compounds in a chemical equation.

ester   An organic compound with the general formula $RCOOR$.

ester linkage   A type of bond with the general structure —COO—. Ester linkages join glycerol to fatty acids.

ether   An organic compound with the general formula ROR.

evaporation   A process in which molecules of a liquid, undergoing constant random motion, acquire enough energy to overcome attractions to neighbors and enter the gas phase.

excited state   An unstable state for an atom or molecule in which energy has been absorbed but not reemitted, raising an electron from the ground state into a higher energy orbital.

exothermic   Describes a process that releases heat energy.

exothermic reaction   A chemical reaction that releases energy to the surroundings.

experiment   A procedure that makes use of observable predictions to test a theory.

exponent   A number that represents the number of times a term is multiplied by itself. For example, in 2^4 the exponent is 4 and represents $2 \times 2 \times 2 \times 2$.

exponential part   One part of a number expressed in scientific notation; it represents the number of places the decimal point has moved.

Fahrenheit (°F) scale   The temperature scale that is most familiar in the United States; water freezes at 32 °F and boils at 212 °F.

family (of elements)   A group elements that have similar outer electron configurations and therefore similar properties. Families occur in vertical columns in the periodic table.

family (of organic compounds)   A group of organic compounds with the same functional group.

fatty acid   A type of lipid consisting of a carboxylic acid with a long hydrocarbon tail.

film badge dosimeter   Badges used to measure radiation exposure, consisting of photographic film held in a small case that is pinned to clothing.

fission, nuclear   The process by which a heavy nucleus is split into nuclei of smaller masses and energy is emitted.

formula mass   The average mass of the molecules (or formula units) that compose a compound.

formula unit   The basic unit of ionic compounds; the smallest electrically neutral collection of cations and anions that compose the compound.

freezing point depression   The decrease in the freezing point of a solvent caused by the presence of a solute.

frequency   The number of wave cycles or crests that pass through a stationary point in one second.

fuel cell   A voltaic cell in which the reactants are constantly replenished.

functional group   A set of atoms that characterizes a family of organic compounds.

fusion, nuclear   The combination of light atomic nuclei to form heavier ones with emission of large amounts of energy.

galvanic (voltaic) cell An electrochemical cell that spontaneously produces electrical current.

gamma radiation High-energy, short-wavelength electromagnetic radiation emitted by an atomic nucleus.

gamma rays The shortest-wavelength, most energetic form of electromagnetic radiation. Gamma ray photons are represented by the symbol $_{0}^{0}\gamma$.

gas A state of matter in which atoms or molecules are widely separated and free to move relative to one another.

gas evolution reaction A reaction that occurs in liquids and forms a gas as one of the products.

gas formation One type of evidence of a chemical reaction, a gas forms when two substances are mixed together.

Geiger-Müller counter A radioactivity detector consisting of a chamber filled with argon gas that discharges electrical signals when high-energy particles pass through it.

gene A sequence of codons within a DNA molecule that codes for a single protein. Genes vary in length from hundreds to thousands of codons.

genetic material The inheritable blueprint for making organisms.

glycogen A type of polysaccharide; it has a structure similar to that of starch, but the chain is highly branched.

glycolipid A biological molecule composed of a nonpolar fatty acid and hydrocarbon chain and a polar section composed of a sugar molecule such as glucose.

glycoside linkage The link between monosaccharides in a polysaccharide.

ground state The state of an atom or molecule in which the electrons occupy the lowest possible energy orbitals available.

group (of elements) Elements that have similar outer electron configurations and therefore similar properties. Groups occur in vertical columns in the periodic table.

half-cell A compartment in which the oxidation or reduction half-reaction occurs in a galvanic or voltaic cell.

half-life The time it takes for one-half of the parent nuclides in a radioactive sample to decay to the daughter nuclides.

half-reaction Either the oxidation part or the reduction part of a redox reaction.

halogens The Group 7A elements, which are very reactive nonmetals.

heat absorption One type of evidence of a chemical reaction, involving the intake of energy.

heat capacity The quantity of heat energy required to change the temperature of a given amount of a substance by 1 °C.

heat emission One type of evidence of a chemical reaction, involving the evolution of thermal energy.

heat of fusion The amount of heat required to melt one mole of a solid at its melting point with no change in temperature.

heat of vaporization The amount of heat required to vaporize one mole of a liquid at its boiling point with no change in temperature.

heterogeneous mixture A mixture, such as oil and water, that has two or more regions with different compositions.

homogeneous mixture A mixture, such as salt water, that has the same composition throughout.

human genome All of the genetic material of a human being; the total DNA of a human cell.

Hund's rule A rule stating that when filling orbitals of equal energy, electrons will occupy empty orbitals singly before pairing with other electrons.

hydrocarbon A compound that contains only carbon and hydrogen atoms.

hydrogen bond A strong dipole–dipole interaction between molecules containing hydrogen directly bonded to a small, highly electronegative atom, such as N, O, or F.

hydrogenation The chemical addition of hydrogen to a compound.

hydronium ion The H_3O^+ ion. Chemists often use $H^+(aq)$ and $H_3O^+(aq)$ interchangeably to mean the same thing—a hydronium ion.

hypothesis A theory before it has become well established; a tentative explanation for an observation or scientific problem that can be tested by further investigation.

hypoxia A shortage of oxygen in the tissues of the body.

ideal gas law A law that combines the four properties of a gas—pressure (P), volume (V), temperature (T), and number of moles (n) in a single equation showing their interrelatedness: $PV = nRT$ (R = ideal gas constant).

indicator A substance that changes color with acidity level, often used to detect the endpoint of a titration.

infrared (IR) light The fraction of the electromagnetic spectrum between visible light and microwaves. Infrared light is invisible to the human eye.

insoluble Not soluble in water.

instantaneous dipole A type of intermolecular force resulting from transient shifts in electron density within an atom or molecule.

intermolecular forces Attractive forces that exist between molecules.

International System (SI) The standard set of units for science measurements, based on the metric system.

ion An atom (or group of atoms) that has gained or lost one or more electrons, so that it has an electric charge.

ion product constant (K_w) The product of the H_3O^+ ion concentration and the OH^- ion concentration in an aqueous solution. At room temperature, $K_w = 1.0 \times 10^{-14}$.

ionic bond The bond that results when a metal and a nonmetal combine in a chemical reaction. In an ionic bond, the metal transfers one or more electrons to the nonmetal.

ionic compound A compound formed between a metal and one or more nonmetals.

ionic solid A solid compound composed of metals and nonmetals joined by ionic bonds.

ionization The forming of ions.

ionization energy The energy required to remove an electron from an atom in the gaseous state.

ionizing power The ability of radiation to ionize other molecules and atoms.

isomers Molecules with the same molecular formula but different structures.

isoosmotic   Describes solutions having osmotic pressure equal to that of bodily fluids.

isotope scanning   The use of radioactive isotopes to identify disease in the body.

isotopes   Atoms with the same number of protons but different numbers of neutrons.

Kelvin (K) scale   The temperature scale that assigns 0 K to the coldest temperature possible, absolute zero ($-273\,°C$ or $-459\,°F$), the temperature at which molecular motion stops. The size of the kelvin is identical to that of the Celsius degree.

ketone   An organic compound with the general formula $RCOR$.

kilogram (kg)   The SI standard unit of mass.

kilowatt-hour (kWh)   A unit of energy equal to 3.6 million joules.

kinetic energy   Energy associated with the motion of an object.

kinetic molecular theory   A simple model for gases that predicts the behavior of most gases under many conditions.

Le Châtelier's principle   A principle stating that when a chemical system at equilibrium is disturbed, the system shifts in a direction that minimizes the disturbance.

lead-acid storage battery   An automobile battery consisting of six electrochemical cells wired in series. Each cell produces 2 volts for a total of 12 volts.

Lewis structure   A drawing that represents chemical bonds between atoms as shared or transferred electrons; the valence electrons of atoms are represented as dots.

Lewis theory   A simple theory for chemical bonding involving diagrams showing bonds between atoms as lines or dots. In this theory, atoms bond together to obtain stable octets (8 valence electrons).

light emission   One type of evidence of a chemical reaction, involving the giving off of electromagnetic radiation.

limiting reactant   The reactant that limits the amount of product formed in a chemical reaction.

linear   Describes the molecular geometry of a molecule containing 2 electron groups (2 bonding groups and no lone pairs).

linearly related   A relationship between two variables such that, when they are plotted one against the other, the graph produced is a straight line.

lipid   A cellular component that is insoluble in water, but soluble in nonpolar solvents.

lipid bilayer   A structure formed by lipids in the cell membrane.

liquid   A state of matter in which atoms or molecules are packed close to each other (about as closely as in a solid) but are free to move around and by each other.

logarithmic scale   A scale involving logarithms. A logarithm entails an exponent that indicates the power to which a number is raised to produce a given number (e.g., the logarithm of 100 to the base 10 is 2).

lone pair   Electrons that are only on one atom in a Lewis structure.

main-group elements   Groups 1A–8A on the periodic table. These groups have properties that tend to be predictable based on their position in the periodic table.

mass   A measure of the quantity of matter within an object.

mass number (A)   The sum of the number of neutrons and protons in an atom.

mass percent composition (or mass percent)   The percentage, by mass, of each element in a compound.

matter   Anything that occupies space and has mass. Matter exists in three different states: solid, liquid, and gas.

melting point   The temperature at which a solid turns into a liquid.

messenger RNA (mRNA)   Long chainlike molecules that act as blueprints for the construction of proteins.

metallic atomic solid   An atomic solid, such as iron, which is held together by metallic bonds that, in the simplest model, consist of positively charged ions in a sea of electrons.

metallic character   The properties typical of a metal, especially the tendency to lose electrons in chemical reactions. Elements become more metallic as you move from right to left across the periodic table.

metalloids   Those elements that fall along the boundary between the metals and the nonmetals in the periodic table; their properties are intermediate between those of metals and those of nonmetals.

metals   Elements that tend to lose electrons in chemical reactions. They are found at the left side and in the center of the periodic table.

meter (m)   The SI standard unit of length.

metric system   The unit system commonly used throughout most of the world.

microwaves   The part of the electromagnetic spectrum between the infrared region and the radio wave region. Microwaves are efficiently absorbed by water molecules and can therefore be used to heat water-containing substances.

millimeter of mercury (mm Hg)   A unit of pressure that originates from the method used to measure pressure with a barometer. Also called a *torr*.

miscibility   The ability of two liquids to mix without separating into two phases, or the ability of one liquid to mix with (dissolve in) another liquid.

mixture   A substance composed of two or more different types of atoms or molecules combined in variable proportions.

molality (m)   A common unit of solution concentration, defined as the number of moles of solute per kilogram of solvent.

molar mass   The mass of one mole of atoms of an element. An element's molar mass in grams per mole is numerically equivalent to the element's atomic mass in amu.

molar solubility   The solubility of a substance in units of moles per liter (mol/L).

molar volume   The volume occupied by one mole of gas under standard temperature and pressure conditions (22.4 L).

molarity (M)   A common unit of solution concentration, defined as the number of moles of solute per liter of solution.

mole   Avogadro's number (6.022×10^{23}) of particles—especially, of atoms, ions, or molecules. A mole of any element has a mass in grams that is numerically equivalent to its atomic mass in amu.

molecular compound   A compound formed from two or more nonmetals. Molecular compounds have distinct molecules as their simplest identifiable units.

molecular element   An element that does not normally exist in nature with single atoms as the basic unit. These elements usually exist as diatomic molecules—two atoms of that element bonded together—as their basic units.

molecular equation   A chemical equation showing the complete, neutral formulas for every compound in a reaction.

molecular formula   A formula for a compound that gives the specific number of each type of atom in a molecule.

molecular geometry   The geometrical arrangement of the atoms in a molecule.

molecular solid   A solid whose composite units are molecules.

molecule   Two or more atoms joined in a specific arrangement by chemical bounds. A molecule is the smallest identifiable unit of a molecular compound.

monomer   An individual repeating unit that makes up a polymer.

monoprotic acid   An acid containing only one ionizable proton.

monosaccharide   A carbohydrate that cannot be decomposed into simpler carbohydrates.

monosubstituted benzene   A benzene in which one of the hydrogen atoms has been replaced by another atom or group of atoms.

net ionic equation   An equation that shows only the species that actually participate in a reaction.

neutral solution   A solution in which the concentrations of H_3O^+ and OH^- are equal (pH = 7).

neutralization   A reaction that takes place when an acid and a base are mixed; the $H^+(aq)$ from the acid combines with the $OH^-(aq)$ from the base to form $H_2O(l)$.

neutron   A nuclear particle with no electrical charge and nearly the same mass as a proton.

nitrogen narcosis   An increase in nitrogen concentration in bodily tissues and fluids that results in feelings of drunkenness.

noble gases   The Group 8A elements, which are chemically inert gases.

nonbonding atomic solid   An atomic solid that is held together by relatively weak dispersion forces.

nonelectrolyte solution   A solution containing a solute that dissolves as molecules; therefore, the solution does not conduct electricity.

nonmetals   Elements that tend to gain electrons in chemical reactions. They are found at the upper right side of the periodic table.

nonpolar molecule   A molecule that does not have a net dipole moment.

nonvolatile   Describes a compound that does not vaporize easily.

normal boiling point   The boiling point of a liquid at a pressure of 1 atmosphere.

normal alkane (or *n*-alkane)   An alkane composed of carbon atoms bonded in a straight chain with no branches.

nuclear equation   An equation that represents the changes that occur during radioactivity and other nuclear processes.

nuclear radiation   The energetic particles emitted from the nucleus of an atom when it is undergoing a nuclear process.

nuclear theory of the atom   A theory stating that most of the atom's mass and all of its positive charge is contained in a small, dense nucleus. Most of the volume of the atom is empty space occupied by negatively charged electrons.

nucleic acids   Biological molecules, such as deoxyribonucleic acid (DNA) and ribonucleic acid (RNA), that store and transmit genetic information.

nucleotide   An individual unit of a nucleic acid. Nucleic acids are polymers of nucleotides.

nucleus (of a cell)   The part of the cell that contains the genetic material.

nucleus (of an atom)   The small core containing most of the atom's mass and all of its positive charge. The nucleus is made up of protons and neutrons.

observation   The first step in the scientific method. An observation must measure or describe something about the physical world.

octet   The number of electrons, eight, around atoms with stable Lewis structures.

octet rule   A rule that states that an atom will give up, accept, or share electrons in order to achieve a filled outer electron shell, which usually consists of 8 electrons.

orbital diagram   An electron configuration in which electrons are represented as arrows in boxes corresponding to orbitals of a particular atom.

orbital   The region around the nucleus of an atom where an electron is most likely to be found.

organic chemistry   The study of carbon-containing compounds and their reactions.

organic molecule   A molecule whose main structural component is carbon.

osmosis   The flow of solvent from a lower-concentration solution through a semipermeable membrane to a higher-concentration solution.

osmotic pressure   The pressure produced on the surface of a semipermeable membrane by osmosis or the pressure required to stop osmotic flow.

oxidation   The gain of oxygen, the loss of hydrogen, or the loss of electrons (the most fundamental definition).

oxidation state (or oxidation number)   A number that can be used as an aid in writing formulas and balancing equations. It is computed for each element based on the number of electrons assigned to it in a scheme where the most electronegative element is assigned all of the bonding electrons.

oxidation–reduction (redox) reaction   A reaction in which electrons are transferred from one substance to another.

oxidizing agent   In a redox reaction, the substance being reduced. Oxidizing agents tend to gain electrons easily.

oxyacid   An acid containing hydrogen, a nonmetal, and oxygen.

oxyanion   An anion containing oxygen. Most polyatomic ions are oxyanions.

oxygen toxicity   The result of increased oxygen concentration in bodily tissues.

parent nuclide   The original nuclide in a nuclear decay.

partial pressure   The pressure due to any individual component in a gas mixture.

pascal (Pa)   The SI unit of pressure, defined as 1 newton per square meter.

Pauli exclusion principle   A principle stating that no more than two electrons can occupy an orbital and that the two electrons must have opposite spins.

penetrating power   The ability of a radioactive particle to penetrate matter.

peptide bond   The bond between the amine end of one amino acid and the carboxylic acid end of another. Amino acids link together via peptide bonds to form proteins.

percent natural abundance   The percentage amount of each isotope of an element in a naturally occurring sample of the element.

percent yield   In a chemical reaction, the percentage of the theoretical yield that was actually attained.

period   A horizontal row of the periodic table.

periodic law   A law that states that when the elements are arranged in order of increasing relative mass, certain sets of properties recur periodically.

periodic table   An arrangement of the elements in which atomic number increases from left to right and elements with similar properties fall in columns called families or groups.

permanent dipole   A separation of charge resulting from the unequal sharing of electrons between atoms.

pH scale   A scale used to quantify acidity or basicity. A pH of 7 is neutral; a pH lower than 7 is acidic; and a pH greater than 7 is basic. The pH is defined as follows: $pH = -\log[H_3O^+]$.

phenyl group   The term for a benzene ring when other substituents are attached to it.

phospholipid   A lipid with the same basic structure as a triglyceride, except that one of the fatty acid groups is replaced with a phosphate group.

phosphorescence   The slow, long-lived emission of light that sometimes follows the absorption of light by some atoms and molecules.

photon   A particle of light or a packet of light energy.

physical change   A change in which matter does not change its composition even though its appearance might change.

physical properties   Those properties that a substance displays without changing its composition.

polar covalent bond   A covalent bond between atoms of different electronegativities. Polar covalent bonds have a dipole moment.

polar molecule   A molecule with polar bonds that add together to create a net dipole moment.

polyatomic ion   An ion composed of a group of atoms with an overall charge.

polymer   A molecule with many similar units, called monomers, bonded together in a long chain.

polypeptide   A short chain of amino acids joined by peptide bonds.

polysaccharide   A long, chainlike molecule composed of many linked monosaccharide units. Polysaccharides are polymers of monosaccharides

positron   A nuclear particle that has the mass of an electron but carries a +1 charge.

positron emission   Expulsion of a positron from an unstable atomic nucleus. In positron emission, a proton is transformed into a neutron.

potential energy   The energy of a body that is associated with its position or the arrangement of its parts.

precipitate   An insoluble product formed through the reaction of two solutions containing soluble compounds.

precipitation reaction   A reaction that forms a solid or precipitate when two aqueous solutions are mixed.

prefix multipliers   Prefixes used by the SI system with the standard units. These multipliers change the value of the unit by powers of 10.

pressure   The force exerted per unit area by gaseous molecules as they collide with the surfaces around them.

primary protein structure   The sequence of amino acids in a protein's chain. Primary protein structure is maintained by the covalent peptide bonds between individual amino acids.

principal quantum number   A number that indicates the shell that an electron occupies.

principal shell   The shell indicated by the principal quantum number.

products   The final substances produced in a chemical reaction; represented on the right side of a chemical equation.

properties   The characteristics we use to distinguish one substance from another.

protein   A biological molecule composed of a long chain of amino acids joined by peptide bonds. In living organisms, proteins serve many varied and important functions.

proton   A positively charged nuclear particle. A proton's mass is approximately 1 amu.

pure substance   A substance composed of only one type of atom or molecule.

quantification   The assigning of a number to an observation so as to specify a quantity or property precisely.

quantum (*pl.* quanta)   The precise amount of energy possessed by a photon; the difference in energy between two atomic orbitals.

quantum number (*n*)   An integer that specifies the energy of an orbital. The higher the quantum number n, the greater the distance between the electron and the nucleus and the higher its energy.

quantum-mechanical model   The foundation of modern chemistry; explains how electrons exist in atoms, and how they affect the chemical and physical properties of elements.

quaternary structure   In a protein, the way that individual chains fit together to compose the protein. Quaternary structure is maintained by interactions between the R groups of amino acids on the different chains.

R group (side chain)   An organic group attached to the central carbon atom of an amino acid.

radio waves   The longest-wavelength and least energetic form of electromagnetic radiation.

radioactive   Describes a substance that emits tiny, invisible, energetic particles from the nuclei of its component atoms.

radioactivity   The emission of tiny, invisible, energetic particles from the unstable nuclei of atoms. Many of these particles can penetrate matter.

radiocarbon dating   A technique used to estimate the age of fossils and artifacts through the measurement of natural radioactivity of carbon atoms in the environment.

radiotherapy   Treatment of disease with radiation, such as the use of gamma rays to kill rapidly dividing cancer cells.

random coil   The name given to an irregular pattern of a secondary protein structure.

rate of a chemical reaction (reaction rate)   The amount of reactant that changes to product in a given period of time. Also defined as the amount of a product that forms in a given period of time.

reactants   The initial substances in a chemical reaction, represented on the left side of a chemical equation.

recrystallization   A technique used to purify a solid; involves dissolving the solid in a solvent at high temperature, creating a saturated solution, then cooling the solution to cause the crystallization of the solid.

reducing agent   In a redox reaction, the substance being oxidized. Reducing agents tend to lose electrons easily.

reduction   The loss of oxygen, the gain of hydrogen, or the gain of electrons (the most fundamental definition).

rem   Stands for *roentgen equivalent man;* a weighted measure of radiation exposure that accounts for the ionizing power of the different types of radiation.

resonance structures   Two or more Lewis structures that are necessary to describe the bonding in a molecule or ion.

reversible reaction   A reaction that is able to proceed in both the forward and reverse directions.

RNA (ribonucleic acid)   Long chainlike molecules that occur throughout cells and take part in the construction of proteins.

salt   An ionic compound that usually remains dissolved in a solution after an acid–base reaction has occurred.

salt bridge   An inverted, U-shaped tube containing a strong electrolyte; completes the circuit in an electrochemical cell by allowing the flow of ions between the two half-cells.

saturated fat   A triglyceride composed of saturated fatty acids. Saturated fat tends to be solid at room temperature.

saturated hydrocarbon   A hydrocarbon that contains no double or triple bonds between the carbon atoms.

saturated solution   A solution that holds the maximum amount of solute under the solution conditions. If additional solute is added to a saturated solution, it will not dissolve.

scientific law   A statement that summarizes past observations and predicts future ones. Scientific laws are usually formulated from a series of related observations.

scientific method   The way that scientists learn about the natural world. The scientific method involves observations, laws, hypotheses, theories, and experimentation.

scientific notation   A system used to write very big or very small numbers, often containing many zeros, more compactly and precisely. A number written in scientific notation consists of a decimal part and an exponential part (10 raised to a particular exponent).

scintillation counter   A device used to detect radioactivity in which energetic particles traverse a material that emits ultraviolet or visible light when excited by their passage. The light is detected and turned into an electrical signal.

second (s)   The SI standard unit of time.

secondary protein structure   Short-range periodic or repeating patterns often found in proteins. Secondary protein structure is maintained by interactions between amino acids that are fairly close together in the linear sequence of the protein chain or adjacent to each other on neighboring chains.

semiconductor   A compound or element exhibiting intermediate electrical conductivity that can be changed and controlled.

semipermeable membrane   A membrane that selectively allows some substances to pass through but not others.

SI units   The most convenient system of units for science measurements, based on the metric system. The set of standard units agreed on by scientists throughout the world.

significant digits (figures)   The non-place-holding digits in a reported measurement; they represent the precision of a measured quantity.

simple carbohydrate (simple sugar)   A monosaccharide or disaccharide.

single bond   A chemical bond in which one electron pair is shared between two atoms.

solid   A state of matter in which atoms or molecules are packed close to each other in fixed locations.

solid formation   One type of evidence of a chemical reaction, involving the formation of a solid.

solubility   The amount of a compound, usually in grams, that will dissolve in a certain amount of solvent.

solubility rules   A set of empirical rules used to determine whether an ionic compound is soluble.

solubility-product constant (K_{sp})   The equilibrium expression for a chemical equation that represents the dissolving of an ionic compound in solution.

soluble   Dissolves in solution.

solute   The minority component of a solution.

solution   A homogenous mixture of two or more substances.

solvent   The majority component of a solution.

specific heat capacity (or specific heat)   The heat capacity of a substance in joules per gram degree celsius (J/g °C).

spectator ions   Ions that do not participate in a reaction; they appear unchanged on both sides of a chemical equation.

standard temperature and pressure (STP)   Conditions often assumed in calculations involving gases: $T = 0\,°C$ (273 K) and $P = 1$ atm.

starch   A common polysaccharide composed of repeating glucose units.

states of matter   The three forms in which matter can exist: solid, liquid, and gas.

steroid   A biological compound containing a 17-carbon 4-ring system.

stock solution   A concentrated form in which solutions are often stored.

stoichiometry   The numerical relationships among chemical quantities in a balanced chemical equation. Stoichiometry allows us to predict the amounts of products that form in a chemical reaction based on the amounts of reactants.

strong acid   An acid that completely ionizes in solution.

strong base   A base that completely dissociates in solution.

strong electrolyte   A substance whose aqueous solutions are good conductors of electricity.

strong electrolyte solution   A solution containing a solute that dissociates into ions; therefore, a solution that conducts electricity well.

structural formula   A two-dimensional representation of molecules that not only shows the number and type of atoms, but also how the atoms are bonded together.

sublimation   A physical change in which a substance is converted from its solid form directly into its gaseous form.

subshell   In quantum mechanics, specifies the shape of the orbital and is represented by different letters (s, p, d, f).

substituent   An atom or group of atoms that has been substituted for a hydrogen atom in an organic compound.

substitution reaction   A reaction in which one or more atoms are replaced by one or more different atoms.

supersaturated solution   A solution holding more than the normal maximum amount of solute.

surface tension   The tendency of liquids to minimize their surface area, resulting in a "skin" on the surface of the liquid.

synthesis   A reaction in which simpler substances combine to form more complex substances; $A + B \longrightarrow AB$.

temporary dipole   A type of intermolecular force resulting from transient shifts in electron density within an atom or molecule.

terminal atom   An atom that is located at the end of a molecule or chain.

tertiary structure   A protein's structure that consists of the large-scale bends and folds due to interactions between the R groups of amino acids that are separated by large distances in the linear sequence of the protein chain.

tetrahedral   The molecular geometry of a molecule containing 4 electron groups (4 bonding groups and no lone pairs).

theoretical yield   The amount of product that can be made in a chemical reaction based on the amount of limiting reactant.

theory   A proposed explanation for observations and laws. A theory presents a model of the way nature works and predicts behavior that extends well beyond the observations and laws from which it was formed.

titration   A laboratory procedure used to determine the amount of a substance in solution. In a titration, a reactant in a solution of known concentration is reacted with another reactant in a solution of unknown concentration until the reaction reaches the endpoint.

torr   A unit of pressure named after the Italian physicist Evangelista Torricelli. Also called a millimeter of mercury.

transition metals   The elements in the middle of the periodic table whose properties tend to be less predictable based simply on their position in the periodic table. Transition metals lose electrons in their chemical reactions, but do not necessarily acquire noble gas configurations.

triglyceride   A fat or oil; a tryglyceride is a tri-ester composed of glycerol with three fatty acids attached.

trigonal planar   The molecular geometry of a molecule containing 3 electron groups, 3 bonding groups, and no lone pairs.

trigonal pyramidal   The molecular geometry of a molecule containing 4 electron groups, 3 bonding groups, and 1 lone pair.

triple bond   A chemical bond consisting of three electron pairs shared between two atoms. In general, triple bonds are shorter and stronger than double bonds.

Type I compounds   Compounds containing metals that always form cations with the same charge.

Type II compounds   Compounds containing metals that can form cations with different charges.

ultraviolet (UV) light   The fraction of the electromagnetic spectrum between the visible region and the X-ray region. UV light is invisible to the human eye.

units   Previously agreed-on quantities used to report experimental measurements. Units are vital in chemistry.

unsaturated fat (or oil)   A triglyceride composed of unsaturated fatty acids. Unsaturated fats tend to be liquids at room temperature.

unsaturated hydrocarbon   A hydrocarbon that contains one or more double or triple bonds between its carbon atoms.

unsaturated solution   A solution holding less than the maximum possible amount of solute under the solution conditions.

valence electrons   The electrons in the outermost principal shell of an atom; they are involved in chemical bonding.

valence shell electron pair repulsion (VSEPR)   A theory that allows prediction of the shapes of molecules based on the idea that electrons—either as lone pairs or as bonding pairs—repel one another.

vapor pressure   The partial pressure of a vapor in dynamic equilibrium with its liquid.

vaporization   The phase transition between a liquid and a gas.

viscosity   The resistance of a liquid to flow; manifestation of intermolecular forces.

visible light   The fraction of the electromagnetic spectrum that is visible to the human eye, bounded by wavelengths of 400 nm (violet) and 780 nm (red).

vital force   A mystical or supernatural power that, it was once believed, was possessed only by living organisms and allowed them to produce organic compounds.

vitalism   The belief that living things contain a nonphysical "force" that allows them to synthesize organic compounds.

volatile   Tending to vaporize easily.

voltage   The potential difference between two electrodes; the driving force that causes electrons to flow.

volume   A measure of space. Any unit of length, when cubed, becomes a unit of volume.

wavelength   The distance between adjacent wave crests in a wave.

weak acid   An acid that does not completely ionize in solution.

weak base   A base that does not completely dissociate in solution.

weak electrolyte   A substance whose aqueous solutions are poor conductors of electricity.

X-rays   The portion of the electromagnetic spectrum between the ultraviolet (UV) region and the gamma-ray region.

ANSWERS TO ODD-NUMBERED EXERCISES

Note: Answers in the Questions section are written as briefly as possible. Student answers may vary and still be correct.

Chapter 1
Questions

1. Soda fizzes due to the interactions between carbon dioxide and water under high pressures. At room temperature, carbon dioxide is a gas and water is a liquid. Through the use of pressure, the makers of soda force the carbon dioxide gas to dissolve in the water. When the can is sealed, the solution remains mixed. When the can is opened, the pressure is released and the carbon dioxide molecules escape in bubbles of gas.

3. Chemists study molecules and interactions at the molecular level to learn about and explain macroscopic events. Chemists attempt to explain why ordinary things are as they are.

5. Chemistry is the science that seeks to understand what matter does by studying what atoms and molecules do.

7. The scientific method is the way chemists investigate the chemical world. The first step consists of observing the natural world. Later observations can be combined to create a scientific law, which summarizes and predicts behavior. Theories are models that strive to explain the cause of the observed phenomenon. Theories are tested through experiment. When a theory is not well established, it is sometimes referred to as a hypothesis.

9. A law is simply a general statement that summarizes and predicts observed behavior. Theories seek to explain the causes of observed behavior.

11. To say "It is just a theory" makes it seem as if theories are easily discardable. However, many theories are very well established and are as close to truth as we get in science. Established theories are backed up with years of experimental evidence, and they are the pinnacle of scientific understanding.

13. The atomic theory states that all matter is composed of small, indestructible particles called atoms. John Dalton formulated this theory.

Problems

15. Carbon dioxide contains one carbon atom and two oxygen atoms. Water contains one oxygen atom and two hydrogen atoms.

17. **a.** observation   **b.** theory
    c. law   **d.** observation

19. **a.** All atoms contain a degree of chemical reactivity. The larger the size of an atom, the higher the chemical reactivity of that atom.

    b. There are many correct answers. One example is: Conceivably, when the size of an atom is increased, the surface area of the atom is also increased; an atom with a greater surface area is more likely to react chemically.

Chapter 2
Questions

1. Without units, the results are unclear and it is hard to keep track of what each separate measurement entails.

3. Often scientists work with very large or very small numbers that contain a lot of zeros. Scientific notation allows these numbers to be written more compactly, and the information is more organized.

5. Zeros count as significant digits when they are interior zeros (zeros between two numbers) and when they are trailing zeros (zeros after a decimal point). Zeros are **not** significant digits when they are leading zeros, which are zeros to the left of the first nonzero number.

7. For calculations involving only multiplication and division, the result carries the same number of significant figures as the factor with the fewest significant figures.

9. When rounding numbers, one must round down if the last (or left-most) digit dropped is four or less, or one must round up if the last (or left-most) digit is five or more.

11. The basic SI unit of length is the meter. The kilogram is the SI unit of mass. Lastly, the second is the SI unit of time.

13. For measuring a Frisbee, the unit would be the meter and the prefix multiplier would be *centi*-. The final measurement would be in centimeters.

15. **a.** 2.42 cm   **b.** 1.69 cm
    c. 21.58 cm   **d.** 20.85 cm

17. Units act as a guide in the calculation and are able to show if the calculation is off track. The units must be followed in the calculation, so that the answer is correctly written and understood.

19. A conversion factor is a quantity used to relate two separate units. They are constructed from any two quantities known to be equivalent.

21. The solution map for converting grams to pounds is:

$$\frac{1 \text{ lb}}{453.59 \text{ g}}$$

23. The solution map for converting meters to feet is:

$$\frac{100 \text{ cm}}{1 \text{ m}} \qquad \frac{1 \text{ ft}}{30.48 \text{ cm}}$$

25. The density of a substance is the ratio of its mass to its volume. Density is a fundamental property of materials and differs from one substance to another. Density can be used to relate two separate units, thus working as a conversion factor. Density is a conversion factor between mass and volume.

Problems

27. **a.** 3.2667×10^7 **b.** 1.193×10^6
    c. 1.8175×10^7 **d.** 4.81×10^5
29. **a.** 7.461×10^{-11} m **b.** 1.58×10^{-5} mi
    c. 6.32×10^{-7} m **d.** 1.5×10^{-5} m
31. **a.** 602,200,000,000,000,000,000,000
    b. 0.000000000000000000016 C
    c. 299,000,000 m/s
    d. 344 m/s
33. **a.** 3,890,000,000 **b.** 0.00059
    c. 8,680,000,000,000 **d.** 0.0000000786
35. 2,000,000,000 2×10^9
    1,211,000,000 1.211×10^9
    0.000874 8.74×10^{-4}
    320,000,000,000 3.2×10^{11}
37. **a.** 54.9 mL **b.** 48.7 °C
    c. 5.550 mL **d.** 46.83 °C
39. **a.** 0.005050 **b.** 0.00000000000000060
    c. 220,103 **d.** 0.00108
41. **a.** 4 **b.** 4
    c. 6 **d.** 5
43. **a.** correct **b.** 3
    c. 7 **d.** correct
45. **a.** 343.0 **b.** 0.009651
    c. 3.526×10^{-8} **d.** 1.127×10^9
47. **a.** 2.3 **b.** 2.4
    c. 2.3 **d.** 2.4
49. **a.** 42.3 **b.** correct
    c. correct **d.** 0.0456
51. **a.** 0.054 **b.** 0.619
    c. 1.2×10^8 **d.** 6.6
53. **a.** 4.22×10^3 **b.** correct
    c. 3.9969 **d.** correct
55. **a.** 200.6 **b.** 41.4
    c. 183.3 **d.** 1.22

57. **a.** correct **b.** 1.0982
    c. correct **d.** 3.53
59. **a.** 3.9×10^3 **b.** 632
    c. 8.93×10^4 **d.** 6.34
61. **a.** 3.15×10^3 **b.** correct
    c. correct **d.** correct
63. **a.** 2.14×10^3 g **b.** 6.172 m
    c. 1.316×10^{-3} kg **d.** 25.6 mL
65. **a.** 0.588 L **b.** 34.1 μg
    c. 10.1 ns **d.** 2.19×10^{-12} m
67. **a.** 57.2 cm **b.** 38.4 m
    c. 0.754 km **d.** 61 mm
69. **a.** 15.7 in **b.** 91.2 ft
    c. 6.21 mi **d.** 8478 lb
71. 5.08×10^8 m 5.08×10^5 km   508 Mm
    5.08×10^{-1} Gm 5.08×10^{-4} Tm
    2.7976×10^{10} m 2.7976×10^7 km   27,976 Mm
    2.7976×10^1 Gm 2.7976×10^{-2} Tm
    1.77×10^{12} m 1.77×10^9 km 1.77×10^6 Mm
    1.77×10^3 Gm   1.77 Tm
    1.5×10^8 m 1.5×10^5 km 1.5×10^2 Mm
    0.15 Gm 1.5×10^{-4} Tm
    4.23×10^{11} m 4.23×10^8 km 4.23×10^5 Mm
    423 Gm   0.423 Tm
73. **a.** 2.255×10^7 kg **b.** 2.255×10^4 Mg
    c. 2.255×10^{13} mg **d.** 2.255×10^4 metric tons
75. 1.1×10^3 g
77. 5.0×10^1 min
79. 4.7×10^3 cm^3
81. **a.** 1.0×10^6 m^2 **b.** 1.0×10^{-6} m^3
    c. 1.0×10^{-9} m^3
83. **a.** 6.2×10^5 pm^3 **b.** 6.2×10^{-4} nm^3
    c. 6.2×10^{-1} Å^3
85. **a.** 2.15×10^{-4} km^2 **b.** 2.15×10^4 dm^2
    c. 2.15×10^6 cm^2
87. 1.49×10^6 mi^2
89. 11.4 g/cm^3, lead
91. 1.26 g/cm^3
93. Yes, the density of the crown is 19.3 g/cm^3
95. **a.** 463 g **b.** 3.7 L
97. **a.** 3.38×10^4 g (gold); 5.25×10^3 g (sand)
    b. Yes, the mass of the bag of sand is different from the mass of the gold vase; thus, the weight-sensitive pedestal will sound the alarm.
99. 10.6 g/cm^3
101. $2.7 \times 10^3 \dfrac{\text{kg}}{\text{m}^3}$
103. 2.5×10^5 lbs
105. 1.19×10^5 kg
107. 3.0×10^1 km/L
109. 108 km; 47.2 km
111. 9.1×10^{10} g/cm^3

Chapter 3

Questions

1. Matter is defined as anything that occupies space and possesses mass. It can be thought of as the physical material that makes up the universe.

3. The three states of matter are solid, liquid, and gas.

5. In a crystalline solid, the atoms/molecules are arranged in geometric patterns with repeating order. In amorphous solids, the atoms/molecules do not have long-range order.

7. The atoms/molecules in gases are not in contact with each other and are free to move relative to one another. The spacing between separate atoms/molecules is very far apart. A gas has no fixed volume or shape; rather it assumes both the shape and the volume of the container it occupies.

9. A mixture is two or more pure substances combined in variable proportions.

11. Pure substances are those composed of only one type of atom or molecule.

13. A mixture is formed when two or more pure substances are mixed together; however a new substance is not formed. A compound is formed when two or more elements are bonded together and form a new substance.

15. In a physical change the composition of the substance does not change, even though its appearance might change. However, in a chemical change, the substance undergoes a change in its composition.

17. Energy is defined as the capacity to do work.

19. Some different kinds of energy are kinetic, potential, electrical, chemical, and thermal.

21. Three common units for temperature are kelvin, Celsius, and Fahrenheit. They differ in how they define zero and in the size of the respective degrees.

23. Heat capacity is the quantity of heat energy required to change the temperature of a given amount of the substance by 1 °C.

25. $°F = \dfrac{9}{5}(°C) + 32$

Problems

27. **a.** element **b.** element
 c. compound **d.** compound

29. **a.** homogeneous **b.** heterogeneous
 c. homogeneous **d.** homogeneous

31. **a.** pure substance-element
 b. mixture-homogeneous
 c. mixture-heterogeneous
 d. mixture-heterogeneous

33. **a.** chemical **b.** physical
 c. physical **d.** chemical

35. physical–colorless; odorless; gas at room temperature; one liter has a mass of 1.260 g under standard conditions; mixes with acetone chemical–flammable; polymerizes to form polyethylene

37. **a.** chemical **b.** physical
 c. chemical **d.** chemical

39. **a.** physical **b.** chemical

41. 2.10×10^2 kg

43. **a.** Yes **b.** No

45. 15.1 g of water

47. **a.** 7.77 cal **b.** 2.35×10^3 J
 c. 8.53×10^3 cal **d.** 1.20 kJ

49. **a.** 9.0×10^7 J **b.** 0.249 Cal
 c. 1.31×10^{-4} kWh **d.** 1.1×10^4 cal

51.

J	cal	Cal	kWh
225	53.8	5.38×10^{-2}	6.25×10^{-5}
3.44×10^6	8.21×10^5	8.21×10^2	9.54×10^{-1}
1.06×10^9	2.54×10^8	2.54×10^5	295
6.49×10^5	1.55×10^5	155	1.80×10^{-1}

53. 3.44×10^9 J

55. 8×10^2 kJ; 17 days

57. **a.** 1.00×10^2 °C **b.** -3.2×10^2 °F
 c. 298 K **d.** 3.10×10^2 K

59. -62 °C, 211 K

61. 159 K, -173 °F

63.

0.0 K	-459.4 °F	-273.0 °C
301 K	82.5 °F	28.1 °C
282 K	47 °F	8.5 °C

65. 1.0×10^4 J

67. 8.7×10^5 J

69. 58 °

71. 31 °

73. 1.0×10^1 °C

75. 0.24 J/g °C; silver

77. 2.2 J/g °C;

79. When warm drinks are placed into the ice, they release heat, which then melts the ice. The prechilled drinks, on the other hand, are already cold, so they do not release much heat.

81. 49 °C

83. 70.2 J

85. 1.7×10^4 kJ

87. 67 °C

89. 6.0 kWh

91. 22 g of fuel

93. 78 g

95. 27.2 °C

97. **a.** pure substance **b.** pure substance
 c. pure substance **d.** mixture

99. physical change

101. Small temperature changes in the ocean have a great impact on global weather because of the high heat capacity of water.

103. **a.** Sacramento is farther inland than San Francisco, so Sacramento is not as close to the ocean. The ocean water has a high heat capacity and will be able to keep San Francisco cooler in hot days of summer. However, Sacramento is away from the ocean in a valley, so it will experience high temperatures in the summer.

 b. San Francisco is located right next to the ocean, so the high heat capacity of the seawater keeps the temperature in the city from dropping. In the winter, the ocean actually helps to keep the city warmer, compared to an inland city like Sacramento.

Chapter 4

Questions

1. It is important to understand atoms because they compose matter and the properties of atoms determine matter's properties. The atom is the key to connecting the microscopic world with the macroscopic world.

3. Democritus theorized that matter was ultimately composed of small, indivisible particles called atoms. Upon dividing matter, one would find tiny, indestructible atoms.

5. Rutherford's gold foil experiment involved sending positively charged alpha particles through a thin sheet of gold foil and detecting if there was any deflection of the particles. He found that most passed straight through, yet some particles showed some deflection. This result contradicts the plum-pudding model of the atom because the plum-pudding model does not explain the deflection of the alpha-particles.

7.
Particle	Mass (kg)	Mass (amu)	Charge
Proton	1.67262×10^{-27}	1	+1
Neutron	1.67493×10^{-27}	1	0
Electron	0.00091×10^{-27}	0.00055	−1

9. Matter is usually charge neutral due to protons and electrons having opposite charges. If matter were not charge neutral, many unnatural things would occur, such as objects repelling or attracting each other.

11. A chemical symbol is a unique one- or two-letter abbreviation for an element. It is listed below the atomic number for that element on the periodic table.

13. Mendeleev noticed that many patterns were evident when elements were organized by increasing mass; from this he formulated the periodic law. He also organized the elements based on this law and created the basis for the periodic table being used today.

15. The periodic table is organized by listing the elements in order of increasing atomic number.

17. Nonmetals have varied properties (solid, liquid, or gas at room temperature); however, as a whole they tend to be poor conductors of heat and electricity and they all tend to gain electrons when they undergo chemical changes. They are located toward the upper right side of the periodic table.

19. Each column within the main group elements in the periodic table is labeled as a family or group of elements. The elements within a group usually have similar chemical properties.

21. An ion is an atom or group of atoms that has lost or gained electrons and has become charged.

23. **a.** ion charge = +1   **b.** ion charge = +2
    c. ion charge = +3   **d.** ion charge = −2
    e. ion charge = −1

25. The percent natural abundance of isotopes is the relative amount of each different isotope in a naturally occurring sample of a given element.

27. Isotopes are noted in this manner, $^{A}_{Z}X$. X represents the chemical symbol, A represents the mass number, and Z represents the atomic number.

Problems

29. **a.** Correct.
    b. False; different elements contain different types of atoms according to Dalton.
    c. False; one cannot have 1.5 hydrogen atoms; combinations must be in simple, whole-number ratios.
    d. Correct.

31. **a.** Correct.
    b. False; most of the volume of the atom is empty space occupied by tiny, negatively charged electrons.
    c. False, the number of negatively charged particles outside the nucleus equals the number of positively charged particles inside the nucleus.
    d. False, the majority of the mass of an atom is found in the nucleus.

33. a, b, d

35. b, d

37. approximately 1.8×10^3 electrons

39. 5.4×10^{-4} g

41. **a.** 27   **b.** 77   **c.** 92
    d. 14   **e.** 4

43. **a.** 25   **b.** 47   **c.** 79
    d. 82   **e.** 16

45. **a.** C, 6   **b.** N, 7   **c.** Na, 11
    d. K, 19   **e.** Cu, 29

47. **a.** gold, 79   **b.** silicon, 14
    c. nickel, 28   **d.** zinc, 30
    e. tungsten, 74

49.
Element Name	Element Symbol	Atomic Number
Gold	Au	79
Tin	Sn	50
Arsenic	As	33
Copper	Cu	29
Iron	Fe	26
Mercury	Hg	80

51. **a.** metal   **b.** metal   **c.** nonmetal
    d. nonmetal   **e.** metalloid

53. a, d, e

55. a, b

57. c, d

59. a, b, e

61. **a.** halogen   **b.** noble gas
    c. halogen   **d.** neither
    e. noble gas

63. **a.** 6A   **b.** 3A   **c.** 4A
    d. 4A   **e.** 5A

65. b, oxygen; it is in the same group or family.

67. b, chlorine and fluorine; they are in the same family or group.

69.
Chemical Symbol	Group Number	Group Name	Metal or Nonmetal
K	1A	Alkali Metals	Metals
Br	7A	Halogens	Nonmetal
Sr	2A	Alkaline Earth	Metal
He	8A	Noble Gas	Nonmetal
Ar	8A	Noble Gas	Nonmetal

71. **a.** e^-　　**b.** O^{2-}
　　c. $2e^-$　　**d.** Cl^-
73. **a.** -2　　**b.** $+3$
　　c. $+4$　　**d.** -1
75. **a.** 19 protons, 18 electrons
　　b. 16 protons, 18 electrons
　　c. 38 protons, 36 electrons
　　d. 24 protons, 21 electrons
77. **a.** False; Ti^{2+} has 22 protons and 20 electrons.
　　b. True
　　c. False; Mg^{2+} has 12 protons and 10 electrons
　　d. True
79. **a.** Rb^+　　**b.** K^+
　　c. Al^{3+}　　**d.** O^{2-}
81. **a.** 3 electrons lost　　**b.** 1 electron lost
　　c. 1 electron gained　　**d.** 2 electrons gained
83.

Symbol	Ion Commonly Formed	Number of Electrons in Ion	Number of Protons in Ion
Te	Te^{2-}	54	52
In	In^{3+}	46	49
Sr	Sr^{2+}	36	38
Mg	Mg^{2+}	10	12
Cl	Cl^-	18	17

85. **a.** $Z = 1$, $A = 2$　　**b.** $Z = 24$, $A = 51$
　　c. $Z = 20$, $A = 40$　　**d.** $Z = 73$, $A = 181$
87. **a.** $^{16}_{8}O$　　**b.** $^{19}_{9}F$
　　c. $^{23}_{11}Na$　　**d.** $^{27}_{13}Al$
89. **a.** $^{60}_{27}Co$　　**b.** $^{22}_{10}Ne$
　　c. $^{131}_{53}I$　　**d.** $^{244}_{94}Pu$
91. **a.** 11 protons, 12 neutrons
　　b. 88 protons, 178 neutrons
　　c. 82 protons, 126 neutrons
　　d. 7 protons, 7 neutrons
93. 6 protons, 8 neutrons, $^{14}_{6}C$
95. 85.47 amu
97. **a.** 49.31%　　**b.** 78.92 amu
99. 121.8 amu, Sb
101. 7.8×10^{17} electrons
103. $6.8 \times 10^{-13}\%$
105.

Number Symbol	Number of Protons	Number of Neutrons	A (Mass Number)	Natural Abundance
Sr-84 or $^{84}_{38}Sr$	38	46	84	0.56%
Sr-86 or $^{86}_{38}Sr$	38	48	86	9.86%
Sr-87 or $^{87}_{38}Sr$	38	49	87	7.00%
Sr-88 or $^{88}_{38}Sr$	38	50	88	82.58%

Atomic mass of Sr = 87.62 amu
107.

Symbol	Z	A	Number of Protons	Number of Electrons	Number of Neutrons	Charge
Zn^+	30	64	30	29	34	1+
Mn^{3+}	25	55	25	22	30	3+
P	15	31	15	15	16	0
O^{2-}	8	16	8	10	8	2−
S^{2-}	16	34	16	18	18	2−

109. 153 amu, 52.2%

111. The atomic theory and nuclear model of the atom are both theories because they attempt to provide a broader understanding and model behavior of chemical systems.
113. **a.** Nt-304 = 72%; Nt-305 = 4%; Nt-306 = 24%
　　b.

120
Nt
304.5

Chapter 5

Questions

1. Yes; when elements combine with other elements, a compound is created. Each compound is unique and contains properties different from those of the elements that compose it.
3. The law of constant composition states that all samples of a given compound have the same proportions of their constituent elements. Joseph Proust formulated this law.
5. The more metallic element is generally listed first in a chemical formula.
7. An atomic element is one that exists in nature with a single atom as the basic unit. A molecular element is one that exists as a diatomic molecule as the basis unit. Molecular elements include H_2, N_2, O_2, F_2, Cl_2, Br_2, and I_2.
9. The systematic name can be directly derived by looking at the compound's formula. The common name for a compound acts like a nickname and can only be learned through familiarity.
11. The block that contains the elements for Type II compounds is known as the transition metals.
13. The basic form for the names of Type II ionic compounds is to have the name of the metal cation first, followed by the charge of the metal cation (in parentheses, using Roman numerals), and finally the base name of the nonmetal anion with -ide attached to the end.
15. For compounds containing a polyatomic anion, the name of the cation is first, followed by the name for the polyatomic anion. Also, if the compound contains both a polyatomic cation and a polyatomic anion, one would just use the names of both polyatomic ions.
17. The form for naming molecular compounds is to have the first element preceded by a prefix to indicate the number of atoms present. This is then followed by the second element with its corresponding prefix and -ide placed on the end of the second element.
19. To correctly name a binary acid one must begin the first word with *hydro-*, which is followed by the base name of the nonmetal plus -ic added on the end. Finally, the word *acid* follows the first word.
21. To name an acid with oxyanions ending with -ite, one must take the base name of the oxyanion and attach -ous to it; the word *acid* follows this.

Problems

23. Yes; the ratios of sodium to chlorine in both samples were equal.
25. 2.06×10^3 g

27.

	Mass N$_2$O	Mass N	Mass O
Sample A	2.85	1.82	1.03
Sample B	4.55	2.91	1.64
Sample C	3.74	2.39	1.35
Sample D	1.74	1.11	0.63

29. NBr$_3$

31. **a.** Fe$_2$O$_3$ **b.** PCl$_3$
 c. PCl$_5$ **d.** Ag$_2$O

33. **a.** 4 **b.** 4
 c. 6 **d.** 4

35. **a.** magnesium, 1; chlorine, 2
 b. sodium, 1; nitrogen, 1; oxygen, 3
 c. calcium, 1; nitrogen, 2; oxygen, 4
 d. strontium, 1; oxygen, 2; hydrogen, 2

37. **a.** atomic **b.** molecular
 c. molecular **d.** atomic

39. **a.** molecular **b.** ionic
 c. ionic **d.** molecular

41. helium → single atoms
 CCl$_4$ → molecules
 K$_2$SO$_4$ → formula units
 bromine → diatomic molecules

43. **a.** formula units **b.** single atoms
 c. molecules **d.** molecules

45. **a.** ionic, Type I **b.** molecular
 c. molecular **d.** ionic, Type II

47. **a.** SrO **b.** Na$_2$O
 c. Al$_2$S$_3$ **d.** MgBr$_2$

49. **a.** KC$_2$H$_3$O$_2$ **b.** K$_2$CrO$_4$
 c. K$_3$PO$_4$ **d.** KCN

51. **a.** K$_3$N, K$_2$O, KF **b.** Ba$_3$N$_2$, BaO, BaF$_2$
 c. AlN, Al$_2$O$_3$, AlF$_3$

53. **a.** cesium chloride **b.** strontium bromide
 c. potassium oxide **d.** lithium fluoride

55. **a.** chromium(II) chloride
 b. chromium(III) chloride
 c. tin(IV) oxide
 d. lead(II) iodide

57. **a.** Type II, chromium(III) oxide
 b. Type I, sodium iodide
 c. Type I, calcium bromide
 d. Type II, tin(II) oxide

59. **a.** barium nitrate **b.** lead(II) acetate
 c. ammonium iodide **d.** potassium chlorate
 e. cobalt(II) sulfate **f.** sodium perchlorate

61. **a.** hypobromite ion **b.** bromite ion
 c. bromate ion **d.** perbromate ion

63. **a.** CuBr$_2$ **b.** AgNO$_3$
 c. KOH **d.** Na$_2$SO$_4$
 e. KHSO$_4$ **f.** NaHCO$_3$

65. **a.** sulfur dioxide
 b. nitrogen triiodide
 c. bromine pentafluoride
 d. nitrogen monoxide
 e. tetranitrogen tetraselenide

67. **a.** CO **b.** S$_2$F$_4$
 c. Cl$_2$O **d.** PF$_5$
 e. BBr$_3$ **f.** P$_2$S$_5$

69. **a.** PBr$_5$ phosphorus pentabromide
 b. P$_2$O$_3$ diphosphorus trioxide
 c. SF$_4$ sulfur tetraflouride
 d. correct

71. **a.** chlorous acid **b.** hydroiodic acid
 c. sulfuric acid **d.** nitric acid

73. **a.** H$_3$PO$_4$ **b.** HBr
 c. H$_2$SO$_3$

75. **a.** 47.02 amu **b.** 110.98 amu
 c. 153.81 amu **d.** 148.33 amu

77. PBr$_3$, Ag$_2$O, PtO$_2$, Al(NO$_3$)$_3$

79. **a.** CH$_4$ **b.** SO$_3$ **c.** NO$_2$

81. **a.** 12 **b.** 4
 c. 12 **d.** 7

83. **a.** 8 **b.** 12 **c.** 12

85.

Formula	Type	Name
N$_2$H$_4$	molecular	dinitrogen tetrahydride
KCl	ionic	potassium chloride
H$_2$CrO$_4$	acid	chromic acid
Co(CN)$_3$	ionic	cobalt(III) cyanide

87. **a.** calcium nitrite **b.** potassium oxide
 c. phosphorus trichloride **d.** correct
 e. potassium iodite

89. **a.** Sn(SO$_4$)$_2$ 310.8 amu **b.** HNO$_2$ 47.02 amu
 c. NaHCO$_3$ 84.01 amu **d.** PF$_5$ 125.97 amu

91. **a.** platinum(IV) oxide 227.08 amu
 b. dinitrogen pentoxide 108.02 amu
 c. aluminum chlorate 277.33 amu
 d. phosphorous pentabromide 430.47 amu

93. **a.** molecular element **b.** atomic element
 c. ionic compound **d.** molecular compound

95. **a.** NaOCl; NaOH **b.** CaCO$_3$; NaHCO$_3$;
 c. Al(OH)$_3$; Mg(OH)$_2$
 d. NaHCO$_3$, Ca$_3$(PO$_4$)$_2$, NaAl(SO$_4$)$_2$

Chapter 6
Questions

1. Chemical composition lets us determine how much of a particular element is contained within a particular compound.
3. There are 6.022×10^{23} atoms in 1 mole of atoms.
5. One mole of any element has a mass equal to its atomic mass in grams.
7. **a.** 30.97 g **b.** 195.08 g **c.** 12.01 g **d.** 52.00 g
9. Each element has a different atomic mass number. So, the subscripts that represent mole ratios cannot be used to represent the ratios of grams of a compound. The grams per mole of one element always differs from the grams per mole of a different element.
11. **a.** 11.19 g H ≡ 100 g H$_2$O
 b. 53.29 g O ≡ 100 g fructose
 c. 84.12 g C ≡ 100 g octane
 d. 52.14 g C ≡ 100 g ethanol

13. The empirical formula gives the smallest whole number ratio of each type of atom. The molecular formula gives the specific number of each type of atom in the molecule. The molecular formula is always a multiple of the empirical formula.

15. The empirical formula mass of a compound is the sum of the masses of all the atoms in the empirical formula.

Problems

17. 3.6×10^{24} atoms

19. **a.** 2.0×10^{24} atoms   **b.** 5.8×10^{21} atoms
    c. 1.38×10^{25} atoms   **d.** 1.29×10^{23} atoms

21.
Element	Moles	Number of Atoms
Ne	0.552	3.32×10^{23}
Ar	5.40	3.25×10^{24}
Xe	1.78	1.07×10^{24}
He	1.79×10^{-4}	1.08×10^{20}

23. **a.** 72.7 dozen   **b.** 6.06 gross
    c. 1.74 reams   **d.** 1.45×10^{-21} moles

25. 0.356 mol

27. 28.6 g

29. **a.** 2.36×10^{-2} mol   **b.** 0.571 mol
    c. 0.476 mol   **d.** 4.9×10^{-3} mol

31.
Element	Moles	Mass
Ne	1.11	22.5 g
Ar	0.117	4.67 g
Xe	7.62	1.00 kg
He	1.44×10^{-4}	5.76×10^{-4} g

33. 8.07×10^{18} atoms

35. 8.44×10^{22} atoms

37. **a.** 8.80×10^{22} atoms   **b.** 4.87×10^{23} atoms
    c. 2.84×10^{22} atoms   **d.** 7.02×10^{23} atoms

39. 2.6×10^{21} atoms

41. 1.61×10^{25} atoms

43.
Element	Mass	Moles	Number of Atoms
Na	38.5 mg	1.67×10^{-3}	1.01×10^{21}
C	13.5 g	1.12	6.74×10^{23}
V	1.81×10^{-20} g	3.55×10^{-22}	214
Hg	1.44 kg	7.18	4.32×10^{24}

45. **a.** 0.945 mol   **b.** 0.903 mol
    c. 109 mol   **d.** 8.65×10^{-6} mol

47.
Compound	Mass	Moles
H_2O	112 kg	6.22×10^3
N_2O	6.33 g	0.144
SO_2	156	2.44
CH_2Cl_2	5.46	0.0643

49. 6.20×10^{21} molecules

51. **a.** 1.2×10^{23} molecules
    b. 1.21×10^{24} molecules
    c. 3.5×10^{23} molecules
    d. 6.4×10^{22} molecules

53. 0.10 mg

55. 9.4 mol Cl

57. d, 3 mol O

59. **a.** 3.8 mol C   **b.** 0.546 mol C
    c. 19.6 mol C   **d.** 183 mol C

61. **a.** 2 moles H per mole of molecules; 8 H atoms present
    b. 4 moles H per mole of molecules; 20 H atoms present
    c. 3 moles H per mole of molecules; 9 H atoms present

63. **a.** 32 g   **b.** 43 g   **c.** 31 g   **d.** 19 g

65. **a.** 1.4×10^3 kg   **b.** 1.4×10^3 kg
    c. 2.1×10^3 kg

67. 84.8% Sr

69. 36.1% Ca; 63.9% Cl

71. 10.7 g

73. 6.6 mg

75. **a.** 63.65%   **b.** 46.68%
    c. 30.45%   **d.** 25.94%

77. **a.** 39.99% C; 6.73% H; 53.28% O
    b. 26.09% C; 4.39% H; 69.52% O
    c. 60.93% C; 15.37% H; 23.69% N
    d. 54.48% C; 13.74% H; 31.78% N

79. Fe_3O_4, 72.36% Fe; Fe_2O_3, 69.94% Fe; $FeCO_3$, 48.20% Fe; magnetite

81. NO_2

83. **a.** NiI_2 **b.** $SeBr_4$ **c.** $BeSO_4$

85. C_2H_6N

87. **a.** C_3H_6O **b.** $C_5H_{10}O_2$ **c.** $C_9H_{10}O_2$

89. P_2O_3

91. NCl_3

93. C_4H_8

95. **a.** C_6Cl_6 **b.** C_2HCl_3 **c.** $C_6H_3Cl_3$

97. 2.43×10^{23} atoms

99. 2×10^{21} molecules

101.
Substance	Mass	Moles	Number of Particles
Ar	0.018 g	4.5×10^{-4}	2.7×10^{20}
NO_2	8.33×10^{-3} g	1.81×10^{-4}	1.09×10^{20}
K	22.4 mg	5.73×10^{-4}	3.45×10^{20}
C_8H_{18}	3.76 kg	32.9	1.98×10^{25}

103. **a.** CuI_2: 20.03% Cu; 79.97% I
     b. $NaNO_3$: 27.05% Na; 16.48% N; 56.47% O
     c. $PbSO_4$: 68.32% Pb; 10.57% S; 21.10% O
     d. CaF_2: 51.33% Ca; 48.67% F

105. 1.8×10^3 kg rock

107. 59 kg Cl

109. 1.1×10^2 g H

111.
Formula	Molar Mass	%C (by mass)	%H (by mass)
C_2H_4	28.06	85.60%	14.40%
C_4H_{10}	58.12	82.66%	17.34%
C_4H_8	56.12	85.60%	14.40%
C_3H_8	44.09	81.71%	18.29

113. $C_4H_6O_2$

115. $C_{10}H_{14}N_2$

117. **a.** 1×10^{57} atoms per star
     b. 1×10^{68} atoms per galaxy
     c. 1×10^{79} atoms in the universe

119. $C_{16}H_{10}$

Chapter 7

Questions

1. A chemical reaction is the change of one or more substances into different substances, for example burning wood, rusting iron, and protein synthesis.

3. The main evidences of a chemical reaction are a color change, the formation of a solid, the formation of a gas, the emission of light, and the emission or absorption of heat.

5. **a.** gas   **b.** liquid
   c. solid   **d.** aqueous

7. **a.** reactants: 4 Ag, 2 O, 1 C products: 4 Ag, 2 O, 1 C balanced: yes
   b. reactants: 1 Pb, 2 N, 6 O, 2 Na, 2 Cl products: 1 Pb, 2 N, 6 O, 2 Na, 2 Cl balanced: yes
   c. reactants: 3 C, 8 H, 2 O products: 3 C, 8 H, 10 O balanced: no

9. If a compound dissolves in water than it is soluble. If it does not dissolve in water, it is insoluble.

11. When ionic compounds containing polyatomic ions dissolve in water, the polyatomic ions usually dissolve as intact units.

13. The solubility rules are a set of empirical rules for ionic compounds that were deduced from observations on many compounds. The rules help us determine whether particular compounds will be soluble or insoluble.

15. The precipitate will always be insoluble; it is the solid that forms upon mixing two aqueous solutions.

17. A complete ionic equation shows the reactants and products as they are actually present in solution. The net ionic equation shows only the species that actually change during the reaction. Spectator ions are shown in the complete ionic equation but are not shown in the net ionic equation. An example of each:

   Complete ionic equation:

   $Na^+(aq) + OH^-(aq) + H^+(aq) + NO_3^-(aq) \longrightarrow$
   $H_2O(l) + Na^+(aq) + NO_3^-(aq)$

   Net ionic equation:

   $H^+(aq) + OH^-(aq) \longrightarrow H_2O(l)$

19. An acid is a compound characterized by its sour taste, its ability to dissolve some metals, and its tendency to form H^+ ions in solution. A base is a compound characterized by its bitter taste, its slippery feel, and its tendency to form OH^- ions in solution.

21. A redox reaction is a reaction involving the transfer of electrons. An example of a redox reaction is the rusting of iron: $4\,Fe(s) + 3\,O_2(g) \longrightarrow 2\,Fe_2O_3(s)$

23. You can classify chemical reactions by either 1) the type of chemistry occurring during the reaction, such as acid–base chemistry verses precipitation chemistry, or 2) by studying what happens to atoms during the reaction. We use both methods for classifying reactions so we can study the similarities and differences between reactions.

25. Two examples of synthesis reactions:

   $2\,Na(s) + Cl_2(g) \longrightarrow 2\,NaCl(s)$

   $CaO(s) + CO_2(g) \longrightarrow CaCO_3(s)$

27. Two examples of single-displacement reactions:

   $2\,Na(s) + 2\,HOH(l) \longrightarrow 2\,NaOH(aq) + H_2(g)$

   $Zn(s) + CuCl_2(aq) \longrightarrow ZnCl_2(aq) + Cu(s)$

Problems:

29. **a.** Yes; there is a color change showing a chemical reaction.
   b. No; the state of the compound changes, but no chemical reaction takes place.
   c. Yes; there is a formation of a solid in a previously clear solution.
   d. Yes; there is a formation of a gas when the yeast was added to the solution.

31. Yes; a chemical reaction has occurred; for the presence of the bubbles is evidence for the formation of a gas.

33. Yes; a chemical reaction has occurred. We know this due to the color change of the hair.

35. **a.** $2\,Cu(s) + S(s) \longrightarrow Cu_2S(s)$
   b. $2\,SO_2(g) + O_2(g) \longrightarrow 2\,SO_3(g)$
   c. $4\,HCl(aq) + MnO_2(s) \longrightarrow$
   $\qquad 2\,H_2O(l) + Cl_2(g) + MnCl_2(aq)$
   d. $2\,C_6H_6(l) + 15\,O_2(g) \longrightarrow 12\,CO_2(g) + 6\,H_2O(l)$

37. **a.** $Mg(s) + 2\,CuNO_3(aq) \longrightarrow 2\,Cu(s) + Mg(NO_3)_2(aq)$
   b. $2\,N_2O_5(g) \longrightarrow 4\,NO_2(g) + O_2(g)$
   c. $Ca(s) + 2\,HNO_3(aq) \longrightarrow H_2(g) + Ca(NO_3)_2(aq)$
   d. $2\,CH_3OH(l) + 3\,O_2(g) \longrightarrow 2\,CO_2(g) + 4\,H_2O(g)$

39. $2\,H_2(g) + O_2(g) \longrightarrow 2\,H_2O(l);$
   $\qquad Cl(g) + O_3(g) \longrightarrow ClO(g) + O_2(g)$

41. $2\,Na(s) + 2\,H_2O(l) \longrightarrow H_2(g) + 2\,NaOH(aq)$

43. $2\,SO_2(g) + O_2(g) + 2\,H_2O(l) \longrightarrow 2\,H_2SO_4(aq)$

45. $V_2O_5(s) + 2\,H_2(g) \longrightarrow V_2O_3(s) + 2\,H_2O(l)$

47. $C_{12}H_{22}O_{11}(aq) + H_2O(l) \longrightarrow$
   $\qquad 4\,CO_2(g) + 4\,C_2H_5OH(aq)$

49. **a.** $3\,N_2H_4(l) \longrightarrow 4\,NH_3(g) + N_2(g)$
   b. $3\,H_2(g) + N_2(g) \longrightarrow 2\,NH_3(g)$
   c. $Cu_2O(s) + C(s) \longrightarrow 2\,Cu(s) + CO(g)$
   d. $H_2(g) + Cl_2(g) \longrightarrow 2\,HCl(g)$

51. **a.** $BaO_2(s) + H_2SO_4(aq) \longrightarrow BaSO_4(s) + H_2O_2(aq)$
   b. $2\,Co(NO_3)_3(aq) + 3\,(NH_4)_2S(aq) \longrightarrow$
   $\qquad\qquad\qquad Co_2S_3(s) + 6\,NH_4NO_3(aq)$
   c. $Li_2O(s) + H_2O(l) \longrightarrow 2\,LiOH(aq)$
   d. $Hg_2(C_2H_3O_2)_2(aq) + 2\,KCl(aq) \longrightarrow$
   $\qquad\qquad\qquad Hg_2Cl_2(s) + 2\,KC_2H_3O_2(aq)$

53. **a.** $2\,Rb(s) + 2\,H_2O(l) \longrightarrow 2\,RbOH(aq) + H_2(g)$
   b. Ok
   c. $2\,NiS(s) + 3\,O_2(g) \longrightarrow 2\,NiO(s) + 2\,SO_2(g)$
   d. $3\,PbO(s) + 2\,NH_3(g) \longrightarrow 3\,Pb(s) + N_2(g) + 3\,H_2O(l)$

55. $C_6H_{12}O_6(aq) + 6\,O_2(g) \longrightarrow 6\,CO_2(g) + 6\,H_2O(l)$

57. $2\,NO(g) + 2\,CO(g) \longrightarrow N_2(g) + 2\,CO_2(g)$

59. **a.** soluble; Na^+ and NO_3^-
   b. soluble; Pb^{2+} and $C_2H_3O_2^-$
   c. insoluble
   d. soluble; NH_4^+ and S^{2-}

61. $AgCl; BaSO_4; CuCO_3; Fe_2S_3$

63.
Soluble	Insoluble
K_2S	Hg_2I_2
BaS	$Cu_3(PO_4)_2$
NH_4Cl	MgS
Na_2CO_3	$CaSO_4$
K_2SO_4	$PbSO_4$
SrS	$PbCl_2$
Li_2S	Hg_2Cl_2

65. **a.** $NH_4Cl(aq) + AgNO_3(aq) \longrightarrow AgCl(s) + NH_4NO_3(aq)$
   b. NO REACTION
   c. $CrCl_2(aq) + Li_2CO_3(aq) \longrightarrow CrCO_3(s) + 2\,LiCl(aq)$
   d. $3\,KOH(aq) + FeCl_3(aq) \longrightarrow Fe(OH)_3(s) + 3\,KCl(aq)$

67. **a.** $Na_2CO_3(aq) + Pb(NO_3)_2(aq) \longrightarrow$
$$PbCO_3(s) + 2\,NaNO_3(aq)$$
   b. $K_2SO_4(aq) + Pb(CH_3CO_2)_2(aq) \longrightarrow$
$$PbSO_4(s) + 2\,KCH_3CO_2(aq)$$
   c. $Cu(NO_3)_2(aq) + BaS(aq) \longrightarrow CuS(s) + Ba(NO_3)_2(aq)$
   d. NO REACTION

69. **a.** correct   **b.** NO REACTION
   c. correct
   d. $Pb(NO_3)_2(aq) + 2\,LiCl(aq) \longrightarrow$
$$PbCl_2(s) + 2\,LiNO_3(aq)$$

71. $K^+, C_2H_3O_2^-$

73. **a.** $Ag^+(aq) + NO_3^-(aq) + K^+(aq) + Cl^-(aq) \longrightarrow$
$$AgCl(s) + K^+(aq) + NO_3^-(aq)$$
$Ag^+(aq) + Cl^-(aq) \longrightarrow AgCl(s)$
   b. $Ca^{2+}(aq) + S^{2-}(aq) + Cu^{2+}(aq) + 2\,Cl^-(aq) \longrightarrow$
$$CuS(s) + Ca^{2+}(aq) + 2\,Cl^-(aq)$$
$Cu^{2+}(aq) + S^{2-}(aq) \longrightarrow CuS(s)$
   c. $Na^+(aq) + OH^-(aq) + H^+(aq) + NO_3^-(aq) \longrightarrow$
$$H_2O(l) + Na^+(aq) + NO_3^-(aq)$$
$H^+(aq) + OH^-(aq) \longrightarrow H_2O(l)$
   d. $6\,K^+(aq) + 2\,PO_4^{3-}(aq) + 3\,Ni^{2+}(aq) + 6\,Cl^-(aq) \longrightarrow$
$$Ni_3(PO_4)_2(s) + 6\,K^+(aq) + 6\,Cl^-(aq)$$
$3\,Ni^{2+}(aq) + 2\,PO_4^{3-}(aq) \longrightarrow Ni_3(PO_4)_2(s)$

75. $Hg_2^{2+}(aq) + 2\,NO_3^-(aq) + 2\,Na^+(aq) + 2\,Cl^-(aq) \longrightarrow$
$$Hg_2Cl_2(s) + 2\,Na^+(aq) + 2\,NO_3^-(aq)$$
$Hg_2^{2+}(aq) + 2\,Cl^-(aq) \longrightarrow Hg_2Cl_2(s)$

77. **a.** $2\,Na^+(aq) + CO_3^{2-}(aq) + Pb^{2+}(aq) + 2\,NO_3^-(aq)$
$$\longrightarrow PbCO_3(s) + 2\,Na^+(aq) + 2\,NO_3^-(aq)$$
$Pb^{2+}(aq) + CO_3^{2-}(aq) \longrightarrow PbCO_3(s)$
   b. $2\,K^+(aq) + SO_4^{2-}(aq) + Pb^{2+}(aq) + 2\,CH_3CO_2^-(aq)$
$$\longrightarrow PbSO_4(s) + 2\,K^+(aq) + 2\,CH_3CO_2^-(aq)$$
$Pb^{2+}(aq) + SO_4^{2-}(aq) \longrightarrow PbSO_4(s)$
   c. $Cu^{2+}(aq) + 2\,NO_3^-(aq) + Ba^{2+}(aq) + S^{2-}(aq) \longrightarrow$
$$CuS(s) + Ba^{2+}(aq) + 2\,NO_3^-(aq)$$
$Cu^{2+}(aq) + S^{2-}(aq) \longrightarrow CuS(s)$
   d. NO REACTION

79. $HCl(aq) + KOH(aq) \longrightarrow H_2O(l) + KCl(aq)$
$H^+(aq) + OH^-(aq) \longrightarrow H_2O(l)$

81. **a.** $2\,HCl(aq) + Ba(OH)_2(aq) \longrightarrow 2\,H_2O(l) + BaCl_2(aq)$
   b. $H_2SO_4(aq) + 2\,KOH(aq) \longrightarrow 2\,H_2O(l) + K_2SO_4(aq)$
   c. $HClO_4(aq) + NaOH(aq) \longrightarrow H_2O(l) + NaClO_4(aq)$

83. **a.** $HBr(aq) + NaHCO_3(aq) \longrightarrow$
$$H_2O(l) + CO_2(g) + NaBr(aq)$$
   b. $NH_4I(aq) + KOH(aq) \longrightarrow H_2O(l) + NH_3(g) + KI(aq)$
   c. $2\,HNO_3(aq) + K_2SO_3(aq) \longrightarrow$
$$H_2O(l) + SO_2(g) + 2\,KNO_3(aq)$$
   d. $2\,HI(aq) + Li_2S(aq) \longrightarrow H_2S(g) + 2\,LiI(aq)$

85. b and d are redox reactions; a and c are not.

87. **a.** $2\,C_2H_6(g) + 7\,O_2(g) \longrightarrow 4\,CO_2(g) + 6\,H_2O(g)$
   b. $2\,Ca(s) + O_2(g) \longrightarrow 2\,CaO(s)$
   c. $2\,C_3H_8O(l) + 9\,O_2(g) \longrightarrow 6\,CO_2(g) + 8\,H_2O(g)$
   d. $2\,C_4H_{10}S(l) + 15\,O_2(g) \longrightarrow$
$$8\,CO_2(g) + 10\,H_2O(g) + 2\,SO_2(g)$$

89. **a.** $2\,K(s) + Cl_2(g) \longrightarrow 2\,KCl(s)$
   b. $Ca(s) + Cl_2(g) \longrightarrow CaCl_2(s)$
   c. $2\,Al(s) + 3\,Cl_2(g) \longrightarrow 2\,AlCl_3(s)$
   d. $Zn(s) + Cl_2(g) \longrightarrow ZnCl_2(s)$

91. **a.** double displacement
   b. synthesis or combination
   c. single displacement
   d. decomposition

93. **a.** synthesis
   b. decomposition
   c. synthesis

95. **a.** $2\,Na^+(aq) + 2\,I^-(aq) + Hg_2^+(aq) + 2\,NO_3^-(aq) \longrightarrow$
$$Hg_2I_2(s) + 2\,Na^+(aq) + 2\,NO_3^-(aq)$$
$Hg_2^+(aq) + 2\,I^-(aq) \longrightarrow Hg_2I_2(s)$
   b. $2\,H^+(aq) + ClO_4^-(aq) + Ba^{2+}(aq) + 2\,OH^-(aq) \longrightarrow$
$$2\,H_2O(l) + Ba^{2+}(aq) + ClO_4^-(aq)$$
$H^+(aq) + OH^-(aq) \longrightarrow H_2O(s)$
   c. NO REACTION
   d. $2\,H^+(aq) + 2\,Cl^-(aq) + 2\,Li^+(aq) + CO_3^{2-}(aq) \longrightarrow$
$$H_2O(l) + CO_2(g) + 2\,Li^+(aq) + 2\,Cl^-(aq)$$
$2\,H^+(aq) + CO_3^{2-}(aq) \longrightarrow H_2O(l) + CO_2(g)$

97. **a.** NO REACTION
   b. NO REACTION
   c. $K^+(aq) + HSO_3^-(aq) + H^+(aq) + NO_3^-(aq) \longrightarrow$
$$H_2O(l) + SO_2(g) + K^+(aq) + NO_3^-(aq)$$
$H^+(aq) + HSO_3^-(aq) \longrightarrow H_2O(l) + SO_2(g)$
   d. $Mn^{3+}(aq) + 3\,Cl^-(aq) + 3\,K^+(aq) + PO_4^{3-}(aq) \longrightarrow$
$$MnPO_4(s) + 3\,K^+(aq) + 3\,Cl^-(aq)$$
$Mn^{3+}(aq) + PO_4^{3-}(aq) \longrightarrow MnPO_4(s)$

99. **a.** acid–base; $KOH(aq) + HC_2H_3O_2(aq) \longrightarrow$
$$H_2O(l) + KC_2H_3O_2(aq)$$
   b. gas evolution; $2\,HBr(aq) + K_2CO_3(aq) \longrightarrow$
$$H_2O(l) + CO_2(g) + 2\,KBr(aq)$$
   c. synthesis; $2\,H_2(g) + O_2(g) \longrightarrow 2\,H_2O(l)$
   d. precipitation; $2\,NH_4Cl(aq) + Pb(NO_3)_2(aq) \longrightarrow$
$$PbCl_2(s) + 2\,NH_4NO_3(aq)$$

101. **a.** oxidation–reduction; single displacement
   b. gas evolution; acid–base
   c. gas evolution; double displacement
   d. precipitation; double displacement

103. $3\,CaCl_2(aq) + 2\,Na_3PO_4(aq) \longrightarrow$

$$Ca_3(PO_4)_2(s) + 6\,NaCl(aq)$$

$3\,Ca^{2+}(aq) + 6\,Cl^-(aq) + 6\,Na^+(aq) + 2\,PO_4^{3-}(aq) \longrightarrow$

$$Ca_3(PO_4)_2(s) + 6\,Na^+(aq) + 6\,Cl^-(aq)$$

$3\,Ca^{2+}(aq) + 2\,PO_4^{3-}(aq) \longrightarrow Ca_3(PO_4)_2(s)$

$3\,Mg(NO_3)_2(aq) + 2\,Na_3PO_4(aq) \longrightarrow$

$$Mg_3(PO_4)_2(s) + 6\,NaNO_3(aq)$$

$3\,Mg^{2+}(aq) + 6\,NO_3^-(aq) + 6\,Na^+(aq) + 2\,PO_4^{3-}(aq) \longrightarrow$

$$Mg_3(PO_4)_2(s) + 6\,Na^+(aq) + 6\,NO_3^-(aq)$$

$3\,Mg^{2+}(aq) + 2\,PO_4^{3-}(aq) \longrightarrow Mg_3(PO_4)_2(s)$

105. *Correct answers may vary, representative correct answers are:

a. addition of a solution containing SO_4^{2-};
$Pb^{2+}(aq) + SO_4^{2-}(aq) \longrightarrow PbSO_4(s)$

b. addition of a solution containing SO_4^{2-};
$Ca^{2+}(aq) + SO_4^{2-}(aq) \longrightarrow CaSO_4(s)$

c. addition of a solution containing SO_4^{2-};
$Ba^{2+}(aq) + SO_4^{2-}(aq) \longrightarrow BaSO_4(s)$

d. addition of a solution containing Cl^-;
$Hg_2^{2+}(aq) + 2\,Cl^-(aq) \longrightarrow Hg_2Cl_2(s)$

107. Ca^{2+} and Cu^{2+} were present in the original solution.

1st: $Ca^{2+}(aq) + SO_4^{2-}(aq) \longrightarrow CaSO_4(s)$

2nd: $Cu^{2+}(aq) + CO_3^{2-}(aq) \longrightarrow CuCO_3(s)$

109. a. chemical; **b.** physical

Chapter 8
Questions

1. Reaction stoichiometry is very important to chemistry. It gives us a numerical relationship between the reactants and products that allows chemists to plan and carry out chemical reactions to obtain products in the desired quantities,

e.g., How much CO_2 is produced when a given amount of C_8H_{10} is burned?

How much $H_2(g)$ is produced when a given amount of water decomposes?

3. 1 mol $N_2 \equiv$ 2 mol NH_3

3 mol $H_2 \equiv$ 2 mol NH_3

5. 1 mol $Cl_2 \equiv$ 2 mol $NaCl$

7. mass A $\longrightarrow$ moles A $\longrightarrow$ moles B $\longrightarrow$

mass B (A = reactant, B = product)

9. The limiting reactant is the reactant that limits the amount of product in a chemical reaction.

11. The actual yield is the amount of product actually produced by a chemical reaction. The percent yield is the percentage of the theoretical yield that was actually attained.

13. d

Problems

15. a. 1 mol C   **b.** 0.5 mol C
c. 2 mol C   **d.** 1 mol C

17. a. 2.6 mol NO_2 **b.** 11.6 mol NO_2
c. 8.90×10^3 mol NO_2 **d.** 2.012×10^{-3} mol NO_2

19. a. 2.96 mol HCl
b. 2.96 mol H_2O
c. 0.740 mol Na_2O_2
d. 0.987 mol SO_3

21. a. 1.2 mol PbO(s), 1.2 mol $SO_2(g)$
b. 0.80 mol PbO(s), 0.80 mol $SO_2(g)$
c. 7.9 mol PbO(s), 7.9 mol $SO_2(g)$
d. 5.3 mol PbO(s), 5.3 mol $SO_2(g)$

23.

mol N_2H_4	mol N_2O_4	mol N_2	mol H_2O
4	2	6	8
6	3	9	12
4	2	6	8
11	5.5	16.5	22
3	1.5	4.5	6
8.26	4.13	12.4	16.5

25. $2\,C_4H_{10}(g) + 13\,O_2(g) \longrightarrow$

$$8\,CO_2(g) + 10\,H_2O(g); 32\text{ mol } O_2$$

27. a. $Pb(s) + 2\,AgNO_3(aq) \longrightarrow Pb(NO_3)_2(aq) + 2\,Ag(s)$
b. 19 mol $AgNO_3$
c. 56.8 mol Ag

29. a. 0.213 g O_2 **b.** 0.385 g O_2
c. 96 g O_2 **d.** 3.4×10^{-4} g O_2

31. a. 3.0 g NaCl   **b.** 3.2 g $CaCO_3$
c. 3.0 g MgO   **d.** 2.3 g NaOH

33. a. 8.9 g Al_2O_3, 9.7 g Fe   **b.** 3.0 g Al_2O_3, 3.3 g Fe

35.

Mass CH_4	Mass O_2	Mass CO_2	Mass H_2O
0.645 g	2.57 g	1.77 g	1.45 g
22.32 g	89.00 g	61.20 g	50.09 g
5.044 g	20.11 g	13.83 g	11.32 g
1.07 g	4.28 g	2.94 g	2.41 g
3.18 kg	12.7 kg	8.72 kg	7.14 kg
8.57×10^2 kg	3.42×10^3 kg	2.35×10^3 kg	1.92×10^3 kg

37. a. 2.3 g HCl   **b.** 4.3 g HNO_3
c. 2.2 g H_2SO_4

39. 123 g H_2SO_4, 2.53 g H_2

41. a. 2 mol A   **b.** 1.8 mol A
c. 4 mol B   **d.** 40 mol B

43. a. 1.5 mol C   **b.** 3 mol C
c. 3 mol C   **d.** 96 mol C

45. a. 1 mol K   **b.** 1.8 mol K
c. 1 mol Cl_2 **d.** 14.6 mol K

47. a. 1.3 mol MnO_3 **b.** 4.8 mol MnO_3
c. 0.107 mol MnO_3 **d.** 27.5 mol MnO_3

49. a. 2 Cl_2 **b.** 3 Cl_2 **c.** 2 Cl_2

51. a. 1.0 g F_2 **b.** 10.5 g Li
c. 6.79×10^3 g F_2

53. a. 1.3 g $AlCl_3$ **b.** 24.8 g $AlCl_3$
c. 2.17 g $AlCl_3$

55. 74.6%

57. CaO; 25.7 g $CaCO_3$; 75.4%

59. O_2; 5.07 g NiO; 95.9%

61. Pb^{2+}; 262.7 g $PbCl_2$; 96.09%

63. 0.152 g Ba^{2+}

65. 1.5 g HCl

67. 3.1 kg CO_2

69. 4.7 g Na_3PO_4

71. 469 g Zn

73. $2 NH_4NO_3(s) \longrightarrow 2 N_2(g) + O_2(g) + 4 H_2O(l)$;
2.00×10^2 g O_2

75. salicylic acid ($C_7H_6O_3$); 2.71 g $C_9H_8O_4$; 74.1%

77. NH_3; 120 kg CH_4N_2O; 72.9%

79. 2.4 mg $C_4H_6O_4S_2$

81. b; the loudest explosion will occur when the ratio is 2 hydrogen to 1 oxygen, for that is the ratio that occurs in water.

83. 2.2×10^{13} kg CO_2 per year; 1.4×10^2 years

Chapter 9

Questions

1. Both the Bohr model and the quantum mechanical model for the atom were developed in the early 1900s. These models serve to explain how electrons are arranged within the atomic structure and how the electrons affect the chemical and physical properties of each element.

3. Light travels at a speed of 3.0×10^8 m/s. The speed of light is extremely fast, for a flash of light from the equator could circle our earth 7 times in one second.

5. A blue object appears blue because when white light is present the object absorbs all wavelengths of light except blue, which it reflects.

7. Wavelength and frequency are inversely related; the longer the wavelength, the lower the frequency, and vice versa.

9. X-rays pass through many substances that block visible light and are therefore used to image bones and organs.

11. Ultraviolet light contains enough energy to damage biological molecules, and excessive exposure increases the risk of skin cancer and cataracts.

13. Microwaves can only heat things containing water, and therefore the food, which contains water, becomes hot, but the plate does not.

15. The Bohr model is a representation for the atom in which electrons travel around the nucleus in circular orbits with a fixed energy at specific, fixed distances from the nucleus.

17. The Bohr orbit describes the path of an electron as an orbit or trajectory (a specified path). A quantum mechanical orbital describes the path of an electron using a probability map.

19. The e^- has wave particle duality, which means the path of an electron is not predictable. The motion of a baseball is predictable. A probability map shows a statistical, reproducible pattern of where the electron is located.

21. The subshells are s (1 orbital which contains a maximum of 2 electrons); p (3 orbitals which contain a maximum of 6 electrons); d (5 orbitals which contain a maximum of 10 electrons); and f (7 orbitals which contain a maximum of 14 electrons).

23. The Pauli exclusion principle states that separate orbitals may hold no more than 2 electrons, and when 2 electrons are present in a single orbital, they must have opposite spins. When writing electron configurations, the principle means that no box can have more than 2 arrows, and the arrows will point in opposite directions.

25. [Ne] represents $1s^2 2s^2 2p^6$
[Kr] represents $1s^2 2s^2 2p^6 3s^2 3p^6 4s^2 3d^{10} 4p^6$

27.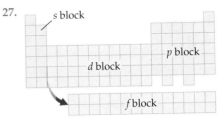

29. Group 1 elements form 1+ ions because they lose one valence electron in the outer s shell to obtain a noble gas configuration. Group 7 elements form 1− ions because they gain an electron to fill their outer p orbital to obtain a noble gas configuration.

Problems

31. infrared

33. radiowaves < microwaves < infrared < ultraviolet

35. gamma, ultraviolet, or X-rays

37. **a.** microwaves < X-rays < gamma rays
b. microwaves < X-rays < gamma rays
c. gamma rays < X-ray < microwaves

39. energies, distances

41. $n = 6 \longrightarrow n = 2$: 410 nm
$n = 5 \longrightarrow n = 2$: 434 nm

43.

The 2s and 3p orbitals are bigger than the 1s and 2p orbitals.

45. Electron in the 2s orbital

47. $2p \longrightarrow 1s$

49. **a.** $1s^2 2s^2 2p^2$ **b.** $1s^2 2s^2 2p^6 3s^1$
c. $1s^2 2s^2 2p^6 3s^2 3p^6$ **d.** $1s^2 2s^2 2p^6 3s^2 3p^2$

51. **a.** Be ⇅ | ⇅
       1s 2s

b. C ⇅ | ⇅ | ↑ | ↑ |
     1s 2s   2p

c. F ⇅ | ⇅ | ⇅ | ⇅ | ↑
     1s 2s   2p

d. Ne ⇅ | ⇅ | ⇅ | ⇅ | ⇅
      1s 2s   2p

53. **a.** $[Ar] 4s^2 3d^{10} 4p^1$
    b. $[Ar] 4s^2 3d^{10} 4p^3$
    c. $[Kr] 5s^1$
    d. $[Kr] 5s^2 4d^{10} 5p^2$
55. **a.** $[Ar] 4s^2 3d^2$
    b. $[Ar] 4s^2 3d^3$
    c. $[Ar] 4s^1 3d^5$
    d. $[Ar] 4s^2 3d^5$
57. Valence electrons are <u>underlined</u>
    a. $1s^2 2s^2 \underline{2p^1}$
    b. $1s^2 2s^2 \underline{2p^3}$
    c. $1s^2 2s^2 2p^6 3s^2 3p^6 4s^2 3d^{10} 4p^6 \underline{5s^2} 4d^{10} \underline{5p^3}$
    d. $1s^2 2s^2 2p^6 3s^2 3p^6 \underline{4s^1}$
59. **a.** Si $\boxed{\uparrow\downarrow}$ $\boxed{\uparrow}$ $\boxed{\uparrow}$ $\boxed{}$ 2 unpaired electrons

   $3s$ $3p$

   b. Ca $\boxed{\uparrow\downarrow}$ 0 unpaired electrons

   $4s$

   c. Cl $\boxed{\uparrow\downarrow}$ $\boxed{\uparrow\downarrow}$ $\boxed{\uparrow\downarrow}$ $\boxed{\uparrow}$ 1 unpaired electron

   $3s$ $3p$

   d. Ar $\boxed{\uparrow\downarrow}$ $\boxed{\uparrow\downarrow}$ $\boxed{\uparrow\downarrow}$ $\boxed{\uparrow\downarrow}$ 0 unpaired electrons

   $3s$ $3p$

61. **a.** 6   **b.** 6
    c. 7   **d.** 1
63. **a.** ns^1 **b.** ns^2
    c. $ns^2 np^3$ **d.** $ns^2 np^5$
65. **a.** $[Ne] 3s^2 3p^1$ **b.** $[He] 2s^2$
    c. $[Kr] 5s^2 4d^{10} 5p^1$ **d.** $[Kr] 5s^2 4d^2$
67. **a.** $[Ar] 4s^2 3d^{10} 4p^3$ **b.** $[Xe] 6s^2$
    c. $[Ar] 4s^2 3d^8$ **d.** $[Xe] 6s^2 4f^{14} 5d^{10} 6p^3$
69. **a.** 2   **b.** 3
    c. 5   **d.** 6
71. Period 1 has two elements. Period 2 has eight elements. The number of subshells is equal to the principle quantum number. For Period 1, $n = 1$ and the s subshell contains only two elements. For Period 2, $n = 2$ and contains s and p subshells that have a total of 8 elements.
73. **a.** Al   **b.** S
    c. Ar   **d.** Mg
75. **a.** Cl   **b.** Ga
    c. Fe   **d.** Rb
77. **a.** Na   **b.** Ge
    c. cannot tell   **d.** P
79. Pb < Sn < Te < S < Cl
81. **a.** In   **b.** Si
    c. Pb   **d.** C
83. F < S < Si < Ge < Ca < Rb
85. **a.** Sr   **b.** Bi
    c. cannot tell   **d.** As

87. S < Se < Sb < In < Ba < Fr
89. $18 \, e^-$
91. Alkali metals have the general electron configuration of ns^1. If they lose their one s electron, they will obtain the electron configuration of a noble gas. This loss of an electron will give the alkali metal a +1 charge.
93. **a.** $1s^2 2s^2 2p^6 3s^2 3p^6$
    b. $1s^2 2s^2 2p^6 3s^2 3p^6$
    c. $1s^2 2s^2 2p^6 3s^2 3p^6$
    d. $1s^2 2s^2 2p^6 3s^2 3p^6 4s^2 3d^{10} 4p^6$
95. Metals tend to form positive ions because they tend to lose electrons. Elements on the left side of the periodic table have only a few extra electrons, which they will lose to gain a noble gas configuration. Metalloids tend to be elements with 3 to 5 valence electrons; they could lose or gain electrons to obtain a noble gas configuration. Nonmetals tend to gain electrons to fill their almost full valence shell, so they tend to form negative ions and are on the right side of the table.
97. **a.** Can only have 2 in the s shell and 6 in the p shell: $1s^2 2s^2 2p^6 3s^2 3p^3$.
    b. There is no $2d$ subshell: $1s^2 2s^2 2p^6 3s^2 3p^2$.
    c. There is no $1p$ subshell: $1s^2 2s^2 2p^3$.
    d. Can only have 6 in the p shell: $1s^2 2s^2 2p^6 3s^2 3p^3$.
99. Bromine is highly reactive because it reacts quickly to gain an electron and obtain a stable valence shell. Krypton is a noble gas because it already has a stable valence shell.
101. K
103. 660 nm
105. 8 min, 19 sec
107. The quantum-mechanical model provided the ability to understand and predict chemical bonding, which is the basic level of understanding of matter and how it interacts. This model was critical in the areas of lasers, computers, semiconductors, and drug design. The quantum-mechanical model for the atom is considered the foundation of modern chemistry.
109. **a.** 1.5×10^{-34} m
     b. 1.88×10^{-10} m
     electrons have particle-wave duality whereas golf balls do not.
111. Ultraviolet light is the only one of these three types of light that contains enough energy to break chemical bonds in biological molecules.

Chapter 10

Questions

 1. Bonding theories predict how atoms bond together to form molecules and also predict what combinations of atoms form molecules and what combinations do not. Likewise, bonding theories explain the shapes of molecules, which in turn determine many of their physical and chemical properties.
 3. Ne: $1s^2 2s^2 2p^6$, 8 valence electrons
    Ar: $1s^2 2s^2 2p^6 3s^2 3p^6$, 8 valence electrons
 5. According to Lewis theory, a chemical bond is the sharing or transfer of electrons to attain stable electron configurations among the bonding atoms.

7. The Lewis structure for potassium has 1 valence electron while the Lewis structure for monatomic chlorine has 7 valence electrons. From these structures we can determine that if potassium gives up its one valence electron to chlorine, K^+ and Cl^- are formed; therefore the formula must be KCl.

9. Double and triple bonds are shorter and stronger than single bonds.

11. You determine the number of electrons that go into the Lewis structure of a molecule by summing the valence electrons of each atom in the molecule.

13. The octet rule is not sophisticated enough to be correct every time. For example, some molecules that exist in nature have an odd number of valence electrons, and thus will not have octets on all their constituent atoms. Some elements tend to form compounds in nature in which they have more (sulfur) or less (boron) than 8 valence electrons.

15. VSEPR theory predicts the shape of molecules using the idea that electron groups repel each other.

17. **a.** 180 °   **b.** 120 °   **c.** 109.5 °

19. Electronegativity is the ability of an element to attract electrons within a covalent bond.

21. A polar covalent bond is a covalent bond that has a dipole moment.

23. It is important to know if a molecule is polar or nonpolar in order to determine how it will react with other molecules.

Problems

25. **a.** $1s^2 2s^2 2p^3$, $\cdot \ddot{N}:$

    b. $1s^2 2s^2 2p^2$, $\cdot \dot{C} \cdot$

    c. $1s^2 2s^2 2p^6 3s^2 3p^5$, $:\ddot{C}l\cdot$

    d. $1s^2 2s^2 2p^6 3s^2 3p^6$, $:\ddot{A}r:$

27. **a.** $K\cdot$

    b. $\dot{A}l:$

    c. $\cdot \dot{P}:$

    d. $:\ddot{A}r:$

29. $:\ddot{X}:$ Halogens tend to gain one electron in a chemical reaction.

31. $M:$ Alkaline earth metals tend to lose two electrons in a chemical reaction.

33. **a.** $\left[:\ddot{C}l: \right]^-$ **b.** $\left[:\ddot{S}e: \right]^{2-}$

    c. Na^+ **d.** Mg^{2+}

35. **a.** Kr   **b.** Ne

    c. Kr   **d.** Xe

37. **a.** Ionic   **b.** Covalent

    c. Ionic   **d.** Covalent

39. **a.** $Na^+ \left[:\ddot{F}: \right]^-$ **b.** $Ca^{2+} \left[:\ddot{O}: \right]^{2-}$

    c. $\left[:\ddot{B}r: \right]^- Sr^{2+} \left[:\ddot{B}r: \right]^-$ **d.** $K^+ \left[:\ddot{O}: \right]^{2-} K^+$

41. **a.** SrSe   **b.** $BaCl_2$
    c. Na_2S **d.** Al_2O_3

43. **a.** $Li^+ \left[:\ddot{F}: \right]^-$ **b.** $Li^+ \left[:\ddot{O}: \right]^{2-} Li^+$

    c. $Li^+ \left[:\ddot{N}: \right]^{3-} Li^+$
              Li^+

45. **a.** $Cs^+ \left[:\ddot{C}l: \right]^-$

    b. $Ba^{2+} \left[:\ddot{O}: \right]^{2-}$

    c. $\left[:\ddot{I}: \right]^- Ca^{2+} \left[:\ddot{I}: \right]^-$

47. **a.** $H - \overset{\displaystyle H}{\underset{\displaystyle H}{\ddot{P}}} - H$ **b.** $:\ddot{C}l - \ddot{S} - \ddot{C}l:$

    c. $:\ddot{F} - \ddot{F}:$ **d.** $H - \ddot{I}:$

49. **a.** $\ddot{O} = \ddot{O}$ **b.** $:C \equiv O:$

    c. $H - \ddot{O} - \ddot{N} - \ddot{O}:$ **d.** $:\ddot{O} = \ddot{S} - \ddot{O}:$

51. **a.** $H - C \equiv C - H$ **b.** $H - \overset{\displaystyle |}{C} = \overset{\displaystyle |}{C} - H$ with H, H below

    c. $H - \ddot{N} = \ddot{N} - H$ **d.** $H - \overset{\displaystyle |}{\ddot{N}} - \overset{\displaystyle |}{\ddot{N}} - H$ with H, H below

53. **a.** $:N \equiv N:$

    b. $\ddot{S} = Si = \ddot{S}$

    c. $H - \ddot{O} - H$

    d. $:\ddot{I} - \ddot{N} - \ddot{I}:$ with $:\ddot{I}:$ below

55. **a.** $\ddot{O} = \ddot{S}e - \ddot{O}: \longleftrightarrow :\ddot{O} - \ddot{S}e = \ddot{O}$

    b.
$$\left[\ddot{O} = C - \ddot{O}: \atop :\ddot{O}: \right]^{2-} \longleftrightarrow \left[:\ddot{O} - C = \ddot{O} \atop :\ddot{O}: \right]^{2-} \longleftrightarrow \left[:\ddot{O} - C - \ddot{O}: \atop :O: \right]^{2-}$$

    c. $\left[:\ddot{C}l - \ddot{O}: \right]^-$

    d. $\left[:\ddot{O} - \ddot{C}l - \ddot{O}: \right]^-$

57. **a.** $\left[:\ddot{O} - \overset{\displaystyle :\ddot{O}:}{\underset{\displaystyle :O:}{P}} - \ddot{O}: \right]^{3-}$

    b. $[:C \equiv N:]$

    c. $\left[:\ddot{O} = \ddot{N} - \ddot{O}: \right]^- \longleftrightarrow \left[:\ddot{O} - \ddot{N} = \ddot{O}: \right]^-$

    d. $\left[:\ddot{O} - \overset{\displaystyle |}{\underset{\displaystyle :O:}{S}} - \ddot{O}: \right]^{2-}$

59. a. $:\ddot{C}l-B-\ddot{C}l:$
    $\quad\quad\quad\;\;|$
    $\quad\quad\quad:\ddot{C}l:$

b. $\ddot{O}=\dot{N}-\ddot{O}: \longleftrightarrow :\ddot{O}-\dot{N}=\ddot{O}$

c. $H-B-H$
    $\quad\quad\;\;|$
    $\quad\quad\;\;H$

61. a. 4   b. 4
    c. 4   d. 2

63. a. 3 bonding groups, 1 lone pair
    b. 2 bonding groups, 2 lone pairs
    c. 4 bonding groups, 0 lone pairs
    d. 2 bonding groups, 0 lone pairs

65. a. tetrahedral
    b. trigonal planar
    c. linear
    d. trigonal planar

67. a. $109.5\,°$ b. $120\,°$
    c. $180\,°$ d. $120\,°$

69. a. linear, linear
    b. trigonal planar, bent
    c. tetrahedral, bent
    d. tetrahedral, trigonal pyramidal

71. a. $180\,°$
    b. $120\,°$
    c. $109.5\,°$
    d. $109.5\,°$

73. a. linear, linear
    b. trigonal planar, bent
    c. tetrahedral, trigonal pyramidal

75. a. trigonal planar   b. bent
    c. trigonal planar   d. tetrahedral

77. a. 1.2
    b. 1.8
    c. 2.8

79. Rb < Ca < Ga < Si < Cl

81. a. polar covalent   b. ionic
    c. pure covalent   d. polar covalent

83. H_2 < ICl < HBr < CO

85. a. polar   b. nonpolar
    c. nonpolar   d. polar

87. a. $(+):C\equiv O:(-)$
    b. nonpolar
    c. nonpolar
    d. $(+)\, H-\ddot{B}r:(-)$

89. a. nonpolar   b. polar
    c. nonpolar   d. polar

91. a. nonpolar   b. polar
    c. nonpolar   d. polar

93. a. $1s^2 2s^2 2p^6 3s^2 3p^6 \underline{4s^2}$, $Ca:$ (underlined electrons are the ones included)

b. $1s^2 2s^2 2p^3 3s^2 3p^6 \underline{4s^2} 3d^{10} \underline{4p^1}$, $\dot{Ga}:$
c. $[Ar]\,\underline{4s^2}3d^{10}\underline{4p^3}$, $\cdot\dot{A}s:$ d. $[Kr]\,\underline{5s^2}4d^{10}\underline{5p^5}$, $\dot{\ddot{I}}:$

95. a. ionic, $K^+\left[:\ddot{\underset{..}{S}}:\right]^{2-}K^+$ b. covalent, $H-\overset{\displaystyle\ddot{O}:}{\underset{|}{C}}-\ddot{F}:$

c. ionic, $Mg^{2+}\left[:\ddot{\underset{..}{Se}}:\right]^{2-}$ d. covalent, $\ddot{B}r-\overset{\displaystyle:\ddot{B}r:}{\underset{|}{P}}-\ddot{B}r:$

97. $:\ddot{C}l-\overset{\displaystyle\dot{\ddot{O}}}{\underset{\|}{C}}-\ddot{C}l:$ polar, $\underset{\displaystyle Cl\quad\quad Cl}{\overset{\displaystyle O}{\underset{\|}{C}}}$

99. $\underset{\displaystyle H}{\overset{\displaystyle H}{\underset{|}{\overset{|}{H-C}}}}-\overset{\displaystyle \ddot{O}}{\underset{\|}{C}}-\ddot{O}H$ $H^{|||}\underset{\displaystyle H}{\overset{\displaystyle H}{\underset{\blacktriangle}{C}}}-\underset{\displaystyle OH}{\overset{\displaystyle O}{\underset{\diagdown}{\overset{\diagup\!\!\!\|}{C}}}}$

101.

$H:\ddot{C}l: + Na^+\left[:\ddot{O}:H\right]^- \longrightarrow H:\ddot{O}:H + Na^+\left[:\ddot{C}l:\right]^-$

103. $K\cdot,\; :\ddot{C}l-\ddot{C}l:,\; K^+\left[:\ddot{C}l:\right]^-$, Cl reduced, K oxidized

105. a. $K^+\left[:\ddot{O}:H\right]^-$
    b.
    $K^+\left[:\ddot{O}=\ddot{N}:\ddot{O}:\right]^- \longleftrightarrow K^+\left[:\ddot{O}:\overset{\displaystyle\dot{\ddot{O}}}{\underset{\|}{N}}:\ddot{O}:\right]^- \longleftrightarrow K^+\left[:\ddot{O}:\ddot{N}=\ddot{O}:\right]^-$

    c. $Li^+\left[:\ddot{I}:\ddot{O}:\right]^-$
    d.
    $Ba^{2+}\left[\overset{\displaystyle:\ddot{O}:}{\underset{:\ddot{O}:\;\;\;:\ddot{O}:}{\overset{\|}{C}}}\right]^{2-} \longleftrightarrow Ba^{2+}\left[\overset{\displaystyle:\ddot{O}:}{\underset{:\ddot{O}:\;\;\;:\ddot{O}:}{C}}\right]^{2-} \longleftrightarrow Ba^{2+}\left[\overset{\displaystyle:\ddot{O}:}{\underset{:\ddot{O}:\;\;\;:\ddot{O}:}{C}}\right]^{2-}$

107. a. $\underset{\displaystyle:\ddot{F}:\quad:\ddot{F}:}{\overset{\displaystyle:\ddot{F}:\;\;:\ddot{F}:\;\;:\ddot{F}:}{P}}$ b. $\underset{\displaystyle:\ddot{F}:\quad:\ddot{F}:}{\overset{\displaystyle:\ddot{F}:\;\;:\ddot{F}:}{\ddot{S}}}$ c. $\underset{\displaystyle:\ddot{F}:\quad:\ddot{F}:}{\overset{\displaystyle:\ddot{F}:\;\;:\ddot{F}:}{\ddot{Se}}}$

109. CH_2O_2 or $H-\overset{\displaystyle O}{\underset{\|}{C}}-\ddot{O}-H$

111. a. $\left[:\ddot{O}-\ddot{O}\cdot\right]^-$ b. $\left[:\ddot{O}\cdot\right]^-$

    c. $\cdot\ddot{O}-H$ d. $H-\underset{\displaystyle H}{\overset{\displaystyle H}{\underset{|}{\overset{|}{C}}}}-\ddot{O}-\ddot{O}\cdot$

113. a. The structure has 2 bonding electron pairs and 2 lone pairs. The Lewis structure is analogous to that of water, and the molecular geometry is bent. b. Correct c. The structure has 3 bonding electron pairs and 1 lone pair. The Lewis structure is analogous to that of NH_3, and the geometry is trigonal pyramidal.

Chapter 13

Questions

1. A solution is a homogeneous mixture of two or more substances. Some examples are air, seawater, soda water, and brass.

3. In a solution, the solvent is the majority component of the mixture and the solute is the minority component. For example, in a seawater solution, the water is the solvent and the salt content is the solute.

5. Solubility is the amount of the compound, usually in grams, that will dissolve in a specified amount of solvent.

7. In solutions with solids, soluble ionic solids form strong electrolyte solutions, while soluble molecular solids form nonelectrolyte solutions. Strong electrolyte solutions are solutions containing solutes that dissociate into ions, for example, $BaCl_2$ and NaOH.

9. Recrystallization is a common way to purify a solid. In recrystallization, enough solid is put into high-temperature water until a saturated solution is created. Then the solution cools slowly, and crystals result from the solution. The crystalline structure tends to reject impurities, resulting in a purer solid.

11. The bubbles formed on the bottom of a pot of heated water (before boiling) are dissolved air coming out of the solution. These gases come out of solution because the solubility of the dissolved nitrogen and oxygen decreases as the temperature of the water rises.

13. The higher the pressure above a liquid, the more soluble the gas is in the liquid.

15. A dilute solution is one containing small amounts of a solute relative to solvent and a concentrated solution is one containing large amounts of solute relative to solvent.

17. Molarity is a common unit of concentration of a solution defined as moles of solute per liter of solution.

19. The boiling point of a solution containing a nonvolatile solute is higher than the boiling point of the pure solvent. The melting point of the solution, however is lower.

21. Molality is a common unit of concentration of a solution expressed as number of moles of solute per kilogram of solvent.

23. Water tends to move from lower concentrations to higher concentrations and when the salt water is being passed through the human body, the salt content draws the water out of the body, causing dehydration.

Problems

25. c, d

27. **a.** solute: salt, solvent: water
    b. solute: sugar, solvent: water
    c. solute: CO_2, solvent: water

29. **a.** hexane **b.** water
    c. ethyl ether **d.** water

31. ions, strong electrolyte solution

33. unsaturated

35. recrystallization

37. **a.** no **b.** yes **c.** yes

39. At room temperature water contains some dissolved oxygen gas; however, the boiling of the water will remove dissolved gases.

41. Under higher pressure the gas (nitrogen) will be more easily dissolved in the blood. To reverse this process, the diver should ascend to relieve the pressure.

43. **a.** 8.11% **b.** 10.3% **c.** 6.37%

45. 13%

47.
Mass Solute	Mass Solvent	Mass Solution	Mass%
15.5	238.1	253.6	6.11%
22.8	167.2	190.0	12.0%
28.8	183.3	212.1	13.6%
56.9	315.2	372.1	15.3%

49. 9.6 g

51. **a.** 2.7 g **b.** 13.7 mg **c.** 0.99 kg

53. **a.** 3.3×10^3 g
    b. 77 g
    c. 15 g

55. 1.6×10^2 g

57. 1.3×10^3 g

59. 1.4×10^4 mL

61. **a.** 0.52 M **b.** 0.263 M **c.** 0.199 M

63. **a.** 0.149 M **b.** 0.461 M **c.** 3.00×10^{-2} M

65. 0.60 M

67. **a.** 1.8 mol **b.** 0.38 mol **c.** 0.238 mol

69. **a.** 0.39 L **b.** 0.056 L **c.** 0.10 L

71.
Solute	Mass Solute	Mol Solute	Volume Solution	Molarity
KNO_3	22.5 g	0.223	125 mL	1.78 M
$NaHCO_3$	2.10 g	0.0250	250.0 mL	0.100 M
$C_{12}H_{22}O_{11}$	55.38 g	0.162	1.08 L	0.150 M

73. 4.8 g

75. 19 g

77. 8.8 L

79. 0.38 M

81. Dilute 0.045 L of the stock solution to 2.5 L.

83. 6.0×10^2 mL

85. 17.7 mL

87. **a.** 0.025 L **b.** 0.020 L **c.** 1.03 L

89. 4.45 mL

91. 0.373 M

93. 1.2 L

95. **a.** 1.0 m **b.** 3.92 m **c.** 0.52 m

97. 1.28 m

99. **a.** −1.6 °C **b.** −2.70 °C
    c. −8.9 °C **d.** −4.37 °C

101. **a.** 100.060 °C **b.** 100.993 °C
     c. 101.99 °C **d.** 101.11 °C

103. −1.27 °C, 100.348 °C

105. 2.28 M, 12.3%

107. 0.43 L

109. 319 mL

111. 0.17 L

113. 9.00 mL

115. 79.5 mL

117. $-3.22\ °C$, $100.885\ °C$
119. $-1.56\ °C$, $100.431\ °C$
121. $1.8 \times 10^2\ \text{g/mol}$
123. **a.** Water will flow from left to right.
     b. Water will flow from right to left.
     c. Water won't flow between the two.
125. $3 \times 10^4\ \text{L}$

INDEX